P9-DWV-597

THE Downy Waterfowl OF NORTH AMERICA

Colleen Helgeson Nelson

DELTA STATION PRESS

Published by
Delta Station Press
Delta Waterfowl Foundation
102 Wilmot Road, Suite 410
Deerfield, Illinois 60015
and
Delta Waterfowl and Wetlands Research Station
R.R.1
Portage la Prairie, Manitoba
Canada
R1N 3A1

ISBN. 1 55056 219 3

Printed and bound in Canada by
Friesen Printers
Altona, Manitoba, Canada

Text and illustrations
by Colleen Helgeson Nelson

Dustjacket and Page ii: Richardson's Canada Goose, Branta canadensis hutchinsii
Jenny Lind Island, Queen Maud Gulf, Northwest Territories (UFS[DM]: measurements) and Baffin Island, Northwest Territories (CESJ: color and pattern). Spider Plant or Whiplash, Saxifraga flagellaris Willd.

This book is dedicated to the memory of those
who encouraged my interest in birds:
my parents, Alvin H. Helgeson and Burdella B. Helgeson Myers,
my sixth-grade teacher, Georgia E. Pettingill,
and my colleague in zoology, Robert M. Hedrick.

This book is made possible through the support of a few dedicated individuals who contributed generously towards ensuring that the knowledge gained through thirty years' study of downy waterfowl would be made available to others interested in the study of waterfowl.

We appreciate the support of :

Charles H. Bell, James F. Bell Foundation, Richard Borden, Wallace C. Dayton, Clayton R. Gaylord, Edson I. Gaylord, James G. Laidlaw, Daniel W. LeBlond, Curtis and Edith Munson Foundation, Richard T. Schroeder, Harold C. Stuart, David Ulhlein, Waterfowl Research Foundation, William B. Webster, III, R. Howard Webster, and Robert Winthrop.

Table of Contents

List of Illustrations

Measured drawings

Preface

South from Lake Manitoba to the Assiniboine River and west from White Horse Plains to the Carberry Sand Hills, stretches a flat expanse of prairie called the Portage Plains. In winter a snowy vastness broken only by isolated farms and leafless wind-breaks, the plains in summer unfold in vistas of green, dark groves rising among fields of oats, barley, wheat, rye, and blue-flowered flax. A line of trees, seeming at times to ring the horizon, marks the winding course of the Assiniboine. At the north edge of the plains lies the Delta Marsh, an array of interlocking bays, creeks, and channels extending the width of Lake Manitoba's south shore. The tiny fishing village for which the marsh is named houses the Delta Waterfowl and Wetlands Research Station. There, in 1962, I began to paint from life the day-old young of the North American waterfowl, a project suggested to me three years earlier by the late H. A. ('Al') Hochbaum, then director at Delta. I did not guess that I would spend more than a dozen summers there, or that my research would take me to Slimbridge and Tunstead in England as well as to other museums and aviaries in the United States and Canada. Nor did I realize, at first, the complexity of the task that I had undertaken. Surely, neither Al nor I had any idea that more than twenty years would be needed to finish the work.

Painting the downy birds occupied nearly all of the first year, but gradually, the scientific aspects of the work claimed most of my attention. Color evaluation, diagnostic characters of plumage and structure, and unique developmental changes among certain closely related species presented problems that I could seldom resist trying to solve. Eight summers passed most pleasantly in this way.

Slowly, the book planned as the end-product of these diverse efforts began to take shape in my mind's eye. For a number of years, I visualized it as an elegant folio, with a color plate for each species, but eventually abandoned that idea as impractical. The other extreme, a modest field guide illustrated solely with line drawings, I rejected as inadequate. Generic accounts evolved into tribal accounts—a practical way of dealing with many morphological and behavioral relationships, but the initial species accounts, written between the hours of four and seven on countless winter mornings, were consigned to the waste-basket after one critical reader commented, "They aren't very interesting, are they?"

Several hundred sets of weights and measurements, gathered mostly during the initial years of my research, form the first appendix to the book; problems encountered in color evaluation suggested that precise color descriptions of each species would make a useful second appendix; and a list of geographical sources of the specimens examined follows each species account. Of necessity, I learned more about statistics, colorimetry, and toponymy than I ever planned to do. The Identification Keys, begun in 1967, were meant as an appendix to the folio. They became, after many revisions and the addition of several hundred drawings, a third appendix in the book.

In limiting the scope of my research to a description of the color, pattern, structure, and behavior of the downy young, I had to leave unexplored—for lack of time, skill, or facilties—many fascinating problems that emerged during the course of my study. Nevertheless, I hope that the information presented here will prove useful in future waterfowl research.

C.H.N.

June 1992
Winnipeg, Manitoba

Acknowledgments

During my first summer of research, when a friend asked me how long I thought it would take to complete my study of the downy waterfowl, I replied confidently, "About ten years," thinking privately that I would spend no more than five at it. Looking back over the intervening thirty years, I realize that the project has been both manageable and finite largely because of the generosity of the persons and institutions named below. I am most grateful to all of them.

When I wrote to biologists and aviculturalists, many of whom I had never met, asking for 'a clutch or two' of star-pipped eggs, I hardly dared to hope that they would respond. But they did, magnificently. The following individuals provided live birds and eggs for my research: J. Barr, J. C. Bartonek, B. D. J. Batt, K. E. Bednarik, F. C. Bellrose, E. G. Bolen, W. J. Breckenridge, R. G. Bromley, W. F. Carrick, J. W. Chadwick, R. Cole, R. Crompton, M. Denny, A. J. Erskine, R. M. Evans, G. Freeman, R. W. Fuller, W. L. Gelston, L. F. Gunther, D. R. Halladay, D. R. M. Hatch, B. L. Hilliker, the late H. A. Hochbaum, S. T. Johnstone, D. Jury, the late S. C. Kendeigh, J. G. King, L. LaGrange, F. B. Lee, T. W. Locke, the late J. J. Lynch, C. D. MacInnes, R. H. Mackay, D. F. McKinney, M. K. McNicholl, J. Malcolm, W. E. Mercer, E. Mikula, G. Moisan, D. Muir, J. E. Myers, R. Ortlied, P. Ould, the late A. J. Pakulak, D. F. Parmelee, H. J. Posten, the late D. G. Raveling, A. Reed, R. W. Ritcey, M. G. Smart, J. H. Stoudt, L. G. Sugden, M. R. Szymczak, J. Tester, R. D. Trethewey, the late L. M. Tuck, K. Vermeer, P. Ward, D. W. Warner, C. Willey, and R. D. Wood. M. Giffin, C. R. Nelson, Jr., F. W. B. Nelson, and L. T. Simmons assisted with field collections. In addition, the late W. F. Palsson was employed to collect the eggs of several Icelandic species for my use at the Round Lake Waterfowl Station, Round Lake, Minnesota.

My observations were carried on at aviaries here and abroad. For the use of research, library, and rearing facilities, and for assistance of many kinds: the Delta Waterfowl and Wetlands Research Station (DWWRS; M. G. Anderson, B. D. J. Batt, the late J. Black, D. Caswell, N. Godfrey, L. M. Gretsinger, the late H. A. Hochbaum, P. Hope, R. E. Jones, S. Kennedy, M. Koppen, N. Mulder, K. W. Risi, B. Vincent, E. K. Ward, P. Ward, M. Wayland, D. Wielicki, and my half-time assistant in 1964, D. A. Manuwal); the Round Lake Waterfowl Station (RLWS; K. L. Hansen, J. Sather, the late K. Sather, R. Schuman, M. G. Smart); the University of Manitoba Field Station [Delta Marsh] (UFS[DM]; H. Lees, the late B. E. Murray, J. M. W. Shay, E. R. Waygood, H. E. Welch; UFS[DM] also furnished sound recording apparatus, pens, and rearing equipment); and the Wildfowl Trust [Slimbridge], England (WT[S]; S. T. Johnstone, J. Kear, M. R. Lubbock, G. V. T. Matthews, the late P. M. Scott). The late J. P. Williams, whose waterfowl collection at Old Farm, Tunstead (JPWT), Norfolk, must surely have been one of the most beautiful in the world, permitted me to observe its denizens during a three-month stay in England. R. W. Elgas (RWEBT; Big Timber, Mont.), E. R. Pace (PWPS; Provincial Wildlife Park, Shubenacadie, N. S.), C. G. Roots (APZ; Assiniboine Park Zoo, Winnipeg, Man.), and the late C. E. Strutz (CESJ; Jamestown, N. D.) also allowed observations at their aviaries. In addition, F. W. J. Davis gave me and my colleague, M. V. Tascona, the use of the University of Winnipeg microbiology laboratory in the summer of 1973.

On many occasions, biologists at the Delta Waterfowl and Wetlands Research Station permitted me to observe and examine their experimental birds: J. C. Bartee, J. C. Bartonek, J. A.

Barzen, B. D. J. Batt, C. W. Dane, D. Eggeman, S. Evarts, K. E. Kostow, the late J. K. Lowther, D. F. McKinney, L. W. Oring, P. Ould, R. B. Owen, Jr., and J. M. Rhymer.

During five years when I raised birds in my studio-laboratory at home (NWPW), I used elevated observation pens built for my use by the maintenance staff at Delta and at Canada Cement Company, Ltd., Fort Whyte, Manitoba. I gave older birds to other aviaries: the Delta Waterfowl and Wetlands Research Station, the Fort Whyte Nature Centre, the Niska Propagation and Research Centre (NPRC) Guelph, Ontario, and L. T. Simmons's aviary, Winnipeg (LTSW).

Certain field observations, measurements, photographs, and color transparencies or evaluations of live young birds of several species were loaned or given by B. D. J. Batt, E. G. Bolen, B. W. Cain, I. de Benedetto, W. L. Gelston, D. Grice, S. A. Hatch, C. Henderson, J. Kear, F. F. Knowlton, K. E. Kostow, M. B. Maj, S. D. MacDonald, D. W. Moulton, N. Murdoch, the late H. R. Murdy, E. R. Pace, T. Pogson, A. Reed, J. P. Ryder, C. E. Smith, V. D. Stotts, D. E. Trauger, and R. D. Trethewey; D. F. McKinney loaned a film made in Alaska of adult Steller's Eiders; K. C. Parkes provided taxonomic notes on a series of scaup specimens; M. Desfayes, N. J. Scott, Jr., C. D. Stutzenbaker, and D. E. Timm permitted me to examine unpublished manuscript and tabular data; C. R. Nelson, Jr., F. W. B. Nelson, O. Tivoli, and M. Welch assisted with sound recordings; and J. C. Bartonek, A. Kansas, C. R. Nelson, Jr., and B. Sucharoff developed and printed photographs. I acknowledge the contribution of several downy specimens from Max Miller, Seymour, Connecticut (MMS). Several capable assistants helped with the preparation of study skins: M. J. Bossenmaier, the late L. E. Kansas, G. R. McLean, D. A. Manuwal, and J. L. Wylie. C. Collins and the conservation staff at the Manitoba Museum of Man and Nature provided distilled water almost daily for my painting.

The necessary permits to collect, capture, and ship live birds and their eggs as well as prepared specimens of endangered species were provided by the Canadian Wildlife Service (J. Heppes, W. R. Miller [also advised on methods of shipping eggs], D. A. Munro, J. C. Shaver, E. F. Whitney), the U. S. Fish and Wildlife Service (D. Donahoo, C. H. Lawrence, A. T. Studholme), and various state and provincial wildlife departments. A. R. Singleton, Canada Agriculture, gave advice and help in expediting international shipments.

Museums have loaned specimens, allowed me to examine collections, and provided work space when I visited. For great patience and many courtesies shown by curators and their staff: Academy of Natural Sciences of Philadelphia (ANSP; the late J. Bond, F. B. Gill), American Museum of Natural History, New York (AMNH; D. Amadon, J. Farrand, Jr., W. E. Lanyon), J. F. Bell [Minnesota] Museum of Natural History, Minneapolis (BMNH; J. T. Klicka, D. F. Parmelee, H. B. Tordoff, D.W. Warner), Bernice Pauahi Bishop Museum, Honolulu (BPBM; A. Ziegler), British Museum (Natural History), Tring (BM[NH]; G. S. Cowles, I. C. J. Galbraith), Carnegie Museum [of Natural History], Pittsburgh (CM; M. H. Clench, J. M. Loughlin, M. Niedermeyer, K. C. Parkes, D. S. Wood), Commonwealth Scientific and Industrial Research Organization, Australia ([Australian National Wildlife Collection] ANWC; P. Fullagar, R. Schodde, J. Wombey), Delta Study Collection, Delta, Manitoba (D; B. D. J. Batt), Denver Museum of Natural History, Colorado (DEN; B. Webb), Field Museum of Natural History, Chicago (FMNH; E. R. Blake, J. W. Fitzpatrick, D. Maurer, M. A. Traylor, D. E. Willard), Florida Museum of Natural History, [formerly, University of Florida State Museum of Natural History], Gainesville (FIMNH; the late O. L. Austin, Jr.), Icelandic Museum of Natural History, Reykjavik [formerly, Reykjavik Museum RM (RM used for bird specimens)]; (IMNH; the late F. Gudmundsson, A. Petersen), Los Angeles County Museum, California (LACM; the late R. W. Schreiber), Louisiana State Museum of Natural Science, [formerly, Louisiana State University Museum of Zoology], Baton Rouge (LSUMZ; the late G. H. Lowery, Jr.), Manitoba Department of Natural Resources, Winnipeg (MDNR; R. W. Nero), Museum of Southwestern Biology, Albuquerque (MSB; J. C. Bednarz, J. S. Findley, D. J. Hafner), Museum of Vertebrate Zoology, Berkeley (MVZ; V. Dziadosz, N. K. Johnson), Canadian Museum of Science, [formerly, National Museum of Canada], Ottawa (NMC; W. E. Godfrey, M. Gosselin, S. D. MacDonald, H. Ouellet), New Mexico Natural Resources Department (W. S. Huey), Oregon State University Fish and Wildlife Collection, Corvallis (OSUFW; B. J. Verts), Prairie Migratory Bird Research Centre Study Collection, Saskatoon, Saskatchewan (PMBRC; J. B. Gollop), Puget Sound Museum, [formerly, Puget Sound Museum of Natural History], Tacoma, Washington (PSM; G. Alcorn, D. Paulson), Royal British Columbia Museum, [formerly, British Columbia Provincial Museum], Victoria (RBCM; R. W. Campbell), Royal Ontario Museum, Toronto (ROM; J. C. Barlow, J. Dick, R. James), San Diego Natural History Museum, California (SDNHM; A. M. Rea), Texas Cooperative Wildlife Collection, Texas A. and M. University, College Station (TCWC; K. A. Arnold), United States National Museum [of

25/7/64
v.3626
Ruddies swim along, snapping bills just below surface of water in feeding.

Natural History], Washington, D. C. (USNM; R. C. Banks, M. R. Browning, J. Weske, R. Zusi), University of Alaska Museum, College (UAM; B. Kessel), University of Alberta Museum of Zoology, Edmonton (UAMZ; D. A. Boag, V. Lewin, N. Panter), University of British Columbia [Vertebrate Museum], Vancouver (UBC; M. F. Jackson), University of Kansas Museum of Natural History, Lawrence (KUMNH; the late R. M. Mengel), University of Manitoba Zoology Museum, Winnipeg (UMZM; S. G. Sealy), University of Michigan Museum of Zoology, Ann Arbor (UMMZ; R. W. Storer), University of Minnesota Field Biology Program [David F. Parmelee Collection], Minneapolis (UMFBP [DFP]; D. F. Parmelee), University of Nebraska Museum of Zoology, Lincoln (UNMZ; P. W. Freeman), University of North Dakota, Grand Forks (UND; L. W. Oring), Oklahoma Museum of Natural History; [formerly, University of Oklahoma Stovall Museum of Science and History], Norman (OU; the late G. M. Sutton), University of Oregon Museum of Natural History, Eugene (UOMNH; E. Gustafson), University of Regina Department of Biology, Saskatchewan (URDB; D. H. Sheppard), Utah Museum of Natural History, [formerly, University of Utah Museum of Zoology], Salt Lake City (UMNH; W. H. Behle, J. W. Wyckoff), [University of Washington Thomas] Burke [Memorial] Museum, Seattle (UWBM; S. Rohwer, J. Rozdilsky, C. Wood), University of Wisconsin Department of Wildlife Ecology, Madison (UWDWE; R. A. McCabe), University of Wisconsin [Richter Natural History Collection], Green Bay (UWGB[RC]; R. S. Cook, T. C. Erdman, H. J. Harris), [Rob and Bessie] Welder Wildlife Foundation, Sinton, Texas (WWF; the late C. Cottam), the Wildfowl Trust [Slimbridge], England (M. Brown), and the Zoological Museum of Copenhagen, Denmark (ZMK; the late F. Salomonsen).

The preparation of the appendices required a good deal of special assistance. The late L. E. Kansas helped tabulate nearly 2000 sets of data for statistical analysis; B. F. Harnish programmed and ran the calculations of them and S. A. Harnish assisted; F. D. Caswell, G. S. Hochbaum, B. Macpherson, and J. B. E. O'Malley gave helpful consultations; and B. F. Harnish and G. S. Hochbaum analysed data on scaup and goldeneyes. H. A. MacDiarmid, G. Szecker, and G. Wyszecki advised on illuminants and supplied useful references; R. L. Hombach assisted with colorimetric tabulations, and L. K. Forster acted as second observer for the preparation of a color synonymy.

Collectors, aviculturists, and curators and staff of museums and aviaries furnished much information on the origins of live and prepared specimens examined. As well, many persons and institutions furnished place names from field data or other special sources: British Columbia Ministry of Transportation and Highways (D. G. H. Raven), Canada Department of Fisheries and Oceans (R. W. Watts), Canadian Permanent Committee on Geographic Names (R. Leduc, A. Rayburn, W. B. Yeo; G. Holm [Man.], D. F. Pearson, N. Michaud-Oystryk [B.C.]), Det Gronlandske Landsbibliotek (H. Rhode), Hudson's Bay Company Library, Hudson's Bay House (C. Preston), Minnesota Department of Natural Resources (C. Henderson, J. Idstrom, L. L. Johnson), National Museum of Canada (the late V. M. Humphreys, H. Ouellet), Province of Saskatchewan Archives (E. E. Morgan), State of North Carolina Division of Archives and History, U. S. Board of Geographic Names (D. Johnson, N. Michalas, D. Orth, R. Payne, R. R. Randall), U. S. Forest Service Information, Yakima, Washington (P. Hart, D. O'Connor, E. Oram), University of Manitoba Dafoe Library (Icelandic Special Collections: S. Johnson; Maps: H. Larimer, D. Phelan), University of Massachusetts (A. C. Bent collections: the late L. M. Bartlett), University of Minnesota (Map Library: L. Anderson); for place names in Alaska (B. Kessel, D. McKnight), Arizona (S. Liston, A. M. Rea), British Columbia (A. J. Erskine, I. M. Cowan), Delaware (H. E. Carey), Minnesota (F. B. Lee, G. A. Swanson), Saskatchewan (J. McConnell, R. G. McKee, F. Mowat), Texas (H. L. Brookshire), Cameroon (D. E. Willard), Costa Rica (L. D. Gomez), Greenland (the late P. Holting), Iceland (H. Bessasson, R. Glendenning, A. Petersen), Madagascar (the late J.T. Delacour), Mexico (R. W. Dickerman), Panama (G. S. Cowles), CIS [formerly, USSR] (G. S. Cowles, W. E. Lanyon), and sources of certain captive species (T. Jones).

For certain translations, I thank B. Cunnings, the late P. Holting (Danish); S. Boning, E. Burley, C. Dyck, Multilingual Services Division of the Canadian Secretary of State (German); C. A. Agard, J. A. Martin (Haitian [French]); R. Glendenning (Icelandic); Y. de Forest (Japanese); L. Kinsbergen, J. Boning (Nederlands); V. Hatten, B. Rotoff, G. Sudomlak (Russian); and O. Tivoli (Spanish).

The assistance of librarians at the Carnegie Museum (G. McKiernan), the Delta Waterfowl and Wetlands Research Station (P. Calder, B. Hales, D. L. Kelly, M. M. Lizotte, P. G. Murphy, the late S. Rutledge), Louisiana State University (A. M. Ipinza), the Manitoba Museum of Man and Nature (J. Carnegie, P. Gendre, K. Gillespie, V. E. Hatten, W. G. Scharbach, C. Shields, C. Steffan), Scripps Institution of Oceanography [Marine Biology Research Division] (S. Stoltz), the University of Lund [UB2], Sweden (L. Sagner), and the University of Manitoba (P. Anthony, R. Bennett, C. Brault, K. Chamberlain, P. Moore, W. Westelaken) proved indispensable to my research. In addition, G. V. T. Matthews supplied publication dates for the first five issues of the Wildfowl Trust's Annual Report, and C. S. Holohan loaned several volumes from his personal library.

B. A. Anderson, E. M. Billington, C. M. Clifford, and B. E. Mackenzie typed successive drafts of the manuscript; K. D. Pooley, P. Bukowski, L. Damant, L. T. Duhamel, M. Fisher, B. C. Glassey, L. Goulet, M. Jesson, N. Jesson, D. Lapsley, S. L. Lopez, V. M. Molter, L. Nicholls, D. L. Turner, and J. J. Warrington typed portions of it. A. Bell, G. M. Dickmeis, L. M. Gregory, V. E. Hatten, K. J. Hughes, A. P.

Kansas, H. A. and W. M. M. MacDiarmid, L. Mark, C. R. Nelson, Jr., F. W. B. Nelson, K. B. Nelson, M. C. Nelson, R. W. and R. F. Nero, L. M. Phillips, M. D. Rieber, R. Wolfe, and R. E. Wrigley proofed parts of the final manuscript.

Manuscript portions were read by M. G. Anderson, T. W. Barry, J. C. Bartonek, C. K. Bluhm, E. G. Bolen, the late J. Bond, A. H. Brush, M. Carrick, F. Cooke, D. I. Eisenhauer, L. H. Fredrickson, H. Hays, J. P. Hubbard, A. F. Lee, the late J. J. Lynch, S. D. MacDonald, D. F. McKinney, M. R. McLandress, H. L. Mendall, D. W. Moulton, L. W. Oring, H. Ouellet, K. C. Parkes, A. Petersen, M. R. Petersen, the late D. G. Raveling, A. Reed, J. P. Ryder, F. W. Schueler, N. J. Scott, Jr., R. W. Storer, V. D. Stotts, C. D. Stutzenbaker, D. E. Trauger, P. Ward, M. W. Weller, R. A. Wishart, and R. E. Wrigley. R. C. Banks, F. C. Bellrose, H. J. Boyd, the late R. M. Mengel, and S. G. Sealy read critically the entire manuscript and made detailed suggestions for its improvement. The comments and constructive criticism of all of these readers have taken the manuscript well beyond my first realizations of it.

A number of colleagues tested the Identification Keys and made suggestions for their improvement. From the Canadian Wildlife Service: F. G. Cooch, S. Curtis, C. Hyslop, L. Metras, J.-P. Savard; from the Carnegie Museum: M. H. Clench, J. M. Loughlin, K. C. Parkes; from Ducks Unlimited (Canada): R. Basiuk, C. Cuthbert, A. Lane, J. Missler, E. E. Mowbray, T. G. Neraasen, P. Ould, T. Sopuck; from the Delta Waterfowl and Wetlands Research Station: J. A. Barzen; from the Manitoba Department of Natural Resources: E. F. Bossenmaier, R. W. Nero; from the Manitoba Museum of Man and Nature: B. A. Anderson, R. H. Breuer, H. W. R. Copland, J. E. Dubois, K. L. Johnson, O. Johnston, L. S. Kinsbergen, G. E. Lammers, W. B. McKillop, W. B. Preston, J. L. Wiley, R. E. Wrigley; from the National Museum of Canada: B. DiLabio, M. Gosselin, H. Ouellet, R. Poulin; and from the University of Manitoba: S. G. Sealy.

The readers are not responsible for any shortcomings that may appear in this work. Those are all mine.

Representatives of several institutions kindly granted permission to quote from published works. These were: T. and A. D. Poyser, Calton, England: tabular data from *The Hawaiian Goose*, by Janet Kear and Andrew J. Berger, © 1980; John Wiens, former editor of *The Auk*: tabular data from "Body weights of newly hatched Anatidae," by Glen Smart (*Auk* 82: 645-48); the Purdue University Research Foundation: day-old weights from "Ecology and behavior of the Emperor Goose (*Anser canagicus* Sewastianov) in Alaska" by David I. Eisenhauer (Master's thesis, Purdue University 1976); and the University of California (Berkeley) Museum of Vertebrate Zoology: certain data from an unpublished field notebook by H. S. Swarth.

Several owners of C. H. Nelson downy waterfowl paintings graciously allowed me to use them as references during preparation of the composite plates: Joanne Ariza, Catherine Auld and Edward McLachlan; Jacques Collin and Karen Collin; Sheila Feltham; Peter and Liivi Forster; Mitchell Giffin; Barbara Harnish; Ben Harnish; Alvin, Jr., and Jacquelyn Helgeson; Denis and Marguerite Jesson; Winston and Kathleen Leathers; the Manitoba Museum of Man and Nature; Patrick Nelson; Michael and Linda Radcliffe; Karen Nelson; Holly Rattray; Harvey and Karen Schipper; Barry and Rena Shenkarow; Roy and Myrtle Simmons; May Tascona; Tony Tascona; Charles and Roine Thomsen; and Joel and Cathy Weinstein.

Financial assistance for my research came from the Frank M. Chapman Fund of the American Museum of Natural History (1962-63), the RESA - Society of the Sigma Xi (Grants-in-Aid of Research: 1963-64), the Josselyn Van Tyne Memorial Fund of the American Ornithologists' Union (1966), the Canada Council (short-term artist's grant with travel allowance: 1969; Explorations Programme grants: 1973-74, 1980), Manitoba Arts Council (materials grant: 1980), the National Museum of

Natural Sciences, Ottawa (1981), and the Carnegie Museum, Pittsburgh (per diem from International Program for Visiting Museum Specialists: 1966-67, 1974, 1976, 1978-79, 1982, 1984). Their support has made possible the completion of this work.

Several colleagues wrote letters on my behalf, and others advised on various aspects of the project: G. Adaskin, J. C. Barlow, E. F. Bossenmaier, W. J. Breckenridge, N. M. Curry, W. C. Dilger, W. H. Elder, G. M. Genthon, J. W. Graham, J. Kear, the late S. C. Kendeigh, W. Leathers, C. Lindgren, W. R. Miller, R. S. Palmer, R. J. Raikow, G. Swinton, M. V. Tascona, A. T. Tascona, A. W. Vincent, and D. W. Warner. I am particularly indebted to the late H. Albert Hochbaum, who gave invaluable advice and criticism during my first years at Delta, and to Bruce Batt, Kenneth Parkes, and Peter Ward, who were unfailing sources of advice and encouragement throughout the project. I am also grateful to Charles Potter, Jr., Alan Scarth, Q.C., and Peter Ward for their efforts in putting forth this book for publication.

I am greatly indebted to J. E. Dubois, G. E. Lammers, R. W. Nero, H. Ouellet, and R. E. Wrigley for the use of office and laboratory space and secretarial services at the Manitoba Museum of Man and Nature and, more recently, at the National Museum of Canada, and for their encouragement and support of my research. The museums' tranquil ambience and the many kindnesses of friends and colleagues have made my work a joy.

For most generous hospitality during visits to museums and aviaries, I thank Lloyd and Frances Burdette, Patricia Burdette, Mary and the late Harry Clench, Charles and Dorothy Dane, Robert and Elizabeth Elgas, Arnold and Mildred Helgeson, Joan and the late Al Hochbaum, John and Irene Meader, Arthur and Hazel Mudry,Charlotte Murray, Eldon and Ruth Pace, Kenneth and Ellen Parkes, Frances Rosewarne, Miriam Sharick, Ruth and the late Carl Strutz, B. J. and Leslie Verts, Peter and Joyce Ward, and the late Jack Williams and his family.

During most of the years that I researched this project, I had small children at home. My four youngest ones have never known a mother who was not interested in downy waterfowl. I am grateful to those who cared for my children

so that I could do research and paint: Barbara Benning, Esther Berg, Teresa Bobik, Shirley Carr, Annette Filby, Susan Good, Sandra and Susan Gossen, Elaine and Ilona Grymonpré, Marguerite Harkness, Ruth Hombach, Audrey Kansas, Myrna Lye, Kelly and Michael McCaughey, Philip and Reginald Pratt, Carla Rattray, Marnie Rieber, Cathy Tascona, Christina Veveris, Terri Wicks, and Valerie Wright.

Family members have assisted in many ways, large and small, with my research and the preparation of the manuscript, especially the late Burdella Myers; Edna and the late Alvin Helgeson, Sr.; Christopher, John, Kathleen, and Patrick Nelson; P. J. Henderson; and the late Carl R., Sr., and the late Margaret Nelson. Finally, I wish to thank my husband, Carl, on whose talents, good sense, patience, and support I have relied throughout the course of my work.

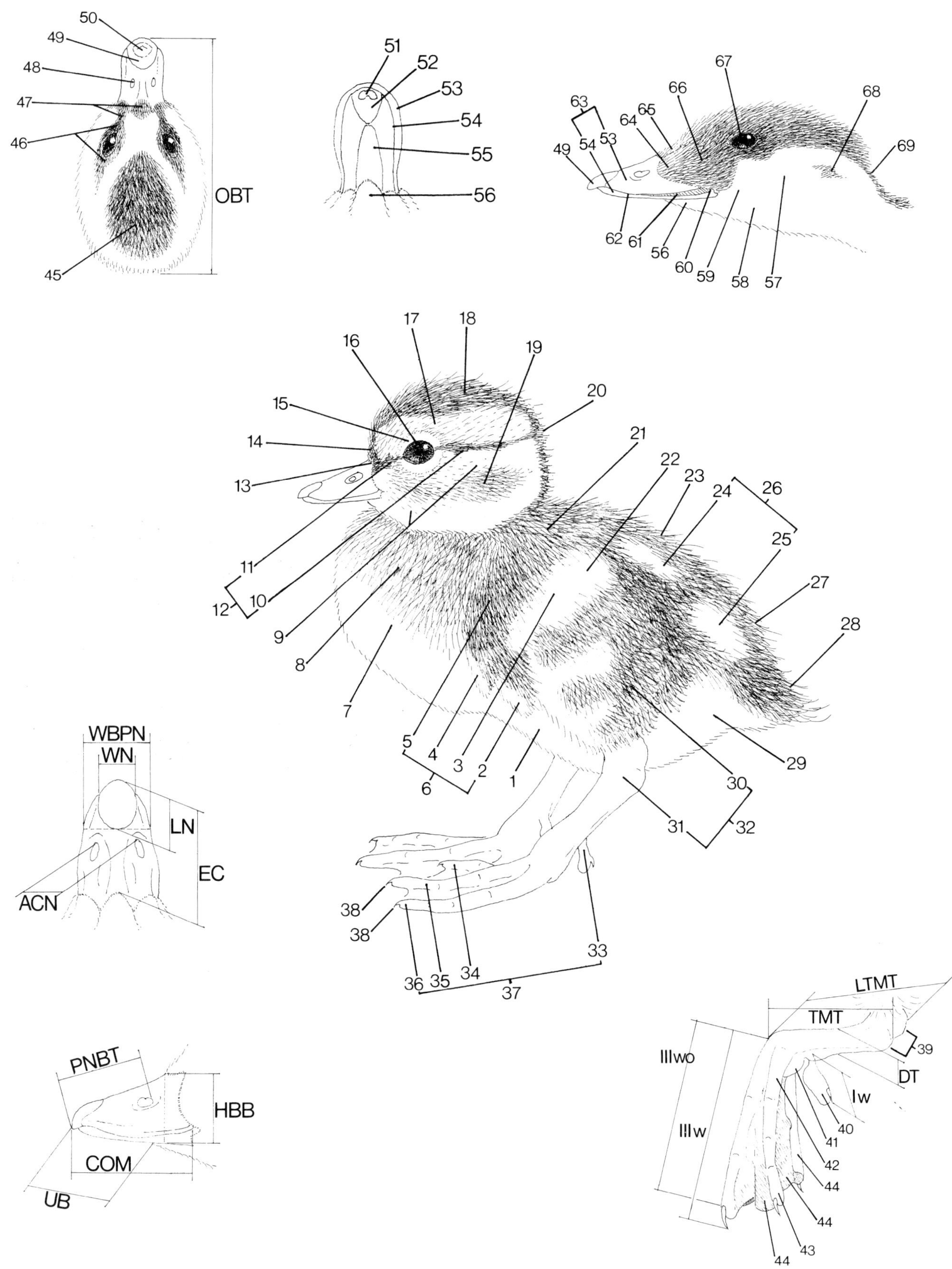

Relative scale of figures not consistent.

Illustrated Glossary

1. Belly
2. (Primaries)
3. (Secondaries)
4. (Alula)
5. (Coverts)
6. Wing
7. Breast
8. Breast-band
9. 'Cheek' (area)
10. Post-ocular stripe
11. Pre-ocular stripe
12. Eye-stripe
13. 'Horn' of bill
14. Forehead
15. Eye-ring
16. Eyelid rim
17. Supraorbital stripe
18. Crown
19. 'Cheek-stripe'
20. Occiput
21. Yoke
22. Wing-patch [pattern]
23. Back
24. Shoulder-spot
25. Rump-spot
26. Dorsal spots
27. Rump
28. Tail
29. Undertail
30. Tibiotarsus
31 Tarsometatarsus
32. Leg
33. Hallux (I)
34. Inner toe (II)
35. Middle toe (III)
36. Outer toe (IV)
37. Digits
38. Claw
39. 'Heel'
40. Lobe of hallux
41. Metatarsal pad
42. Proximal phalanx
43. Distal phalanx
44. Web (3)
45. Crown-patch
46. 'Mask'
47. 'Bridle'
48. Nostril
49. [Upper] nail (2) (dertrum)
50. [Upper] egg-tooth
51. Lower egg-tooth (of dabbling duck)
52. Lower nail
53. Upper mandible (maxilla)
54. Lower mandible
55. Chin [bare portion]
56. Chin [feathered portion]
57. 'Cheek-patch' [pattern]
58. Throat
59. Malar region
60. Rictus
61. Lamellae
62. Tomium of upper mandible
63. Bill
64. Lateral feathering
65. Mesial feathering
66. Lore
67. Iris
68. Ear-spot
69. Hindneck (nape)

EC: Length of exposed culmen
PNBT: Distance from posterior corner of nostril to tip of bill
LN: Length of nail
WN: Width of nail at juncture with bill
WBPN: Width of bill at posterior of nail
UB: Distance from tip of chin feathering to tip of upper mandible
COM: Commissure; length of bill from gape to tip
HBB: Height of bill at base
ACN or DACN: Distance between anterior corners of nostrils
TMT: Length of tarsometatarsal bone from posterior end at mid-heel to anterior end on fron of foot at middle toe
LTMT: "Long" tarsus; length from back of heel (distal end of tibiotarsal bone) to anterior end of tarsometatarsal bone on front of foot at middle toe
DT: Antero-posterior diameter (depth) of tarsus at mid-point
IIIw: Length of middle toe with claw,
IIIwo: Length of III without claw
Iw: Length of hallux with claw
OBT: Length of head from occiput to bill-tip

Introduction

As I stated in the preface, this work started out to be simply a record, in watercolor, of the day-old young of the North American waterfowl—at most, a few summers' work. Once I realized that more than painting was needed to complete the record of the downy waterfowl, I felt I had no choice but to continue and to augment the pictorial record begun in 1962. A quarter of a century later, I found myself the possessor of more than twenty notebooks of behavioral, colorimetric, and museum data; hundreds of measured line drawings and color portraits; and several thousand life sketches and sets of mensural data. I knew the whereabouts of nearly every downy waterfowl skin in North America (and many abroad). I knew also that there still existed no single publication on the downy waterfowl of North America.

Except for F. E. Blaauw's descriptions (published between 1899 and 1916) of newly hatched waterfowl from his aviary in The Netherlands, descriptions and portraits of downy young included in several 19th and early 20th century works (e.g., Baird, Brewer, and Ridgway 1884; Coues 1903; Millais 1913; Forbush 1925) seem to have been made from museum specimens. Often minutely detailed, these portraits and verbal descriptions nonetheless reflect the color changes that take place in stored specimens, i.e., 'redder' or 'browner' hues than those found in the plumage of live birds, and greatly altered color attributes of the unfeathered parts. Live birds evidently were used for many later portrayals (e.g., A. C. Meinertzhagen, M. A. Koekkek, and G. E. Lodge *in* Witherby et al. [1939] 1943; A. Brooks and H. Grönvold *in* Phillips 1922-26; J. Larsen *in* Schiøler 1925-26; T. M. Shortt *in* Kortright 1942; P. M. Scott *in* Delacour 1954-64; C. H. Nelson *in* Palmer 1976; and R. Hines *in* Bellrose 1980). S. T. ("Tommy") Johnstone's descriptions of live hatchlings from the Wildfowl Trust collection at Slimbridge often included photographs by P. Talbot-Ponsonby, Philippa Scott, E. E. Jackson, and others. Photographs of live downy young are also included in Heinroth and Heinroth (1928), Kuroda (1939), and F. Todd (1979).

Recent works by Fjeldså (1977; *Guide to the precocial young of European birds*) and Harrison (field guides to nest, eggs, and nestlings of British and European [1975] and North American [1978] birds) identify both anatid and non-anatid young; Harrison's works also treat altricial young.

Fjeldså's paintings appear to have been made largely from fresh material (i.e., sketches and photos of live or newly dead young), although his use of published waterfowl references results in erroneous representation of the natal plumage of the Magpie Goose, *Anseranas* (Clark 1978). This minor flaw is more than offset by Fjeldså's assessment of intraspecific pattern variation in palaearctic downy waterfowl (Fjeldså 1977: figs. 10-11) and by his numerous, lively ink-sketches.

Burton's paintings (*in* Harrison 1975, 1978), on the other hand, seem to have been based mainly on published references and museum skins. The result is the perpetuation of errors in colors of the unfeathered parts and in plumage pattern. In general, the feet of Burton's downy waterfowl are too small.

The primary object of my research has been to provide detailed descriptions, drawings, color portraits, and diagnostic identification of live, day-old young of North American waterfowl. I have used the Munsell color notation and the verbal nomenclature based upon it (Kelly and Judd 1976) to make the descriptions, not only for the sake of consistency but also to encourage their use by other biologists. The keys to identification are based mainly on characters of structure and pattern. They are intended primarily for use in field and museum with birds in the hand, although the plumage patterns shown may also serve to identify some downy young seen at a distance.

The taxonomic importance of the downy young has been pointed out by A. C. Meinertzhagen (1924), Moffitt (1932), Mayr (1945), Delacour and Mayr (1945), Johnsgard (1961b, 1965), Storer (1967), Jehl (1968b), and others. I found that color and pattern characters of downy waterfowl suggested taxonomic arrangements somewhat different from those now generally accepted. In most cases, these departures are supported by evidence from other sources. I have discussed these views elsewhere under Taxonomy, pp. 4-5, in various tribal accounts, and in the Discussion, pp. 147-56.

Materials and Methods

Observation

Live birds were the basis of the sketches, descriptions, and color portraits, as well as of the measured drawings of bills included in the Identification Keys. Some portraits for which I had no live models were done from well-prepared museum skins, and a few others from descriptions and color transparencies provided by others. The life-size ink drawings in the Identification Keys are based almost entirely on museum specimens (see Appendix C).

I weighed and measured the day-old birds (see Appendix A), color-evaluated (see Appendix B), and color-sketched them. Using a Uher 4000 Report-l tape recorder, I recorded the voices of about 25 species, following the methods described by Kear (1968). Having placed the birds in an elevated pen, I sat beside it to observe, photograph, and sketch them at eye-level. Downy birds that died during rearing, as well as day-old birds of many species collected at Delta during 1964, were prepared as study specimens for the Delta Study Collection, Portage la Prairie and the Manitoba Museum of

Man and Nature, Winnipeg.

Color evaluation

Standard illumination and viewing methods were essential to proper color evaluation. Most times, I used north daylight or one of two lamp-booths (C. Nelson 1982) to evaluate the colors of both live and prepared specimens. Other times, I used Macbeth lamps or shaded daylight of various kinds. Before 1975, I simply held the live birds away from both glare and shadow, in a position where the colors seemed 'right', and made evaluations whenever the birds were still—the artist's method. After 1975, I used the more consistent procedures recommended by the CIE (Commission International de l'Eclairage [International Lighting Commission]) for illumination and viewing (CIE 1971). In this method, a horizontal specimen illuminated by beams of light at about 45° (as from a window) is viewed more or less directly from above (normal), a horizontal specimen under direct (normal) illumination (as in the lamp-booths) at approximately 45°.

Color nomenclature

Color notation of the *Munsell Soil Color Charts* (1973 [hues 5R to 5Y, with 7 additional hue charts: 7.5Y, 10Y, 2.5GY, 5GY, 5PB, 7.5PB, Gley]) is used throughout the text. Hues not included in the augmented soils collections were evaluated from the *Munsell Book of Color*

(1929, matte samples; 1966, glossy samples). Use of the Munsell notations permitted quantification of three attributes of color: *hue* (e.g., yellow [Y], yellow-red [YR], green-yellow [GY]), *value* (e.g., dark [2.5/ to 4.4/], medium [4.5/ to 6.4/], light [6.5/ to 8.5/]), and *chroma* (e.g., vivid [/14 and higher], strong [/5 to /12], moderate [/2.5 to /4.5], dull or grayish [/0.5 to /2.4]). Where necessary, Munsell notations were

derived from older terminologies of Ridgway (1912) or Villalobos-Dominguez and Villalobos (1947), using a color synonymy prepared with the assistance of a second observer.

Most verbal color names are from *Color—Universal Language and Dictionary of Names* (Kelly and Judd 1976); these correlate directly with Munsell notations made, in most cases, from live birds. In certain other cases, I used generic names (Palmer and Reilly 1956) or commonly understood terms, followed by equivalent color dictionary terms in brackets, e.g., grayish rosy buff [=dull yellowish red].

Aviculture

Incubation and rearing techniques, developed at the Delta Waterfowl and Wetlands Research Station for prairie species (Ward and Batt 1973), worked equally well for most others. Only the sea-ducks needed special treatment: plenty of space, water for diving, and live animal food. Swimming pools were built into elevated observation pens used at Delta (DWWRS; UFS[DM]) and in my studio-laboratory at home. Portable brooder pens (Ward and Batt 1973: 51, fig. 41) modeled after pens used in J. P. Williams's aviary at Tunstead, Norwich, were also used. These combined shelter with an infrared lamp for warmth; a small, exposed grassy area; a swimming tank; and predator-proof wire screens at both top and bottom of the pen.

Wild eggs that I imported for my research usually had been incubated by their natural mothers to the point of hatching (i.e., star-pipped) before collection and shipment. Shipping crates (i.e., Ward and Batt 1973: 16, fig. 9), containing molded paper trays to prevent breakage, were designed to allow hatching during transport if necessary. Broody bantam hens incubated and reared the eggs of captives at Slimbridge and Tunstead in England.

Prepared specimens

Museum specimens were an indispensable aid to my research. They provided most of the data on the few species that I did not see alive, they confirmed or supplemented plumage and structural data from the live birds, and they allowed me to assess individual and geographical variation. Acronyms are mainly from Choate and Genoways (1975); some were obtained from curators or museum labels; and a few, such as aviary acronyms, were assigned by the author.

Identification keys

I began work on the Identification Keys in 1967. I hoped to provide a guide to museum specimens of downy waterfowl based on pattern rather than color. The use of color alone as an identifying character can be misleading—nor does color indicate taxonomic relatedness, as Portenko (1972 [1981]) believed. Furthermore, colors of museum skins often change over time; patterns do not. I felt that such a guide would be especially useful for teaching collections, which often have more than their share of misidentified specimens. The life-sized bills of day-old young provide a scale against which specimens of unknown age can be measured.

Geographical area

The geographical area covered by this book extends from Greenland west to the western Aleutian Islands, south to the Hawaiian Islands, Mexico, and Central America, as far as but not including, Colombia. The West Indies, the Netherlands' Antilles, and Baja California are also included. The reader is directed to the range maps in *The Handbook of North American Birds,* vols. 2 and 3 (Palmer 1976), and to the distribution sections of the *A.O.U. Check-list of North American Birds,* 6th ed. (A.O.U. 1983). Exact geographic locations, museum acronyms, and numbers of bird specimens examined follow each species account under "Source of Specimens." Museum catalog numbers are not given.

Taxonomy and nomenclature

Based as it is on the phenetic relationships of pattern, structure, and color in newly hatched waterfowl, the classification used here may be expected to differ in some ways from other recent systems. Nevertheless, there is substantial agreement between this classification and various others derived from analysis of anatomical and osteological characters (e.g., Humphrey 1958a; Woolfenden 1961; Livezey 1986), DNA (e.g., Kessler and Avise 1984; Quinn, Shields and Wilson 1991), blood and muscle tissue (Numachi et al. 1983; Oates et al. 1983), behavior (Johnsgard 1965, 1978, 1979), and vocalizations (Kear 1968). There are also certain parallels with more "eclectic" (Raikow 1985b: 189) taxonomies (e.g., Delacour and Mayr 1945; A.O.U. 1957, 1983).

In general, pattern [="color pattern"; Jehl 1968b: 7] is the element of the plumage that shows relatedness at the tribal and generic levels (e.g., Kear 1968; Fjeldså 1977), whereas structural details and color characters are more useful in distinguishing species and subspecies. My object in retaining as tribes, genera, full species, or subspecies taxa previously merged by other authors (e.g., Heinroth and Heinroth 1928, vol. 3; Delacour and Mayr 1945; Johnsgard 1965, 1979; A.O.U. 1983) is simply to elucidate what appear to be natural groupings (whether or not recognized nomenclaturally by other authors), as defined by characters of the newly hatched young. Many ornithologists believe such characters to be conservative and hence useful taxonomically.

Within the Anatidae, I have followed the tribal designations of the *A.O.U. Checklist of North American Birds*, 6th ed. (1983), with the addition of the tribe *Somateriini*, following studies by Humphrey ([1955] n.d., 1958a; tracheal anatomy, adult female and downy plumages) and Brush (1976; feather proteins). Although Brush merged Cygnini with Anserini (as did Delacour and Mayr 1945; Johnsgard 1965; and others), distinctive characters of the downy plumage and unfeathered parts of cygnets support Woolfenden's (1961) and Livezey's (1986) separation of the two tribes on the basis of osteology (see Discussion, pp. 147-56, for proposed departures from tribal order).

Genera follow Woolfenden's (1961) allocations, except that *Mareca* and *Philacte* (A.O.U. 1957; Livezey 1991 re: *Mareca*). are retained. Well-marked differences in the downy plumage pattern separate *Mareca* from *Anas*, and *Philacte* from *Anser.*

Order and nomenclature of species follow Voous (1973; based largely on Johnsgard 1965) for the whistling-ducks, swans, *Anser* (but A.O.U. 1983 for *Branta* and *Nesochen*), perching ducks, *Aythya*, eiders, and sea-ducks (except order of *Bucephala* spp.: *islandica, clangula, albeola*), but the order of the stiff-tails is reversed: *Oxyura jamaicensis, Nomonyx dominicus.* Order of species in the Anatini also follows Voous (1973), except that the two pintail species are placed near the Green-winged Teal, the three mallard-like species recognized by Palmer (1976, vol. 2)—*A. fulvigula, A. rubripes, A. diazi*—appear in that order before the Northern Mallard, and the Hawaiian and Laysan ducks follow it, preceding the blue-winged ducks.

Downy young collected with the known

range of an accepted subspecies, exhibiting geographical variation or characters believed typical of the group, were assigned to that subspecies. Certain downy specimens proved difficult to classify because knowledge of adults and downy young from some parts of the breeding range was incomplete or lacking, e.g., Greater White-fronted Goose and Canada Goose. Regarding the latter species, I have used 11 of Delacour's (1951) subspecies (the 12th, *asiatica* Aldrich, presumed extinct), despite Palmer's (1976, vol. 2) persuasive argument for the recognition of only eight, because Delacour's nomenclature reflects better the diversity of form, color, and pattern among the downy young (see also Van Wagner and Baker 1986; Shields and Wilson 1987b).

English names are those of the A.O.U. 1983, except for certain subspecific names which follow Delacour (1954) and Palmer (1976); English names of South American endemics follow Blake (1977). Unless otherwise acknowledged, French names are taken from Ouellet and Gosselin (1983), Spanish names from Sada, Phillips, and Ramos (1987).

Results

Attributes of downy young waterfowl are often quite different from those of their adult counterparts. Whereas vocalizations and behavior—if peculiar to the very young—can be shown clearly to have developmental connections to the adult condition (e.g., Tinbergen 1939; Caswell 1972), colors and patterns of the downy young cannot. They are both unique and transitory. In this work, I have tried to describe the behavioral and morphological qualities of the downy young in some detail, for their biologic, taxonomic, and intrinsic value.

Colors

Plumage

The colors of plumage and unfeathered parts of all downy waterfowl usually consist of several *values* and *chromas* of the same *hue* or closely related *hues*; these related colors often characterize a tribe, genus, species, or group of species. Although clearly parts of an integrated whole (i.e., the total appearance of a species), the colors will be discussed here in two major categories: base color, the lighter one, and pattern color, the darker (as defined by Johnsgard 1965). Three base colors occur in the plumage: yellow, white, and grayish rosy buff. Yellow appears most often in Anatini and Aythyini, and in some downy whistling-ducks, geese, and perching ducks; white is found in cygnets, in other downy perching ducks, geese, and whistling-ducks, in *A. acuta*, and in Mergini ducklings; and grayish rosy buff [=dull yellowish red; Kelly and Judd 1976] is restricted to downy eiders. *Hues* rom 2.5Y to 7.5Y characterize most yellow downies, but *hues* of *Anser*, and of some *Branta* and *Dendrocygna* downies are more greenish, ranging to 10Y, 1.25GY, or 2.5GY. *Hues* of Laysan and Masked ducklings are more orange (1.5Y; e.g., dark yellow or deep yellow), and the *hue* of the American Wigeon's secondary base color is 10YR, a strong (but dull in some specimens) brownish yellow (Kelly and Judd 1976).

Pattern color of the downy young is always basically gray or black, but some lighter values seem to acquire hue from the underlying base color. For example, the light or medium gray pattern colors of the geese—seldom dark except in 'blue' phase Snow and Ross' goslings—show up as olive-gray, olive-green, or olive-yellow (some *Branta* goslings), or strong greenish olive or grayish yellow-green (certain downy *Anser*), so that the entire aspect of the birds becomes primarily that of the bright or brilliant base color. Even the 'blackest' pattern color appears to have a degree of *chroma* if the base color is sufficiently brilliant, as in downy Black-bellied Whistling-ducks. In downy mergansers, the yellowish red secondary pattern color lends a distinct 'reddish' cast to their dark grayish heads and, in *Mergus* ducklings, to their blackish face-stripes, as well.

In wild downy young of all species, the

chroma of the natal colors diminishes rapidly (i.e., becomes duller, especially greenish yellow colors), and their *value* increases (i.e., grows paler), so that after 7-10 days of exposure to sunlight, little remains of any bright or brilliant colors present at hatching. Colors are further-dulled by plumage wear and by growth of new gray underdown over the entire body—a process which begins at about 10 days in the Gadwall (Oring 1968)—but the *hue* of the natal colors in newly hatched and some older birds

often remains the same. For example, the bright yellow *hue* of a live, day-old Canvasback was 6Y 8/8; that of a live, four-day-old duckling was "straw yellow" (Dzubin 1959: 258), the same yellow, if somewhat paler and duller (Ridgway's [1912] 'straw yellow'=Hamly's [1949] Munsell 6Y 8.4/6).

Colorants. "Eumelanin...the black or dark brown [pigment of] crows *Corvus* spp. Blackbird *Turdus merula*...and...others" (Vevers 1964) probably also is responsible for the dark pattern color of downy waterfowl, but the colorants producing the yellow and rosy buff base colors are incompletely known. Oring (1968) suggested that carotenes were the source of the yellow color in downy Gadwalls, whereas Völker (1934) proposed that phaeomelanin, rather than carotenoids, produces the yellow color of downy domestic chicks and ducklings. Brush (1981: 542) stated that some form of melanin is the colorant of "most hatchlings," and reported further that "ethanolic extracts of the bills and feathers of the head, face, and neck...[of a downy] coot (*Fulica atra*) ...produced a yellow-orange solution with no distinct visible spectral bands (Brush and Zamlauski, unpubl.)." An experiment by M. Tascona and C. Nelson (unpubl.) using a methanolic extract of the tips of yellow down feathers from a day-old Northern Mallard, *A. p. platyrhynchos*, had similar undetermined results: spectrophotometric analysis disclosed no recognizeable carotenoid maxima, nor could the maxima recorded be assigned to any colorant known to these researchers.

Structural colors. Iridescent colors appear on several species. The Harlequin duckling has faint greenish blue ('turquoise') iridescence on the dorsum (Palmer 1976, vol. 3), and there seems to be a weak iridescence on the backs of some downy Oldsquaws (purple) and Common and Red-breasted mergansers (bluish green). Light yellow Canada goslings have many glistening 'gold-tipped' down plumes, but dark yellow goslings have almost none. Trumpeter and Whistling cygnets (live Whoopers not seen) appear to have a 'silver' iridescence on head and breast.

Iridescent colors (e.g., blue, green, copper) found on the specula of adults of various *Anas* species are produced by the interference of melanin granules in the barbules of the contour feathers (Rutschke 1966); the ultrastructure of the barbules of iridescent down plumes may be similar. However, the 'silvery' aspect of the *Olor* cygnets' white plumage probably results from the reflection of incident light by the colorless but [presumably] regularly structured barbules (see H. Fox and Vevers 1960).

The possible adaptive significance of structural colors in downy waterfowl is unclear, although both the 'silvery' down of *Olor* cygnets and the dark bluish greenish gray dorsal color of Harlequin ducklings may help to conceal them from aerial predators: the *Olor* cygnets' white down is the color of new-fallen snow—a frequent component of their tundra nest-sites, and MacDonald pointed out that the Harlequin ducklings' dorsal color resembles that of wet stones in the swift-running streams of their habitat (Stewart MacDonald, pers. comm. 1984).

Variation

Variations in color and pattern of the plumage are of three kinds: individual, continuous, and discontinuous. Individual variation consists of small differences in prominence of the pattern elements, or in color attributes of the plumage and unfeathered parts. Such variations are widespread. They appear random and unrelated to geographical origin or to sex. Continuous variation describes the range of individual or geographic differences for a given character, and assumes a more or less evenly graded series representing the extremes of variation as well as all intermediates (e.g., geographical variants in Canada goslings; belly colors of adult Brant from Prince Patrick Island [Manning, Höhn, and Macpherson 1956: pl. 7]; see also extremes of pattern color continua for Green-winged Teal, pl. 6, & Redhead, pl. 8). Such small variations, common to wild individuals of all species, have little effect upon the stability of pattern characters within tribes (e.g., Dendrocygnini), genera (e.g., *Mareca*, *Somateria*), and species groups (e.g., blue-winged ducks, pochards, scaup).

Color phases represent discontinuous variation, i.e., distinct variants whose characteristics do not seem to overlap. These appear in swans (*C. olor, O. buccinator*), some geese (*A. rossii, A. caerulescens*) and whistling-ducks (*D. bicolor* has dark and pale variants in pattern color, *D. autumnalis* has 'dark' and pale variants in base color). Variants for brown face and yellow face, occurring in the American Wigeon, are often clearly distinguishable from one another, but at other times display overlapping characters.

Well-marked color phases characterize the Ross' and Snow goslings (adult Snow Geese also polymorphic). Of five color classes described by Cooke and Cooch (1968) in the downy Lesser Snow Goose, the two lightest (Classes 0 and 1) and the two darkest (Classes 3 and 4) are well-separated in color and pattern. The intermediate Class 2, apparently rather uncommon (Cooke and Cooch 1968), shows characters of both light and dark phases, but more of the latter.

Color phases in the Ross' gosling are more complex (Ryder [1967: 36] named 7 color categories), although the darkest ("dark gray") and lightest ("white") gray phases are easily distinguished, as are the "black yellow" and "light yellow" categories. The great variety of intermediates in both gray and yellow phases suggests more or less continuous variation in both.

Unfeatherd parts

Eyes. Downy young of most species have brown or hazel eyes at all stages, but the eyes of a few change progressively in the immature plumages before achieving the adult color, which is usually yellow or red, sometimes brown. Such changes are known in the goldeneyes (C. Nelson 1983), in downy *Mergus*, in various *Aythya* species (Weller 1957; see also scaup accounts, pp. 106-10), in the Northern Cinnamon Teal (Spencer 1953), and in the Australian Black Swan (Frith 1982).

According to H. Fox and Vevers (1960: 13), yellow and brown [also certain red?] eye-colors are produced by "melanin pigment granules of these colours in the stroma of the iris," but the blue eye-colors of some mammals [e.g., cats; man] are structural, the result of Tyndall scattering, i.e., "minute protein particles in the iris...which scatter the incident white light...causing blueness." Blue eye-color in mammals may also result from the reflection of incident light through the cornea by a blue *tapetum lucidum*, as in the Gaur, *Bos gaurus* (Inverarity 1889; Dunbar Brander 1926). However, the brilliance of the purple-blue eye-color of downy goldeneyes (up to Munsell /12 in direct natural or artificial daylight; C. Nelson 1983) suggests the involvement of other factors, such as structural modifications of the inner eye producing iridescence, perhaps in combination with "red carotenoids...or reddish brown melanins [which would] give a...violet appearance" (D. Fox 1976: 39). Eye shine is a less likely concomitant: neither Van Rossem (1927) nor Walker (1939) reported purple-blue eye-shine in any avian group that they observed, nor do birds have a true *tapetum lucidum* (Wood 1917).

Bill. Except for *Olor* cygnets, whose bills and feet derive their pink color from the red blood pigment, haemoglobin (Parmelee, Stephens, and Schmidt 1967; see also D. Fox 1971, 1976 [pl. 3] re: flamingo nestlings), the upper mandibles of downy anatids are dark colored, presumably melanic. *Value* of the bill color ranges between 3/ (dark) and 5/ (medium); the basically gray tones often have tints of other *hues* (e.g., 'greenish' in Barrow's Goldeneye, 'purplish' in White-winged Scoter, 'bluish' in Gadwall and Redhead, 'reddish orange' in Northern Shoveler, etc.).

Colors of the lower mandible vary among the tribes. Dark colors, matching those of the upper mandible, appear in downy *Cygnus*, all goslings, greater eiders (*Somateria*), and most Mergini ducklings, while light dull yellow or pinkish yellow colors characterize downy whistling-ducks, Anatini, Aythyini, Hooded and Red-breasted mergansers, Oxyurini, and probably also the lesser eider, *Polysticta*. The Harlequin Duck's pinkish nail and tomia are unique among the Mergini; evidently, these lighter bill colors also take their pinkish hues from haemoglobin. A grayish spot appearing proximally on the rami of individuals of many species does not appear to have taxonomic significance.

Color and pattern of feet. The colors and pattern of the feet vary both within and among tribes. In general, the feet of swans, whistling-ducks, and geese lack strongly contrasting patterns, whereas many ducks have them. Ducklings of some *Dendrocygna* species have brightly colored feet, but the pattern is quite low-contrast. All goslings and downy *Cygnus* have essentially dark feet, with a line of lighter color that runs from the metatarsal pad up the back of the tarsus to the heel (except *A. albifrons* and [perhaps] *A. brachyrhynchus* appear to lack the contrasting color). This light line—barely discernible on the matte black feet of Pacific Brant, Barnacle, and Cackling goslings and absent altogether on the shiny black feet of the Class 4 Snow gosling—is low-contrast in paler footed, yellow-plumaged individuals.

Base color of the feet of certain Cairinini and of some Anatini, Aythyini, and Mergini ducklings is usually of light or medium *value*, with a strongly contrasting darker pattern color. However, both downy Anatini and—to a lesser extent—Aythyini show considerable individual variation in the contrast of pattern and base colors. Most consistently monochromatic or low-contrast are the feet of American Wigeon, Northern Pintail, Green-winged Teal, Mottled, American Black, Mexican, and [perhaps—no live birds examined] Hawaiian ducklings. On the feet of other Anatini, brownish gray pattern colors contrast well (e.g., many Blue-winged Teals and Northern Shovelers) to poorly (e.g., most Northern Cinnamon Teals) with the predominantly orange or yellow-orange base colors. The pattern and base colors of downy *Aythya* feet contrast best in the Ring-necked duckling and least well in the downy Redhead, with Canvasback and scaup intermediate.

Harlequins, some Oldsquaws, and Red-breasted Mergansers have quite light-colored, low-contrast feet, relative to the darker, monochromatic feet of Somateriini and other Mergini. The stiff-tailed ducklings have almost uniformly blackish feet.

Foot colors of half-grown downies and feathered juveniles are usually bluish gray or brownish gray, whatever the species, but sometimes they have tints of dull pink (Laysan Duck), dull green (certain Canada goslings), dull violet (White-winged Scoter), or dull yellow (Gadwall).

Color changes in dried specimens.

Changes in the appearance of color attributes (i.e., *hue, value, chroma*) may take place in the plumage of prepared specimens after a period of storage. These changes, often quite dramatic (e.g., in *Catharus dryas* subspp.: A. Phillips and Rook 1965; in trogons: Parkes 1970), are usually caused by 'foxing' or fading. 'Foxing' is the condition in which certain yellow-red plumage colors of stored specimens become 'rusty', and the dark colors become 'brownish'. Characteristically a long-term process, 'foxing' may proceed in a matter of months in some species (e.g., Gray Jay, Boreal Chickadee; Henri Ouellet, letter to the author, November 1984). Fading or bleaching, a color change that results from the exposure of specimens to light (as in museum exhibits: Lusk 1975; G. Thomson 1978), may affect nearly all colors except (possibly) some melanins and (perhaps) structural colors. In some organic colorants (e.g., "the dye, Cyanine, in collodion film"), the rate of fading increases directly "with the amount of oxygen in the atmosphere" (Giles 1966: 101; re: textile colors). Melanin, a more stable organic compound than cyanine, might be expected to fade more slowly, although the light phaeomelanins seem to deteriorate more quickly than the dark eumelanins. In general, fading of dried specimens takes place slowly under variable, ambient illumination (e.g., conventional incandescent or fluorescent lamps) but proceeds rapidly on both specimens and live birds in ultraviolet light. McKillop (1986) observed that certain colors of dried insect specimens changed markedly in *hue, value,* and *chroma* when exposed continuously to ultraviolet radiation.

Colors termed 'faded' may not necessarily have reached that state by having been exposed to light. Parkes (1970: 345) states that "[presumed] carotenoid pigments [of trogons] fade, often quite rapidly, in museum specimens, even when kept in total darkness." A marked susceptibility of certain colorants to rapid fading (as in carotenoid "cosmetic coloration" described by Vevers 1985) could explain the transitory nature of the pale pink or yellow colors found on the breasts of Common Mergansers and on some larids and thrushes. However, the plumage of other species having known carotenoid colorants (e.g., Northern Oriole, Yellow Warbler; M. Tascona and C. Nelson, unpubl.) retains its color attributes during long periods of storage in museum cabinets.

Unfortunately, a lack of precise knowledge of the colorants in the plumage and unfeathered parts of downy waterfowl prevents a proper understanding of either 'foxing' or fading. If one can assume, from the suggestions of Völker (1934), Vevers (1964), and Brush (1981), that light and dark melanins (phaeomelanins and eumelanins, respectively), are the colorants of downy waterfowl plumage, then 'foxing' might be considered the product of the gradual oxidation of melanic pigments, occurring in the absence of light. It is also possible that the light phaeomelanins of the base color, which usually tint the tips of the dorsal plumes, may oxidize more quickly than the dark [more stable?] eumelanins of the pattern color, thereby lending a 'foxy' aspect to virtually the entire plumage of some specimens. The shift of *hue* toward red is particularly obvious in the greenish yellow plumage of *Aythya* ducklings and of certain downy Anserinae. For example, the *hue* of a live, day-old Canvasback duckling's cheeks and belly is typically 6Y to 7.5Y, with *chroma* /8 to /10, whereas the *hue* of certain dried specimens may shift markedly toward red (e.g., to 2.5Y), the *chroma* may lose up to six Munsell steps (down to /4), and the *value* become noticeably paler. In other examples, the dark brownish grays of live eider and scoter ducklings become dark, grayish browns in museum specimens (e.g., "bister," "clove brown," "mummy brown" [Ridgway 1912]), and the neutral blackish gray of live, day-old West Indian Whistling-ducks becomes dark grayish yellowish brown in dried specimens.

Color changes of the bill and feet are even more obvious. Dark [presumably melanic] colors become darker and grayer when the modifying reddish tints of the blood pigment beneath the skin are gone, as in downy *Cygnus*, many goslings, and most sea-ducklings. The change is more striking in the light-colored lower mandibles, nails, and tarsi of live downies of surface-feeding ducklings, stiff-tailed ducklings, and some Mergini. The pink bill and feet of live *Olor* cygnets become dull yellow in dried specimens (Parmelee, Stephens, and Schmidt 1967).

Plumage Pattern

Eye-stripe

The eye-stripe includes several quite different patterns. The conspicuous eye-stripe of *Aix* and northern hemisphere *Cairina* ducklings begins at the eye, whereas the well-marked stripe of *Anas* ducklings nearly always starts at the bill (except Laysan Duck often has stripes poorly marked).

In *Mareca* and downy diving ducks, eye-stripes are inconspicuous or lacking; yellow *Aythya* ducklings have poorly defined eye- and cheek-stripes rather similar to those of American Wigeons (*Mareca*), but some individual *Aythya* which are a bit darker in over all body color have quite noticeable eye-stripes.

Downy *Mergus* and eiders have face-stripes quite unlike those of other species or of one another. The two dark stripes of downy *Mergus* ducklings run nearly parallel from the bill, laterally along the face, to the back of the head. The upper stripe borders closely the *lower* edge of the dark 'reddish' crown color (*Lophodytes* has only a faint eye-line, no cheek-stripes), while the lower stripe diffuses behind the eye, 'bleeding' onto the white cheeks and merging with the wash of light pattern color at the side of the head (compare merganser spp., pl. 9). The single thin stripe on *Somateria* and *Polysticta* ducklings rims the *upper* edge of the dark cheek-patch in downies of both genera (pl. 7). In contrast, the white-cheeked ducklings (except *Mergus*) have no stripes at all.

The eye-stripes of geese, often poorly defined, are usually inconspicuous or absent behind the eye. In front of the eye, the stripe characteristically appears as a blotchy dark 'spot' in *Anser* goslings, or as part of a 'mask' or 'bridle' in *Branta* goslings. Cygnets have no stripes, only faint smudges, if anything, nor do downy whistling-ducks have discrete dark eye-stripes: their dark crown color reaches eye-level, broken (in 3 of 4 North American spp.) by a short, pale supraorbital stripe.

Cheek-patch

The cheek-patch ('cheek', as used here, refers to "the whole side of the head" between eye-level and throat [A. Thomson 1964: 827]) has many variations among the downy waterfowl. By definition (Illustrated Glossary), it is an area contrasting in *value* with either base color or pattern color. Whistling-ducklings have a line of pale base color running all around the head between dark crown and dark occipital 'T' stripe (pl. 1)—the lateral arm of the dark 'T' stripe extends forward onto the cheek—but well-marked cheek-patches are usually low-contrast or absent in other downy Anserinae. Snow, Ross', Emperor, and *Branta* goslings lack a contrasting cheek-patch (except gray cheeks of Pacific Brant often show low contrast with darker hood and [if present] white chin-patch), but downy *Nesochen* has a dark cheek-patch continuous with the dark 'mask' and ear-spot (compare gosling figs. on pls. 3, 4 & 5). Greater White-fronted and Pink-footed goslings often have dusky cheek-patches more or less joined to the darker, blotchy pre-ocular stripe (pl. 1). The cheek-patch is never more than a shadow on downy cygnets (pl. 2).

Downy Anatinae have varied, often well-marked cheek patterns. Both Cairinini and Anatini ducklings characteristically lack dark cheek-patches, but Green-winged Teal, Northern Pintail, and Northern Shoveler ducklings sometimes have smudgy, incomplete dark cheek-stripes, and downy Gadwalls, Northern Cinnamon Teals, and Laysan Ducks occasionally have diffuse, grayish cheek-patches contrasting poorly with the adjacent base color (pls. 6 & 7). In *Aythya* ducklings, the broken, irregular cheek-stripe often widens into a dusky area below and in front of the eye on the dark scaup, but almost never does so in the yellow pochard ducklings. Most downy eiders have a wide, dark grayish cheek-patch extending from lore to nape, contrasting well with the light supraorbital stripe, but blending with the paler color of the throat. The Spectacled Eider is an exception: its cheek-patch is reduced to a narrow stripe by the peculiar dark 'spectacle' superimposed upon it. The large, white or gray-white cheek-patch of many Mergini ducklings varies individually within the tribe. A white or yellow cheek-patch, crossed by a single, usually quite prominent stripe, occurs also in the stiff-tails (compare cheek-patch forms on pls. 8 & 9; see also Mergini account, pp. 120-24, and Discussion, pp. 147-56).

Dorsal pattern

Dorsal spots vary in number, size, and shape within and among the various tribes. Downy whistling-ducks have either a bold, conspicuous dorsal pattern (*D. viduata, D. autumnalis, D. arborea*) or almost none (*D. bicolor*). The northern cygnets (*Olor*) as well as the goslings of all species (except [usually] Emperor, Brant, and Hawaiian geese) have wing-patches and shoulder-spots; the southern cygnets (*Cygnus*) characteristically lack both. North American Cairinini and Anatini ducklings have, consistently, four dorsal spots and (usually) conspicuous wing-patches, but dorsal patterns of the diving ducklings vary widely. The yellow *Aythya* ducklings (also downy *Bucephala* and mergansers) have prominent wing-patches and four-spotted dorsal patterns, but scaup, eiders, most scoters, and the Oldsquaw do not. The Masked duckling has four distinct dorsal spots and the Ruddy Duck two, but both lack wing-patches. Often present, but seldom prominent, are two or four dorsal spots on Harlequin, Steller's Eider and some White-winged Scoter ducklings.

Tibial pattern

In general, the darker the downy bird over all, the less extensive is the light-colored tibial pattern. The pattern in Anatini ducklings has two or three 'fingers' of light base color reaching from the inner side of the tibiotarsus into the dark pattern color at the outer side. A similar pattern appears in *Aix, Cairina,* and yellow pochards (some *Aythya*), all yellow goslings (extensive in light variants of *Anser* and *Branta*), *Olor* cygnets, and *Bucephala*. The tibial pattern is intermediate in darker yellow scaup (other *Aythya*), gray-backed *Dendrocygna, Histrionicus,* and *Lophodytes*. It is virtually lacking in Brant and Emperor goslings, downy *Cygnus, Somateria, Polysticta, Clangula, Melanitta, Nomonyx,* and *Oxyura,* but is strikingly 'scalloped' in spotted-backed *Dendrocygna* ducklings and downy *Mergus merganser* and *M. serrator.*

Structure

Bill

Downy anatids of all species have dorsoventrally flattened bills, the structural peculiarities of which parallel to some extent those of their adult counterparts. The persistence of bill characters typical for the species in downies newly hatched to half-grown (and older) suggests that these characters may represent specializations for obtaining particular kinds of food, as documented by Collias and Collias (1963), Weller (1968b), and others. For example, downy cygnets and whistling-ducks have wide bills, with wide nails (figs. G-13, 1-2), whereas the equally wide-nailed bills of goslings are higher at the base, tapering toward the tip (figs. G-16, G-18). The bills of downy perching ducks, American Wigeons, and Gadwalls also are high-bridged and tapering (figs. G-47, 5-6, 5-61); the Northern Shovelers have the longest, most spatulate bills of all downy Anatini (figs. 5-26, 5-36). Among the diving species, bills of scaup ducklings are wider and flatter than those of other downy pochards, whereas eider ducklings have high-bridged, more or less straight-sided bills with wide, often rather pointed nails. Bill shape in the Mergini varies from narrow and attenuated (mergansers) to somewhat laterally compressed (Harlequin [most], *Bucephala* [intermediate], Oldsquaw [least]), to wide and rather flat (scoters). Bills of North American Oxyurini ducklings are generally wide and much flattened, but differ markedly in shape and nail structure (figs. G-82, G-83).

Bill characters of the downy young, especially the size and shape of the nail and its proportions relative to those of other parts of the bill, often were diagnostic for certain genera or species-pairs with closely similar pattern and plumage colors (e.g., swans, pochards, scaup, goldeneyes). Because linear growth proceeds at different rates throughout the bill (e.g., culmen length [EC] fastest, nail width [WN] slowest; C. Nelson unpubl. data), these differences can often be expressed as ratios derived from a series of developmental measurements (see scaup and goldeneyes, Table l, Appendix A).

Feet

All downy waterfowl have webbed feet, but the extent of the webbed area varies from group to group. Except for being proportionately larger than the feet of their adult counterparts, hatchlings' feet are entirely similar in structure to those of the adults, reflecting both their role in locomotion and obtaining food and their adaptation to aquatic life. For example, whistling-ducklings have rather small web areas, similar to those of geese (figs. G-6, G-7); adults of both groups obtain most of their food by grazing (e.g., Bolen and Forsyth 1967). The terrestrial Hawaiian Goose, with feet webbed only half-way to the tips of the toes, has a small paddle area relative to that of other North American geese (Miller 1937). The American Wigeon, a grazer among dabblers (Kortright 1942; Rijnsdorp 1986), has the smallest paddle index among the Anatini (Raikow 1973). Swans, although similar in many ways to geese, are generally more aquatic. They have very large paddle areas (fig. G-8) to aid in swimming and taxiing and, presumably, to help balance their heavy bodies when "dipping their heads and...tilting like ducks" to obtain food (M. Owen and Kear 1972: 58).

The paddle areas of diving species are the largest, relative to body proportions, among the Anatinae (Raikow 1973). The outer toe (IV) of diving ducklings is usually as long as or even longer than the middle toe (III), and the hallux (I) is deeply lobed (compare feet of ducklings of diving and dabbling spp. in figs. G-39 and G-41, respectively). These characters have "obvious functional significance in swimming and diving" (Raikow 1973: 304). Interestingly, Raikow found the paddle index of eiders more like that of dabbling ducks than like that of other divers (see also Humphrey 1958a).

The scutes and rete of the feet have thin, glossy, often brightly colored sheaths at hatching, which begin to slough off after a week or ten days. Remnants of them may persist for several weeks, their darker or brighter hues still recognizeable against the paler, grayer colors of older birds' feet.

Egg-teeth

All downy waterfowl possess a deciduous egg-tooth, near the tip of the culmen on the upper nail, which usually scales off (dehisces) by the second or third day after hatching. Cygnets and goslings also have a small 'tooth-like' projection beneath the deciduous tooth. This persists for a week or more. The upper egg-tooth may be homologous both to the func-

Plate 1

1 Fulvous Whistling-duck, Dendrocygna bicolor
Gray and 'silver' variants. RLWS captives.

2 Northern Black-bellied Whistling-duck, D. autumnalis, D.a. fulgens
Brilliant and pale variants. Lake Mathis, Texas (DWWRS; UFS[DM]).

3 White-faced Whistling-duck, D. viduata
E Maromandia, Madagascar (BM[NH] [6-7 d.]: color and pattern) and captives (AMNH [1-2 d.]: color. WT[S] [2-3 d.]: measurements and pattern).

4 West Indian Whistling duck, D. arborea.
RLWS captives

5 Pink-footed Goose, Anser brachyrhynchus
Darker and lighter variants. Thjorsarver, Iceland (RM).

Greater White-fronted Goose, A. albifrons

6 Pacific White-fronted Goose, A. a. frontalis. Kuguklik River, Alaska (OSUFW).

7 A. a. gambelli? Perry River, Northwest Territories (FMNH).

8 A. a. gambelli? Adelaide Peninsula, Northwest Territories (NMC).

9 Greenland White fronted Goose, A. a. flavirostris. Greenland. (WT[S] captives [1 d.: measurements, and 5 d.: color]).

Plate 1

tional egg-tooth observed in some viviparous snakes (e.g., Copperhead, *Agkistrodon contortrix;* Fitch 1960), and to the tiny, apparently non-functional structure reported by Klauber (1956) in embryos and new-born young of other viviparous species (e.g., Timber Rattlesnake, *Crotalus horridus*) and in embryos and newly hatched young of some oviparous species (e.g., Plains Hog-nosed Snake, *Heterodon masicus*, & Smooth Green Snake, *Ophiodrys vernalis*; William Preston, pers. comm. 1989).

At least some members of all anatid tribes have also an egg-tooth at the tip of the lower nail (to my knowledge, undescribed in new-born reptiles). This structure, heretofore catalogued in fewer than 20 families of birds (Clark 1961; Anatidae not included), was described by Tjeenk Willink (1899) in embryos of the Moorhen (*Gallinula chloropus*), a bustard (*Otis atra* [=*Afrotis atra*; Peters 1934]), and several charadriiform families (e.g., Tjeenk Willink's fig. 13: *Oedicnemus crepitans* [=*Burhinus oedicnemus*; Sharpe 1896, Peters 1934]). Tjeenk Willink also observed a whitish lower egg-tooth on newly hatched young of the Oystercatcher, Black Tern, and Avocet. Even earlier, Weinland (1857 [no other data; *in* Tjeenk Willink 1899]) had found a lower egg-tooth on [an embryo or newly hatched?] *Tringa pusilla* [=*Calidris pusilla*; A.O.U. 1983] and suggested that other members of the genus might also possess them. More recently, Jehl (1968a) and Sealy (1970) added the Phalaropodidae and the Alcidae to the list of families some of whose downy chicks have an egg-tooth on the lower mandible.

Parkes and Clark (1964: 148) cautioned against interpreting the absence of culmen egg-teeth on newly hatched young as "negative evidence," pointing out "that the egg-tooth may have been lost in some of these during the preservation or later handling." Their caution applies equally to the lower egg-tooth, which is usually lost within a few hours of hatching in many sandpipers (Jehl 1968a) but is evidently more persistent in the American Woodcock (Wetherbee and Bartlett 1962) and in certain alcids (Sealy 1970).

In all anatid species on which the lower egg-tooth was observed, it nearly always dehisced within a few hours of hatching. Rarely, remnants of it persisted for about two days. In day-old whistling-ducks, swans, and geese, the lower egg-tooth is customarily lacking or fragmentary (however, note thin but complete lower egg-tooth on a newly hatched Brant [NMC; fig. 3-79). Gadow (1891 [*in* Parkes and Clark 1964]) asserted that avian embryos of all species possess [upper] egg-teeth. By implication, all avian species may also have lower egg-teeth, but many (as possibly in some Anserinae) may be lost even before hatching.

The lower egg-tooth in all downy North American Anserinae is thin and scale-like (as in Red-necked Phalarope; Jehl 1968a), but differed somewhat among the various duck tribes. Perching ducks, Anatini, Aythyini, *Bucephala*, and *Oxyura* had small, raised (except *Bucephala* sometimes rather flat), bi-lobed structures (see figs. 4-2, 5-47, 6-4, 8-45, 9-5; also Sealy 1970 re: Pigeon Guillemot and Kittlitz's Murrelet); the other ducks (all diving species) had a thin lower egg-tooth resembling that of the Anserinae (e.g., figs. 7-47, 8-2, 8-16, 8-70). A lower egg-tooth raised and thickened medially, as reported in chicks of the American Woodcock (Wetherbee and Bartlett 1962) and the Solitary Sandpiper (Jehl 1968a: fig. l), did not appear on any downy North American anatid. Neither did an egg-tooth "encompassing...the entire tip of the upper mandible" (Jehl 1968a: 328).

The upper egg-tooth is used in hatching. According to Driver (1960b: 202), the " 'upward nod' [aided by the hatching muscle; Fisher 1958]...involves the raising of the bill...[which] enables the [upper] egg-tooth to be brought into contact with the shell," making a line of cracks around its larger end as the duckling slowly turns within it. On the other hand, the function of the lower egg-tooth is unclear. Jehl (1968a: 328) observed that it "plays no obvious role in rupturing the egg shell or membrane [of hatching sandpipers]" but does seem to shield the "delicate tip of the lower mandible [from] possible damage...during the hatching process." He believes that this protective function may apply to chicks whose upper and lower mandibles are of approximately equal length, e.g., scolopacids (Jehl 1968a), certain alcids (murres, guillemots, murrelets; Sealy 1970), and terns (Tjeenk Willink 1899; McNicholl 1983). Jehl (1968a: 329) suggested that in "gulls, jaegers, and plovers, which lack a lower egg-tooth," the tip of the longer upper mandible overhangs and protects the tip of the shorter lower one.

Although the upper mandible overhangs the lower both medially and laterally in all species of waterfowl, the egg-teeth may still serve briefly to protect the hatchling's bill, which is softer and fleshier than that of charadriiform young. Even the upper and lower nails do not harden appreciably until the young anatid is several days old.

Oil gland

Waterfowl of nearly all species begin to use the oil gland [=uropygium, or preen gland] within hours after hatching. Exceptions are the downy young of screamers (*Chauna*: Anhimidae) and of the Cape Barren Goose (*Cereopsis*: Anserinae). In these species, parent birds use oil from their own glands to waterproof the down of their offspring, whose oil glands do not function during the first two weeks of life (*Wildfowl* 23, 1972: pl. 6, Philippa Scott photo and caption).

Elder (1954) and Kear (1972) propose that preening behavior is probably innate. Elder suggested (p. 19) that "the stimulation of the duck's bill...apparently...induces flow of the gland's secretion." If this is the case, the gland almost certainly commences to function within the first day of life. I used Elder's (1954) technique to test for the presence of oil in the gland. Namely, press a cigarette paper gently onto the gland and observe whether an oil spot appears; if it does, the gland is functional. An eight-hour Bufflehead and a nine-hour Wood Duck had functional oil glands, but a two-hour Wood Duck and a five-hour White-winged Scoter did not. Glands of other species tested at 24 hours also secreted oil (i.e., Black-bellied Whistling-duck, Canada Goose, Canvasback, Ruddy Duck). In the species not tested, the oil gland was assumed to be functional for waterproofing feathers if the birds appeared healthy and preened frequently and vigorously.

Vocalizations

Calls of newly hatched waterfowl, like those of domestic chicks (*Gallus gallus*; Andrew 1964) fall into two general categories: twitters and peeps (Scoville and Gottlieb 1980; Kostow 1981; and others), or "pleasure notes" and "distress calls," respectively (Collias 1952: 131). Andrew (1964: 65) believes that these two types of calls represent "the extreme variants of a continuous series of patterns [forming] a single system of responses, of which the twitter proper is the lowest intensity form." Kear (1968), Caswell (1972), and Kostow (1981) observed similar continua among captive and wild downy waterfowl. However, Scoville and Gottlieb (1980: 1095) criticized the attempts of some authors (e.g., Andrew 1964; Gottlieb and Vandenbergh 1968; Kear 1968) to "establish...vocalization categories on the basis of their auditory distinctiveness to the human observer." They pointed out that the observer's perceptions of the parameters of vocalizations are not necessarily the same as "those of the animals under study." Nevertheless, I have used Kear's (1968) terminology of vocalizations, in part because I have modeled my methods of vocalization-research on hers, in part because her findings on the possible taxonomic significance of vocalizations parallel some of my own regarding downy plumages, but mostly because her work is based upon hundreds of hours of close, consistent observations of the newly hatched young of more than 100 species of waterfowl—a survey to which all others of similar intent must inevitably be compared.

Low amplitude vocalizations described by Kear (1968: 94) include "clicks" ['tapping' before hatching], the repetitive "pleasure calls" [conversation, greeting, contact, or contentment calls], and "sleepy calls" [soft twitters or trills emitted just prior to falling asleep]. Discrete, loud (high amplitude) vocalizations include the "distress call," "whistle," "shriek," and ("in the only goose to feed its young...*Anseranas*" [p. 104]) the "begging call." The "hiss," although discrete and forceful, is not especially loud (note that Kear's terminology is used hereafter without quotation marks).

Vocalizations begin even before the hatchling emerges from the shell (e.g., Collias 1952; Nice 1962; Fischer 1965; Kear 1968). Driver (1965: 315) confirmed that the 'clicks' or 'taps' heard from Common Eider embryos "2-3 days" prior to hatching are produced, not by the impact of the egg-tooth upon the shell, as is often supposed, but "simultaneously with respiratory movement" (see also McCoshen and Thompson 1968). Vince (1964) demonstrated that 'clicking' of unhatched embryos facilitates hatching in the Northern Bobwhite, *Colinus virginianus,* and White (1984) induced accelerated hatch time in the domestic chick by prenatal auditory stimulation with a mechanical click. Both studies suggest that 'clicks' may help to coordinate hatch times within waterfowl broods as well.

Gottlieb and Vandenbergh (1968: 307) found that calls which they evoked by stimulation of Peking Duck embryos (domestic Mallard, *Anas platyrhynchos* var. *domesticus*) at about three days before hatching were quite similar in form and frequency of utterance to those emitted after hatching, i.e., " 'distress', 'contentment', and brooding-like calls." Würdinger (1970) reported similar calls in unhatched goslings of four species. In a later study of Peking embryo vocalizations, Scoville and Gottlieb (1980: 1103) reported that distress calls were absent prior to hatching, and that contentment calls (i.e., "short-fast notes") predominated in the vocal repertoires of embryos and of ducklings up to two days of age, a pattern also characteristic of wild Northern Mallards (Caswell 1972). The frequent occurrence of vocalizations consisting of "short-fast notes," as well as the emission of "low-pitched notes [by] an undisturbed embryo" (Gottlieb and Vandenbergh 1968: 311), suggest that these low intensity vocalizations may be sounded almost spontaneously or, as Andrew (1964: 75) proposed regarding the domestic chick, may occur in response to "any stimulus [having] 'intrinsic contrast'...with background stimulation."

The wild Northern Mallard hen, "normally silent...during incubation," responds to the predominantly low intensity vocalizations of late-stage embryos with calls that "gradually increase in frequency and intensity" from the time the first egg is pipped until hatching is complete (McKinney 1969: 618). Gottlieb (1965: 18) established that such "auditory stimulation...initiates parental recognition [and exodus from the nest] in [ducklings of] ground-nesting as well as hole-nesting species" (see also Fabricius 1951 [Northern Shoveler, Tufted Duck, Common Eider]; Collias and Collias 1956 [Canvasback, Blue-winged Teal]; Boyd and

Fabricius 1965 & Bjärvall 1968 [Northern Mallard]; Grice and Rogers 1965 [Wood Duck]; Siegfried 1977 [Ruddy Duck]; Frazer and Kirkpatrick 1979 [Emperor Goose]; and Cabot et al. 1984 [Barnacle Goose]). Indeed, maintenance of the parent-offspring bond may be based more on recognition of species-typical vocalizations of the young than on recognition of characteristic plumage patterns (see Goodwin 1984).

In newly hatched waterfowl, vocalizations accompanied nearly all activities. Caswell (1972: 75) found that Northern Mallard ducklings reared by their mothers in flight pens "were extremely vocal, being silent only when in alert positions or when being brooded." Among day-old hatchery anatids of all species that I observed, vocalizations also formed a continuum, rising and falling in pitch, becoming softer or louder, and ceasing only when the birds fell asleep. Even then, the silence could be broken by softly trilled sleepy calls or by a single 'protesting' note from some sleeper aroused.

The low intensity pleasure call appeared to be the basic unit of the continuum. Uttered softly when 'conversing' with siblings, in situations of warmth and comfort, and while feeding and preening (Kear 1968), it was repeated for as long as those circumstances continued. When the stimulus situation changed, so did the type of vocalization. Goslings (and eiders) engaged in bill-fighting or down-pulling voiced the two-syllabled greeting call (sometimes omitting the second syllable) loudly and emphatically. Preening birds, which had fed and were growing sleepy, called more and more softly, their pleasure calls becoming sporadic, "the syllables not separated at the correct pitch and loudness [until] long, low...trills emerged" (Kear 1968: 99). The trills, in turn, became softer, almost formless, and finally ceased altogether as the birds fell asleep.

The distress call is a loud, sustained, evenly accented piping "with a remarkably constant note interval" (Kostow 1981: 19), the chief function of which is to draw the attention of the female to the young (Collias 1962; Gaioni and Evans 1986). The call is prefaced by a short series of notes increasing in volume as they rise (usually) about a major 6th (M6) in pitch. Superficially rather similar in all of the species that I observed, the distress call was nevertheless shown by Kear (1968) to have potential taxonomic significance at both generic and tribal levels. Kear observes (p. 102) that "the shape of the [isolation distress] note [in sonagrams] and the frequency range it covers tend to be similar in closely related species and differ in more distantly related ones." For example, calls of three species of wigeon are obviously different from those of three species of Cairinini as well as from those of three species of Aythyini (her fig. 11) and *Anas smithii* (her fig. 10). However, she noted (p. 103) that a "gradation of form" could be shown between calls of the wigeons and their allies (Falcated Duck, Gadwall) and the more distantly related Anatini species. In another example, Kear confirmed the opinion of Johnsgard (1967a) [as did later studies by Raikow 1971 and Brush 1976] that the affinities of the unusual White-backed Duck, *Thalassornis leuconotus*, lie more with the whistling-ducks than with the stiff-tails, where Delacour and Mayr (1945) had placed it provisionally.

Only *Dendrocygna* ducklings whistled (Kear 1968: fig. 16b). The sound appeared early (1-2 d.), but was not frequently uttered until a day or two after that, and was then nearly always interspersed with pleasure calls, squeals, or steadily reiterated chatter (see Dendrocygnini, pp. 21-24).

The shriek, a single piercing note voiced by a young bird in extreme discomfort (Kear 1968: fig. 17), immediately arrested the attention of nearby young of all species whenever it sounded.

The hiss described by Kear (1968: fig. 19) in a 10-day-old Mute Swan did not appear in my very young captive cygnets, although some bantam-reared goslings hissed at two days

(Néné, Dusky Canada Goose) and goslings of most other species hissed frequently after five or six days. Weller (1968a: 198) described a "neck-stretch and mouth-open hissing display" in Black-headed ducklings *Heteronetta atricapilla*, less than seven days old, whereas Black-bellied Whistling-ducks, White-winged Scoters, and Ruddy Ducks hissed forcefully, but almost inaudibly, when but one or two days old.

Fabricius (1951), Driver (1960b), Kear (1968), Kostow (1981), and others noted several refinements of the vocal repertoire. They differentiated at least three forms of the pleasure call, according to the context in which it was emitted: contentment calls, contact calls, and greeting calls. Fabricius (1951: 161-62) and Kear (1968) listed feeding, drinking, bathing, preening, and "reaching a warm spot" after deprivation as stimuli which, having a "low threshold of response," elicit short, quiet, rapidly reiterated syllables (see also Andrew 1975). The same call evidently serves to establish and maintain contact between brood members (Fabricius 1951; Driver 1960b; Collias 1962), between goslings and parents (Würdinger 1970), and between the hen and her brood (Scoville and Gottlieb 1980). Kostow (1981: 42) found that the "spatial distribution [among individuals of a foraging (*Aythya*) brood] corresponds to the maximum possible distance at which soft calls [twitters, trills] can be reliably detected" against what Schleidt (1973: 375) has termed "the ambient noise." Fabricius (1951) implied a higher threshold of response for the greeting call; Driver (1960b) and Kear (1968) associated it with up-and-down movements of the head and neck ("light yellow" Ross', pl. 3, and Pacific Brant goslings, pl. 4; see also Kear's fig. 4).

Among day-old waterfowl of all species that I observed, the amplitude of the pleasure calls uttered during feeding or foraging was usually higher (i.e., louder) than that of contentment calls, the rhythm was more regular, and the number of syllables in the call was often reduced. For example, goslings frequently omitted the second, accented upward note(s) of the pleasure call, substituting a pause of the same time value, so that the rhythmic structure of the call was maintained.

Fabricius (1951), Collias (1962), and Kear (1968) described, besides the isolation distress call, or "Pfeifen des Verlassenseins" (Lorenz 1935: 180), a slower, harsher call uttered by cold or wet ducklings. Fabricius (1951) described a polysyllabic distress call of downy Common Eiders, *Somateria m. mollissima* (as opposed to the monosyllabic calls of Anatini ducklings; Lorenz [1941] n.d.); the ascending prefatory distress notes of other *Somateria* species are also 'angular', two-syllabled, and not regularly spaced. However, Driver (1960b) described only monosyllabic notes in Common Eiders, *S. m. sedentaria*, from the Belcher Islands; he reported (p. 203) a call of undescribed form which he termed the "question or investigatory note," the function of which, he suggested, was to alert siblings to possible danger from intruders.

Fabricius (1951: 162) also reported a "note of terror...a prolonged whirr...released in 24-hour-old tufted ducks [*Aythya fuligula*] when they saw flying gulls." I did not hear this note from any of the very young hand-raised birds with which I worked (nor was it catalogued by Kear 1968), but Lesser Scaup females, *Aythya affinis*, about seven weeks old sometimes greeted my approach with a low-pitched, faintly 'metallic' whirring call (see also Oxyurini, p. 142-44). However, the two calls may be quite unrelated; the ontogeny of vocalizations in *Oxyurini* and in most species of *Aythya* has not been determined.

In addition to characterizing more or less discrete calls, i.e., those in which "the ranges of the [acoustical] characteristics do not overlap" (Kostow 1981: 19), Kear (1968), Caswell (1972), and others recognized several intermediate types of calls. Sometimes, these calls are emitted singly or in short bouts, but other times they represent a quite prolonged transition between one type of call and another in response to a gradual change in the stimulus situation, such as a growing realization of hunger (i.e., pleasure call toward distress) or sleepiness (i.e., pleasure call toward sleepy trill).

The close relationship of the vocalizations of downy waterfowl to those of the adults has been suggested by Lorenz ([1941] n.d.), Kear (1968), and others. The low frequency pleasure calls of the downy young give rise to the adult calls of both sexes in the Northern Mallard (Caswell 1972) and the Graylag Goose, *Anser anser* (Fischer 1965), and distress calls become "lament-calls...and...distance-calls" in adult Bar-headed, Snow, White-fronted, and Canada geese (Würdinger 1970: 300). However, the ontogeny of vocalizations for most other species is incompletely known.

Behavior

Note that behavior terminology (capitalized, without quotation marks) is that of Johnsgard (1965) unless referred to McKinney (1965), to another specific source (e.g., Driver 1960c), or to the author (e.g., 'Forward-neck-stretch').

Day-old waterfowl of nearly all species are capable or running, swimming, diving, reaching the oil gland, and preening all feathered areas, although their movements generally lack the grace and ease of execution that mark the actions of older birds. For example, the heavy cygnets (ca. 200 g) move almost ponderously, Ruddy ducklings (unable to run) scoot along on their bellies, and hatchlings of all species (but especially cygnets and diving ducks) usually brace themselves with feet apart and tail held downward to maintain balance while preening.

Many behavior patterns typical of adult waterfowl appear in partly-developed form in the day-old young, confirming Tinbergen's (1939: 216) observation that "an innate activity does not always function at birth, but...new reactions [associated with it] may appear gradually and pass through a slow maturation process." These patterns include comfort movements, threat postures, chin-lifting [not known whether precursor of pre-flight or sexual displays or both], head-bobbing, and habits and postures used in feeding. McKinney (1965) noted that two comfort movements, the Wing-flap and the Tail-wag [McKinney's terminology], were absent in hatchery-reared Northern Mallards less than one day old, but present in those a day or two older. These movements appeared similarly in the young of all other species that I observed (Wing-flap also in swimming wild goldeneye ducklings [ca. 1 d.] observed by Myres [1957: fig. 4]). Although often enacted separately, the two movements also are part of a 'defecation ritual' performed on land. The order of the components of the ritual is virtually invariable: 'Forward-neck-stretch', Wing-flap, defecation, Tail-wag, resting posture. The Tail-wag, the last element to develop, was seen occasionally in birds one or two days old (e.g., Barrow's Goldeneye), more frequently in those three or four days old (e.g., Néné, Canvasback, Oldsquaw), almost invariably in birds five or six days old (e.g., Gadwall, Northern Pintail, White-winged Scoter), and appeared fully developed in birds about a week old (Northern Shoveler, other dabblers, et al.). McKinney's (1965: 178) observations regarding the order of appearance of other comfort movements of the Northern Mallard duckling (e.g., "scratching...oiling, nibbling") apply also to the young of other species. These similarities, together with his conclusion (p. 205) that "almost all comfort movements [of adults of more than 120 species] are of universal occurrence in basic situations in the family," suggests strongly a parallel sequence in their development among the downy young of all species. Nice's (1962: 47, Table 8) observations of 12 duck species immediately before and after hatching disclosed that many comfort movements appeared within the first few hours after hatching, some ("nibbling, preening...yawning") as much as seven minutes *before* hatching.

McKinney (1965: 179) found that day-old Mallard ducklings had longer naps with relatively shorter periods of activity than did birds a few days older. He was "sure that the [pen-reared] birds' behavior was quite different from that of wild ducklings." However, hatchery-reared young of all other anatids that I observed exhibited similar rhythms, an observation which suggests that these rhythms may be under strong internal control in all species. In day-old birds, feeding and drinking occupy but 15 to 20 minutes, and are often preceded or followed by an exploratory excursion around the enclosure, led by one of the more 'adventurous' members of the group. Preening takes 15 to 30 minutes with only infrequent oiling sequences (McKinney 1965), but naps often last for 30 to 45 minutes or more, although interrupted frequently by short periods of preening and resettling. Newly hatched birds crowd closely together as they sleep, presumably to conserve heat and possibly manifesting, even in the absence of the female, the "brooding reflex" which Driver (1960c: 416) described in the nidifugous young of several species (e.g., downy goldeneyes; Myres 1957). Sometimes, they form a low pyramid with their downy bodies, tumbled together in utter relaxation. Inevitably, those at the bottom of the heap work their way out, wiggling and protesting, to clamber atop the other sleepers. In contrast, half-grown downies and feathered juveniles sleep less frequently, without crowding, and often rest, awake, for long periods.

If the familial (i.e., typically anatid) and cyclic character of certain activities is apparent in the downy young, even more so is the species-typical character of other activities. For example, among the Anserinae, threat postures similar to those of adult birds appear during the first one to three days of life (e.g., *D. autumnalis,* pl. 1; *O. columbianus*, pl. 2; and *B. bernicla*, pl. 4), while the up-and-down head and neck movements used in greeting (Kear 1968: fig. 4) were also observed in a Triumph Ceremony between an Aleutian Canada Goose and her four three-day-old goslings (see Anserini, pp. 36-41; also Atlantic Canada and Giant Canada goslings, pl. 5). In the Anatinae, the "special greeting movements [of]...newly hatched...eiders and shovellers...are included in the courtship display of the adults" (Fabricius 1951: 161), and the Chin-lifting observed in downy Gadwalls (Lorenz [1941] n.d.) may reappear in the adult female's inciting display (Johnsgard 1965). Among the Mergini, the quiet White-winged Scoter ducklings become even more silent as adults ("Sehr stille"; Bauer and Glutz von Blotzheim 1969: 326) and the head-bobbing observed in day-old *Bucephala* ducklings seems clearly to anticipate both "head-bobbing" in adult male Buffleheads (Erskine 1972: 28-29, fig. e) and "pumping" displays of courting male goldeneyes (Myres 1957; Palmer 1976, vol. 2: 415 & fig. p. 411).

Collias and Collias (1963) observed feeding techniques in young ducklings (10 prairie spp. up to 1 wk. of age) and found that those associated with adults of certain species were also more or less characteristic of downy young. Ducklings develop and refine these techniques as they grow. For example, among the divers, ducklings one or two days old make shorter, shallower dives than ducklings a few days older, and they use surface-feeding techniques (also "tilting" in ducklings of *A. fuligula, S. mollissima*; Fabricius 1951: 161) at least as frequently as diving during the first few days after hatching (e.g., wild Hooded Merganser and Ring-necked ducklings: Beard 1964; captive ducklings of *Aythya* spp.: Bartonek and Hickey 1969). However, Aythyini, Somateriini (Driver 1960a), Mergini, and Ruddy ducklings adopt consistent head-under-water searching and diving for food within the first week of hatching; Ruddy ducklings also strain for food (Oxyurini, pp. 142-44; see also Collias and Collias 1963). Downy cygnets and geese, as well as perching, dabbling, and whistling-ducks usually prefer pecking, dabbling, straining, or tilting for food, although the techniques often overlap considerably within tribes. For example, older ducklings of certain dabblers sometimes dive. Fabricius (1951: 161) reported "spontaneous...bottom-divings...by...shovellers...about 2 weeks old." Moreover, McKinney described "head-under the surface while swimming, surface-dabbling, and up-ending" as the three food-gathering techniques "universal in [adult] *Anas*." He went on to say that "diving is widely used by dabbling ducks as a feeding method... [e.g.,]...in Cape Teal, *A. capensis* (Frank McKinney, letter to the author, November 1983)." Diving is also a well-known escape mechanism for adults and young of many species (e.g., Wetmore 1916; Hochbaum 1944; Driver 1960b; Bengtson 1966; Stewart 1967; Rylander and Bolen 1970; Alison 1976; Nymeyer 1977).

Interest in fly-snatching and proficiency at it differ somewhat from group to group. Hatchery-reared Anserinae generally pay less attention to flying insects than do young Anatinae. However, S. Hansen (1984) reported very young wild Trumpeter cygnets feeding actively on small flies that swarmed abundantly above the surface of their natal slough, and Eisenhauer (1976) reported that Emperor nestlings ate nearby black flies disturbed by observers. Newly hatched eider (Driver 1960a) and Anatini ducklings notice insects but do not always attempt to catch them, although individuals of many species vigorously pursue insects at a day or two of age. Most become expert fly-snatchers by the end of their first week. Downy Wood Ducks, Aythyini, and Mergini ducklings show consistent skill at pursuit and capture of flying insects when but one or two days old: Harlequin, Oldsquaw, and merganser ducklings regularly caught flies and mosquitos, and a Red-breasted Merganser (-l d.), settled in my lap for measuring, lunged at a passing mosquito and would have fallen if I had not caught him.

Whereas the rhythms of feeding, preening, and sleeping, as well as certain habits or mannerisms typical of particular species, appear spontaneously in naïve, incubator-hatched, day-old young, some behavior patterns (e.g., threat postures, head and neck signals [Black and Barrow 1985, re: Canada goslings], avoidance behavior, liveliness) seem to develop earlier and 'better' in downy young incubated and reared by natural or foster mothers. The day-old incubator birds are more curious and excitable, easily distracted by the slightest sound. They 'answer' quickly when spoken to, and show no fear of human presence. Cooch (1958) and Eisenhauer (1976) reported similar differences between pen-reared and wild goslings. Bluhm observed "that broods of captive Canvasback ducklings that had been incubated, hatched, and brooded by their natural mothers showed increased and exaggerated avoidance behavior and increased 'flightiness'" compared to those hatched using an artificial incubator (Cynthia Bluhm, letter to the author, August 1984).

In comparison, bantam-reared young (such as those at Slimbridge and Tunstead), watched and 'herded' by the hen, were guarded in their responses to my conversation, and scurried to her if I approached too quickly; some older goslings even adopted a threat posture. A cuckoo's call from the nearby wood, or the shadow of a hawk passing overhead, drew a low "Cluck!" from the bantam hen, which caused the young birds to fall silent and run to her for shelter. Other observers report similar behavior in wild ducklings (e.g., Caswell 1972 [Northern Mallards]; Driver 1960b [Hudson Bay Eider]; Michael Anderson, pers. comm. 1987 [Canvasback]). Mendenhall and Milne (1985) suggested that such protective behavior contributes to the survival of Eider ducklings in Scotland. They observed that flying gulls never attacked ducklings that had reached a female's side in response to her alarm call.

Whistling-ducks, tribe Dendrocygnini

North American genus: *Dendrocygna* Swainson

DISTRIBUTION AND TAXONOMY. Whistling-ducks are found in tropical and sub-tropical habitats world-wide (J. Phillips 1922; Delacour 1954; Bolen and Rylander 1983). The breeding range of the Fulvous Whistling-duck, *Dendrocygna bicolor,* one of the largest known among birds, spans four continents (J. Phillips 1922). In contrast, the populations of two other species, the West Indian Whistling-duck, *D. arborea*, and the Spotted Whistling-duck, *D. guttata*, are restricted to islands (Bolen and Rylander 1983).

The tribe Dendrocygnini, as defined by Delacour and Mayr (1945), included only the whistling-ducks in a single genus, *Dendrocygna.* Subsequent research by Johnsgard (1967a), Kear (1967, 1968), Raikow (1971), and Brush (1976) suggested that the peculiar White-backed Duck, *Thalassornis leuconotus*, of Africa and Madagascar—placed provisionally by Delacour and Mayr (1945), Delacour (1959), and Woolfenden (1961) with the stiff-tails—should also be included in the tribe. Kear's (1968: fig. 12c) study of vocalizations showed conclusively that the distress calls of newly hatched *Thalassornis* are like those of *Dendrocygna* ducklings rather than like downy *Oxyura.* Johnsgard (1979) considered *Thalassornis* a member of the subfamily, *Dendrocygninae*, whereas Sibley, Ahlquist, and Monroe (1988) assigned full family status (Dendrocygnidae) to the whistling-ducks, but did not list family members. However, Livezey (1986: 739), finding "pervasive...convergence between *Thalassornis* and the stiff-tailed ducks...in adaptations for diving"—e. g., the Madagascan White-backed Duck, *T. l. insularis*, dives proficiently (Scott and Lubbock 1974)—placed *Dendrocygna* and *Thalassornis* in separate subfamilies of the Anatidae—Dendrocygninae and Thalassorninae—rather than as sister genera in the same tribe.

Kear had earlier (1967) described newly hatched *Thalassornis* as heavy (more than 50 g), having morphological characters of both *Dendrocygna* and *Oxyura* ducklings (e. g., Philippa Scott photo [in *Annual Report of the [Severn] Wildfowl Trust 1965-6* 18, 1967] and Peter Scott painting [*in* Delacour 1959: pl. 19]). Two wild-caught, newly hatched *T. l. leuconotus* (FMNH; Kenya: Lake Naivasha) also combined characters of both whistling- and stiff-tailed ducklings. Their bills and heads were somewhat like those of whistling-ducks (but with poor contrast between the occipital 'T' stripe and the dark crown color), and their base color was striking dark chestnut, similar in *hue* to barred juveniles of both groups. They had lobed halluxes and bi-lobed, elevated lower egg-teeth like those of stiff-tailed ducklings, rather than downy whistling-ducks' long, unlobed halluxes and flat, scale-like lower egg-teeth.

I found no evidence in the downy young for or against the subspecies proposed by Friedmann (1947) for adult Fulvous and White-faced, *D. viduata*, whistling-ducks, but I did find consistent pattern differences—as did Delacour (1954)—between the northern and southern representatives of the Black-bellied Whistling-duck; these correlated with Friedmann's (1947) geographical allocation of the races for that species. I have used Banks's (1978) nomenclature for the two subspecies: *D. a. fulgens* Friedmann [=*lucida* Friedmann and *autumnalis* Linnaeus] for the Northern Black-bellied Whistling-duck, and *D. a. autumnalis* Linnaeus [=*discolor* Sclater and Salvin] for the Southern Black-bellied Whistling-duck.

APPEARANCE AND BEHAVIOR. Downy whistling-ducks have an appearance and behavior unique among waterfowl species. All have long necks, long tarsi and halluxes, and wide, dorsoventrally flattened bills. A distinctive, dark, occipital 'T' stripe is separated from the darker crown by a light stripe running all around the head (see pl. 1). Other peculiarities include small web areas (reminiscent of geese; see figs. G-6, G-7), an extremely short tail, and down so sparse that the duckling's pink skin can be seen when it preens. They also have thick eyelid-rims and, in at least two North American species, light-colored rims around the slightly raised nostrils.

The Fulvous and Wandering, *D. arcuata*, whistling-ducks are widely regarded as a superspecies (e.g., Delacour and Mayr 1945; Johnsgard 1965, 1979; Bolen and Rylander 1983). Downy young of the two species are similarly patterned in gray and white but the gray of *D. arcuata australis* may be quite blackish whereas that of *D. a. arcuata* is medium. Ducklings of the other species are black and yellow or black and white, their colors arranged in patterns of spots and stripes so dazzling that their brilliance is apparent even in black-and-white photographs (e.g., 8 young Black-bellied ducklings in *Annual Report of the [Severn] Wildfowl Trust 1963-64* 16, 1965: Philippa Scott photo).

Both Fulvous and Black-bellied ducklings have distinct color variants. In the former, 'silver-gray' appears occasionally in place of medium gray pattern color, while in the latter, a strong, rich yellow sometimes replaces the more characteristic pale yellow base color (see pl. 1). There is no discernible variation in the base color of the Fulvous duckling or in the pattern color of the Black-bellied duckling. The bright plumage colors reported by Palmer (1976, vol. 2) in downy West Indian Whistling-ducks may represent a variant from the usual exceedingly pale base color, but I have not confirmed this in the specimens that I examined.

Most downy whistling-ducks lack a distinct breast-band, except for the Fulvous duckling, which often has a light gray one. A downy East Indian Wandering Whistling-duck, *D. a. arcuata* (BMNH; Philippine Islands: Siquijor Island) also had a faint gray breast-band, but blackish gray and white ducklings of *D. a. australis* (ANWC; Australia: Northern Territory: S. Alligator River Bridge), had extensive, well-marked blackish gray bands. In all other species, the band, if present at all, is simply a scattering of thinly-spaced dark plumes that often form a loose, central spot at the top of the breast (Blaauw 1912; J. Phillips 1922: Brooks pl. 13). The "cheek patch" to which Johnsgard (1965: 15) referred is actually a lateral arm of the occipital 'T' stripe in all species except (sometimes) the White-faced Whistling-duck. In ducklings of this species, the lateral arm often is separated from the median stripe, forming a large, slanted patch over the ear (compare whistling-duck patterns on pl. 1).

Delacour's (1954: 33) description of adult whistling-ducks as "delightful...quaint and graceful" applies equally to the ducklings, whose behavior is as distinctive as their plumage. Day-old whistling-ducks of the three species that I observed (*D. bicolor, D. arborea, D. autumnalis*) customarily fell asleep on their feet, standing up at first, then sinking gradually to rest on the heels, with the head falling farther and farther forward, often until the bill was tucked beneath the breast, pointing tailward. Older ducklings slept less on their feet, more on their bellies, with chins on the floor and feet trailing out behind. None appeared to depend greatly on water, as downy sea-ducks and stifftails do. According to Bolen and Rylander (1983), adult whistling-ducks adapt interspecifically to water, e.g., Plumed, *D. eytoni*, and White-faced whistling-ducks swim slowly and awkwardly and are reluctant to dive, whereas Wandering, Fulvous, and Indian, *D. javanica*, whistling-ducks swim and dive with ease.

Walking erect and with deliberation, as if on spongy ground, downy whistling-ducks seem almost sluggish when compared to the lively ducklings of certain other species, such as the Wood Duck, *Aix sponsa*, and the goldeneyes, *Bucephala* spp. The appearance is deceptive, as I learned one day when six little West Indian ducklings climbed the sides of their wooden pen, teetered perilously on its edge, and planed lightly down to run, chattering and squealing, in all directions. Ducklings of another hole-nesting species, the Black-bellied Whistling-duck, are also adept at climbing; downy young of both species have long, strongly decurved claws (Rylander and Bolen 1970: fig. 3). The downy young of ground-nesting species, such as the Fulvous and White-faced whistling-ducks (Delacour 1954), are less well-adapted for climbing, with claws not markedly decurved (Rylander and Bolen 1970).

The Head-low-and-forward posture noted by Johnsgard (1965) in adults of several *Dendrocygna* species appeared in day-old Black-bellied ducklings. I could sometimes elicit the posture by placing a foreign object in their pen. With tiny wings outstretched, the ducklings would advance upon the object, drawing their heads back slightly with each step, then thrusting them forward, with bills open, 'hissing' (see dark yellow variant, pl. 1).

Johnsgard (1965) and McKinney (1965) reported mutual nibbling in adults of all *Dendrocygna* species (e.g., McKinney's pl. 7: White-faced Whistling-ducks) except the Fulvous and Black-bellied whistling-ducks. I observed mutual nibbling only in Black-bellied ducklings, but the prevalence of this behavior in adults of the tribe suggests that it probably occurs among the downy young of other species as well.

Whistling-ducks are noisy even as newly hatched young. The four-syllabled, somewhat 'metallic', conversation call; (see Kear 1968: fig. 16a, *D. bicolor*) is quietly and rapidly given and then immediately reiterated, so that the effect is one of constant chattering, interspersed frequently with squeals and whistles much like those of adult birds. First heard at one or two days of age, the whistle is a high-frequency call of variable but generally ascending pitch, delivered from an upright "whistling posture" (Kear 1968: fig. 15). It may take several forms, depending on the stimulus situation, and (possibly) on the species. The Fulvous duckling has a soft, slurred, descending whistle; the ascending whistle of the Black-bellied duckling often is accompanied by a little upward and forward movement of the head. If repeated softly and persistently in a squealy tone, the whistle seems to indicate discomfort: it is uttered frequently by very wet birds as they preen themselves dry, or by a duckling buried beneath a group of sleepers. In all three species that I observed, the whistle often is preceded by one or more firm, disyllabic notes, lightly accented on the second syllable, or it can be followed by rapid polysyllabic chatter or by evenly accented monosyllables all on one pitch. Other times, it is unaccompanied. Uttered loudly and followed by the polysyllabic chatter, it may also be a greeting. A brood of Black-bellied ducklings, imprinted to me, customarily saluted me in this way each morning. The greeting was followed by rapid, low-amplitude conversation calls as the ducklings crowded toward the observation screen to settle down just a few inches from my face.

The daily rhythms of feeding and sleeping described for day-old Northern Mallards (McKinney 1965) are quite similar in newly hatched young of the other anatid species that I saw. I offer the following observations of day-old Black-bellied Whistling-ducks, hatched from wild eggs collected in Texas, as an example of these activities. Like Fulvous and West Indian ducklings, the Black-bellied ducklings strained their food in the water, with great puddling and splashing, making an audible clatter with rapid movements of their mandibles. They eventually abandoned attempts to strain turkey starter, their usual captive fare, but used the method successfully to extract most of the duckweed, *Lemna trisulca*, and small pond invertebrates from their swimming pool. The feeding session, about 20 minutes long, was accompanied by irregular, accented monosyllabic calls and a few chattering calls, all quickly and softly uttered. There were no whistles.

As the ducklings became satiated, they retired, a few at a time, to preen and sleep. One sleepyhead fell into the pool, squealed with alarm, splashed three times, and scrambled out to preen dry, still protesting. Over the next half-hour, the short, accented feeding calls gave way to quiet polysyllabic chatter, with a few squeals and whistles as the ducklings jostled and preened, dozed, and were roused again by the settling movements of the sleepers. As the birds grew sleepier, the calls became quieter, trailing away into soft, squealy whistles as all fell soundly asleep, heads drooping slowly and heels sinking to the floor. At last, only two ducklings remained standing, face to face, each with its head on the other's shoulder. Silence. Five minutes later, the first soft chatters and squeals sounded as the ducklings awoke, stretched, and straggled by twos and threes toward the food tray to recommence feeding.

Fulvous Whistling-duck

Dendrocygne fauve. Pato Pijije Alioscuro.
Dendrocygna bicolor (Vieillot)

APPEARANCE. The Fulvous Whistling-ducklings have long necks and gray and white plumage. Usually, they lack the pale superciliary line and conspicuous wing-patches and dorsal spots. They are unique among North American whistling-ducks. Most Fulvous ducklings have medium gray and white plumage, but a few have plumage 'silver-gray' and white (both variants shown on pl. 1).

VARIATION. Two specimens had yellow base color (Texas [OSUFW]; Louisiana [Lynch 1943]). The "supraloreal spot" (Dickey and Van Rossem 1923: 47; see normal gray variant, pl. 1) was sometimes linear (figs. 1-7, 1-8; APZ, RLWS: 6 live) or, rarely, extended all across the forehead, forming a buffy white 'V' in front view (RLWS: 1 live). Location of the supraloreal spot and shortness of the lateral arm of the 'T' stripe, shown by Burton (*in* Harrison 1978: pl. 3), are incorrect. Conspicuous wing-patches (APZ: 1 live; Meanley and Meanley 1959: fig. 5; MVZ; OSUFW) and four dorsal spots (Palmer 1976, vol. 2: 370, C. Nelson col. pl. and Hines *in* Bellrose 1980: pl. 23) are uncommon. The presence of dorsal spots is apparently unrelated to that of other light pattern elements.

DISCUSSION. The unusual 'silver-gray' plumage was the only one illustrated by Delacour (1954: Scott pl. 4) and Harrison (1978: Burton pl. 3). Delacour later (1964: Scott pl. 5) portrayed the more common, darker form. The genetic mechanism behind the color difference is unknown. Of the 53 specimens that I examined, only two live birds were pale. Lynch suggested that the pale plumage may be caused by a recessive gene; pale ducklings have hatched from eggs laid by both pale and seemingly normal parents in his aviary. He saw no intermediates in any plumage, although he noted that pale adults displayed varying degrees of paleness (John Lynch, letter to the author, September 1968).

I found no differences among wild and captive Fulvous ducklings that could be considered subspecific, such as Friedmann (1947) found for adult birds. However, a large sample of wild ducklings from all parts of the range might disclose some consistent geographical pattern variation in the downy young of both Fulvous and Wandering whistling-ducks, which have quite similar plumage. For example, wild-caught downy *D. arcuata* specimens from the Philippine Islands (BMNH; *arcuata*, ca. 5 d.) and Australia (ANWC; *australis*, 2-3 d.) had prominent superciliary stripes, but the stripes were absent in three *D. arcuata* ducklings reared at the Wildfowl Trust, Slimbridge (WT[S]; *Annual Report of the [Severn] Wildfowl Trust 1963-64* 16, 1965: Philippa Scott photo). In a Fulvous duckling photographed by F. Todd (1979: fig. 1.152), the pale supraloral spot was replaced by a well-marked stripe like that of Australian and Philippine *D. arcuata* specimens.

SOURCE OF SPECIMENS. **California**: *Merced County*: Los Baños (MVZ-1: figs. 1-5, 1-6). **Louisiana**: *Lafayette Parish*: Lafayette (LSUMZ-1: figs. 1-7, 1-8). **Texas**: *Harris* and *Waller* counties—50 to 65 km W Houston (OSUFW-1; PSM-2: UWBM-1). *Nueces County*: Corpus Christi (AMNH-2). COLOMBIA: **Valle del Cauca**: Valle Vijes (ROM-1). **Captive origin** (APZ, RLWS, WT[S]-36 live: figs. 1-2 to 1-4; APZ-1 dead [*ss*: MMMN-1]; BMNH-1; MVZ-1; PSM-2; WT[S]-l; CM-2 alcoholics).

OTHER REFERENCES. Bellrose 1976. Bolen and Rylander 1983. Brown, Urban, and Newman 1982. Cogswell 1977. Coues (1872) 1903, vol. 2. Grinnell, Bryant, and Storer 1918 (quoted *in* Bent 1925). Harrison 1978. Johnsgard 1965. Kortright 1942. Kuroda 1939. J. Phillips 1922.

White-faced Whistling-duck
Dendrocygne veuf. Yaguaso Cariblanco (Venezuela; Desfayes unpubl.).
Dendrocygna viduata (Linnaeus)

APPEARANCE. In the downy White-faced Whistling-duck, the rump-spots are continuous with the pale undertail color or separated from it by only a thin line of dark down; the cheek-stripe has a pronounced anterior droop and is detached from the median occipital stripe or connected to it by just a few dark plumes. The supraorbital stripe was wider in front of the eye than behind it in three specimens and more or less evenly wide in two others, but the supraorbital spot noted by Palmer (1976, vol. 2) was not present on any specimen (see pl. 1 and figs. 1-10 to 1-12). Compared to ducklings of other North American *Dendrocygna* species, the downy White-faced Whistling-duck's bill is longer and the tarsi shorter. Together with the West Indian and Black-bellied ducklings, the White-faced duckling lacks the downy Fulvous Whistling-duck's swan-like crook of the neck.

DISCUSSION. Four of the five prepared specimens examined had pale yellow base color. Delacour (1924, 1954) and Mackworth-Praed and Grant (1970; African population) also describe pale base color for the downy White-faced Whistling-duck. However, J. Phillips's (1922: 18) description—"light sulphur-yellow"—and Scott's portrait of a very yellow duckling (*in* Delacour 1954: pl. 4) suggest the possibility of some variation. An aviary specimen (AMNH; ca. 7 d.) was also quite yellow, and one of the Madagascar ducklings (BM[NH]), bore traces of yellow color on the lores and supraorbital stripe (its sibling was a bit paler and duller over all). Differences among individuals, differences in age of the ducklings at the time of collection, changes in plumage color after preparation and storage, or a combination of these factors could have caused the variations observed. In any case, neither the specimens nor Delacour's

(1924) descriptions of the live duckling suggest a clear-cut variation in base color for downy White-faced Whistling-ducks.

SOURCE OF SPECIMENS. MADAGASCAR [=MALAGASY REPUBLIC]: 1 day E Maromandia [overland from Antananarivo] (BM[NH]-2). **Captive origin** (AMNH-2; WT[S]-1: figs. 1-10 to 1-12).

OTHER REFERENCES. Bolen and Rylander 1983. Brown, Urban, and Newman 1982, vol. 1. Friedmann 1947. McLachlan and Liversidge 1972.

West Indian Whistling-duck

Dendrocygne des Antilles. Chiriría (Puerto Rico; Desfayes unpubl.).
Dendrocygna arborea (Linnaeus)

APPEARANCE. Downy West Indian and Black-bellied whistling-ducks share the same bold plumage pattern (see pl. 1), but the West Indian duckling is larger and heavier (see Table 1, Appendix A), its base color is much paler, its pale supraorbital stripes nearly always meet above the bill to form a pale forehead, and its

toes and tarsi are grayish green, grayish blue, or bluish gray rather than olive-yellow as in the small Black-bellied duckling.

VARIATION. In two specimens, the dark crown color extended in a thin line all the way to the bill (RLWS: 1 live; BM[NH]); two others had the pale forehead extremely narrow (FMNH). The cheek-stripes of two live ducklings were long and heavy (APZ; Nancy Murdoch color transparency) and those of three others curved upward in front of the eye and connected loosely to the pre-ocular stripes (BM[NH]; FMNH).

DISCUSSION. Most authors (e.g., Blaauw 1912; Delacour 1954), emphasized the pale base color of the West Indian duckling. The "rich" or "vivid" colors described by Palmer (1976, vol. 2: 27, 29) for ducklings of this species were confined to the lores and supraorbital stripes of the live specimens that I examined and, although truly brilliant, were also extremely pale.

SOURCE OF SPECIMENS. BRITISH VIRGIN ISLANDS: Virgin Gorda Island (FMNH-2: figs. 1-18, 1-19). VIRGIN ISLANDS (U. S.): Saint Croix Island (FMNH-2: figs. 1-16, 1-17). **Captive origin** (RLWS-6 live: figs. 1-13 to 1-15; BM[NH]-1; APZ-1 color transparency).

OTHER REFERENCES. Bolen 1973. Bolen and Rylander 1983. Johnsgard 1965. J. Phillips 1922. Rylander and Bolen 1970.

Black-bellied Whistling-duck

Dendrocygne à ventre noir. Pato Pijije Aliblanco.
Dendrocygna autumnalis (Linnaeus)

APPEARANCE. *Dendrocygna's* striking pattern of spots and stripes is best displayed in the brilliant yellow and black plumage of the downy Black-bellied Whistling-duck; Johnstone (1957b: 24) aptly termed the contrast "wasp-like". A quite wide, yellow supraorbital stripe (usually extending past the eye), a cheek-stripe ending just under the eye, and a narrow dark forehead are also characteristic. Most Black-bellied ducklings have pale yellow base color, but a few North American *D. a. fulgens* [=*D. a. lucida* Friedmann and *D. a. autumnalis* Linnaeus; Banks 1978] have dark, strong yellow base color (see both variants on pl. 1; also DISCUSSION, below).

VARIATION. Seventeen of 75 live, wild-caught ducklings from seven broods had narrow yellow foreheads (Brian Cain, letter to the author, October 1968; DWWRS; UFS[DM]), and one live duckling (UFS[DM]) had a prominent yellow forehead. The cheek-stripes of a few individuals were long and heavy (DWWRS, UFS[DM]), extending forward of eye-level.

D. a. autumnalis Linnaeus [=*D. a. discolor* Sclater and Salvin; Banks 1978]. Compared to *fulgens*, the yellow supraorbital stripe is narrower than the dark transocular stripe, which usually extends only to the eye or slightly beyond, and the cheek-stripe is wider and longer. *Autumnalis* gives the impression of narrower yellow stripes, wider black ones; *fulgens* opposite. The unfeathered parts of two *autumnalis* ducklings from Venezuela were more generally 'greenish' than those of downy *fulgens*: irides "grayish brown", upper mandible "greenish gray", lower mandible "mustard yellow", feet "olive green" (CM-1 [ca. 7 d.], tag data; coll. J. L. Ariay [author's translation from the Spanish]); an older duckling (CM-1 [ca. 2 wk.]) had "dark grayish brown" irides (*fulgens* nearly black), "greenish gray" upper mandible, and "clear, dark greenish gray-brown" feet (bill and feet of half-grown *fulgens* bluish gray).

DISCUSSION. Of 21 live Black-bellied duckings examined, 17 were pale yellow and four were dark (i.e., 'bright' or strong yellow), such as those depicted by Shortt (*in* Kortright 1942: pl. 35), Scott (*in* Delacour 1954: pl. 4), C. Nelson (*in* Palmer 1976, vol. 2: 370), Burton (*in* Harrison 1978: pl. 3; note absence of yellow shoulder-spot), and Hines (*in* Bellrose 1980: pl. 22). Bolen stated that the 'yellower' birds were unusual in Texas broods that he had examined

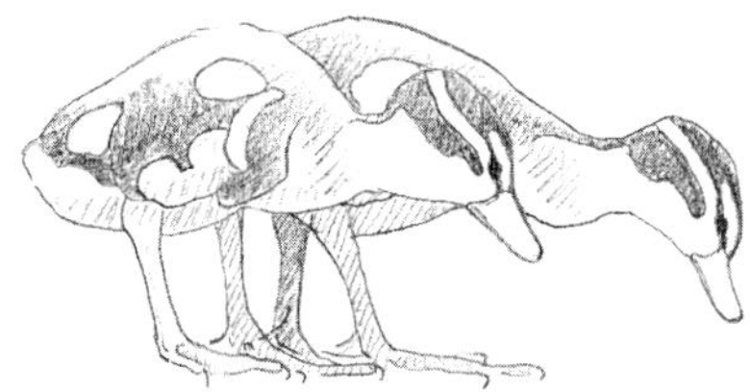

(Eric Bolen, letter to the author, March 1965).

Cain later provided color data on 94 Black-bellied ducklings (5 broods, 7 individuals) from his study area near Kingsville, Texas. He and Steven Labuda found 43 'bright' and 44 'pale' ducklings distributed more or less evenly among three of the broods and selectively within two others: one brood of 10 was entirely 'pale'; another brood of 19 had 17 'bright' and two 'pale' individuals. All broods were less than 36 hours old, except the last, which was about seven days old. Of seven individual birds, three were 'bright' and four were 'pale' (Brian Cain, letter to the author, October 1968).

The data from Cain and Labuda—gathered in the field without a color standard—suggest not only that the two yellow color variants can be recognized easily, but also that they may be about equally common in the Kingsville area: all three 'bright' ducklings among the 20 study skins examined also came from Texas. They may even represent true color phases rather than the "individual variation" suggested by Palmer (1976, vol. 2: 29).

SOURCE OF SPECIMENS. **Texas**: *San Patricio County*: Lake Mathis (WWF-1), near Mathis (DWWRS, UFS[DM]-21 live: figs. 1-20 to 1-22 [*ss*: D-2; MMMN-2: figs. 1-23, 1-24; UND-1]; PSM-2; 3 color transparencies). COSTA RICA: **Guanacaste:** Ballena (FMNH-1;LACM-1: figs. 1-25, 1-26). MEXICO: **Nayarit**: San Blas (BMNH-3). **Vera Cruz**: Rio Jaltepec at Highway 105 bridge (BMNH-4). BRAZIL: **Bahia**: Rio Preto: Santa Rita de Cassia (LACM-1). COLOMBIA: **Antioquia**: Cuturú (AMNH-1). PANAMA: **Coclé**: Aguadulce (BM[NH]-1). VENEZUELA: **Carabobo**: El Paíto (CM-1); Lago di Valencia (CM-1). **Cojedes**: Hato Nuevo (CM-1). **Captive origin** (USNM-1; WT[S]-1).

OTHER REFERENCES. *Annual Report of the [Severn] Wildfowl Trust 1958-59* 11, 1960; *1960-61* 13, 1962; *1963-64* 16, 1965. Baird, Brewer, and Ridgway 1884, vol. 1 (quoted *in* Bent 1925). Bellrose 1976. Blake 1977. Bolen and Forsyth 1967. Bolen and Rylander 1983. Bolen, McDaniel, and Cottam 1964. Coues (1872) 1903, vol. 2. *Defensa de la Naturaleza* 2 (5), July 1972. Grinnell, Bryant, and Storer 1918. Johnsgard 1965. J. Phillips 1922. Ridgway (1887) 1896. *Wildfowl* 27, 1976.

Swans, tribe Cygnini

North American genera: *Cygnus* Bechstein, *Olor* Wagler

DISTRIBUTION AND TAXONOMY. Commanding the attention and admiration of even the most casual observer, the large, graceful swans also fire the interest of specialists in behavior, ecology, genetics, and taxonomy. Many authors include the swans in the Anserini because of behavioral (Delacour and Mayr 1945; Johnsgard 1965, 1978, 1979), biochemical (Brush 1976), and certain genetic (Numachi et al. 1983) similarities. However, because of distinctive characters of the downy young and what I believe to be an evolutionary history divergent from that of geese, I have retained the swans in Cygnini, following Woolfenden (1961), A.O.U. (1983), and Livezey (1986).

At least one species of swan is native to every continent except Africa, from which fossil swans are known (Howard 1964). Adults of five species are entirely white (i. e., *Coscoroba, Cygnus olor*, 3 *Olor* spp.), but those of two others, the Black Swan, *Cygnus atratus*, and the Black-necked Swan, *C. melanocoryphus*, have extensive areas of black feathers. Cygnet plumages of all species are essentially white or gray, with little or no contrasting pattern, except for *Coscoroba*, which has a distinctive, *Dendrocygna*-like pattern, bill, and feet (FMNH; Paraguay: Chaco; see also Scott et al. 1972: pl. 2 [upper]). On the basis of these and other similarities, many authors (e.g., Heinroth and Heinroth 1928, vol. 3; Peters 1931, vol. 1; Delacour and Mayr 1945; Cramp and Simmons 1977; A.O.U. 1983) place all swan species, excluding *Coscoroba*, in one genus, *Cygnus.*

Delacour (1954), using the single genus, nevertheless considered the northern swans to be distinct and very closely related; his group contains two species, *C. cygnus* [2 subspp.: palaearctic *cygnus* and nearctic *buccinator*] and *C. columbianus* [2 subspp.: palaearctic *bewickii* and nearctic *columbianus*], with the southern swans (*C. olor, C. atratus, C. melanocoryphus*, no subspecies) forming a second—but less obviously related—group. As well as having widely different geographical distributions, adults of the two groups are further distinguished by certain genetic differences (Numachi

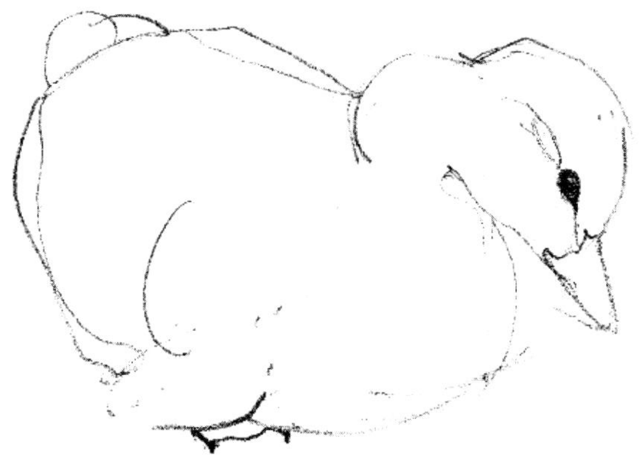

et al. 1983), and by differences in tracheal anatomy (Wetmore 1951; Boyd 1972), osteology (Woolfenden 1961; Livezey 1986), philopterid parasites (*Ornithobius* spp.; Timmermann 1963), and behavior (Johnsgard 1961b, 1963, 1965). Both Howard (1964: 255) and Brodkorb (*in* Howard 1964: 261) recognized, respectively, a "whistling-type" and a "mute type" among fossil swans from western North America. Characters of the downy plumage and unfeathered parts separate the cygnets into the same two groups (C. Nelson 1976b), with no overlap of characters and no intergrades. In this work, the northern and southern swans are treated as separate genera, *Cygnus* and *Olor*, following Wetmore (1951; re: white swans), Parkes (1958), Woolfenden (1961), and Livezey (1986). *Coscoroba*, recognized as having certain affinities with the whistling-ducks (Delacour and Mayr 1945), is included as a tribal member, following Woolfenden (1961), Scott et al. (1972), Johnsgard (1979), and Livezey (1986).

Plate 2

Note: Unless otherwise indicated, all portraits depict day-old waterfowl. The place where the specimens were housed, if different from their place of origin, appears in parentheses. Birds of captive origin are so designated.

1 Mute Swan, Cygnus olor

Gray phase. Little Compton, Long Pond, Rhode Island (NWPW).

White Phase. Traverse City, Michigan (NWPW).

2 Whistling Swan, Olor c. columbianus

Between Bethel and Hazen Bay, Alaska: "the flats" (RLWS [2d.]).

3 Trumpeter Swan, O. buccinator

Gray variant. Wolf Lake, Grande Prairie, Alberta (NMC: color) and Lonesome Lake, British Columbia (WT[S] captives: measurements).

Leucistic variant. Lacreek National Wildlife Refuge, South Dakota (Minnesota Department of Natural Resources captives: Carroll Henderson color transparencies (7-10 d.]) and Red Rock Lakes Migratory Waterfowl Refuge, Montana (DWWRS captives [2 d.]: measurements).

Plate 2

Authorities also differ concerning the classification of the northern swan species. Peters (1931, vol. 1) catalogued four full species (*C. cygnus, C. bewickii, C. columbianus, C. buccinator*), whereas Delacour and Mayr (1945) and Johansen (1956) merged Trumpeter with Whooper [as *C. cygnus*] and Bewick's with Whistling [as *C. columbianus*] to make two. Portenko ([1972] 1981) and Johnsgard (1974) placed all northern swans within a single species, *C. cygnus*, although Johnsgard (1978, 1979) later re-classified the one species as four. Species classification used herein follows Parkes (1958), Palmer (1976, vol. 2), and the A.O.U. (1983). These sources consider the palaearctic Bewick's and nearctic Whistling swans as subspecies of the Tundra Swan, *O. columbianus*, and the Trumpeter and Whooper swans as separate species.

APPEARANCE AND BEHAVIOR. Although Delacour and Mayr (1945: 8) considered the northern swans "the most primitive [of swans]," certain evidence from the downy plumages suggests that the opposite may be true. All adult *Cygnus* and *Olor* have the lore unfeathered from bill to eye, but only the Black Swan, *C. atratus*, resident in Australia and New Zealand, displays this character in the natal plumage (Stejneger 1883; Palmer 1976, vol. 2). Young cygnets of the other five species show various degrees of loreal feathering thought to be adaptations to their colder breeding habitats (compare fig. 11, *C. atratus*, with figs. 8, 14, 17, 20, 23, 26, all *in* C. Nelson 1976b). However, in half-grown cygnets of the three North American species, a return to the more 'primitive' unfeathered lore of the downy Black Swan takes place, as the soft loreal down is transformed into a 'V' of withered, twisted nubs narrowing from bill to eye (figs. 2-7, 2-14, 2-21; not examined: half-grown cygnets of Black, Black-necked, Bewick's, and Whooper swans). There is apparently considerable individual variation in the age at which this transformation takes place: two of five gray-feathered Trumpeter siblings shown by S. Hansen (1984: 49, photo) have partly bare lores, but the other three cygnets, as well as gray-headed juvenal Bewick's Swans of approximately the same age depicted by Scott et al. (1972: pl. 40, Philippa Scott photo), are feathered between eye and bill. In contrast, a half-grown, partly downy Black-necked Swan portrayed by Scott et al. (1972: pl. 15 [lower], Russ Kinne photo) has entirely bare lores.

Southern cygnets have measurably darker, 'yellower' pattern color than do northern cygnets. The plumage of downy Mute and Black swans has none of the 'silvery' brilliance that characterizes northern cygnets. Even the downy Black-necked Swan, so white it looks almost 'painted', is actually the darkest of the three southern species at the *base* of the dorsal down (C. Nelson 1976b). Downy *Cygnus* lack dorsal spots and wing-patches, and have dark-colored bills (except nail) and feet. The opposite is true of the paler, 'bluish' and 'silvery', dorsally patterned *Olor* cygnets whose virtually unpigmented bills and feet take their pink color from the red pigment of blood beneath the skin (Parmelee, Stephens, and Schmidt 1967).

Downy cygnets of both genera have short, heavy tarsi with large, rounded paddle areas (figs. G-5, G-6) and glossy, finely reticulate, loose-fitting skin. Claws of the live *Olor* cygnets are longer, slimmer, and more sharply pointed than those of the downy Mute Swan, and their halluxes are shorter and thinner.

The adult swans' habit of drawing up one foot to rest at the side of the body develops early. Day-old Whistling (RLWS) and Trumpeter swans (DWWRS) rested their wrinkled pink feet in this way; so did Delta's two-day-old Trumpeters as they floated on their pond. Wild, month-old Idaho Trumpeter cygnets often rest one foot while "paddling with the other...canting a bit on the water—like tiny, listing ships" (S. Hansen 1984: 45).

Preening and oiling occupy much of the cygnets' time awake. Day-old Trumpeter Swans (DWWRS) reached the oil gland, then nibbled and preened their own and their mother's feathers. Lowther observed these two-day-old cygnets Head-shaking after preening (James Lowther, pers. comm. 1964). Three Mute cygnets (1 d.; NWPW) followed a 10-minute swim with prolonged oiling and preening, including mutual preening, accompanied by soft, ascending polysyllabic calls. They braced themselves as Ruddies do, with feet outstretched on either side, and tails touching the floor of their pen. Walking slowly, almost clumsily, they had difficulty balancing their heavy bodies, and often tumbled over while belly-preening or trying to reach the oil gland. Delta's captive, day-old Trumpeter cygnets, too, standing on their mother's back to preen, frequently lost their balance and toppled off into the grass. A two-day-old Mute cygnet fell repeatedly while trying to walk and to preen its tibial plumage at the same time.

Southern swan parents often carry their young on their backs (e.g., Gould 1873: pl. 8; Johnsgard and Kear 1968), but the habit was not documented in northern swans until Hammer (1970: 325, photo p. 324) observed a very young wild Trumpeter cygnet at Lacreek National Wildlife Refuge, South Dakota, which "climbed onto [a swimming adult's] back, quickly turned around, sat down, and began preening." Bailey, Bangs, and Berns (1980) later saw Alaskan Trumpeters from two different families back-carrying their young.

Cygnets of both groups dabble when feeding. Mute cygnets (4 d.), which often swam with their entire heads and necks submerged, dipped each bit of food into water before ingesting it. Delta's day-old Trumpeters 'nibbled' constantly on the nest materials, on the grass around it, and on their mother's and one another's plumage. Two-day-old Delta cygnets were led to water by their mother, where they dabbled and pecked at materials that she had stirred up by 'trampling'. S. Hansen (1984) observed 'trampling' by both parents in wild Trumpeter families; so did Evans (1975) in captive Bewick's Swans.

The calls and behavior of cygnets and goslings share many similarities. For example, the structure of the sleepy call (Kear 1968: fig. 7) given by the Whooper cygnet (calls of Trumpeter and Tundra cygnets presumed similar) resembles that of *Anser* goslings [more than *Branta*], and the greeting calls of both Mute and *Olor* cygnets have two or three syllables lightly accented on the second, as in goslings, but sounding deeper and more resonant. Captive Trumpeter cygnets (DWWRS) uttered sporadic but frequent short trills and monosyllabic conversation calls [=first syllable of greeting call] as they moved about the nest, climbing in and out of their mother's plumage. Chin-lifting accompanies the soft, two-syllabled greeting call in day-old cygnets of all three North American species, but Bill-dipping before the Chin-lift was observed only in day-old Whistling Swans.

Like goslings, day-old cygnets engage in frequent, vigorous bill-fighting and 'heel-nipping', e.g., a downy Mute Swan leaned out, as it swam in the pool, and tweaked sharply the bill and foot of a sibling resting beside it. The Delta Trumpeters fought with their bills, bumping and pushing beneath their mother's wings; S. Hansen (1984: 41, photo) reported bill-fighting in wild., 10-day-old Trumpeters. A 'silvery', pink-billed Whistling cygnet (RLWS; captive hatched from wild Alaskan eggs)—in my eyes, the very picture of exquisite innocence—was quickly moved to other quarters after it seized a day-old teal by the bill and shook it roughly back and forth. The Head-down-and-forward posture, typical of goslings, is absent, but cygnets only one or two days old sometimes arch their long necks as in the adult threat posture.

Mute Swan

Cygne tuberculé. Cisne Vulgar.

Cygnus olor

APPEARANCE. Compared to Tundra and Trumpeter cygnets, the plumage of the downy Mute Swan is grayer and browner (gray phase) or whiter and yellower (white phase). Its bill and feet are heavily pigmented (dark gray or black in gray phase, light brown in white phase), its lateral bill feathering runs almost straight up from the rictus to the 'horn' of the bill, and it lacks both dorsal spots and prominent wing-patches (narrow, inconspicuous wing-patches form 'shadow pattern' on a few individuals). The mesial bill feathering, usually short and rounded in dorsal view (figs. 2-1, 2-4), is occasionally long and pointed in both nearctic (fig. 2-6) and palaearctic cygnets (Witherby et al. [1939] 1943, vol. 3). The pinkish gray nail (entirely white or yellowish white in prepared specimens) contrasts well with the dark bill (see 2 color phases on pl. 2; also C. Nelson 1976a, frontispiece, for dorsal views).

VARIATION. Northrepps (*in* Dresser 1871-81, vol. 6), Delacour (1954), Palmer (1976, vol. 2), and Cramp and Simmons (1977) described entirely white plumage for white-phase cygnets. Pinkish bill and foot colors were also noted on some [young?] palaearctic cygnets by Northrepps (*in* Dresser 1871-81, vol. 6), Stejneger (1883), and Bauer and Glutz von Blotzheim (1968), whereas the bill and feet of a four-week-old palaearctic cygnet were "greenish grey" (Gurney 1877: 59). No live, feral North American cygnet had the combination of pink or grayish pink feet and dark bill portrayed by Boyd (1972) and Fjeldså (1977).

DISCUSSION. The Mute Swan's striking 'gray' and 'white' color phases can be readily identified in all plumage classes. Although it appears quite white when compared directly to 'gray' cygnets, the 'white' cygnet has discernible color at hatching (Gurney 1877; Stejneger 1883; C. Nelson 1976a; Fjeldså 1977). Admittedly, the 'brilliance' of this color—an extremely pale, dull yellowish brown at hatching—fades quickly, so that the older downy cygnet does appear essentially white or yellowish white. The *value* contrast between the 'gray' and 'white' plumages becomes even greater in feathered (i.e., not downy) juveniles (Scott et al. 1972: pl. 8, B. Thyselius photo).

Described by Yarrell in 1838 as a full species, *Cygnus immutabilis* (='Unchanging Swan', i.e., all plumages white), the white or 'Polish' phase of the Mute Swan was shown by Munro, Smith, and Kupa (1968) to result from the action of a single sex-linked gene (see Kear [1972: 107] for diagram of sex-linked color inheritance). According to Kear (1972: 108), "the domestication of the Mute Swan in some European locations has undoubtedly encouraged the spread of the white phase." The Traverse City flock (fed in fall and winter by local residents [Gelston 1970], hence, semi-domesticated) appears to have a higher proportion of white phase birds (ca. 45%) than that found in the feral Rhode Island population (ca. 30%) by Munro, Smith, and Kupa (1968); Gelston (1970) tallied 50 'Polish' cygnets among 111 hatched in eight northern Michigan counties during a single year. Loss of gray pigment beyond that normal for the white phase may accompany the recessive phenotypes: blue irides were found on about a dozen individuals in a feral Michigan flock (Gelston 1970).

The Mute Swan, native to Europe and Asia, was introduced to North America as an ornamental bird for parks, zoos, and country estates. According to Halla (1966: 2), "escapees from [certain of] these captive flocks are believed responsible for the feral swans on the Atlantic coast," which, "as of 1982, numbered about 3500 adults" (James Myers, telephone interview, 3 January 1984). In Michigan, Gelston (1970) traced the Traverse City flock, at that time comprising about 300 birds, to a single pair of adults imported from England in 1918 by a wealthy Iowa landowner. Smaller feral flocks exist in British Columbia, Ontario, Oregon, and other parts of North America.

Attractive as they are to human observers, Mute Swans sometimes present problems in conservation and management. Aggressive behavior of both captive and breeding pairs (e.g. Minton 1968; Kear 1972) may effectively prevent some other species from using available nesting habitat: Halla (1966: 4) found Northern

Mallards and American Black Ducks nesting within six meters of feral Mute Swans in Rhode Island, but observed that "no other swan or goose [was] allowed to nest nearby." Willey (1968) also noted tolerance of other species, but found more often intolerance so extreme that no other species was allowed to occupy the body of water defended by the Mute Swan pair.

SOURCE OF SPECIMENS. **Michigan**: *Grand Traverse County*: 0.4 km N Traverse City on East Bay (NWPW-3 live). **Oregon**: *Lincoln County*: Devil's Lake (OSUFW-1). **Rhode Island**: *Newport County*: Little Compton: Long Pond (NWPW-3 live: figs. 2-1 to 2-3). *Washington County*: South Kingston Township: Trustom Pond (6 frozen [*ss*: MMMN-2: figs. 2-4, 2-5). ENGLAND: River Thames (BM[NH]-1), River Thames at Sunbury (BM[NH]-1). **Captive origin** (PSM-2; ROM-2: figs. 2-6, 2-7; UWBM-1).

OTHER REFERENCES. Bannerman 1957, vol. 6. Dement'ev and Gladkov ([1952] 1967, vol. 4). Gould 1873. Harrison 1975. Heinroth and Heinroth 1928, 3. F. Todd 1979. Scherner 1984. *Wildfowl* 31: 52. Wilmore 1974.

Tundra Swan

Cygne siffleur. Cisne Menor.
Olor columbianus (Ord)

APPEARANCE. Both Tundra (represented by the nearctic Whistling Swan, *O. c. columbianus*) and Trumpeter (*O. buccinator*) cygnets have pale, 'bluish' gray and white plumage, with prominent white wing-patches and two large white shoulder-spots (pale interscapular area also noted by Dement'ev and Gladkov [1952] 1967, vol. 4, in cygnets of palaearctic Bewick's [*O. "Cygnus" columbianus bewickii*], Jankowski's [*"Cygnus bewickii jankowskii"*], and Whooper [*O. "Cygnus" cygnus cygnus*] swans). The plumage is 'silvery', almost iridescent, the irides are dark grayish brown, and the bill and feet are pink. Relative to the Trumpeter cygnet, the downy Whistling cygnet is smaller, with shorter, rounder head and smaller bill proportions. The forehead rises more abruptly (comparison also true of palaearctic Bewick's and Whooper cygnets; Bauer and Glutz von Blotzheim 1968). The Whistling cygnet's longer, fluffier head down effectively conceals the lobed outline of the bill feathering (compare figs. 2-8 to 2-14 and 2-15 to 2-21; see also photos, pls. 26 and 32, *in* Scott et al. 1972) and the posterior border of the nail is usually rounded (figs. 2-15, 2-18). The nostril is small and oval (longer and more pointed anteriorly in older downies) and its front rim usually falls within the anterior half of the commissure (figs 2-17, 2-19); compare Whistling and Trumpeter cygnets on pl. 2).

In no case was the morphometric variation described in adult Tundra (Whistling) Swans (Miller et al. 1988) observed in the downy young.

VARIATION. Five of eight live Alaskan cygnets had measurably darker plumage, with darker pink bills and feet, than the three hatched a few days later. Parmelee, Stephens, and Schmidt (1967) found similar variations among four downy Whistling siblings collected on Victoria Island, NWT. They noted that dorsal and ventral down colors of one female cygnet contrasted more strongly than those of other brood members. This specimen (UMFBP[DFP]) and that of a male sibling (OSUFW) had prominent white wing-patches and shoulder-spots, unlike another, much paler, male sibling (UMFBP[DFP]) on which the dorsal markings were barely discernible. Evans and Lebret (1973: 62) reported "pale blue" irides in a captive, leucistic Bewick's Swan.

DISCUSSION. Despite the appearance of several excellent descriptions of the bill and foot colors of live *O. columbianus* cygnets (e.g., Bailey 1948; Snyder 1957; Wilmore 1974; Palmer 1976, vol. 2), published errors persist. Scott's portrayal (*in* Delacour 1954: pl. 4) of yellow-footed *Olor* cygnets (downy Whistling Swan with yellow bill, bills of Trumpeter and Bewick's pinkish) does not agree with Delacour's accurate description in the text (p. 73 et al.). Nor did Burton's portrait (*in* Harrison 1978: pl. 3) of a yellow-billed, yellow-footed Trumpeter cygnet match Harrison's correct evaluation of the two North American species (p. 69). Parmelee, Stephens, and Schmidt (1967: 36) established the source of such errors when they observed that the pink bills and feet of live cygnets became "pale yellow" after the cygnets had been preserved as study skins (such as described by D. G. Elliot *in* Bent 1925).

The juvenal Whistling Swan "retains dark feathers only on the head and upper neck in contrast to the Trumpeter cygnet," which is quite dark-feathered all over (H. Hansen et al. 1971: 54; compare their figs. 42 [Trumpeter cygnet] and 43 [Whistling cygnet]). Both the demarcation between dark forehead and pale lores and the rather sharp contrast between dark crown and lighter occiput of the 9 1/2-month-old Whistling cygnet are reminiscent of the head patterns of *Coscoroba* and some *Dendrocygna* ducklings.

SOURCE OF SPECIMENS. **Northwest Territories**: *District of Franklin*: Victoria Island: Cambridge Bay (OSUFW-1; UMFBP[DFP]-2). *District of Keewatin*: Adelaide Peninsula near E side Sherman Basin (NMC-4: figs. 2-18, 2-19). Southampton Island: Bay of God's Mercy (MMMN-1), Hut Point (CM-1: figs. 2-20, 2-21). *District of Mackenzie*: Mackenzie Delta: Kendall Island (CM-2), 4.8 km S Kendall island—69° 26' N, 135° 18' W (USNM-1). **Alaska**: between Bethel and Hazen Bay: "the flats" (RLWS-8 live: figs. 2-15 to 2-17). Point Barrow: Chipp River (FMNH-1). RUSSIA: **Siberia**: Yenisey River: between Gol'chikha and Korsakovskiye Islands (BM[NH]-1), 2 days N Tolstyy Nos [enroute to Yeniseysk aboard *S. S. Yenisei*] (BM[NH]-1) [unpubl. notebooks of H. L. Popham, 1895, -97, at British Museum (Natural History)]. **Captive origin** (WT[S]-1).

OTHER REFERENCES. Bailey and Niedrach 1965, vol. 1. Bellrose 1976, 1980. Cramp and Simmons 1977. Dement'ev and Gladkov (1952) 1967, vol. 4. Evans 1977. Gabrielson and Lincoln 1959. Johnstone 1957a. Macpherson and Manning 1959. Roberts 1932, vol. 2. Witherby et al. (1939) 1943, vol. 3.

Trumpeter Swan
Cygne trompette. Cisne Trompetero.
Olor buccinator (Richardson)

APPEARANCE. 'Gray' cygnet: see Tundra Swan, pp. 32-33; also Banko (1960: fig. 42) for photograph of 'silvery' down. The plumage of the 'leucistic' cygnet is almost white and its unfeathered parts are yellower than those of the 'gray' cygnet (see cygnets of both color phases on pl. 2; Carrol Henderson, letter to the author, October 1982). Relative to the Tundra cygnet, the downy Trumpeter Swan is larger, with longer proportions of head and bill, a sloping forehead, more 'sculptured' outline of the bill feathering, and shorter, smoother appearance of the head down (compare 2 spp. on pl. 2 and in figs. 2-8 to 2-14, 2-15 to 2-21; see also Scott et al. 1972: photos, pls. 26 (Trumpeter Swan) and 32 (Whistling Swan); Trumpeter's down also shorter and denser than that of Black and Black-necked cygnets [Blaauw 1904]). In young downies, the posterior border of the nail is usually broadly triangular (figs. 2-8, 2-11). The nostril is long, irregularly shaped, and some-

what pointed anteriorly, with its front rim falling about half-way along the commissure (figs. 2-10, 2-12; compare *Olor* cygnets on pl. 2).

VARIATION. The small *value* variations in pattern color occurring in Trumpeter cygnets should not be confused with the color phases described above. Although both captive Slimbridge cygnets were paler than either of two live Delta cygnets, neither was leucistic. Sclater (1870) and Wilmore (1974) described quite dark gray Trumpeter cygnets—palaearctic Whooper and Bewick's cygnets also dark dorsally (Dement'ev and Gladkov ([1952] 1967, vol. 4)—and a few cygnets from the Grande Prairie region, Alberta (NMC), were much darker than others from the same area, especially on the occiput and hindneck. Shea noted similar individual *value* differences among wild cygnets in Yellowstone Park (Ruth Shea, letter to the author, April 1978).

The pink *hue* of the bill and feet may be 'yellower' in pale individuals, 'redder' and 'bluer' in darker ones. The "muted orange-yellow" foot color reported for both color phases by Palmer (1976, vol. 2: 56) was not seen in live birds, but fell within the range of colors observed in prepared specmens: light brownish gray (darker individuals) to grayish yellowish white (paler ones). The difference in the foot colors of live and prepared Trumpeter cygnet specimens parallels almost exactly that observed by Parmelee, Stephens, and Schmidt (1967) in wild Tundra (Whistling) cygnets.

Foot color in feathered 'gray' juveniles varies from "greyish fleshy pink [younger birds?] turning to olive-grey and black" (Delacour 1954: 75) to "yellowish or olive gray-black" (Banko 1960: 62) to "mustard yellow" (D. Munro 1962: 65). Banko (1960) stated that juvenal foot colors were the same in both color phases, but Shea said that an adult [leucistic?] Trumpeter seen near Yellowstone National Park had "pale yellow legs" (Ruth Shea, letter to the author, April 1978). These observations suggest that foot color of juveniles varies widely within the yellow-red range, but the lack of precise color evaluation data for live juveniles (or for live, newly-hatched young) of either phase precludes a proper assessment of the extent of the variation.

The light-colored dorsal spots and wing-patches seen on very young 'gray' cygnets may be inconspicuous on the faded plumage of older cygnets and, presumably, on 'leucistic' cygnets of all ages. The length and softness of the dorsal down also tend to diffuse the outlines of any pattern present.

DISCUSSION. I suspect that 'leucistic' Trumpeter cygnets have measurable amounts of dorsal color at hatching (e.g., an exceedingly pale 'bluish' gray), but, if so, the color fades rapidly. An older cygnet (7-10 d.) appeared dazzling white beside a 'gray' sibling of the same age (C. Henderson color transparencies; see also Banko 1960: 71, W. V. Watson photo of mixed 'gray' and 'white' brood).

Banko (1960: 62) considered the leucistic plumage "rare" among wild cygnets in Yellowstone Park. Shea confirmed that "although the leucistic phase was rather common [in Yellowstone] in the 1930's and 1940's [Palmer (1976, vol. 2: 57) lists..."13%...over a 4-year period," or about 1 in 8], they are apparently very uncommon today. [In 1977,] at least 52 cygnets hatched [in the park], but none were leucistic" (Ruth Shea, letter to the author, April 1978). However, leucistic cygnets have been observed in areas of the Trumpeter's former breeding range, where it has become reestablished, e.g., Idaho (Mary Maj, pers. comm. 1981) and South Dakota. Eggs from Lacreek National Wildllife Refuge, sent to St. Paul for Minnesota's non-game wildlife program, produced 5 cygnets: 4 gray and 1 leucistic (Harold Burgess, letter to the author, July 1982). As far as is known, leucistic cygnets have not been produced in the Alaskan population. The genetic mechanism of the leucistic phase remains unknown.

Physical differences reported by H. Hansen (1973) between Trumpeter Swan populations in Alaska and Montana (he found Alaskan birds larger at all ages than the Montana birds measured by Banko 1960) were not supported by morphological and genetic data obtained by Barrett and Vyse (1982) from populations of adult Trumpeter Swans in Alaska, Alberta (Grande Prairie), and Montana (Red Rock Lakes

National Wildlife Refuge). Barrett and Vyse (1982: 106) found little or no difference in live weights and bill length between Alaska and Montana populations (Alberta birds not measured), but rather, "close genetic relationships among the three populations." However, they did not distinguish between normal and leucistic adults in their sample, if, indeed, there were any of the latter.

SOURCE OF SPECIMENS. **Alberta**: Grande Prairie region: Airport Slough (NMC-1), Buffalo Lake near Sexmith (NMC-1), Clairmont Lake (NMC-1), Hermit Lake (NMC-1), Saskatoon Lake near Wembley (NMC-4), Wolf Lake (NMC-1: figs. 2-11, 2-12). **British Columbia**: *Range 3, Coast District*: parent stock from wintering birds at Lonesome Lake—33.7 km SE Atnarko [Mackay 1954] (WT[S]-2 live captives). **Montana**: *Beaverhead County*: Monida: Red Rock Lakes Migratory Waterfowl Refuge (DWWRS-2 live captives: figs. 2-8 to 2-10; D-3: figs. 2-13, 2-14; OU-1; PSM-2; UND-1). **South Dakota**: *Bennett County*: Lacreek National Wildlife Refuge (UNMZ-1 alcoholic).

OTHER REFERENCES. Boyd 1972. Cooper 1979. Hansen et al. 1971. S. Hansen 1984. Harrison 1978. Johnsgard 1965. *North Dakota Outdoors* 33 (1), 1970. [Smallwood] 1985.

Geese, tribe Anserini

North American genera: *Anser* Brisson, *Philacte* Bannister, *Branta* Scopoli, *Nesochen* Salvadori

DISTRIBUTION AND TAXONOMY. All species of Anserini are holarctic, except for the Cape Barren Goose, *Cereopsis novae-hollandiae*, which is restricted to the coastal islands of Tasmania and southern Australia (Blakers, Davies, and Reilly 1984). Livezey (1986) accords *Cereopsis*, *Anser*, and *Branta* equal status within the tribe, Anserini, whereas Johnsgard (1979), who no longer recognizes the tribe as a taxonomic unit, includes the Cape Barren Goose in the subfamily, Anserinae, only tentatively. The strongly contrasting, achromatic patterns of downy *Cereopsis* resemble closely those of downy sheldgeese, *Chloephaga*, and downy shelducks, *Tadorna*, resemblances which undoubtedly influenced Delacour (1954) to place *Cereopsis* in the tribe, Tadornini. Johnsgard (1965) considered courtship and nest-defense behavior of *Cereopsis* similar to those of holarctic geese but believed certain other of its behavioral characters intermediate between those of shelducks and geese. Kear (1968: 100) found the sleepy trill of day-old *Cereopsis* "unique." Both Woolfenden (1961) and Johnsgard (1978) proposed a separate tribe, Cereopsini, for it, but biochemical (Brush 1976), genetic (Numachi et al. 1983: 71), and osteological (Livezey 1986) evidence suggests that, although "its [genetic] similarity is slight", *Cereopsis* is more closely related to the Anserini than to any other tribe.

The holarctic geese, often referred to as 'true geese', are found chiefly in arctic and subarctic regions, in boreal forests, and in temperate grasslands. Some species are widely distributed, e.g., Bean Goose, *Anser fabalis*, Greater White-fronted Goose, *A. albifrons*, and Brant, *Branta bernicla*, but others, such as the Ross', *A. rossii*, Barnacle, *B. leucopsis*, and Red-breasted, *B. ruficollis*, geese, are restricted to much smaller areas (Delacour 1954; Johnsgard 1979; A.O.U. 1983). No doubt, all Anserine geese—but especially the Snow, *A. caerulescens*, Ross', and Bar-headed, *A. indicus*, geese—experienced considerable fading of pattern colors during the Pleistocene glaciations.

A wide range of intraspecific variation among gosling and adult Canada, *B. canadensis*, Snow, Bean, and Greater White-fronted geese; biological and behavioral peculiarities (e.g., family structure, Triumph Ceremony); and certain generic problems (e.g., *Anser* vs. *Chen* and *Philacte*, *Branta* vs. *Nesochen*) have made the taxonomy of geese the subject of lively discussion for the last hundred years. Most authors (e.g., Delacour and Mayr 1945; Johnsgard 1965, 1978, 1979; Brush 1976; Livezey 1986) recognize only two polytypic genera, *Anser* and *Branta*, for holarctic geese, although certain characters of the downy plumage favor the resurrection of two additional, monotypic genera, *Philacte* (for the Emperor Goose) and *Nesochen* (for the Hawaiian Goose). The retention by the A.O.U. (1983) of the genus, *Chen*, for the Snow and Ross' geese is perhaps understandable, although characters of the downy plumage support the adoption of *Anser* for the white geese as well as the gray (compare head patterns of darker color phases of "*Chen*" and *Anser* goslings on pls. 1, 3, & 4; note virtual obliteration of typical *Anser* pattern in blackish Class 3 & 4 Lesser Snow [*caerulescens*] goslings). However, I believe that the inclusion of the Emperor Goose in *Chen* is unjustified. Adult Emperors do bear a superficial resemblance to adult 'blue' morphs of Lesser Snows (both have white heads and bluish gray body plumage), but Palmer (1976, vol. 2) and Eisenhauer and Kirkpatrick (1977) report different nesting habits, calls, and ecology for the two species. Moreover, Seeb, Wishard, and Oates (unpubl.) present biochemical evidence to support a unique taxonomic position for the Emperor Goose. As well, the plumage of the downy Emperor Goose is at once the least variable and the most distinctive among *Anser*-like goslings: it lacks dorsal spots (but faint wing-patches sometimes present), the yellow base color characteristic of all *Anser* goslings, and a typically Anserine head pattern (dark area around eye and on side of head may obscure eye-stripe [Eisenhauer 1976: fig. 27, 1 h. gosling photo]). The white area around the bill, continuous with white throat and underparts and contrasting well with diffuse gray or dark gray color on the crown and sides of the head, is found on no other gosling (pl. 4; figs. 3-69 to 3-72). Because of these peculiar attributes, I prefer to retain the Emperor Goose in *Philacte*, at the same time recognizing certain affinities with *Anser*.

The case of *Branta* vs. *Nesochen* for the Hawaiian Goose, or Néné, is less clear-cut. Most authors (e.g., Delacour 1954; Johnsgard 1979; Olson and James 1982; Numachi et al. 1983) synonymize *Nesochen* with *Branta*; Humphrey (1958b) also recommends the adoption of *Branta* for the Néné because of its tracheal structure. However, Numachi et al. (1983) and Quinn, Shields, and Wilson (1991) found the Néné genetically distinct from the Canada Goose. Preliminary evidence from Olson and James (1982: 34), that the Hawaiian Goose "or closely related taxa" inhabited all five of the larger Hawaiian islands prior to human settlement, suggests the possibility of radiation independent of the *Branta* species that also formerly inhabited the islands. Color and pattern characters of the downy young support Miller's (1937) and Woolfenden's (1961) use of *Nesochen* on anatomical grounds. The plumage pattern of juvenal *Nesochen* (Miller 1937) and the well-marked, dark crown-cap recall *Branta*, but the downy Néné's dark cap dips downward behind the eye and is usually joined to a heavy 'mask' and ear-spot; a quite distinct dark band connects the crown and yoke (figs. 3-177, 3-178). The Néné's grayish brown back is usually unpatterned; sometimes, there is a 'shadow pattern' of inconspicuous shoulder-spots and wing-patches. Chromatic base color is restricted to an extremely pale yellow wash on a few individuals.

Goslings of North American *Anser* species (i.e., Snow, Ross', Pink-footed, and Greater White-fronted geese) vary greatly in color and pattern; the variation, unlike that in the Canada Goose, appears unrelated to geography (Macpherson and Manning 1959; Cooke and Cooch 1968; Cooke and Ryder 1971; Lensink and Timm unpubl.). Nevertheless, common pattern elements can be recognized in the various color morphs of the downy young. For example, head pattern elements appear superficially quite diversified in *Anser* goslings, but the basic pattern can be shown to vary more or less continuously from pale, thin, and inconspicuous in Bar-headed, Class 0 Snow, and pale or light-colored Ross' goslings (figs. 3-20, 3-22, 3-27), to darker and fairly wide in certain Pink-footed and Greater White-fronted goslings (figs. 3-41, 3-54), to dark and extensive in the darker Pink-footed (fig. 3-47) and dark gray Ross' goslings (compare *Anser* figs. on pls. 1, 3, & 4; note that color phases of Ross' goslings [pl. 3] encompass virtually the entire range of variation in the head pattern of *Anser* spp.).

The loss of melanic pattern color in certain captive *Anser* goslings may also reveal intrageneric similarities, e.g., successive generations of goslings of captive Eastern Greylag, *A. a. rubirostris* (JPWT), and Swan geese, *A. cygnoides* (RLWS), may become increasingly pale, so as to resemble Bar-headed (RLWS), or Class 0 Snow (JPWT; RLWS) goslings. The yellowish olive toes of these pale captives have darker, 'bluish' gray terminal joints, as in Class 0 Snow, Bar-headed, and light yellow Ross' goslings (see E. Koch photo of more conspicuously plumaged [wild-type?] Swan goslings in *Annual Report of the [Severn] Wildfowl Trust 1950-51* 4, 1952; also Delacour 1954: Scott pl. 10).

A well-marked, dark, round crown-cap unifies the *Branta* species. It is most extensive in the Pacific ('Black') Brant, *B. b. nigricans* (DWWRS; JPWT; RLWS) and Red-breasted goslings (RLWS; Delacour 1964: Scott pl. 5; Knystautas and Liutkus 1984: 43, fig. 35), where it reaches forward to the bill and down below eye-level. The cap stops short of the bill in other downy *Branta,* including the Atlantic Brant, *B. b. hrota.* Brant goslings, some downy Barnacle Geese, and all of the darker Canada goslings have also a grayish 'mask' and 'bridle' (compare *Branta* figs. on pls. 4, 5, and frontispiece; see Brant figs. 3-77, 3-84; Barnacle fig. 3-91, and Canada figs. 3-94, 3-95).

Despite extensive studies by Johansen (1945, 1956), Delacour (1951, 1954), Cooch (1961), Hanson (1965), and others, the classification of polytypic goose species is often difficult. Evidence from the downy young supports taxonomic preferences of these authors: Johansen (1956) re: Bean Goose, *Anser fabalis,* and Pink-footed Goose, *A. brachyrhynchus;* Palmer (1976, vol. 2) re: Greater White-fronted Goose, *A. albifrons,* with four subspecies, *albifrons, frontalis, gambelli,* and *flavirostris;* Cooke and Cooch (1968) re: Snow Goose, *A. caerulescens,* with two subspecies, *caerulescens* and *atlanticus;* Palmer (1976, vol. 2) re: Brant, *B. bernicla,* with three subspecies, *bernicla, hrota,* and *nigricans;* and Delacour (1951, 1954) re: Canada Goose, *B. canadensis,* with twelve subspecies, *canadensis, interior, maxima, moffitti, parvipes, taverneri, fulva, occidentalis, leucopareia, asiatica* [presumed extinct], *minima,* and *hutchinsii.*

APPEARANCE. All downy *Anser* and *Branta* have well-marked wing-patches or shoulder-spots or both, except for some color morphs of Snow and Ross' goslings, in which the dorsal pattern is simply a mottled area of somewhat lighter *value* than the back. None have rump-spots, contrary to Delacour and Mayr (1945). The dorsal pattern is typically absent in downy Emperor, Brant, and Hawaiian geese, but is sometimes present as a 'shadow pattern' in all three species. The plain-backed goslings also lack yellow base color. A well-marked breast-band is found consistently only on *B. c. minima* goslings, but a faint one appears occasionally on downy Hawaiian Geese, on other Canada goslings (e.g., a few *fulva, occidentalis, parvipes,* and *taverneri*), and on some darker morphs of the Greater White-fronted Goose (e.g., *flavirostris,* pl. 1). Some Greater White-fronted goslings are also quite grayish on throat and chin (e.g., Adelaide Peninsula *gambelli,* pl. 1). Only the downy Brant has a wide, shallow white 'V' between gray breast and gray belly (compare pattern elements of 4 genera on pls. 1, 3-5).

Details of bill color and structure also differ within and between the genera. The nail color difference which Bent (1925: 191) described for the downy Greater White-fronted Goose—"light-colored...instead of all black as in the Canada [gosling]"—holds true for all North American *Anser, Branta,* and *Nesochen* goslings, except downy Brant, which have the nail dark at the base and white at the tip, as in the Emperor gosling, *Philacte.* In dorsal view, downy *Anser* have longer, more tapering bills than *Branta* goslings, often with longitudinal furrows along the 'horns' or in the nostril area (figs. 3-5, 3-16, 3-33). In lateral view, the upper and lower mandibles of downy *Anser* curve apart at the center of the bill, to reveal the lamellae along the tomia of both (compare *Anser* figs. 3-5, 3-6, & 3-37 with *Branta* figs. 3-94 to 3-98), but the separation is less wide in Emperor (figs. 3-70, 3-72) and Pink-footed goslings; the latter have also a pronounced downward curve of the upper mandible at the rictus (figs. 3-46, 3-48). Bills of all downy *Anser,* Néné, and Brant have a slight downward droop near the tip, but the bills of Canada and Barnacle goslings do not (compare bills of goslings of 4 genera on pls. 1, 3, 4, & 5 and in Anserini figs. 3-1 to 3-178).

VARIATION. A rather narrow range of individual differences constitutes normal variation in downy Emperor, Barnacle, and Hawaiian geese, but more striking variations appear in goslings of other species. The seven 'blue' and white morphs of Lesser Snow adults and the five related color classes of their downy young are well known from genetic studies by Cooke and Cooch (1968). Less well understood is the polymorphic coloration of Ross' goslings, although Cooke and Ryder (1971) showed that variation of the gray pattern color probably results from the action of a single pair of alleles.

Variation in color and size of Canada goslings appears related to geography: pale-bellied adults from the wide eastern range have light, bright yellow downy young; dark-bellied adults from the much narrower western range have dark yellow or 'greenish' yellow goslings (Palmer 1976, vol. 2). Adults and goslings from zones of intergradation between pale-bellied and dark-bellied forms (e.g., Alaskan North Slope; Yukon-Kuskokwim Delta) have somewhat intermediate characters of plumage and (in goslings) unfeathered parts. However, color phases, polymorphic broods, and striking pattern color variations, as Snow and Ross' goslings, are unknown among downy Canada Geese.

Also apparently geographical are pattern and *value* variations among downy Brant, which correspond to the light and dark belly colors of the adults. Polymorphic broods occur in several parts of the Canadian Arctic, where the range of light-bellied birds from the east meets that of dark-bellied birds from the west, e.g., Prince Patrick Island (MacDonald 1954), Banks Island (Manning, Höhn, and Macpherson 1956), Southampton Island (Barry *in* Eagles 1964), and the western Queen Elizabeth Islands (Boyd and Maltby 1979).

The often well-marked variation of base and pattern colors observed in downy young Pink-footed (Scott, Fisher, and Gudmundsson 1953) and Greater White-fronted (Hanson, Queneau, and Scott 1956) geese is largely unstudied. Variation in both species ranges from bright yellow or bright greenish yellow birds with conspicuous dorsal spots to duller yellow birds with dark dorsal color and less conspicuous spots, but the variation is *within* broods of Pink-footed goslings and *between* broods of Greater White-fronted goslings.

BEHAVIOR. The salient characteristic of gosling behavior is aggression, between broods (Frazer and Kirkpatrick 1979 [Emperor Goose]; Mary Carrick, letter to the author, January 1984 [Barnacle Goose]), within broods (Stahlberg 1974 [Greylag]), and between species. The occurrence of a 'peck order' or rank order among both wild and captive birds is well-known among ethologists and aviculturalists (e.g., Schjelderup-Ebbe 1922; Hepp and Hair 1984). Among goslings that I observed, bill-fighting, down-pulling, and 'nipping' of heels and toes occurred frequently among siblings. Four-day-old Todd's Canada Geese (*B. c. interior*; NWPW) seemed quite hostile about the down-pulling: one gosling 'nibbled' at the down of another's nape until it found a good grip, then pulled the plumage sharply and repeatedly. Usually, these encounters lasted only seconds, whereupon the goslings turned to other activities, but sometimes a skirmish persisted for many minutes. Five Great Basin Canada goslings (*B. c. moffitti*; NWPW) spent much of their time bill-fighting and pulling at the down of one another's heads, napes, and backs, while uttering sharp squeals and cries. One hapless warrior, somewhat too intent upon the fray, lost its footing, fell into the swimming pool, then climbed quickly out the other side and into the food tray. Diverted only momentarily, it soon rejoined the fight.

Goslings are also aggressive toward other species. A three-day-old, wild-caught Pacific Brant dominated a group of American Wigeons, *Mareca americana* (3 d.), in the Delta hatchery, pursuing them with head down and forward, to pull their dorsal down. Three captive Hawaiian goslings (JPWT; ca. 3 d.) mobbed their bantam hen, yanking repeatedly at her red comb, and an older Néné (ca. 3 wk.) chased its bantam all around their enclosure.

Threat postures appear even in very young captive goslings. One- to three-day-old Brant (RLWS; incubator-hatched from wild-gathered eggs) threatened pen-mates of all species, apparently without provocation. A bantam-fostered Néné gosling (JPWT; 2 d.) reacted to my hand, thrust slowly into its pen, by spreading its wings, opening its bill, and 'hissing' at me.

Warned by its bantam's cluck, a six-day-old Taverner's Canada Goose (*B. c. taverneri*; JPWT) advanced toward me with head down and bill open when I came too near.

Aggressive displays become ritualized in the Triumph Ceremony. Some goslings just a few days old took part in the ceremony initiated by their captive mothers after defense of the brood-rearing territory and young. A captive Aleutian Canada Goose (*B. c. leucopareia*; CESJ; wild-caught on Buldir Island, Alaska), swimming with her four goslings (3 d.), chased away a Canvasback hen which had ventured too close, then swam back to her young, with neck extended low and head up, calling. The goslings, also with heads and necks extended, bobbing up and down, swam to meet her, repeating rhythmically the two-noted greeting call. In the same way, a captive Cackling Canada Goose (*B. c. minima*; LTSW) rousted an intruding Ross' Goose and returned to greet her lone offspring with calls and head-bobbing, to which the gosling (2 d.) responded in kind.

Exhibiting behavior reminiscent of the Trumpeter cygnets, a day-old Atlantic Brant (1 of 2 hatched by a captive female [PWPS]) climbed onto its mother's back to preen and sleep whenever she 'sat down' to rest. In the same way, downy Lesser White-fronted Geese, *A. erythropus*, perched atop their bantam hen. I did not observe this habit in captive goslings of other species, nor did Johnsgard and Kear (1968) report it in wild geese.

I can add little to Kear's (1968) account of the vocalizations of goslings. Differences and similarities among the calls of the various species show up well in her sonagrams, e.g., the looser, 'squealier' sleepy calls of *Anser* goslings vs. the closer textured (i.e., syllables closely spaced), more trilling ones of *Branta* (her fig. 8). The greeting call in newly hatched goslings of most species has two or three notes lightly accented on the last, higher note, encompassing the interval of a major third (M3) in the eight-tone musical scale. The first *two* syllables of the three-note call occupy the same time interval as the *single* first syllable of the two-note call, so that meter and accent remain constant (but note that ascending three-note calls of Barnacle goslings [5-6 d.] are often accented on the *first* syllable). Goslings customarily repeat the calls several times, with brief pauses between each, alternating the number of syllables, apparently at random. Some goslings (e.g., Néné, Ross', and Cackling geese) often use four- or five-syllabled calls, extending over a larger interval (up to a major sixth [M6]). The vocalizations of very young Emperor goslings, structured much as those in downy *Anser*, have nonetheless a characteristic flat, rather unresonant quality, as do calls of the adults (JPWT captives); the timbre of the downy Néné's calls lies somewhere between those of *Anser* and *Branta*. The conversation call of Pacific Brant goslings sometimes resembles the two-note call of *Anser* and other *Branta* goslings, but other times it is speeded up, with the second (higher) note broken into two syllables of the same pitch.

The basic greeting call also performs other functions. Irregularly sounded and heavily accented, it accompanies agonistic behavior. Quietly uttered and evenly accented (often monosyllabic), it apparently serves to keep siblings together during grazing, as suggested earlier by Collias (1962). The same call sometimes emanates from the egg. Eisenhauer and Kirkpatrick (1977: 43) heard Emperor goslings "peeping [=twittering?] and moving about in eggs up to 48 hours before pipping." The several subspecies of Canada Geese hatched in my incubator twittered often during the two days before hatching. One day, I heard the two-note greeting call from an egg of Todd's Canada Goose, as I turned a clutch of seven in my incubator. I imitated the call and the gosling responded. The 'conversation' went on for a half-minute or more, until the gosling fell silent.

The posture assumed when voicing the greeting call (head down and forward, bobbing up and down [see Atlantic and Giant Canada geese on pl. 5; also Kear 1968: fig. 4]), although observed frequently in very young captive goslings, is better-developed in downies four or five days old. Alternatively, 'seated' Ross' and Greater White-fronted goslings (ca. 3 d.) Chin-lift when uttering the greeting call.

Quiet, ascending pleasure trills accompany preening and settling. The pleasure trills of Canada and Barnacle goslings are close-textured, but those of Pacific Brant goslings (3 d.) have more the form of a musical scale, the first few notes ascending in whole tones and the last in half-tones or less (i.e., chromatically), at once accelerating tempo and diminishing amplitude. Yet, no matter how softly and rapidly the syllables are sounded, the Brant goslings' clear, slightly metallic tones are still distinguishable one from another. In broods of Lesser Snow goslings, pleasure trills give way to a gentle chorus of sleepy calls, which in turn seem almost to unwind, spiraling off into soundlessness as the goslings fall asleep.

Pink-footed Goose

Oie à bec court. Ansár Piquicorto (Cramp and Simmons 1977).
Anser brachyrhynchus Baillon

APPEARANCE. The variable, green-yellow Pink-footed goslings have dark grayish eye-stripes and loreal spots (often joined to form a 'mask'), and gray eyelid rims. Their dark crown color usually fades out below eye-level. The light eye-ring found on most downy Greater [and Lesser; JPWT captives] White-fronted Geese is lacking in the Pink-footed gosling (but see Schiøler 1925: Larsen pl. 82). Usually, the shoulder-spots are continuous with an irregular yellow area on the fronts of the tibiotarsi, as are the yellow sides of the rump with the yellow area on the backs of the tibiae. Dark pattern areas are more extensive, and light ones smaller and duller on darker variants. In some lighter variants, pale olive-gray tips of the dorsal down lend a cloudy or 'milky' appearance to the plumage (dark nape and hindneck probably unusual on otherwise light-colored gosling shown by Fjeldså [1977: pl. 4]). The upper mandible curves sharply downward at the base of the bill (see figs. 3-40, 3-44, 3-48; also Fjeldså [1977: fig. 9] for details of lamellae—note that his figure does not show marked downward curve of upper mandible). Because the base and pattern colors contrast poorly (usually, 0-1.75 Munsell *value* steps), the tarsi and toes appear almost uniformly dark (e.g., grayish yellowish brown [RM], some shade of gray [BM(NH): Spitsbergen; Palmer 1976, vol. 2; Fjeldså 1977], or "black" [Cramp and Simmons 1977: 402]; compare Pink-footed variants with downy Greater White-fronted Geese on pl. 1 and in figs. 3-39 to 3-48 and 3-53 to 3-65; see also dark and light variants by Scott [*in* Cramp and Simmons 1977: pl. 52, and in *Annual Report of the [Severn] Wildfowl Trust 1952-53* 6, 1954: cover ill.]).

The yellow natal down "fades as the gosling grows, until at a later stage the bird is pale grey with only a tinge of greenish" (Scott, Fisher, and Gudmundsson 1953: 89). Older goslings observed by Trevor-Battye in late July on Spitsbergen, "...in an advanced state of *grey*—not yellow—down..." (Trevor-Battye *in* Alphéraky [1904] 1905: 92; see also Dement'ev and Gladkov [1952] 1967, vol. 4), had evidently reached this later, faded stage. Remnants of down clinging to the tips of emerging juvenal feathers in two older goslings (RM 115 & RM 315) had almost no yellow color, but the dark head pattern remained prominent and unfaded (see figs. 3-44, 3-48).

VARIATION. Variation of *value* and *chroma* within broods of newly hatched Pink-footed Geese is well-known from Spitsbergen to Iceland (Newton *in* Alphéraky [1904] 1905; Scott, Fisher, and Gudmundsson 1953; compare Pink-footed variants on pl. 1 and in figs. 3-39 to 3-48). More unusual variants included a newly hatched gray and white Icelandic gosling and its normally colored sibling (RM; coll. A. Gardarsson) and several partly feathered young banded by Scott, Boyd, and Sladen (1953: 89) having white patches on the wings or body, and a "biscuit-coloured gosling [with] pink...bill and legs."

DISCUSSION. Many authors (e.g., Johansen 1945; Delacour and Mayr 1945; Dement'ev and Gladkov [1952] 1967, vol. 4; Delacour 1954; Johnsgard 1965, 1978, 1979) regard the Pink-footed Goose as a subspecies of the Bean Goose. So does Palmer (1976, vol. 2: 113), who views the Pink-footed Goose as the small, light-colored extreme of tundra Bean Geese, with the Novaya Zemblya population "presumed to trend toward Pinkfeet in morphological characters" rather than toward the larger eastern tundra Bean Geese, *fabalis* Latham and *serrirostris* Swinhoe. He believes that a clear separation "between tundra and forest types of Bean Geese does not now exist in Eurasia." On the other hand, Johansen (1956: 93) proposed that the Bean and Pink-footed geese are members of a species group ("Artengruppe") containing "two morphologically and biologically rather distinct [sub]groups," one of which inhabits the tundra, the other the forest. Johansen suggested that the Pink-footed Goose, westernmost of the tundra dwellers, having undergone measurable changes in size and color through long isolation in rather restricted breeding areas in Spitsbergen, Iceland, and E Greenland, has probably evolved to species level.

The darker Bean and lighter Pink-footed goslings could be considered the extremes of a gradient, as many authors consider the adults; similar head patterns and colors of the unfeathered parts of the downy young do suggest a close taxonomic relationship for the Bean and Pink-footed geese (compare Bean and Pink-footed goslings *in* Delacour 1954: Scott pl. 10). However, the resemblance between the dark Bean and the light, variable Pink-footed goslings is no greater than that between the paler Ross' and Class 0 Snow goslings or between downy Greater and Lesser White-fronted geese. Nor has striking intra-brood variation been reported in downy Bean Geese as it has in Pink-footed goslings: live Western Bean goslings (*A. f. fabalis*; JPWT) and a wild-caught Kolyma River Delta gosling (*A. f. serrirostris*; FMNH) were dark-headed and rather dull-colored, as was a *serrirostris* gosling portrayed by Dement'ev and Gladkov ([1952] 1967, vol. 4: fig. 56). On the basis of present information, therefore, I have treated them as separate species, following Johansen (1956), Cramp and Simmons (1977), and Owen, Atkinson-Willes, and Salmon (1983).

SOURCE OF SPECIMENS. ICELAND: **Midhálendi**: Thjórsárver [=region mostly in *Arnessýsla* partly in *Rangárvallasýsla*, comprising the watershed of the River Thjorsá, which forms the boundary between the two counties] (RM-10): *Rangárvallasýsla:* Eyvindarkofaver (RM-1: figs. 3-47, 3-48), small bog S Hestalda (RM-1: figs. 3-43, 3-44). NORWAY: Svalbard: **Spitsbergen**: Gips Valley: Ice Fjord (BM[NH]-1: figs. 3-38, 3-41, 3-42); Prins Karls Forland: Vogel Hoek (BM[NH]-1: figs. 3-45, 3-46). **Captive origin** (WT[S]-1: figs. 3-39, 3-40).

OTHER REFERENCES. Bannerman 1957, vol. 6. Bent 1925. Cabot et al. 1984. Dresser 1871-1881, vol. 6. Harrison 1975. Johnsgard 1965. Koenig 1911 (*in* Schiøler 1925). Ogilvie 1978. F. Todd 1979 (fig. 1.132: head pattern of downy "Pink-footed Goose" is more like that of Class 0 Lesser Snow Goose).

Greater White-fronted Goose

Oie rieuse. Ganso Manchado.
Anser albifrons Scopoli

APPEARANCE. The variable, green-yellow Greater White-fronted goslings have grayish eye-stripes and loreal spots, which, on darker variants, are sometimes joined to form a 'mask'. They have light yellowish brown eyelid rims (=eye-ring) and a rather light supraorbital area separating the dark crown color from the dark eye-stripe (also shown for nominate *albifrons* by J. Gould and H. C. Richter *in* Gould 1873, vol. 5: pl. 4). There is a slight but distinct downward droop of the bill (see pl. 1; also Frank Dufresne photo *in* Brandt 1943: 284). Wing-patches are well defined on all but the darkest Greater

White-fronted goslings, but shoulder-spots may be inconspicuous or even lacking on some darker variants; they are not usually continuous with the light-colored tibial pattern. The contrast between the lighter base color and the darker pattern color of the tarsi (usually, 2-5 Munsell *value* steps), will distinguish at least the lighter-colored variants of *A. albifrons* from all color variants of the similar Pink-footed gosling (compare 2 spp. on pl. 1 and in figs. 3-39 to 3-48; 3-49 to 3-65).

VARIATION. Base colors of Greater White-fronted gosling specimens from Alaska, Northwest Territories, and Greenland (including individuals of *frontalis, gambelli*, and *flavirostris*, as delimited by Palmer 1976, vol. 2), differed chiefly in *value* and *chroma*; pattern colors differed only in *value*. Variation, as far as is known, occurs between broods rather than within them. Light-colored, 'green' goslings, with bright or brilliant base color and light or medium pattern color, came from all breeding areas: Alaska (e.g., Hooper Bay [USNM: Brandt 1943], Kobuk River [pl. 1; MVZ: Grinnell 1900], Kuguklik River [OSUFW; PSM], Naskonat Peninsula [DWWRS: 2 live], Pitt Point [MVZ]); Mackenzie Delta (CM); and Greenland (WT[S]: 1 live captive). Bright yellow goslings with medium pattern color were collected at Perry River (pl. 1; FMNH) and observed at Holitna River, Alaska (Daniel Timm, letter to the author, February 1983). Bright yellow birds with dark pattern color came from Saint Michael (USNM), Chipp River (CM), and the Colville River Delta (AMNH; 2 d. live goslings [color transparencies loaned by Thomas Pogson in letter to the author, December 1983]); Hines (*in* Bellrose 1980: pl. 22) and (Palmer 1976, vol. 2: 242, C. Nelson col. pl.) also depict a bright yellow gosling with dark pattern color.

Four-day-old Greater White-fronts from Cook Inlet were rather dull yellow with dark grayish olive pattern color (Pogson's color transparencies), whereas several goslings from the Alaskan north slope (e.g., Barrow and Chipp River [MVZ], Point Tangent [UMMZ]) with very dull yellow base color, grayish cheeks, and grayish olive pattern color, appeared pale or 'faded' over all, regardless of their age when collected. Grayish yellow goslings with very dark pattern color came from the Adelaide Peninsula (pl. 1; NMC: Macpherson and Manning 1959); the darkest, dullest gosling of all—with a grayish breast-band and blackish tarsi and toes—was a Slimbridge captive from Greenland (pl. 1; WT[S]). The color attributes of eight dark goslings taken by Robert Elgas at Old Crow Flats, Yukon Territory, and the Kugalik River, Northwest Territories, are unknown, but according to Elgas (1970), the goslings subsequently developed adult plumage typical of *gambelli* (his fig. 1).

Dorsal patterns varied in both nearctic and palaearctic goslings. Bright yellow or greenish yellow variants from some areas had quite conspicuous shoulder-spots, but some darker goslings lacked them (e.g., Hooper Bay, Alaska [FMNH: Hanson, Queneau, and Scott 1956: fig. 26]; Redoubt Bay, Alaska ['Tule' goslings; Pogson's color transparencies]). A. C. Meinertzhagen (*in* Witherby et al. [1939] 1943, vol. 3) suggested that the presence of shoulder-spots in Alaskan *frontalis* goslings [location not specified] distinguished that subspecies from the Eurasian *A. a. albifrons*. Most nominate *albifrons* have wing-patches but no shoulder-spots (e.g., Delacour 1954; Harrison 1975), but goslings described by Bauer and Glutz von Blotzheim (1968: 177) had both wing-patches and brownish yellow spots ("Fleckenpaar") behind the wings.

Macpherson and Manning (1959) described rump-spots on six very young Adelaide Peninsula goslings—so did Fjeldså (1977) on downy European *A. a. albifrons*, but I was unable to distinguish rump-spots on any of the specimens that I examined. In defense of my inability to see these spots, I offer this observation. In live goslings, the light color of the belly and undertail may extend almost as far onto the sides of the rump as do the rump-spots of many ducklings. When the dark-feathered tibiae are extended and drawn back, as in the preparation of a study skin, they interrupt the connection of the light rump-side color with that of the light undertail color, creating the impression of a true 'spot'.

Lighter foot and tarsal colors predominated on bright yellow or greenish yellow birds; darker, 'greener' colors of the same *hue* on duller, darker birds. For example, Kalmbach (*in* Brandt 1943: 400, col. pl.) portrayed light grayish olive foot color on a bright greenish yellow Alaska gosling, whereas Macpherson and Manning (1959) evaluated grayish olive and grayish olive-green tarsal colors on their dark Adelaide Peninsula goslings.

DISCUSSION. It is tempting to speculate that the variations described above may characterize Greater White-fronted goslings of a particular subspecies or geographical area, but the downy specimens thus far examined present no conclusive evidence for any but individual variation. Macpherson and Manning (1959: 13), comparing Adelaide Peninsula goslings with those from Hooper Bay, Alaska, and Perry River, NWT (Hanson, Queneau, and Scott 1956: fig. 26), stated that their specimens were more similar to the Alaska goslings than to those from Perry River, and concluded that the differences noted by Hanson and his colleagues were "probably not geographical." I would say further that apparent large differences are ones of degree, involving *value* and *chroma* only, with *hue* remaining more or less constant.

The nature of variation among adult Greater White-fronted Geese is incompletely understood. Studies by Bauer (1979) and Krogman (1979) confirm the existence of a small population of large, dark Greater White-fronted Geese wintering in certain areas of California—the legendary 'Tule Geese' first described by Swarth and Bryant (1917). The morphological characters of this population matched almost exactly those of Greater White-fronted Geese found breeding at Redoubt Bay, Cook Inlet, Alaska, but they differed from those of Greater White-fronts wintering in other parts of California as well as from known adult *frontalis* summering around or near Redoubt Bay (Timm, Wege, and Gilmer 1982). These authors did not recognise the subspecies *elgasi,* proposed by Delacour and Ripley (1975) for the 'Tule Goose', but reserved *gambelli* Hartlaub for the Cook Inlet population. They pointed out that the percentage of Texas recoveries of *gambelli* banded in Cook Inlet exceeded that of *frontalis* banded in the outer Yukon-Kuskokwim Delta (Timm and Dau 1979), which

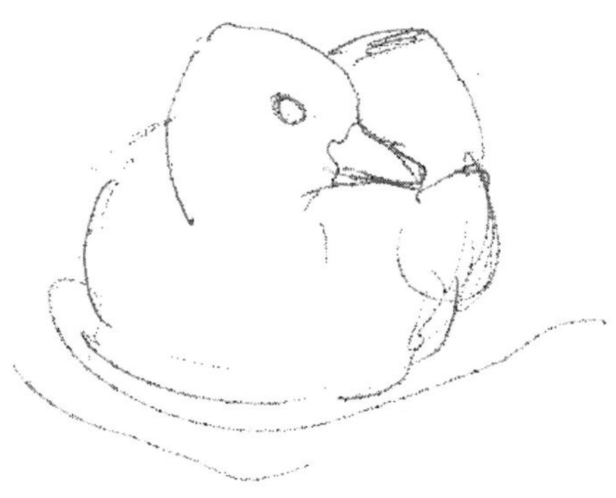

data suggest that a Texas type-locality is quite possible for the 'Tule Goose', even though the great majority of that population winters in California. They noted further studies by Lensink and Timm (unpubl.) showing that "significant differences in average size of morphological characters [of breeding adults] may occur between areas that are relatively close geographically" as well as between those more widely separated. So may differences in the color characters of the downy young (e.g., bright greenish yellow Naskonat Peninsula goslings *vs.* dark, unspotted goslings from Hooper Bay; Elgas's (1970) dark goslings from the Kugalik River, Northwest Territories, *vs.* bright green-yellow goslings from the 'nearby' Mackenzie Delta. Such differences have not yet been correlated with known morphological and

Plate 3

1 Ross' Goose, Anser rossii

Dark yellow variant. Arlone Lake, Northwest Territories (J. P. Ryder color transparencies).

Black yellow variant. Data as for dark yellow variant

Light yellow variant. Arlone Lake, Northwest Territories (UAMZ), and Perry River, Northwest Territories (JPWT captives).

Green yellow variant. Arlone Lake, Northwest Territories (WT[S] captives and J. P. Ryder color transparencies.

Pearly gray variant. Perry River, Northwest Territories (JPWT and WT[S] captives).

Medium gray variant. Karrak Lake, Northwest Territories (LTSW captive).

White variant (J. P. Ryder description; Scott pl. 10 *in* Delacour 1954).

Dark gray variant. Data as for dark yellow and black yellow variants

2 Greater Snow Goose, A. caerulescens atlanticus

Classes 0 and 1. JPWT captives.

Plate 3

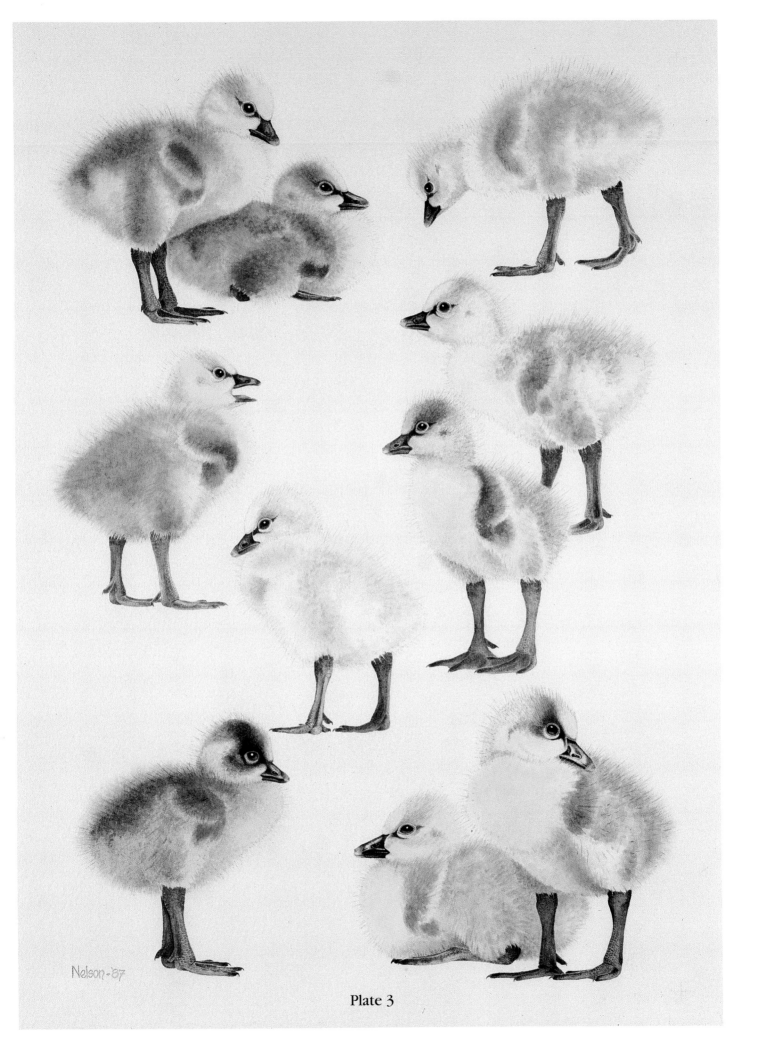

color differences among adults, but the observations of Pogson (color transparencies of Cook Inlet goslings) and Elgas (1970) imply that 'dark' goslings from at least some areas develop into 'dark' adults. Variations in linear measurements and weight, paralleling those of the adults, might also be expected in the downy young, although there are no published data that would either confirm or deny such a comparison.

I agree with Dzubin and Palmer (*in* Palmer 1976, vol. 2: 94), that the collection for comparative study of Greater White-fronted adults and their goslings from various breeding areas in North America would be "rewarding"—even more so if the collectors were to take their color standards with them.

SOURCE OF SPECIMENS. **Northwest Territories**: *District of Keewatin*: Adelaide Peninsula near E side Sherman Basin (NMC-6: figs. 3-62, 3-63). Hanbury River (NMC-1). *District of Mackenzie*: Arctic coast E Fort Anderson (USNM-1). Mackenzie Delta: Loon Channel (CM-4: figs. 3-58, 3-59). Perry River (FMNH-4). **Alaska**: Barrow (FMNH-2; MVZ-2). Chipp River (CM-1; MVZ-1). Colville River Delta (AMNH-1). Hooper Bay (FMNH-3; USNM-2: figs. 3-52, 3-53). Kipnuk: Kuguklik River near Kinak Bay (OSUFW-3; PSM-1). Kobuk River Delta [=Kowak River Delta] (MVZ-2). Naskonat Peninsula about 240 km W Bethel (DWWRS-2 live: figs. 3-49 to 3-51). Pitt Point (MVZ-1). Point Barrow (MVZ-2: figs. 3-54, 3-55). Point Tangent (UMMZ-1: figs. 3-56, 3-57). Saint Michael (USNM-2). Yukon Delta (FMNH-1). GREENLAND (WT[S]-1 live captive; WT[S]-1: figs. 3-64, 3-65). **Captive origin** (PSM-1; USNM-1: figs. 3-60, 3-61).

OTHER REFERENCES. Baird, Brewer, and Ridgway 1884, vol. 1. Bellrose 1976, 1980. Bent 1925. Cramp and Simmons 1977. Dement'ev and Gladkov [1952] 1967, vol. 4. Dresser 1871-1881, vol. 6. Harrison 1978. Johnsgard 1965. Kortright 1942. Ridgway 1895 (quotes Baird, Brewer, and Ridgway 1884, vol. 1). Snyder 1957.

Snow Goose

Oie des neiges. Ganso Ceruleo, Ganso (Ceruleo) Blanco, Ganso (Ceruleo) Cuelliblanco.

Anser caerulescens (Linnaeus)

APPEARANCE. The eye-stripe of Class 0-1 goslings (both subspecies) is wide in front of the eye and narrow and incomplete behind it. Often, it continues as a thin ring of dark plumes all or part way round the eye. The pre-ocular stripe extends downward posteriorly in front of the eye, but narrows immediately below it and disappears. There is no cheek-stripe. The gray crown-patch behind the eye, crescentic in dorsal view, appears in side view as a narrow 'bonnet' that may be quite prominent in older goslings (figs. 3-28 to 3-32, 3-36, 3-37; see also Scott pl. 56 [juv. *caerulescens* and *atlanticus*] *in* Cramp and Simmons 1977). Dark dorsal down plumes give many Class 1 goslings of both subspecies a "frizzled or near-agouti appearance" (Cooke and Cooch 1968: 291). In Class 0-1 goslings in the field, the gray 'bonnet', dark feet, dark eye-line, and an orange-yellow wash on cheeks and forehead can be seen clearly at some distance; vestiges of the orange-yellow color remain throughout the downy state. Yellowish gray to very dark grayish olive tarsal colors described by Heyland for wild Greater Snow goslings on Bylot Island, Northwest Territories (J. D. Heyland, telephone interview, 25 October 1971), are exactly similar to those observed in captive Class 0-1 goslings of both subspecies. The 'bluish' gray claws and terminal joints seen in Class 0 captives of both subspecies are also found in goslings of other *Anser* species, e.g., Ross', Bar-headed, and Swan geese, as well as in those of Emperor Geese.

In *caerulescens* goslings of Classes 2-4, dark elements of the face pattern may be almost entirely concealed by dark down feathers and bright yellow color is confined to the head, while tarsal colors are dusky or blackish. The Class 4 gosling has very shiny black feet.

Character distinctions within the two paler morphs (Classes 0 and 1) and the two darker ones (Classes 3 and 4) may be "somewhat arbitrary" (Cooke and Cooch 1968: 291), but the 'pied' Class 2 morph is dissimilar to both extremes. The Class 2 morph is the rarest in both wild (Cooke and Cooch 1968) and captive flocks (JPWT; RLWS). Two of the captive Class 2 goslings had the yellow eye-ring shown on plate 4, but one of the captives and all three of the wild Class 2 goslings seen by Cooke and Cooch (1968) lacked it. Other yellow markings of the Class 2 captives varied similarly.

Plate 4 shows five color variants of the downy Lesser Snow Goose, *A. c. caerulescens* (Classes 0-4; Cooke and Cooch 1968); plate 3 shows two color variants (Classes 0-1) of the downy Greater Snow, *A. c. atlanticus*. 'Blue' *atlanticus* morphs reported by Palmer (1976, vol. 2) are presumed similar to those of *caerulescens*; Greater Snow goslings are somewhat larger and heavier over all than downy Lesser Snows, with bills slightly deeper at the base (HBB) relative to culmen length (EC; [C. Nelson unpubl. data]). Actual size differences are most apparent in Age B specimens in Table 1, Appendix A.

VARIATION. The gray 'bonnet' is virtually lacking in some very pale Class 0 goslings (e.g., Hines pl. 22 *in* Bellrose 1980). These pale goslings may also have light gray bills (Cooke and Cooch 1968) and grayish irides (Manning *in* Witherby et al. [1939] 1943, vol. 3). Dark, pinkish feet (e.g., Shortt *in* Kortright 1942: pl. 32) and dark orange feet (e.g., Hines *in* Bellrose 1980: pl. 22) were not seen on any color variant. Two dark face-stripes described by D. G. Elliott (*in* Bent 1925) on a Greater Snow gosling (ANSP) were probably artifacts of preparation: the orbits of the specimen, which I have also examined, were not fully stuffed, and the lores are sunken and the skin folded as a result.

Differences in Ridgway (1912) evaluations (Kennard 1927; N. Hollister *in* Kennard 1927) of the foot colors of Greater and Lesser Snow goslings apparently convinced Kennard (who described the Greater Snow Goose as a new full species) that the color difference represented a distinguishing character for young goslings of two *species* rather than a range of variation common to those of two *subspecies*, as we now believe them to be.

DISCUSSION. The taxonomic status of the Snow and 'Blue' geese was not resolved until the latter half of the present century. Some authors (e.g., Blaauw 1899 [first description of polymorphic broods]; Hartert 1920; Salomonsen 1933; Delacour and Mayr 1945; Hanson, Queneau, and Scott 1956; Portenko [1972] 1981), urged recognition of a single species, *A. caerulescens*, for both the white and 'blue' forms, but other authorities regarded these as separate species (e.g., Soper 1942; A.O.U. 1957; W. Todd 1963) or as two subspecies (Manning, Höhn, and Macpherson 1956). Cooch (1961) subsequently stated his belief in the conspecificity of 'Blue' and Snow geese on ecological grounds, but it remained for Cooke and Cooch (1968) to demonstrate that the two forms are genetic morphs of a single species. They concluded that the striking polymorphic plumage of adults and young results from the action of a single gene with an incompletely dominant allele (B) producing 'blue' adults and dark goslings (BB), a recessive allele (b) producing white adults and yellow goslings (bb), and a heterozygous genotype (Bb) producing one or more intermediate phenotypes. More recently, Cooke, Partin, and Rockwell (1988) present historic and genetic evidence to support the idea of separate species (but with viable hybrids) for the two color phases of the Lesser Snow Goose.

SOURCE OF SPECIMENS. **Northwest Territories**: *District of Franklin*: Axel Heiberg Island near Stang Bay (NMC-1: figs. 3-36, 3-37; UMFBP[DFP]-1). W coast Baffin Island: Camp Kungovik—65° 35' N (FMNH-1; NMC-3); S end Taverner Bay (ROM-5: figs. 3-4, 3-5, 3-29, 3-30). Bathurst Island: 45 km W Goodsir Inlet (NMC-1). Queen Maud Gulf: Jenny Lind Island (PSM-1; UMFBP[DFP]-1). *District of Keewatin*:

Adelaide Peninsula near E side Sherman Basin (NMC-4). Southampton Island: Bay of God's Mercy (NMC-3), Boas River (NMC-6). *District of Mackenzie*: Anderson River Delta (UAMZ-2). Mackenzie Delta: Gillham Island (CM-4: figs. 3-27, 3-28), 8 km S Kendall Island (CM-2), Richards Island (CM-7). Perry River (FMNH-1; NMC-1). **Ontario:** *Kenora District:* Cape Nemaskamagow (ROM-2). **Québec:** *Montmorency No.1 County:* Parent stock from migrating birds on Saint Lawrence River near Saint Joachim (PWPS-5 live captives). **Alaska:** Chipp River about 100 km E Barrow (FMNH-1). GREENLAND: *Thule District* [=*Avanersuup kommunia*]: Five Glacier Valley [=Kuusuaq]—W MacCormick Bay [=Iterlassuaq] (ANSP-1). **Captive origin** (JPWT, RLWS, WT[S]-45 live: figs. 3-1 to 3-3, 3-24 to 3-26, 3-33 to 3-35; MVZ-1; NMC-1: figs. 3-31, 3-32; PSM-2; ROM-1; UWGB[RC]-2; UWBM-2).

OTHER REFERENCES. *Annual Report of the [Severn] Wildfowl Trust 1948* 1; *1949-50* 3, 1951; *1951-52* 5, 1953. Bent 1925. Bent, Bangs, and Peters 1927. Dement'ev and Gladkov (1952) 1967, vol. 4. Lemieux 1959. Parmelee, Stephens, and Schmidt 1967. Roberts 1932, vol. 2. Scott 1951a, 1951b (*caerulescens*: Blue X Snow hybrids at Perry River). Snyder 1957. Soper 1930. Thomson 1964.

Ross' Goose

Oie de Ross. Ganso Menor.

Anser rossii (Cassin)

APPEARANCE. The *chroma* of the Ross' goslings' pale plumage is often brilliant. The goslings have unusually dense and fluffy down (Blaauw 1903), a short bill, and short toes relative to tarsal length (John P. Ryder, pers. comm. 1970). Their dark grayish brown irides appear almost black against the pale head down. The Anserine eye-stripe is discrete and well-marked in the paler morphs (figs. 3-19 to 3-22), but becomes part of the dark 'hood' extending below eye-level in the "dark gray" morph (pl. 3). The 'hood' appears as a fairly conspicuous 'bonnet' on some gray and darker yellow morphs, but is marked by just a few dusky down tips in the paler morphs (compare 'bonnet' in figs. 3-19 to 3-22 & on pl. 3). The gray dorsal color is strongly yellow or greenish yellow in the yellow morphs, but is barely tinted yellow in the gray morphs. The feet of yellow morphs are distinctly olive or yellowish olive, whereas gray morphs have more uniformly gray or olive-gray feet. Rare 'blue' morphs of the Ross' gosling resemble Class 4 Lesser Snow goslings except for their smaller size and a white (rather than yellow) chin-patch (McLandress and McLandress 1979). Plate 3 shows eight color variants of the Ross' gosling. The names of seven variants ("light yellow", "yellow-green", "dark yellow", "black-yellow", "dark gray", "pearly gray", and "white") are from Ryder (1967: 36); the eighth variant, medium gray, was named by the author from a captive gosling (Karrack Lake, NWT.; LTSW).

VARIATION. The eight color morphs on plate 3 are meant to represent the relative—but not necessarily absolute—values of Ryder (1967), who found considerable individual variation among the morphs assigned to each category (e.g., yellow color on the belly and undertail of some yellow variants may be paler and duller than that shown on pl. 3).

DISCUSSION. Hanson, Queneau, and Scott (1956) found three times as many gray broods and individuals as yellow ones among downy Ross' Geese at Perry River; the ratio of gray birds to yellow in mixed broods was approximately equal. Williamson (1957: 518) analyzed their data and concluded "that the 'dimorphism' is controlled by a single pair of alleles, that the genotypes are in the proportion, p:2pq:q, and that mating is at random." Ryder (1967: 44), questioning Williamson's hypothesis, suggested that "the problem appears to be not the action of a single pair of alleles but possibly the action of multiple alleles [of a single gene?]." Later, Cooke and Ryder, having analyzed Ryder's field data on 'yellow' and 'gray' broods and individuals, and using the same color names employed by Hanson, Queneau, and Scott (1956) and Williamson (1957), also concluded that gray plumage was dominant over yellow, with the dimorphism controlled by a single pair of alleles.

The agreement of these researchers upon the dominance of the gray allele suggests strongly that the dorsal color of the goslings, at least, can probaby be explained by the hypothesis of simple dominance. Ryder's (1967: 44) hypothesis, "multiple alleles", proposing that two or more pairs of alleles might be required to produce a given color phenotype (e.g., Sinnott, Dunn, and Dobzhansky [1925] 1950: fig. 43) could, in theory, account for the rarity of both the "white" and "dark gray" morphs. However, Cooke feels that, as attractive as the ideas of co-dominance and multiple alleles may be, they must be regarded as speculative in the absence of long-term, field-based family history studies (Fred Cooke, telephone interview, 30 January 1984).

But as yet, there is no satisfactory genetic explanation for the variation of the yellow component of the Ross' goslings' plumage. The range of *values* (i.e., exceedingly pale ['ivory'] to moderate or dark) invites comparison with the *value* range of the gray component (i.e., exceedingly pale ['silver'] to dark gray or blackish, and suggests that the yellow color may also have dominant and recessive forms. In any case, Ryder's (1967) color categories are probably best visualized as recognizeable, concurrent variations of both base color (yellow) and pattern color (gray), whereas the plumage classes described by Cooke and Cooch (1968) in the Lesser Snow gosling involve variations in pattern color only (note combination of dark plumage and bright yellow chin-patch on Classes 2-4 goslings, pl. 4).

The difficulty in accepting a diagnosis of simple dominance involving a single pair of alleles lies not with the mathematics of analysis, but with the colorimetric parameters of the data. 'Gray' and 'yellow' are generic terms and, as such, can be both imprecise and subjective when used to measure color. Ryder's own plumage color designations (1967), taken from Palmer (1962: 4-5, insert based on *Atlas de los Colores* [Villalobos-Dominguez and Villalobos 1947]), prove considerably more informative. However, Ryder's terms reflect his impressions of the predominant color on the *backs* of the goslings (i.e., the pattern color) as they moved away from him in the field (John Ryder, pers. comm. 1970). They do not quantify the lighter, brighter base colors on the faces, breasts, and bellies of the goslings.

The 14 live Ross' goslings that I saw, as well as all of the study skins, color transparencies, field color notes (John Ryder, letter to the author, October 1964), descriptions (John Ryder, pers, comm. 1970), and life-sketches (Scott 1948: 35) show varying degrees of both yellow and gray color in the goslings' plumage and on their feet. With such (evidently) independent variation, predominantly 'gray' morphs may also display yellow color, and the 'yellow' morphs gray. The "pearly gray" gosling (Ryder 1967: 36; see pl. 3) has an exceedingly pale orange-yellow face, and extremely dull orange-yellow [grayish olive] feet, yet it is obviously more gray than yellow, particularly when viewed from the rear. Likewise, the yellow component of the medium gray gosling's plumage is evident only in the pale yellowish gray color of the undertail and in the olive tint of its gray feet. Yellow color in the "white" morph ("the rarest one"; John Ryder, pers. comm. 1970) is restricted to a cream-colored wash on the head and upper breast (see pl. 3; also Scott pl. 10 *in* Delacour 1954). In predominantly yellow goslings, the concentration of gray color ranges from low ("light yellow") to variable medium ("yellow-green", "dark yellow") to relatively high ("black yellow"). In the last-named, both yellow and gray colors are dark, and the yellow is also bright. The opposite condition obtains in the "white" gosling, where both colors are extremely pale.

The "dark gray" gosling is a special case. The pattern color is so extensive and so well-defined that it seems quite unrelated to the more delicate head patterns of the yellow and lighter gray morphs (see 'yellow' and 'gray' goslings on pl. 3). It compares well with dark-headed goslings of other *Anser* species, e.g., Pink-footed and Greater White-fronted goslings (pl. 1 and figs. 3-38 to 3-48, 3-49 to 3-65; see also E. Koch photo of Swan gosling in *Annual Report of the [Severn] Wildfowl Trust 1950-51* 4, 1952).

The dark color variants occurring normally in the Ross' gosling should not be confused with the 'blue' phase young and adults reported by McLandress and McLandress (1979). The 3/4 Ross' X Snow gosling which they describe seems to reflect the dominant effect of the hybrid Ross' X Snow parent rather than the manifestation of a latent 'blue' phase in the Ross' Goose (color transparency loaned by Robert McLandress, letter to the author, March 1983). Probably, the 'blue' gosling's white chin-patch would be yellow if the dark plumage had appeared on one of the bright yellow morphs rather than on a paler one. The McLandresses' suggestions regarding the genetic origin of the 'blue' Ross' Geese are entirely compatible with known plumage characteristics of normal and 'blue' goslings of both Ross' and Snow geese.

SOURCE OF SPECIMENS. **Northwest Territories:** *District of Mackenzie:* Arlone Lake (UAMZ-5: figs. 3-22, 3-23; 21 color transparencies). Karrack Lake (LTSW-1 live: fig. 3-19). Kennett River [=Laine Creek] (FMNH-3: figs. 3-20, 3-21). Perry River region (JPWT, WT[S]-13 live captives: figs. 3-16 to 3-18). **Captive origin** (AMNH-2; OSUFW-1; PSM-1).

OTHER REFERENCES. Barry and Eisenhart 1958. Bent 1925 (descr. from Blaauw 1903). Johnsgard 1965. Snyder 1957.

Emperor Goose

Oie empereur. Oca Imperadora.

Philacte canagica (Sewastianow)

APPEARANCE. Achromatic plumage, poorly defined pattern elements, and a short, wide, black bill with whitish nail-tip and egg-tooth, distinguish the downy Emperor Goose from goslings of all other species (pl. 4; see also Portenko [1972] 1981 re: Siberian goslings). A white area all around the bill remains for about three weeks after hatching, when it is replaced by gray feathers (David Eisenhauer, letter to the author, January 1983). The head-shape, wide in front view (pl. 4) but high and round in side view (Palmer 1976, vol. 2: 242, C. Nelson col. pl.), is distinctive. Compare Emperor figures 3-66 to 3-68 with Brant figures 3-73 to 3-75, 3-79 to 3-82; also Emperor and Brant figures, plate 4.

VARIATION. Published descriptions by Blaauw (1916a: 278; "pearl-grey"), Dement'ev and Gladkov ([1952] 1967, vol. 4: 316; "dark silky gray"), Portenko ([1972] 1981: 134; "bright ash gray"), and others convey not only an aesthetic appreciation of the Emperor gosling's elegant, gray and white plumage, but also the extent of variation in the pattern color. Phillip Headley's photograph (*in* Bureau of Sport Fisheries and Wildlife 1967: 8) shows the extremes of *value* variation in a brood of four goslings.

In some individuals, the pale hindneck is set off against the darker crown-patch, but in other specimens the light and dark areas are not well defined. A few light-colored individuals have a poorly-contrasting crescent of paler down feathers below the eye, which, in two live goslings that I examined, formed a ring around the eye—the "spectacled effect" noted by Palmer (1976, vol. 2: 172). In some goslings with darker plumage, the indistinct eye-stripe is virtually lost in the diffuse dark crown-patch extending below and in front of the eye.

The colors of irides and feet also vary. Most Emperor goslings have grayish brown irides, but Conover (1926) described gray irides on six 36-hour goslings collected at Hooper Bay, Alaska (FMNH). These goslings had olive foot color, as did those portrayed by Kalmbach (*in* Brandt 1943: 400, col. pl.; but pale yellow webs not typical), Scott (1948), Palmer (1976, vol. 2), and Bellrose (1980: Hines pl. 22). Other authors (e.g., Blaauw 1916a, 1916b; Shortt *in* Kortright 1942; Dement'ev and Gladkov [1952] 1967, vol. 4) portray black or blackish feet. Of nine live goslings examined, all had grayish olive-brown feet, but only two of these were dark and none was blackish. The color of the webs and terminal joints was more or less the same as that of the toes and tarsi, not paler as in specimens examined by Palmer (1976, vol. 2).

SOURCE OF SPECIMENS. **Alaska:** Hooper Bay (FMNH-6: figs. 3-69, 3-70). Kipnuk (OSUFW-2): Kuguklik River near Kinak Bay (AMNH-1: figs. 3-71, 3-72; OSUFW-3), N side Kuskokwim Bay near Cape Avinof (MVZ-1; OSUFW-2; PSM-3; ROM-1). Kokechik Bay [=Igiak Bay] (ROM-1). Kuskokwim Delta and Nunivak Island (JPWT, RLWS-9 live captives: figs. 3-66 to 3-68; RLWS-1 frozen).

OTHER REFERENCES. Alphéraky (1904) 1905. Bent 1925 (cites Blaauw 1916b). Bellrose 1976, 1980. Eisenhauer 1976. Frazer and Kirkpatrick 1979. Johnsgard 1965. Kuroda 1939.

Brant

Bernache cravant. Ganso de Collar.
Branta bernicla (Linnaeus)

APPEARANCE. Brant goslings have a dark cap, a dark 'mask' around the eyes, and a wide white 'V' between gray breast and gray belly. They have dark gray or blackish feet; a small, slim bill; and (often) a white chin-patch. Brant appear in North America in two closely-related forms, the paler *hrota* Müller from the eastern Arctic and the darker *nigricans* (Lawrence) from the western (pl. 4; see also Palmer 1976, vol. 2, for N. A. range of 2 subspp.). Nominate *bernicla* Linnaeus is evidently intermediate between *hrota* and *nigricans*, having western representatives closer to *hrota* (Bauer and Glutz von Blotzheim 1968; Cramp and Simmons 1977) and eastern birds more like *nigricans* (Dement'ev and Gladkov [1952] 1967). In older, partly feathered goslings (ear-tufts, scapulars, flanks, and white-tipped secondaries emerged; primaries beginning), the white 'V' is lost, the new breast down is gray as in young downies, and the belly down becomes entirely white.

The Brant gosling bears a superficial resemblance to the downy Emperor Goose, but it has a better-defined plumage pattern, and it lacks the Emperor gosling's wide bill, as well as the white area around it. Some paler *hrota* goslings have head pattern and dark feet similar to those of downy Barnacle Geese, but lack the latter's contrasting plumage pattern and pale yellow base color (see Emperor fig. 3-70, Barnacle figs. 3-91, 3-93 and Brant figs. 3-77, 3-84; compare also 3 spp. on pl. 4).

VARIATION. Variation in over all darkness and definition of pattern elements is common in Brant goslings from all areas, e.g., the base color of live *hrota* goslings from Bear Cove, Southampton Island (PWPS; captives), and Foxe Basin, Baffin Island (Bruce Batt, color transparencies loaned to the author, September 1980), was noticeably paler than that of other *hrota* goslings from the same islands (NMC;

ROM), which were grayer. Also grayer were palaearctic *hrota* goslings depicted by Scott (*in* Cramp and Simmons 1977: pl. 55) and Blossom (*in* M. Owen 1980: pl. 7).

Shoulder-spots, characteristically inconspicuous or absent on all Brant goslings, were evidently better-marked in *hrota* specimens portrayed by Shortt (*in* Kortright 1942: pl. 32), Delacour (1954: Scott pl. 10 [rump-spots also shown]), and Snyder (1957). More typical of *hrota* goslings are the light-colored, inconspicuous wing-patches reported by Witherby et al. ([1939] 1943, vol. 3), Palmer (1976, vol 2), Bellrose (1980: Hines pl. 22; note labels of 2 subspp. reversed), and others. A gosling portrayed by Fjeldså (1977: pl. 5 [subsp. unspecified]) has wing-patches but lacks the dorsal spots described in his text. Shoulder-spots of downy *nigricans* are expressed as a 'shadow pattern'; wing-patches, if present, are always inconspicuous. Both pattern elements may be more prominent on older downies, in which the dorsal color has faded.

The chin-patch and 'V' appeared to differ individually in both *hrota* and *nigricans,* regardless of sex or geographical origin. Most live and prepared specimens displayed both markings, but some lacked the chin-patch, and a few the white 'V' (see also Manning, Höhn, and Macpherson 1956 and Parmelee, Stephens, and Schmidt 1967 re: variation within broods on Banks and Victoria islands, respectively).

The gray plumage of downy Pacific ('Black') Brant is typically dark (e.g., Kokechik Bay, Alaska: RLWS live; Mackenzie Delta, NWT [CM]; Banks Island, NWT [NMC]) with a pronounced 'bluish' cast (RLWS live; Manning, Höhn, and Macpherson 1959; J. P. Williams, Esq., pers. comm., 1964). However, some individuals are paler, with lower contrast of pattern elements, as in goslings from Alaska (Naskonat Peninsula live; WT[S] live captives; Admiralty Bay [ANSP]) and portraits by Scott (*in* Delacour 1964: pl. 5), Burton (*in* Harrison 1978: pl. 3), and Hines (*in* Bellrose 1980: pl. 22; "Atlantic Brant"=Black Brant). Even in the paler *nigricans* goslings, the dark crown cap nearly always extends forward to the bill and downward below eye-level (pl. 4). However, Barry reported a *hrota*-like 'mask' in many individual *nigricans* from western Arctic Canada (Thomas Barry, letter to the author, January 1984).

A striking variation in the breast color of adult Brant of both sexes was found by Manning, Höhn, and Macpherson (1956: pl. 7) among eight birds, six of which (including the lightest and next-darkest individuals) were from Mould Bay, Prince Patrick Island, Northwest Territories, within the zone of intergradation mapped by Palmer (1976, 2: 252). Migrant adult males from New Brunswick and breeding adult males from Banks Island represented, respectively, the next lightest and darkest *values* in the series. In Denmark, Webbe (1958) observed complete gradation of color, from pale *hrota* to dark *bernicla,* among wintering palaearctic adults.

DISCUSSION. Three subspecies are recognized for the Brant: nominate *bernicla,* Atlantic *hrota,* and Pacific *nigricans,* following Salomonsen (1958), Portenko ([1972] 1981), Palmer (1976, vol. 2), and Cramp and Simmons (1977). Both the existence of *hrota* X *nigricans* pairs in arctic Canada (e.g., in NWT at Perry River [Hanson, Queneau, and Scott 1956], Prince Patrick Island [MacDonald 1954], and Southampton Island [Barry *in* Eagles 1964]) and the occurrence of adult plumages intermediate between dark-bellied western and pale-bellied eastern birds (e.g., MacDonald 1954; Manning, Höhn, and Macpherson 1956; Boyd and Maltby

1979) make it difficult to accept the suggestion of a fourth subspecies (i.e., *orientalis* of Delacour and Zimmer 1952, which Johnsgard [1979] places in the eastern arctic Soviet Union]) to describe what may be simply the result of 'hybridization' between the two forms in zones of sympatry. However, the possibility of a fourth subspecies cannot be ruled out entirely. The unique character of adult brant from the western Queen Elizabeth Islands, first noted by Boyd and Maltby (1979), was later confirmed by distinctive patterns of mitochondrial DNA in a Melville Island population of adult *B. b. nigricans* (Shields 1990). The downy young of this unique island population remain undescribed.

SOURCE OF SPECIMENS. **Northwest Territories:** *District of Franklin:* W coast Baffin Island: Taverner Bay (NMC-1; ROM-3). Banks Island: DeSalis Bay (NMC-4: fig. 3-79). Coronation Gulf: Duke of York Archipelago (NMC-2). Foxe Basin: North Spicer Island (DWWRS-2 color transparencies: fig. 3-78). Prince Patrick Island: Mould Bay (USNM-4: figs. 3-85, 3-86). Victoria Island: Cambridge Bay (UMFBP[DFP]-2). *District of Keewatin:* Southampton Island: Bear Cove (PWPS-2 live captives: figs. 3-73 to 3-75), Boas River (NMC-3: figs. 3-76, 3-77). *District of Mackenzie:* Mackenzie Delta: Kendall Island (CM-5). **Alaska:** Barrow (FMNH-3; MVZ-1; SDNHM-3; UMMZ-1). Chipp River (FMNH-1; MVZ-1). Hazen Bay (OSUFW-2; PSM-1). Kokechik Bay [=Igiak Bay] (RLWS-25 live [*ss*: BMNH-1; UMFBP(DFP)-1]). Island in Meade River Delta—70° 56' N, 156° 12' W (MVZ-1). Naskonat Peninsula about 240 km W Bethel (DWWRS-2 live: figs. 3-80 to 3-82 [*ss*: MMMN-1: figs. 3-83, 3-84]). Point Barrow (FMNH-3): Admiralty Bay (ANSP-2; CM-1). Tasekpuk Lake [=Teshekpuk] (SDNHM-1). Captive origin (WT[S]-5 live).

OTHER REFERENCES. Alphéraky (1904) 1905 (descr. from Middendorf [n.d.]). Barry 1956. Bent 1925. Cottam, Lynch, and Nelson 1944. Einarsen 1965. Gavin 1947. Handley 1950. Harrison 1975, 1978. Johnsgard 1965. Linduska 1964 (p. 154: Glen Sherwood photo). Smallwood 1984.

Barnacle Goose

Bernache nonnette. Barnacla Cariblanca.
Branta leucopsis (Bechstein)

APPEARANCE. The combination of small size; blackish bill and feet; and short, dense down (like that of the downy Richardson's Goose, *B. c. hutchinsii*) with contrasting olive-gray pattern color and gray-white or pale yellow base color distinguish the downy Barnacle Goose from other *Branta* goslings. The pale shoulder-spots and rump-side are continuous with the pale color of the underside (pl. 4; Bauer and Glutz von Blotzheim 1968) and the olive-gray pattern color may have a pronounced 'bluish' cast. The olive-gray 'mask' and 'bridle' are at times reduced to a spot at the 'horn' of the bill, a dusky loreal wash, and a partial gray eye-ring (fig. 3-93), but they form, with the blackish bill, the dark eye, and (sometimes) a thin post-orbital line, a continuously darker area that stands out against the pale face (e.g., F. Todd 1979: fig. 6.9). The dark gray or blackish gray feet of Barnacle goslings appear black when viewed from a distance. The gray pattern color of older goslings (8-10 d.) is paler than at hatching, and only faint traces of yellow base color remain on the face. Still older goslings, with flanks and scapulars feathered and secondaries just emerging, have no yellow color at all. Some of these goslings have a quite pointed nail, hooked downward, but others do not.

The equally small Brant gosling has a light gray breast and throat (often with white chin-patch), a white 'V' on the belly, and more blended pattern and base colors; it lacks well-defined dorsal spots and wing-patches, as well as any vestige of yellow color. The downy Richardson's Goose has brilliant yellow base color and a low-contrast dorsal pattern (compare Barnacle gosling with downy Brant [pl. 4] and *B. c. hutchinsii* gosling [frontispiece]).

VARIATION. The "three pairs of spots" noted

by Delacour (1954: 178) and Palmer (1976, vol. 2: 235), as well as the rump-spots described by Cramp and Simmons (1977) and Fjeldså (1977), did not appear on any goslings examined; Burton's Barnacle goslings (*in* Harrison 1975, 1978: pls. 5) lack the dorsal spots described in the text. The extent and continuity of the light areas typical of most live goslings are correctly shown in Scott's portrait (*in* Cramp and Simmons 1977: pl. 54), and in photographs by Johnsgarf (*Annual Report of the [Severn] Wildfowl Trust 1959-60* 12, 1961) and F. Todd (1979: fig, 6.9); the characteristic dark appearance of the winglets appears in both photographs.

SOURCE OF SPECIMENS. **Captive origin** (JPWT, RLWS-14 live: figs. 3-87 to 3-89; AMNH-1; BMNH-1; OSUFW-2: figs. 3-92, 3-93; PSM-3; ROM-5: figs. 3-90, 3-91; WT[S]-1).

OTHER REFERENCES. Alphéraky (1904) 1905. Cabot et al. 1984. Coues (1872) 1903, vol. 2. Dement'ev and Gladkov (1952) 1967 (quote descr. by Tougarinov 1941). M. Owen 1980. Salomonsen and Gitz-Johansen 1950. Schiøler 1925. *Wildfowl* 26, 1975; 27, 1976.

Canada Goose

Bernache du Canada. Ganso Canadiense.
Branta canadensis (Linnaeus)

APPEARANCE. Goslings of all Canada Goose subspecies have yellow or greenish yellow base color, olive pattern color, and a well-marked, round dark 'crown-cap'. Base color is yellower, pattern color lighter olive, and foot color generally lighter in Canada goslings of interior North America, the Atlantic coast, eastern Arctic Canada, and Greenland. Dark foot color and dark pattern elements—'mask', 'bridle', and (sometimes) breast-band—are prominent in the dark grayish olive and greenish yellow downies from the Pacific slope (compare Canada goslings from 11 North American locations on frontispiece and pl. 5; note range of foot colors). Bill color is dark (N 4/) or blackish gray (N 3/) on all subspecies except *hutchinsii*, which may be lighter (N 4.5/; N 5/).

Downy Canada Geese bear a close [if superficial] resemblance to yellow *Anser* goslings (Johnsgard 1965), but their head pattern is more consistent and better-marked, and their nails are entirely dark. In contrast, *Anser* goslings have either more extensive, more diffuse, or much *less* prominent head markings; they also have paler, contrastingly colored nails. Even very young *Anser* goslings have clearly visible lamellae or display some evidence of a 'grinning patch'. Compare *Anser* and *Branta* species on plates 1 and 3-5, *Anser* figures G-25 and G-27 with *Branta* figures G-36 and G-37, and *Anser* figures 3-19 to 3-65 with *Branta* figures 3-76 to 3-173.

VARIATION. Canada goslings vary in size, proportion, plumage characters, definition of pattern, and colors of plumage and feet. These apparently geographical differences parallel, to some extent, those of adults described by Delacour (1951, 1954). In general, the size of both adults and goslings decreases from the southern to the northern part of the range, exemplifying Hanson's (1965: 77) idea of "a selective effect of climate on size." For example, the variation in weight of adult males (ca. 5.0 kg [interior North American *maxima;* Hanson 1965] to ca. 1.5 kg [western Alaskan *minima;* Delacour 1954]) is reflected in that of the downy young: day old *maxima* [n=2; Delta, Manitoba] averaged 121.6 g; day-old *minima* [n=2; Kokechik Bay, Alaska] only 67.6 g. Exposed culmens (EC) of the Delta *maxima* goslings averaged longer (17.7 mm) than those of the Alaskan *minima* (11.1 mm), as did tarsal measurements (STMT). See Table 1, Appendix A, for weights and measurements of Canada goslings from 14 locations.

Body types of the downy young also resemble those of the adults as defined by Delacour (1954). The round-bodied, short-necked types include *hutchinsii, minima, leucopareia,* the as-yet-unnamed race from the Semidi Islands (Hatch and Hatch 1983), and [presumably extinct] *asiatica* (Aldrich 1946).

The long-bodied, long-necked types are *canadensis, interior, maxima, moffitti, fulva, occidentalis, parvipes* and *taverneri.* Downy young *parvipes* and *taverneri* are scaled down versions of larger interior subspecies, as MacInnes and Palmer (*in* Palmer 1976, vol. 2) reported for adult *parvipes,* in which Palmer included *taverneri.*

In goslings, the proportion of tarsus length (STMT) to swim-length (CT=front of chest to tip of tail; meas. not depicted in Glossary) varies with body type. In long-bodied goslings,

the tarsus measurement was 25% to 26% of the swim-length, but in short-bodied *hutchinsii* and *leucopareia,* the proportion was 28% (C. Nelson, unpubl. data). Proportion data for the tiny *minima* goslings are incomplete, but suggest a ratio similar to that of the other short-bodied species.

The plumage and pattern characters of newly-hatched Cackling (*minima*) and Richardson's (*hutchinsii*) geese are quite distinct from each other, supporting Palmer's (1976, vol. 2: 186) statement that "the smallest dark and the smallest light [adult] birds are, within the species, not closely related." Goslings of both subspecies have short bills and feathered chins, but *minima's* greenish yellow and dark grayish olive plumage is long and fluffy, with few iridescent down-tips, and its grayish breast-band, dark 'mask' and 'bridle' are well-marked (pl. 5), whereas lightly-patterned *hutchinsii's* relatively shorter, lemon-yellow and light olive plumage is dense and mat-like, with a veritable aura of iridescent green-gold down-tips (frontispiece; compare *minima* figs. 3-113 to 3-119 and *hutchinsii* figs. 3-127 to 3-134; see also Sutton (1932: pl. 22) and Manning [*in* Witherby et al. (1939) 1943, 3: 218]). Goslings of other Canada subspecies have neither the long, fluffy plumage of *minima* nor the shorter, denser down of *hutchinsii,* but have intermediate down characters.

Minima's well-defined pattern elements—often partly concealed by the long, fluffy dorsal down of very young goslings—are shared by other Pacific slope subspecies (*fulva, occidentalis, leucopareia*), which also have few iridescent down-tips. Dorsal patterns are better-marked in older *minima* and in goslings of other western subspecies, e.g., some downy *leucopareia,* in which the rump-side color extends upward to center back, forming a transverse band of lighter color between back and tail (Anon. 1966: C. E. Strutz photo). Goslings from the Semidi Islands (Hatch and Hatch 1983) resemble closely downy *leucopareia* (2 [ca.] 5 d. goslings; Scott Hatch, color transparencies loaned to author, March 1987). Large goslings from the interior and the Atlantic coast are patterned much as downy *hutchinsii,* having many iridescent golden down-tips, but they vary in general lightness and definition of pattern: *moffitti* is palest over all, *maxima* and *canadensis* are variable but generally a bit darker, and *interior* has the best contrast of pattern and base colors (compare goslings of 4 large subspp. on pl. 5). The patterns of downy *parvipes* and *taverneri* are, in various ways, intermediate between the dark western and the paler eastern goslings: *taverneri's* pattern is nearer to that of Pacific slope goslings (e.g., W Alaska [JPWT; 6 live]; Colville River, Alaska [DEN; Bailey 1948]), but *parvipes'* pattern is more like that of *maxima* or *interior* (e.g., McConnell River, NWT [NPRC; 3 live]; Old

Crow River, YT [USNM]; Great Bear Lake, NWT [NMC]; Southampton Island [CM]); both may have iridescent down-tips (compare darker western with paler eastern and intermediate birds in figs. 3-99 to 3-173, frontispiece, and pl. 5).

Tarsal and foot colors of goslings from the narrow western range are nearly always dark gray, blackish gray, or black, but those of goslings from the large eastern range vary from gray or olive-gray (*hutchinsii*) to medium or light grayish yellowish orange (some *interior*, many *maxima*, *moffitti*, and *canadensis*) to light or pale grayish yellowish green (other *maxima* and *moffitti*) to dark grayish yellowish orange, dark gray, or blackish gray (other *interior*, some coastal *canadensis* and *parvipes*). Tarsal and foot colors of *taverneri* (e.g., W Alaska [JPWT: 6 live]) and other *parvipes* (e.g., Yukon and Northwest territories [CM; NMC; USNM]) are between those of the dark western and the lighter-colored eastern birds, with colors of *taverneri* closer to the western birds and those of *parvipes* closer to the eastern.

DISCUSSION. An understanding of the Canada Goose is complicated by, among other things, the presence of full-grown birds of different sizes at the same time in the same areas, by the appearance of subspecies in areas where they were previously unknown, by the intergrading of subspecies at boundaries of breeding areas (Delacour 1951; Palmer 1976, vol. 2), and by the close physical resemblance of subspecies having different biological characteristics. Palmer's (1976, vol. 2: 188) summation—"such factors [e.g., lack of records from remote areas, local extinctions, heedless transplantation of breeding stock from one area to another] have forever obscured whatever pattern of breeding distribution formerly existed"—is probably all too true. Nevertheless, studies by Morgan, Sulkin, and Henny (1977), Johnson, Timm, and Springer (1979), Shields and Wilson (1987b), and others, as well as evidence from the downy young, provide useful insights into the status of the Canada Goose.

Although there does not seem to be a single geographical area known in which both very large and very small geese can be found nesting side by side, some parts of the range (e.g., Southampton Island, the Yukon Delta) contain breeding Canada Geese of discernibly different sizes, as do the populations of certain migration corridors. For example, the Alaskan Population [Pacific Flyway] has *minima*, *taverneri*, and *leucopareia*, and the Tallgrass Population [Mississippi Flyway] includes *hutchinsii*, *parvipes*, and *maxima* (Bellrose 1976). Large Canada Geese (e.g., *moffitti*, *maxima*; mostly immatures) are known to undertake regular, northward summer molt migrations within the breeding range of the much smaller *parvipes* (Dennis Raveling, pers. comm., 1970; Krohn and Bizeau 1979; Davis et al. 1985). Earlier, Sutton (1932) reported three types of white-cheeked geese on Southampton Island in summer: two smaller subspecies found nesting (*hutchinsii* and *"leucopareia"* [=*parvipes*]) and a large 'honker' (probably *interior*, then undescribed) which apparently did not breed.

Populations of two Canada Goose subspecies thought to be extinct (*leucopareia*, *maxima*; Delacour 1951, 1954) have been rediscovered. Sightings of small Canada Geese in the Aleutian Islands (Kenyon 1961; Jones *in* Kenyon 1961) were further confirmed in 1963, when U. S. Fish and Wildlife Service personnel found a small breeding population of Aleutian Canada Geese, *B. c. leucopareia*, on Buldir Island (Kiracofe 1964). More recently, the discovery of a population of small Canada Geese (genetically indistinguishable from *leucopareia*; Shields and Wilson 1987b) breeding on Kaliktagik Island in the Semidi Islands, southeast of the Alaska Peninsula, has extended the range of *leucopareia* eastward by nearly 1800 km and may include as well the historic range of *asiatica* in the Commander and Kurile islands (Hatch and Hatch 1983). Hanson (1965) documented an extensive range for the Giant Canada Goose, *B. c. maxima*, which includes much of the central North American grasslands, parts of Montana [possibly also Idaho] and Colorado east of the Continental Divide (Will 1969; but note that Canada Geese from Colorado rivers flowing west from the Divide, e.g., Green River system, belong to *moffitti* [Bailey and Niedrach 1965, vol. 1]). Successful captive propagation has allowed reintroduction of both subspecies to parts of their former ranges (e.g., Anon. 1966; Szymczak 1975; Lee et al. 1984).

A change in the composition of the Cook Inlet, Alaska, Canada Goose population is suggested by Johnson, Timm, and Springer (1979: 72), who reported that Canada Geese from Upper Cook Inlet, all of which breed north of the Kustatan Peninsula, belong only to *parvipes* (38 birds examined had "sandy colored" breast feathers), contrary to earlier statements by Delacour (1954), Hansen (1962), Palmer (1976, vol. 2), and others, who named Cook Inlet as the western limit of the breeding range of *occidentalis,* a dark-breasted form. Delacour confined *parvipes* to the Alaskan and northern Canadian interiors, and designated Cook Inlet, together with the Alaska Peninsula, as the southeastern limit of the breeding range for *taverneri.* Palmer (1976, vol. 2) did not extend the combined breeding area of *parvipes* and *taverneri* south of the Alaska Range [i.e., he believed that Canada Geese belonging to *parvipes/taverneri* did not breed in Cook Inlet].

Authorities also disagree about the appearance of *taverneri.* The adults have been considered morphologically similar to *minima* (Bailey 1948; Delacour 1951, 1954; Ogilvie 1978), *leucopareia* (Delacour 1951, 1954), and *parvipes* (A.O.U. 1957; Palmer 1976, vol. 2; Johnsgard 1975, 1978, 1979). Delacour (1954) reserved *taverneri* for the middle-sized, darker colored geese of the North Slope, west central Alaska, and the Alaska Peninsula. He used *parvipes* for the lighter colored eastern geese, but Palmer (1976, vol. 2: 203) viewed the variation in adult *parvipes* and *taverneri* as more or less continuous: "...from pale breasted (*parvipes* narrowly defined) to dusky breasted (some so-called *taverneri* of Alaska)". Johnson, Timm, and Springer (1979) also found the species pair, *parvipes-taverneri,* difficult to separate morphometrically.

Biological as well as morphological differences help to define taxa in some areas (e.g., different nesting ecologies separate *fulva* and *occidentalis* [SE Alaska; Van Horn, Harrington, and Ratti 1979], *parvipes* and *taverneri* [interior and W Alaska and Cook Inlet; Johnson, Timm, and Springer 1979], *parvipes* and *hutchinsii* [Southampton Island; Sutton 1932]), but others remain unidentified, such as the Canada Geese nesting in Prince William Sound (Johnson, Timm, and Springer 1979). Observations by Hansen (1962), Phillip Havens (Donald McKnight, letter to the author, July 1970), and Kurhajec (1977 [cited in Johnson, Timm and Springer 1979]) of *fulva*-like behavior in the middle-sized, dark-breasted geese of Prince William Sound suggest a population intermediate in some ways between *fulva* and *occidentalis.*

However, Grinnell (1910: 372) stated that a dark-footed gosling (1 of 5 newly hatched) collected on Hawkins Island in Prince William Sound was "identical in coloration with...one from the Sitkan district," the area from which adult *fulva* measured by Johnson, Timm, and Springer (1979) were taken. The culmen (EC) of Grinnell's specimen (MVZ; figs. 3-102, 3-103) was longer than those of day-old *occidentalis* (Prince Rupert, B. C.: JPWT captives; figs. 3-99 to 3-101) but about the same as those of day-old, wild *fulva* (Vancouver Island, B. C.; figs. 3-106 to 3-108); the gosling's faint grayish breast-band was similar to that observed on a few individuals of both subspecies. Compare culmen (EC) measurements of *fulva* and *occidentalis* in Table 1, Appendix A; note that wild *occidentalis* goslings from Cordova, Alaska (Copper River Delta) were approximately three days old when measured, hence their culmens were longer than those of day-old young of either subspecies.

Genetic studies by Morgan, Sulkin, and Henny (1977), Van Wagner and Baker (1986), and Shields and Wilson (1987b) confirm a close relationship among Canada Goose subspecies. Morgan, Sulkin, and Henny (1977) and Shields and Wilson (1987b) showed that the small, dark-colored Alaskan subspecies (i.e., *minima, leucopareia, taverneri*) formed a well-defined entity, and all three research groups found one or more of the Alaskan taxa quite distinct from the large, light-colored interior subspecies (as are also the downy young; compare eastern and western Canada goslings on pl. 5). Morgan and his colleagues (1977) found similar serum proteins in the subspecies pairs, *fulva-occidentalis* and *maxima-moffitti*, that appear to justify merging *fulva* with *occidentalis* and *maxima* with *moffitti* as Palmer (1976, vol. 2) and Ogilvie (1978) did, but Van Wagner and Baker (1986; electrophoresis of heart and liver proteins) and Shields and Wilson (1987b; analysis of mtDNA types), finding greater-than-expected differences between populations of *maxima* and *moffitti*, suggested both subspecies be recognized.

The unexpected uniqueness found by Van Wagner and Baker (1986: 940) in the Akimiski Island population of *B. c. interior*—these geese showed, with *B. c. minima*, "the highest genetic variability within populations [of *canadensis* subspecies sampled] and the greatest divergence from other populations"—lends credence to "the possibility...that the more disparate populations [i.e., isolated, as in W Alaska *minima* and Akimiski Island (James Bay) *interior*] have already speciated or are in the process of doing so." Day-old *interior* (e.g., Man.: Churchill: 7 live; NWT: Belcher Is. [ROM]; Ont.: Ft. Severn [ROM]; Qué.: Ungava Penin. [NMC]) are easily distinguished from day-old young of other large Canada subspecies: they usually have dark—even blackish—feet, good contrast of dark olive pattern color and bright yellow base color, and a wash of vivid orange-yellow ("saffron"; W. Todd 1963: 121) at the sides of the head and neck. Somewhat older goslings, collected on Akimiski Island by Hanson (1965: 41) were "markedly darker" [re: dorsal color] than those of *canadensis,* with "underparts...distinctly grayish and the crown of the head...dark brown."

Further genetic, morphometric, and behavioral studies could identify the Canada Geese of Prince William Sound, elucidate possible changes in the Canada Goose population of Cook Inlet, and settle the question of subspecific distinction for *parvipes* and *taverneri*. Analysis of color and mensural characters of live, newly hatched, wild Canada goslings from the Queen Charlotte Islands to Prince William Sound and the Copper River Delta would help to clarify the relationships of the *fulva-occidentalis* pair. Live, newly hatched goslings from the Chagulak and Semidi islands, Prince William Sound, Upper Cook Inlet, Yakutat, and western Alaska (e.g., Kotzebue Basin, outer Yukon-Kuskokwim Delta), as well as from most of the Alaskan and northern Canadian interiors, remain undescribed. Weights and linear measurments, Munsell color evaluations, and collections of such known-age young (and their parents) from these and other breeding areas would provide a much-needed perspective on the intriguing relationships of the Canada Geese.

SOURCE OF SPECIMENS. **Alberta:** Camrose: Pelican Lake (ROM-1). **British Columbia:** *Cariboo District:* Jackpine Lake (NMC-2). *Comiaken District:* Vancouver Island: small island in Quamichan Lake (NWPW-3 live: figs. 3-106 to 3-108). *Kootenay District:* Golden (NMC-1). *Queen Charlotte District:* Queen Charlotte Islands (ROM-2: figs. 3-109, 3-110). *Range 4, Coast District:* Lowe Inlet (MVZ-1). *Range 5, Coast District:* Prince Rupert (JPWT-6 live captives: figs. 3-99 to 3-101). *Yale District,* Similkameen Division: Vaseux Lake (ROM-1). **Manitoba:** Churchill (NWPW-7 live; MDNR-1 frozen: figs. 3-142, 3-143; CM-1). Delta (UFS[DM]-2 live: figs. 3-146 to 3-148; DWWRS-1 dead; D-2: figs. 3-151, 3-152). Northern Indian Lake (NWPW-5 live). **Newfoundland:**

Labrador South District: Red Bay (CM-1): Strait of Belle Isle (CM-1: figs. 3-140, 3-141). *Saint Mary's District:* Avalon Peninsula: Laden Field's Pond—NE Laden Field's Brook (UFS[DM]-2 live: figs. 3-137 to 3-139). **Northwest Territories:** *District of Franklin:* Baffin Island (CESJ-2 live). Boothia Peninsula: Spence Bay (ROM-3). Queen Maud Gulf: Jenny Lind Island: islet in small lake near Water Lake (UFS[DM]-1 dead: figs. 3-127 to 3-129 [*ss:* MMMN-1: figs. 3-133, 3-134]; UMFBP[DFP]-1). *District of Keewatin:* Adelaide Peninsula near E side Sherman Basin (NMC-14: figs. 3-130 to 3-132). Eskimo Point: McConnell River (NPRC-3 live captives: figs. 3-158 to 3-160 [*ss:* MMMN-1]). Hudson Bay: Belcher Islands: Kugong Island (ROM-1). James Bay: Rupert Bay: Dufourmentel Rocks (CM-1), South Twin Island (NMC-1), Weston Island (NMC-4: figs. 3-144, 3-145). Southampton Island: Coral Harbour (CM-1), Ford River (CM-1). *District of Mackenzie:* Great Bear Lake: Keith Arm: Manitou Island (NMC-1: figs. 3-165, 3-166), N shore (NMC-2: figs. 3-163, 3-164). Mackenzie River: site of Old Fort Good Hope—160 km below Good Hope (USNM-1). Perry River (FMNH-1). **Ontario:** *Kenora District:* Fort Severn (ROM-1); Sutton River: 48.2 km below Hawley Lake (ROM-1), 70.8 km below Hawley Lake (ROM-1). **Québec:** *Territory of New Quebec:* Ungava Peninsula: Abloviak Fjord: 8.0 km from head, 4.8 km inland (NMC-1); False

River: Kohlmeister Lake (NMC-1); Kogaluk River: 16.0 km above mouth (CM-2); Lake Ford—59° 13' N, 70° 10' W (NMC-1); Leaf River:19.3 km above first rapids (NMC-1); inland from Povungnituk (ROM-1). **Saskatchewan:** Cypress Lake (NMC-1). Regina: Wascana Park (DWWRS-11 live). **Yukon Territory:** Old Crow: Old Crow River at Timber Creek (USNM-2: figs. 3-161, 3-162). **Alaska:** Admiralty Island: Hasselborg Creek (MVZ-1). Aleutian Islands: Rat Islands: Buldir Island (CESJ-6 live captives; 1 dead: figs. 3-120 to 3-122 [*ss:* PSM-1]; USNM-3: figs. 3-123 to 3-126). Colville River (DEN-5: figs. 3-170, 3-171), near mouth of Kurupa River—69° 10' N, 155° W (UAM-1: figs. 3-172, 3-173). Cordova: Copper River Delta between Copper River and Alaganik Slough (UFS[DM]-3 live). Juneau: near Mendenhall Lake (USNM-1). Kashunuk River 10.5 km SE Old Chevak (UMMZ-1: figs. 3-118, 3-119). Kokechik Bay [=Igiak Bay] (RLWS-2 live; FMNH-3: fig. 3-116). Kupreanof Island: Duncan Canal near Indian Point (USNM-1). N side Kuskokwim Bay near Cape Avinof (OSUFW-1: fig. 3-117). Kuskokwim Delta and Nunivak Island (RLWS-19 live captives). Mitkof Island: near Petersburg Water Reservoir (USNM-2: figs. 3-111, 3-112). Prince William Sound: Hawkins Island: Cedar Bay [=cove, NW side Hawkins Island—60° 33' N, 146° W] (MVZ-1: figs. 3-102, 3-103). Saint Michael (USNM-1). **California:** *Lassen County:* 11.2 km W Wendel (MVZ-1). *Siskiyou County:* Tule Lake (SDNHM-1). **Colorado:** *Moffat County:* Little Snake River (NWPW-5 live: figs. 3-153 to 3-155). **Idaho:** *Caribou County:* Henry (PSM-1). **Michigan:** *Kalamazoo County:* Augusta (UMMZ-1). **Minnesota:** *Marshall County:* Mud Lake (AMNH-1: figs. 3-149, 3-150). *Nobles County:* (RLWS-45 live captives; PSM-2). **Montana:** *Sheridan County:* Medicine Lake (PSM-2). *Sweet Grass County:* Yellowstone River (RWEBT-5 live). **Nevada:** *Elko County:* W side Ruby Lake (MVZ-2). **North Carolina:** *Dare County:* Pea Island National Wildlife Refuge (FMNH-1). **Oregon:** *Harney County:* Frenchglen (SDNHM-1); Malheur Lake (LACM-1). *Lake County:* Paisley (PSM-1): Chewau-can Marsh (OSUFW-1); Silver Lake (OSUFW-1). **Utah:** *Box Elder County:* Brigham City (FMNH-8: figs. 3-156, 3-157). **Washington:** *King County:* Seattle: Green Lake (UWBM-1).

Captive origin (*canadensis*?: PSM-1; *interior:* ROM-1; *minima:* JPWT, LTSW, WT[S]-12 live: figs. 3-113 to 3-115; *moffitti:* PSM-2; *occidentalis:* PSM-1: figs. 3-104, 3-105 *taverneri:* JPWT-6 live: figs. 3-167 to 3-169).

OTHER REFERENCES. Baird, Brewer, and Ridgway 1884, vol. 1. Bent 1925]. Brooks 1926. Cogswell 1977. *Conservator,* Ducks Unlimited (Canada) 6 (2), spring 1985. Cramp and Simmons 1977. Dement'ev and Gladkov (1952) 1967, vol. 4. Frome 1967. Harrison 1975, 1978. Heinroth and Heinroth 1928, vol. 3. Leiff, MacInnes, and Misra 1970. Ridgway 1895. Snyder 1957. Soper 1928 Taverner 1931. Witherby et al. [1939] 1943, vol. 3. Yocom and Harris 1965.

Hawaiian Goose

Bernache néné. Ganso Hawaiense (Allan Phillips, letter to the author, January 1989).
Nesochen sandvicensis (Vigors)

APPEARANCE. Short, velvety brownish gray dorsal down; 'silvery' base color; and olive-gray feet with markedly reduced web areas distinguish the downy Hawaiian Goose, or Néné, from goslings of all other species. The wide, pale supraorbital stripes meet in a 'V' on the forehead (Berger 1981) and the large eye is surrounded by a ring of pale grayish feathers and

a dark 'mask'. A *Branta*-like crown-patch dips downward behind the eye to join with the upper edge of the dark 'mask' and (sometimes) with the dark ear-patch; the ear-spot, nearly always prominent in young goslings, becomes somewhat faded in older downies. The crown and yoke are connected by a continuous wide band of dark pattern color, unlike *Branta* goslings, in which the dark crown and yoke are nearly always separated by paler color on the nape (compare *Nesochen* and *Branta* goslings on pls. 4 & 5). Grayish, inconspicuous dorsal spots are present on most goslings, but wing-patches are faint at best "Nearly-white" wing-tips (Blaauw 1904: 68)—the pale, 'silvery' fronts of the alulae, primaries, and leading edge of the wing—contrast well with the dark pattern color. A slight downward droop of the tapering, high-bridged bill is also characteristic.

VARIATION. The base color of most Néné goslings is gray-white, 'silvery', or faintly cream-colored. Only one gosling had a pale but distinct yellow wash (Munsell 7.5Y 8/3) in the malar region. Pattern color is similar to that described by Delacour (1954) and Kear and Berger (1980), but was more gray and olive in live goslings and more brownish in prepared specimens. The "dark olive-green" pattern color reported by Blaauw (1904: 68) seems unusual, but could have been the result of the illuminant used for evaluation. Johnsgard's (1965: 50) "silvery gray" description is too pale for the *pattern* color of normal, day-old goslings, but describes their *base* color almost perfectly. Goslings having "cottony" down (Johnstone 1959: 39)—a recessive character in which the down is sparse and lacks "...some of the short down plumules..." (Kear and Berger 1980: 52 and pl. 22)—are evidently somewhat paler over all.

The feet of five live goslings and those of four prepared specimens were olive-gray or olive, but a fifth study skin had blackish feet similar to those of live goslings observed by Blaauw (1904) and Kear and Berger (1980).

SOURCE OF SPECIMENS. **Hawaiian Islands:** *Hawaii County:* Hawaii Island: Pohakuloa (OSUFW-3), Volcanoes National Park: Puu Kaone (UWBM-1). **Captive origin** (JPWT-5 live: figs. 3-174 to 3-176, 1 dead; WT[S]-1: figs. 3-177, 3-178).

OTHER REFERENCES. Berger 1972. Kuroda 1939. G. Munro 1944. M. Owen 1980. *Wildfowl* 23, 1972. *Annual Report of the [Severn] Wildfowl Trust 1950-51,* 4, 1952; *1951-52,* 5, 1953; *1960-61,* 13, 1962.

Perching ducks, tribe Cairinini

North American genera: *Cairina* Fleming, *Aix* Boie

DISTRIBUTION AND TAXONOMY. Perching ducks comprising the tribe Cairinini, as described by Delacour and Mayr (1945), are endemic in every continent except Europe. Even there, feral flocks of the introduced Wood Duck, *Aix sponsa*, are known (Fjeldså 1977). All tribal members have tropical or sub-tropical habitats in the southern hemisphere, except for two species, the nearctic Wood Duck and the eastern palaearctic Mandarin Duck, *Aix galericulata*, which are restricted to the north temperate zone (Delacour 1959). The perching ducks vary greatly in size and appearance, from the large, black-and-white Spur-winged Goose, *Plectropterus gambensis*, of Africa to the brilliantly-plumaged Wood and Mandarin ducks, to the tiny pygmy geese, *Nettapus* spp., of Africa and Australasia (Delacour 1959).

The status of the perching ducks as a taxonomic unit is nearly as uncertain today as it was in 1922, when J. Phillips placed the Spur-winged Goose, the Muscovy Duck, *Cairina moschata*, the Comb Duck, *Sarkidiornis melanotos*, and the pygmy geese in the sub-family, Plectropterinae, and removed the Wood and Mandarin ducks to the dabblers, following the Pink-eared Duck, *Malacorhynchus membranaceous*. Delacour and Mayr (1945) erected the tribe Cairinini and included in it not only Phillips's "Plectropterinae" and the Wood and Mandarin ducks, but also the Australian Wood Duck, *Chenonetta jubata*, the White-winged Wood Duck, *Cairina scutulata*, Hartlaub's Duck, *C. hartlaubi* (=*Pteronetta hartlaubi* [Cassin]), and the Brazilian Teal, *Amazonetta brasiliensis*. On the basis of similar osteological characters, Woolfenden (1961) placed *Plectropterus* with the shelducks (Tadornini) and the rest of the perching ducks with the Anatini. Johnsgard (1965) considered the Ringed Teal, *Callonetta leucophrys* (=*Anas leucophrys* of Delacour and Mayr 1945) more of a perching duck than a dabbler in its behavior and placed it in the Cairinini, following Delacour (1936). Kear (1968) found *Callonetta's* isolation distress calls quite similar to those of two perching ducks, *Cairina moschata* and *Sarkidiornis*, but Brush (1976: 489) found its SCM-proteins "unequivocally" like those of Anatini. He found little tribal similarity among six 'cairinine' genera that he examined (*Amazonetta, Chenonetta, Aix, Nettapus, Sarkidiornis, Cairina*), but chose to retain the tribe, Cairinini, pending further investigation. More recently, Livezey (1986: 743), using 120 osteological characters, confirmed the polyphyletic nature of the perching ducks, proposed a unique status for *Plectropterus* (p. 740: "the first of the waterfowl...with scutellate tarsi"), and suggested that *Callonetta* and other cairinines, as well as the dabbling ducks (Anatini), were members of "a poorly resolved grade." Neither Livezey, Woolfenden, nor Johnsgard (1979) accorded tribal status to the perching ducks.

Polyphyletic origin of the Cairinini is supported by the natal characters of tribal members: no single set of plumage or pattern characters (i.e., no avian 'personna') typifies the downy young of all cairinines, unlike, e.g., eiders, pochards, or whistling-ducks, which have distinct pattern elements shared by all tribal members. Pattern elements vary in both form and definition, forming several groups within the tribe, but the resemblance may, in some cases, be superficial. Patterns of *Chenonetta* (ANWC; Australia: ACT: Hall) and *Aix* spp. are similar; so are those of *Callonetta* (FMNH; Paraguay: 200 km W Puerta Casada) and species of *Nettapus* (compare downy young of two genera in Scott pls. 23 & 11 *in* Delacour 1956 & 1959, respectively). *Cairina moschata* and *Sarkidiornis* (FMNH; India: Farrukhabad) share strikng pattern and bill characters not found in *C. scutulata* and *C. hartlaubi*. *A.*

Plate 4

Plate 4

1 Lesser Snow Goose, Anser caerulescens caerulescens
Class 0. RLWS captive.
Class 1. JPWT captive.
Class 2. WT(S) captive.
Class 3. JPWT captive.
Class 4. JPWT captive.

2 Hawaiian Goose, Nesochen sandvicensis
JPWT captives.

3 Emperor Goose, Philacte canagica
RLWS captives.

4 Barnacle Goose, Branta leucopsis
RLWS captives.

Brant, B. bernicla

5 Atlantic Brant, B. b. hrota. Bear Cove, Southampton Island, Northwest Territories (PWPS captives).

6 Pacific (or, Black) Brant, B. b. nigricans. Kokechik Bay, Alaska (RLWS).

Plate 5

Canada Goose, Branta canadensis

1 Atlantic Canada Goose, B. c. canadensis
Laden Field's Pond, Newfoundland (UFS[DM]).

2 Giant Canada Goose, B. c. maxima
Round Lake, Minnesota (RLWS captives).

3 Great Basin Canada Goose, B. c. moffitti
Little Snake River, Colorado (NWPW).

4 Todd's Canada Goose, B. c. interior
Churchill, Manitoba (NWPW).

5 Taverner's Canada Goose, B. c. taverneri
JPWT captives.

6 Lesser Canada Goose, B. c. parvipes
Eskimo Point, Northwest Territories (NPRC captives).

7 Cackling Canada Goose, B. c. minima
Kuskokwim Delta and Nunivak Island, Alaska (RLWS captives).

8 Aleutian Canada Goose, B. c. leucopareia
Buldir Island, Alaska (CESJ captives).

9 Dusky Canada Goose, B. c. occidentalis
Copper River Delta, Alaska (UFS[DM]: color and pattern); Prince Rupert
British Columbia (JPWT captives: measurements).

10 Vancouver Canada Goose, B. c. fulva
Quamichan Lake, British Columbia (NWPW).

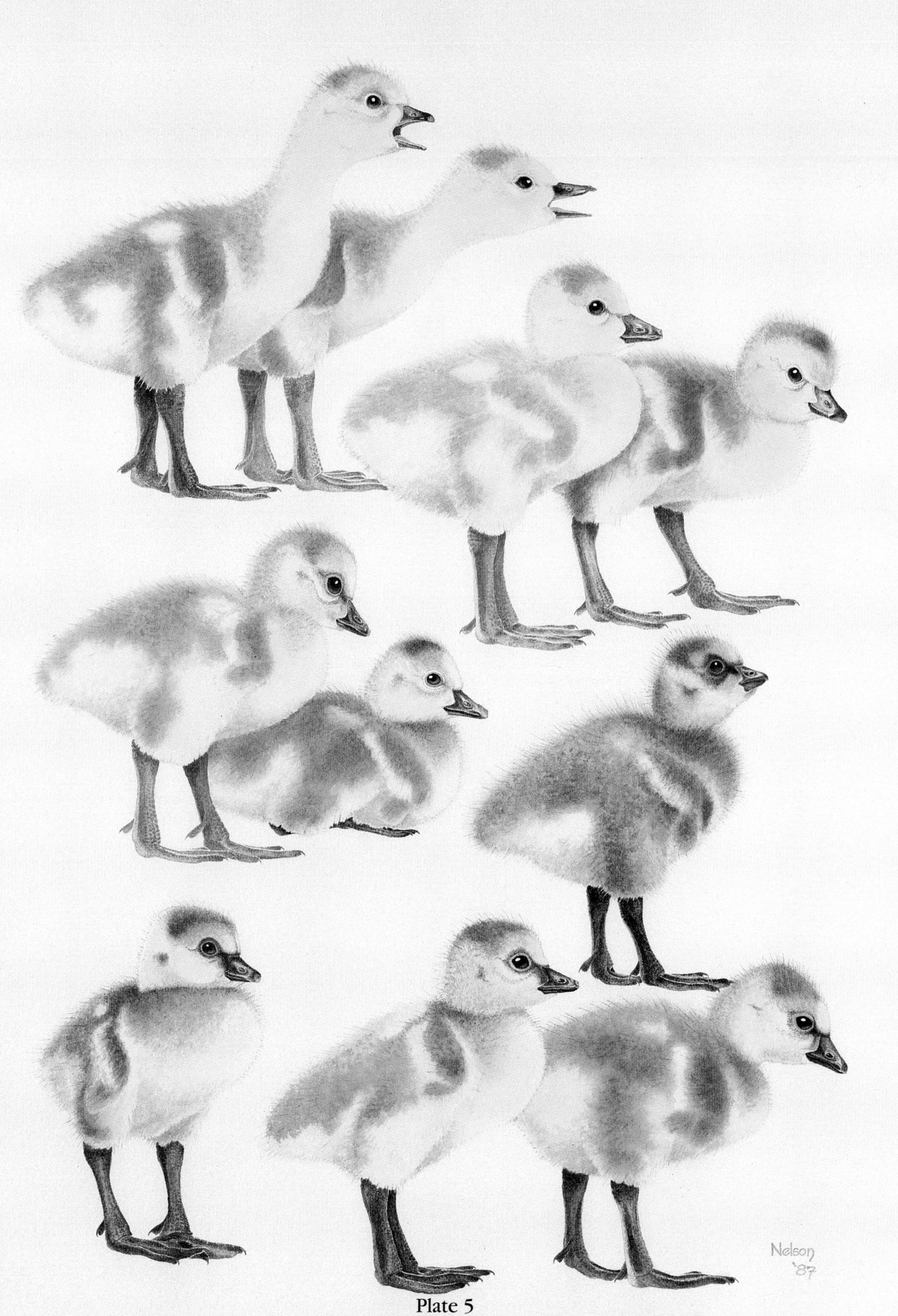

Plate 5

brasiliensis appears somewhat *Anas*-like (USNM; Delaware: Howard Carey Aviary; Delacour 1959: Scott pl. 11) and the large, olive-and-yellow *Plectropterus* (ROM; Kenya: Ruiru) stands alone, with a poorly-defined, *Aythya*-like face pattern. Distinctive eye-to-occiput stripes (De Vis 1897) of the downy young suggest that *Anas waiguensis* (Kear 1975: 107, J. B. Blossom drawings) and *Merganetta* (Kear 1975; Johnsgard 1979) may also belong in the Cairinini.

Subgroups within the tribe have in common certain postures and habits characteristic of most tribal members, but not necessarily exclusive to them. For example, a swimming posture in which the adult bird's posterior is held at shoulder level or higher is reported for *Plectropterus* (Brown, Urban, and Newman 1982) and for *Aix sponsa, Nettapus* spp., and *Chenonetta* (Frith 1982). Arboreal perching has been reported for all species of Cairinini, including the larger ones such as the Comb Duck (Gibbon 1933; Siegfried 1979) and the Spur-winged Goose (Cheesman and Sclater 1935). A Spur-winged gosling (ca. 5 d.) had strongly decurved claws. Cavity-nesting is known in all species, although the Brazilian Teal usually nests on the ground (Delacour 1959). According to Delacour (1959) and Brown, Urban, and Newman (1982), the nests of Hartlaub's Duck (for which the latter authors retain the genus *Pteronetta* Salvadori) have not been found, but they note that the ability of captive ducklings [WT(S)] to cling and climb, using their sharp claws, implies a cavity-nesting habit for this species as well. However, cavity-nesting is known in other tribes, such as whistling-ducks and sea-ducks. Neither is the perching habit confined to the Cairinini, e.g., Scott (1958) described tree-roosting by wild Magpie Geese, *Anseranas semipalmata*. As Woolfenden (1961: 110) observed, "The perching habit characteristic of these [cairinine] genera may not be a reflection of common ancestry."

Intrageneric variation also presents some problems. Although some cairinine genera exhibit little variation in the plumage patterns of their downy young (e.g., *Nettapus, Aix*), the amount of intrageneric variation observed in downy young of the three species placed by Delacour and Mayr (1945) in the genus, *Cairina*—Muscovy Duck, White-winged Wood Duck, Hartlaub's Duck—is at times greater than the degree of *intergeneric* variation among downy young of other perching ducks. For example, the combination of dark eye-stripe (often incomplete or lacking before the eye) and a (sometimes) faint or smudgy cheek-to-ear stripe is shared by downy *Aix* and *Chenonetta* (compare dark variant of *A. sponsa*, pl. 8, with *Chenonetta jubata* ducklings in *Wildfowl* 20 (1969: Philippa Scott photo). Intraspecific pattern variation occurs also on some downy Muscovy Ducks (compare figs. 4-5, 4-7, and pl. 8). Delacour and Mayr's (1945) three *Cairina* species share a bright, often brilliant, yellow base color and rather similar wing-patches and dorsal spots, but they differ markedly in foot color. The tarsi and toes of White-winged [and Muscovy] ducklings are strongly patterned in dark brown and yellow (Johnstone 1972, 1973), whereas those of Hartlaub's duckling are black (Johnstone 1960). Moreover, the Muscovy's forehead is yellow (like that of some Comb ducklings; D'Eath 1967: lower photo facing p. 197) and the forehead is dark to the top of the bill on both Hartlaub's and White-winged ducklings. What may be a more significant difference occurs between the two dark-headed ducklings themselves. "The [Hartlaub's] ducklings appear more like young African Black Ducks, or even Northern Mallards, than they are like Muscovy Ducks or Comb Ducks, their supposed closest relatives" (Johnstone 1960: 70). The connection of eye- and cheek-stripes of *C. scutulata* forms a "divided eye-stripe...not found in other species" (Mackenzie and Kear 1976: 14, fig. 4 [but see *Netta rufina* in Millais 1913, vol. 1]), the upper branch of which "turns up almost at a right angle to the dark brown cap" (Johnstone 1972:

136; E. E. Jackson photo, pl. 15 [but see oblique angle of stripe connection of White-winged Wood duckling *in* F. Todd 1979: fig. 1.138]). The stripe is nonetheless pochard-like (compare with pochard figs. on pl. 8), and there is even a striking 'Aythyan hood' on White-winged Wood ducklings portrayd by Lubbock (1975: E. E. Jackson photo). In contrast, the undivided eye-stripe of *Pteronetta hartlaubi* is heavy and *Anas*-like, and always meets the dark cap at an oblique angle (Johnstone 1960: Philippa Scott photo facing p. 69). Wild downy Hartlaub's Ducks (FMNH; Cameroon: Efulan) had traces of an *Aythya*-like cheek-stripe. The bills of White-winged and Hartlaub's ducklings also resemble the longer, more spatulate bills of dabblers and pochards rather than the shorter, high-bridged, tapering bills of other tribal members such as *Chenonetta, Nettapus*, and *Aix*. In other words, Hartlaub's ducklings and downy White-winged Wood Ducks bear only a superficial resemblance to each other, and neither resembles greatly the downy young of other perching ducks, including the *Anas*-like olive-brown-and-yellow Brazilian Teal ducklings. These have light-colored feet with low-contrast darker pattern, a very narrow dark hindneck, and a complete eye-stripe that outlines heavily the lower half of the eye (USNM; *Annual Report of the [Severn] Wildfowl Trust 1960-61* 13, 1962: P. Talbot-Ponsonby photo). The distinctive plumage of the Hartlaub's duckling might be added to the behavioral (Johnsgard 1960b, 1965) and osteological (Woolfenden 1961; Livezey 1986) evidence cited by these authors to justify the retention of *Pteronetta* for that species.

Genetic analysis of blood samples from *C. moschata, Sarkidiornis,* and *Aix* species (Numachi et al. 1983) showed *A. sponsa* and *A. galericulata* to be virtually indistinguishable at all 10 loci tested, but indicated that the three genera are not closely related within the tribe, but are genetically more like some *Aythya* species (e.g., *A. fuligula, A. marila*) than like most *Anas*, supporting the close relationship of perching ducks and pochards proposed by Delacour and Mayr (1945). Studies by Livezey (1986) and Seeb, Wishard, and Oates (unpubl.) also support the close relationship of *Aix* and *Aythya*.

The weight of evidence for polyphyletic origin of the perching ducks is almost overwhelming. However, I have used the tribe, Cairinini, in this work as a convenient means of emphasizing the distinctive elements of pattern, plumage, and behavior that separate the two North American 'cairinines' (Muscovy Duck, Wood Duck) from the rest of the Anatini, as defined by Woolfenden (1961), Johnsgard (Anatinae; 1979), and Livezey (1986).

APPEARANCE AND BEHAVIOR. Despite differences in size, color, and dorsal pattern, downy young of the Muscovy and Wood ducks have much in common. Ducklings of both species have large, lustrous dark eyes—so do *Chenonetta* ducklings—which stand out against the pale cheeks and the paler superciliary and pre-ocular areas; a single dark stripe runs between dark eye and dark occiput. Slightly longer down plumes on the occiput and hindneck create a maned effect in both (Palmer 1976, vol. 2); yellow or olive-yellow down-tips, more prominent in the Muscovy, give a 'golden' sheen to the dark crown color. Bills of both species are high-bridged, rather short relative to head-length, and somewhat laterally compressed (more so in the Wood Duck); they taper slightly in young downies but become more spatulate in half-grown ducklings. At the same time, the nails become longer, wider, and more pointed (compare young downies in figs. 4-1 to 4-5 and 4-8 to 4-12, with older birds in figs. 4-6 to 4-7, 4-13 to 4-14). As well as their morphological likenesses, newly hatched young of both species share similar vocalizations and behavior, and both can cling to and climb almost any vertical surface.

Wary and extremely shy, 11 captive Muscovy ducklings (WT[S]) stayed close together, maintaining a low-pitched, more or less continuous chatter of three- or four-syllabled conversation calls. I had only to make some small sound or movement to put them on the alert: necks stretched upward, posture almost vertical, and long tails sweeping the grass (pl. 8). Turning a page in my notebook would send them scurrying to the shelter of their brooder.

Day-old Wood Ducks seem unable to keep still. They keep up a running conversation of high-pitched, polysyllabic calls, punctuated by occasional bobbings of the head, frequent attempts to jump out of their pen (accompanied by distress calls), and sudden leaps from one side of the pen to the other. Allowing newly hatched ducklings to jump out of their carrying box or shipping crate into their pen seems to have a calming effect on them (Robert Fuller, telephone interview, 20 May 1964). The lively, nervous behavior of captive Wood ducklings is matched by that of wild ones. Both Beard (1964) and Grice and Rogers (1965) observed very young, wild Wood Duck broods dabbling and gleaning, darting and jumping in pursuit of food. Beard (p. 397) reported that older ducklings, "almost able to fly, [would jump] 8-10 inches out of the water for insects high on a sedge stem." Older captive Wood ducklings (ca. 1 wk.), having lost the urge of the newly hatched to leap and climb, go about quite sedately, with fanned-out, upaised tails and stately, oscillating head movements.

When feeding, downy Wood Ducks reiterate rapid, four-syllabled calls, ascending in pitch a minor third (m3), with scarcely a pause between each one. A rapid, high-pitched distress call, "Ti-ti-ti-ti...!", is often accompanied by a series of movements (observed also in downy American Wigeons, *Mareca americana*) in which the head is brought slightly backward, then thrust upward and forward, and finally returned, briefly, to a resting position on the shoulders. Both the movement and the vocalizations are repeated virtually without interruption until the distress is in some way alleviated. Polysyllabic conversation calls of Muscovy ducklings are quite similar, but lower-pitched. Sleepy calls of both species are short, close-textured trills.

Muscovy Duck

Canard-musqué d' Amérique (Desvillers 1976).
Pato Real.
Cairina moschata (Linnaeus)

APPEARANCE. The boldly patterned yellow and dark brown Muscovy duckling bears a striking, if superficial, resemblance to the downy Ring-necked Duck: both have prominent dorsal spots and wing-patches, a clear yellow forehead continuous with the supraorbital stripes, and dull yellow feet contrastingly patterned with grayish brown (compare ducklings of 2 spp. on pl. 8). However, the dark stripe from eye to nape, the long body with short, heavy tarsi; the short, but distinct, 'mane' of longer down-plumes at the back of the head; and the long, fan-like tail quickly distinguish the downy Muscovy Duck from all other yellow-plumaged North American ducklings. Also, the downy Muscovy's wide nail is hooked downward (Delacour 1959).

Half-fledged ducklings from Colombia [CM] were downy on the face, crown, throat, sides of belly, and back, but had feathered ears, upper neck, center belly, scapulars, flanks, and tail. The last three areas were also iridescent: bright green, dull greenish purple, and faintly purple, respectively. The thin eye-line was clearly defined, the dark yellow down-tips showed up well on the dark crown, and four yellowish white dorsal spots were prominent (as on Class IIb ducklings shown by Woodyard and Bolen 1984: 459, fig. 1).

VARIATION. Four wild-caught ducklings from Brazil and Venezuela (AMNH; FMNH) had rump-spots somewhat larger than shoulder-spots and narrow yellow foreheads (figs. 4-5, 4-7). A well-marked dark stripe ran clearly from eye to occiput in the Venezuelan specimen (fig. 4-4), but was thin in one Brazilian duckling and absent in two others; these had, however, a faint cheek-stripe, extending from the nape forward to eye-level, which was lacking in the other wild specimens. The 'wild-type' captive duckling had the largest, most conspicuous dorsal spots, the widest yellow forehead, a thin—but well-marked—line from eye to occiput, and no cheek-stripe (compare stripe characters of Muscovy and Wood ducklings in figs. 4-1 to 4-7, 4-8 to 4-14, and on pl. 8). Tarsi and toes of the four wild specimens had evidently been some shade of yellow, patterned with a dark brownish color, but those of the captive duckling had areas of pale yellowish pink alternating with areas of dull greenish yellow patterned with grayish brown.

Muscovy ducklings sometimes appear as dark mutants, having dark—yet somehow garish—olive-yellow plumage, yellow chin-patch, and shiny black feet, or with patchy, yellowish pink pigmentation of plumage or unfeathered parts or both (USNM). Short, pale gray bills with transverse culmen ridges are also known (figs. 4-1 to 4-3).

DISCUSSION. According to various early accounts cited by J. Phillips (1922), Spanish explorers in the early 16th century found the Muscovy Duck already domesticated by South American Indians. Imported to Europe later in that century, the species has since been widely domesticated there. Delacour (1959: 130) notes that alterations of body size, color, and facial characters may occur "after two or three generations." Such alterations evidently took place among the wild Muscovies kept at Slimbridge. After several generations, downy progeny of the original wild parents (from Recife, Brazil; S. T. Johnstone, letter to the author, July 1970) were mostly the dark mutant type (Janet Kear, letter to the author, January 1966). The first ten pipping Muscovy eggs sent from Slimbridge produced such mutants, but the eleventh egg held a 'wild-type' duckling (see *Annual Report of the [Severn] Wildfowl Trust 1962-63* 15, 1964: Philippa Scott photo of 'wild-type' and mutant ducklings).

SOURCE OF SPECIMENS. BRAZIL: **Amazonas:** Río Madeira: Santo Antonio de Guajara—near Borba (AMNH-1: figs. 4-4, 4-5). **Ceará:** Quixada (FMNH-2). **Pernambuco:** Recife (WT[S]-11 live captives: figs. 4-1 to 4-3). COLOMBIA: **Choco:** Río Atrato: Santata (CM-3). VENEZUELA: **Bolívar:** Río San Felix: "Las Guacas" [Phelps and Phelps 1950] (AMNH-1: figs. 4-6, 4-7). **Captive origin** (UMMZ-1; USNM-1).

OTHER REFERENCES. Johnsgard 1965, 1978, 1979. Markum and Baldassare 1989. Palmer 1976, vol. 3.

Wood Duck

Canard branchu. Pato Arcoiris.
Aix sponsa (Linnaeus)

APPEARANCE. A dark, well-marked stripe from eye to occiput; a short 'mane'; a dark, almost glossy, pattern color contrasting with a pale, 'sulphury' yellow base color; slim, boldly patterned tarsi and toes; and a long, fan-like blackish tail separate the Wood duckling from those of other North American species. The

dark forehead, widening gradually and evenly from the horns of the dark bill past the pale pre-ocular area, is especially prominent in front view; its 'golden' or 'silvery' aspect is produced by many dull greenish yellow down-tips. Dusky down-tips form a delicate shadow over the face and breast, along the sides, and on the undertail of many ducklings.

VARIATION. Numerous small differences of color and pattern in downy Wood Ducks from many areas raise the possibility of these being related to geographical origin (Palmer 1976, vol.

3). Among live, wild ducklings, I found 12 Vermont birds clearly yellow and brown, a Minnesota duckling essentially black and white, and 38 Ohio and Illinois downies somewhat intermediate. However, subsequent examination of live and prepared specimens from British Columbia, Manitoba, Minnesota, Washington, Oregon, and California disclosed much the same range of variation. Grice also found similar variations among "several thousand newly hatched Wood Ducks" web-tagged in Massachusetts, but did not consider the differences "distinct or unusual" (David Grice, letter to the author, February 1965). Fredrickson found certain wild Missouri Wood Ducks more brightly colored than any described herein; he suggested that the color of the downy young might be influenced by the prenatal crustacean diet of female Wood Ducks (Leigh Fredrickson, letter to the author, July 1983).

Yellow color is absent or greatly reduced in the plumage and foot color of many ducklings hatched from captive stock. Fjeldså (1977: 61) and Harrison (1978: 77), respectively, described "cream coloured" and "grayish-white" ducklings, presumably from such captive (or feral) European Wood Duck specimens (but note the distinctly yellowish duckling shown by Burton *in* Harrison 1978: pl. 4). The feet of these pale captives are usually dull and rather 'pinkish'.

The dark eye-to-occiput stripe is always complete and nearly always thin, except on a few individuals where it is rather wide and uneven. The pre-ocular stripe, characteristically absent in the downy Wood Duck, is indicated in some individuals by a tiny dusky line anterior to or part way around the eye. Often, this faint line connects loosely with an ill-defined dark cheek-stripe. Seldom clearly delineated, the cheek-stripe varies from a barely visible line of dusky down-tips to a smudged stripe of uneven width extending forward from the ear and curving upward behind the lore, leaving a light area below the eye. Such a dark stripe appeared on wild-caught specimens from Ohio, Illinios, Oregon, and British Columbia (see 2 variants on pl. 8). However, a few captives from feral stock (JPWT) had wide or heavy cheek-stripes extending from bill to nape, which were quite similar to the cheek-stripes of *Chenonetta* and *A. galericulata.*

Both dorsal and tibial patterns have certain characteristic variations. The shoulder-spots, evidently missing on Wood ducklings described by Baird, Brewer, and Ridgway (1884, vol. 1; Illinios specimen), J. Phillips (1925), and Grice and Rogers (1965), appear on other ducklings as a cluster of three or four pale plumes or as a single spot a few mm in diameter. The rump- spots, often broken or bar-like, are often somewhat larger (6-7 mm) and the narrow wing-patches—yellow, brownish yellow, or (occasionally) white—are entirely lacking on some individuals. The tibial pattern of some Wood ducklings resembles that of downy *Anas,* but in others is poorly defined and is mottled with light grayish brown or yellowish gray down plumes.

Bold contrast of base and pattern colors marks the feet of newly hatched Wood Ducks; the pale color of the webbed areas adjacent to the toes has a distinctive 'scalloped' outline against the dark centers of the webs. Yellow, greenish yellow, or olive base colors and dark pattern colors were found on wild-caught ducklings from eastern, central (both variants, pl. 8), and western North America (British Columbia: ROM, tag data, coll. J. A. Munro; California: MVZ, H. S. Swarth 1923, unpubl. field notebook). Monochromatic or low-contrast foot colors depicted by Scott (*in* Delacour 1959: pl. 11; dark gray), Burton (*in* Harrison 1978: pl. 4; olive), and Hines (*in* Bellrose 1980: pl. 23; olive-green) are not typical of live, wild North American ducklings.

SOURCE OF SPECIMENS. **British Columbia:** *New Westminster District:* Huntingdon (ROM-1). **Manitoba:** Delta (D-1: figs. 4-13, 4-14). Portage Creek (DWWRS-9 live). **Ontario:** *Frontenac County:* Snow Road (ROM-2). *Norfolk County:* Long Point (ROM-2). *Ontario County:* Uxbridge (ROM-2). *York County:*

Toronto Island (ROM-1). **Québec:** *Gatineau County:* Gatineau River near Chelsea (NMC-1). **California:** *Merced County:* Snelling (MVZ-1). **Illinois:** *Mason County:* Havana: Chautauqua

National Wildlife Refuge (UFS[DM]-18 live). **Minnesota:** *Hennepin County:* Brooklyn Park (BMNH-2); Hayden Lake—SW Champlin: Elm Creek (BMNH-1); Minneapolis (RLWS-7 live): near Minnehaha Creek (BMNH-2); Wayzata (BMNH-1). **Ohio:** *Ottawa County:* Magee Marsh (UFS[DM]-20 live). **Oregon:** *Benton County:* Corvallis (OSUFW-2). *Clatsop County:* Knappa: near Columbia River Slough [probably=collective name for entire complex of sloughs in vicinity of Knappa] (OSUFW-2). *Lincoln County:* Depoe Bay (OSUFW-1). *Multnomah County:* Sauvie Island (PSM-2). *Tillamook County:* Blaine: Silver Falls [=local name for waterfall formerly existing on Nestucca River about 9.6 km SE Blaine] (OSUFW-2); Nehalem (MVZ-1; OSUFW-1). *Yamhill County:* Willamina (PSM-1). **Pennsylvania:** *Crawford County:* Linesville (CM-2). *Delaware County:* Secane (PSM-1). **Vermont:** *Addison County:* Vergennes (DWWRS-12 live: figs. 4-8 to 4-10 [ss: D-1; MMMN-1: figs. 4-11, 4-12; UND-1). **Washington:** *Snohomish County:* Snohomish (UWBM-2). **Captive origin** (JPWT, LTSW, WT[S]-16 live; MVZ-2; ROM-2).

OTHER REFERENCES. Beard 1964. Bent 1923. Cogswell 1977. Grinnell, Bryant, and Storer 1918. Johnsgard 1965. Kortright 1942. Leopold 1951. Linduska 1964. Ridgway 1895. Roberts 1932, vol. 2.

Dabbling ducks, tribe Anatini

North American genera: *Mareca* Stephens, *Anas* Linnaeus

DISTRIBUTION AND TAXONOMY. Dabbling ducks, or river ducks, are the most widely distributed members of the waterfowl family: every continent and many remote islands (Lack 1970; Weller 1980) have representatives of what some authors (e.g., J. Phillips 1922; Delacour 1956) refer to as the 'true ducks'. Yet the tribe is far from unified. Delacour and Mayr (1945: 23), while merging the vast majority of the 'dabbling' species in the genus *Anas*, nevertheless recognized no fewer than 15 subgroups within the genus, as well as a final group of "aberrant river ducks," in which they placed provisionally the monotypic genera, *Hymenolaimus, Malacorhynchus, Rhodonessa,* and *Stictonetta.* Subsequent studies by Woolfenden (1961), Brush (1976), and Livezey (1986) established other tribal affinities for these monotypic genera, and restored the genera *Lophonetta,* Bronze-winged Duck, and *Marmaronetta,* Marbled Teal. Osteological studies by Woolfenden (1961) and Livezey (1986) suggested that perching ducks and dabbling ducks be merged in the tribe Anatini. Johnsgard (1979) included also the pochards in the subfamily, Anatinae, a relationship suggested by Delacour and Mayr (1945) and supported by genetic evidence from Numachi et al. (1983).

However, distinctive natal characters separate North American dabblers from ducklings of the two continental species of perching ducks and from all species of *Aythya.* For that reason, the three groups are treated in this work as separate tribes, following other authors (e.g., Delacour and Mayr 1945; Brush 1976; Palmer 1976, vol. 2). I have resurrected the genus, *Mareca* (A.O.U. 1957), for wigeons and the Falcated Duck, because their downy young share a unique color and pattern.

APPEARANCE. Plumage patterns (pls. 6 & 7; Scott pls. *in* Delacour 1959; Palmer 1976, vol. 2: 370, C. Nelson col. pl.), vocalizations (Kear 1968), and behavior are generally similar among holarctic Anatini ducklings, but certain measurable differences in these characters create several subgroups within the tribe: the wigeons, Falcated Duck, and Gadwall; Green-winged Teal and Northern Pintail; White-cheeked Pintail; the mallards; Laysan Duck; and the blue-winged ducks.

American Wigeon, *Mareca americana,* and Gadwall, *Anas strepera.*

The downy young of the three species of wigeon (American, European, *M. penelope,* & Chiloë, *M. sibilatrix*) and the Falcated Duck, *M. falcata,* are at once closely similar to one another and unequivocally distinct from all other Anatini. All have a yellowish brown secondary base color, which is more reddish in the Falcated duckling, confined entirely to the head and shoulders. The face appears yellowish brown (either strong, moderate, or grayish) and the eye-stripe and ear-spot typical of most *Anas* are faint or absent. Often, there is a pale ring all or part way around the eye. The yellowish brown color intensifies the darker color of crown and yoke, but fades out quickly on the posterior half of the birds, leaving a yellowish white or ivory-yellow primary base color as the only pale color on the rump-spots, belly, and undertail. In a few American Wigeon (DWWRS; Man.: Portage la Prairie) and Falcated ducklings (PSM; 2 captive), nearly all yellow primary base color was absent; these individuals appeared essentially grayish brown and white.

Certain behavioral characteristics also distinguish wigeons from other Anatini. Goose-like posture and behavior typify even day-old American Wigeon (pl. 6; note 'long-legged', upright stance of paler variant, & Head-down-and-forward posture of darker one). Kortright (1942: 186) described adult American Wigeons as "active on land, where they trot about and graze like little geese," and Raikow (1973) found the American Wigeon's adaptation to feeding on land reflected in the lowest paddle index obtained among Anatini species that he measured (such adaptive characters may be convergent in other tribes, e.g., *Chenonetta* is a 'grazer' among the perching ducks; Frith 1982). Wishart (1983) reported differences in calls and courtship behavior between American Wigeon and most other Anatini: male Wigeon have clear, polysyllabic whistles, but most *Anas* males do not; male Wigeon do not perform the Grunt-whistle, the Head-up-tail-up, or the Down-up—all typical of most *Anas* males—but do display the Wings-up, which *Anas* males do not. However, Wishart, as most modern authors, retains wigeons in the genus, *Anas*. Tracheal anatomy (Johnsgard 1961c) and displays of the Falcated Duck are intermediate between those of wigeons and Gadwall: the Grunt-whistle and the Head-up-tail-up are perfomed, but the Down-up is rare or lacking and the Wings-up is undescribed (Johnsgard 1963, 1965).

The resemblance between dorsal coloring of wigeon and Falcated ducklings and that of the downy Gadwall supports the close relationship of these five species suggested by J. Phillips (1923), Delacour (1956), and Johnsgard (1965), who regards the Gadwall as intermediate between the wigeon group and the rest of the Anatini. Prominent on all Gadwall ducklings are large, white or yellowish white rump-spots; buff or buffy yellow wing-patches; and a grayish yellowish brown back mottled with paler down-tips. Dorsal patterns of the wigeon group are similar to those of the Gadwall, but the pale markings were somewhat less conspicuous on downy American Wigeon (DWWRS; Man.: Delta), Chiloë Wigeon (CM; Chile: Elephant Gulf), and Falcated Duck (WT[S], PSM; all captive). A. C. Meinertzhagen (*in* Witherby et al. [1939] 1943, 3: 265) and Cramp and Simmons (1977: 480) described "cinnamon-buff" dorsal down-tips and wing-patches in the downy European Wigeon, *M. penelope*. The downy Gadwall's high-bridged, tapering bill is like those of wigeons, but its yellow face and well-defined eye-stripe are typical of *Anas* ducklings.

Green-winged Teal, *A. crecca*, and Northern Pintail, *A. acuta*.

Green-winged Teal and Northern Pintail ducklings have similar foot colors and plumage patterns; the two species are also rather close genetically (Kessler and Avise 1984). Ducklings of both species have essentially monochromatic foot color (olive-gray or bluish gray in the Northern Pintail; gray, dark gray, or blackish gray in the Green-winged Teal) and blotchy, diffuse cheek-stripes (pl. 6; dark and light variants of both spp.). Dorsal patterns of the downy young are less similar: Northern Pintail ducklings always have a linear arrangement of dorsal spots, but the dark, inconspicuously patterned Green-winged ducklings usually do not. Northern Pintail ducklings have an almost exact counterpart in downy Yellow-billed Pintails, *A. georgica* (FMNH; Chile: Araucania; Colombia: Nariño), while darker Greenwing ducklings are quite similar to southern teal ducklings, e.g., Andaman Teal, *A. gibberifrons* (FMNH; India: S Andaman I.) and Chestnut Teal, *A. castanea* (ANWC; Australia: ACT: Gungahlin).

Day-old Northern Pintail and Green-winged ducklings appear 'long-legged' relative to swim-length (=CT [front of chest to tip of tail, in resting or swimming posture]), an impression emphasized by their horizontal body posture. Downy Northern Pintails have proportionately longer tarsi than, e.g., Northern Mallard ducklings have, but downy Green-winged Teals do not (C. Nelson, unpubl. data). Probably, the teals' small size and slim tarsi contribute to the illusion of long 'legs'.

Good field characters are the dark-faced look of young Northern Pintail and Greenwing ducklings and the 'square-headed' appearance of these species at all ages. The appearance is enhanced in both species by the transverse lines of eye- and cheek-stripes.

White-cheeked Pintail, *A. bahamensis*

Unlike ducklings of the two northern species, the newly hatched White-cheeked Pintail (breeding range tropical and sub-tropical; Delacour 1956) lacks both the 'square-headed' look and the dark cheek-stripe, and is thus typical of many other *Anas* ducklings (Moffitt 1932), such as the Red-billed Pintail, *A. erythrorhyncha* (FMNH; Zambia: Lundazi).

The pre- and post-ocular portions of the eye-stripe differ markedly in width and prominence (compare figs. 5-12, 5-19, & 5-39), and the dorsal spots vary individually from four more or less round spots to a wide stripe from shoulder to rump to pale undertail (pl. 6). The feet are dull orange-yellow (usually with good contrast of the grayish brown pattern color) and the resting posture is more upright than horizontal.

The mallards in North America.

The mallards: Mallard, *A. platyrhynchos;* Mottled Duck, *A. fulvigula*; American Black Duck, *A. rubripes*; and Mexican Duck, *A. diazi.*

Ducklings of the mallard group compare closely in all characters of plumage, posture, and bill structure. Indeed, the five continental taxa (*fulvigula, maculosa, rubripes, diazi, platyrhynchos*), as well as the insular Greenland Mallard (*A. p. conboschas*) and the Hawaiian and Laysan ducks, are widely regarded as members of a single complex (e.g., Delacour 1956; Johnsgard 1961a, 1965, 1979; Numachi et al. 1983), or even as a polytypic species (Johnsgard 1978; see also Morgan, Noe, and Henny 1976 and Ankney et al. 1986 for the American Black Duck, *A. rubripes*). Adults of the insular taxa show certain anatomical (Schiøler 1925, re: Greenland Mallard), behavioral (Johnsgard 1963, 1965, re: Hawaiian and Laysan ducks), and biological differences (Moulton and Weller 1984, re: Laysan Duck) from the basic mallard pattern, but adults of the continental forms have considerable agreement of "morphological, behavioral...electrophoretic" (Johnsgard 1961a: 39) and genetic characters (J. Phillips 1921; Kessler and Avise 1984; re: *platyrhynchos* and *fulvigula*). Delacour and Mayr (1945: 21) viewed sexually monomorphic *fulvigula, rubripes*, and *diazi* as three subspecies of the "Dusky Duck" [*Anas obscura* var. *fulvigula* Ridgway 1874], whereas Palmer (1976, vol. 2) considered them as three full species, representing the 'old' mallard in North America, with dimorphic, green-headed *A. platyrhynchos* representing the 'new'. A. Phillips's (1961) suggestion of *one* genetic change to produce a dimorphic, green-headed mallard thus seems more plausible than Johnsgard's (1961a) proposal of *three* such changes resulting in three closely similar monomorphic mallards. Characters of the downy young as well as differential susceptibility to parasitic infections of *Leucocytozoon simondi* (Fallis and Bennett 1966; Khan and Fallis 1968) and *Sarcocystis* spp. (Mason and Clark 1990) suggest that the two groups should be treated separately. Species names follow Palmer (1976, vol. 2), subspecies Johnsgard (1961a).

The present distribution of 'old' mallards and 'new' is entirely compatible with Rand's (1948) idea of the isolation of monomorphic 'old' forms in southerly refugia during times of maximum glaciation. The subsequent contact of 'old' and 'new' types—as when the dimorphic green-headed Northern Mallard, *A. p. platyrhynchos*, is thought to have re-invaded North America from Asia during one or more of the interglacial periods (Palmer 1976, vol. 2)—has, in the case of the Mexican Duck, *A. diazi*, resulted in allopatric hybridization ("secondary intergradation"; Mayr 1965: 369). Hubbard (1973) proposed the evolution of two New World mallard types in North America, *rubripes* and *diazi/fulvigula,* both of which eventually came into contact with Old World *platyrhynchos*. Hubbard (1977: 5) affirms that both the Northern Mallard and the Mexican Duck "are undeniably closely related forms with a common origin" and may have been in contact for "several thousand years" (p. 45), but despite an "obviously massive gene flow into *diazi* from *platyrhynchos*, [Hubbard remains] convinced that these two forms have had distinct evolutionary histories and should be valued at least for this reason" (John Hubbard, letter to the author, October 1983). A cline of phenotypic variation has been well-documented in these taxa (Hubbard 1977; Scott and Reynolds 1984): zones of Northern Mallard X Mexican Duck hybridization include Hidalgo and Doña Ana counties, New Mexico, and the Río Conchos Valley, Chihuahua, Mexico. However, Scott and Reynolds (1984: 272) found "large genetically uniform populations of...*diazi*...in many areas [and] no evidence that the Northern Mallard genetic influence is actively moving beyond...the Río Conchos Valley."

Sympatry of the American Black Duck and Northern Mallard has occurred largely in this century (Coulter and Mendall 1968), in part because of the clearing of forests for agriculture (Johnsgard 1967b; Palmer 1976, vol. 2). Hybrid pairing occurs in some areas (e.g., Massachusetts: Heusmann and Burrell 1974; Ontario: Brodsky and Weatherhead 1984) and wild adult hybrids are known (e.g., Poole 1929; Johnsgard 1967b), but the zone of hybridization is neither so well-defined, nor the phenotypic variation of the wild population so well-documented as in the Mexican Duck (but see J. Phillips 1921). Sympatry of the Florida and Mottled ducks with the wild Northern Mallard is as yet unknown (Johnsgard 1961a; Palmer 1976, vol. 2), although Weeks (1969 [*in* D. Nelson 1980]), LaHart (1970), and Paulus (1984) observed wild hybrid pairs, and Hubbard (1977) and D. Nelson (1980) described hybrid adults from Colorado and Texas, respectively.

Similarities in pairing chronology and pair bond maintainenance among the three 'old' mallards parallel their close morphological resemblance, and may help to effect reproductive isolation from *A. p. platyrhynchos*—an important factor, considering that both 'old' and 'new' mallards share many of the same wintering areas (Palmer 1976, vol. 2: maps pp. 286, 311, 317, 331). Weller (1965) reported early pair formation in Mottled Ducks, *A. f. maculosa*, in Texas; both Weeks (1969 [*in* LaHart 1970]) and Paulus (1984) cited early pair formation [i.e., in late summer or early autumn, before the arrival of migrant Northern Mallards] as the most important isolating mechanism of Mottled Ducks in Louisiana. So did LaHart (1970) for the Florida Duck, *A. f. fulvigula*. Early pair formation in the American Black Duck (e.g., Trautman 1947; Wright 1954; Stotts and Davis 1960; Hepp and Hair 1983) may help to isolate that species as well. Pair formation also begins early in the Mexican Duck (January; Bevill and Davis 1969), but the initiation of nesting may be delayed until suitable habitat becomes available at the onset of the summer rains (A. Phillips and Dickerman *in* Aldrich and Baer 1970, re: *diazi* in Mexico), whereas Northern Mallards, *A. p. platyrhynchos*, in SW United States usually breed a bit earlier than *diazi* (Hubbard 1977). Defence of space within a summer flock of mixed species (some unpaired) by paired *diazi* males in New Mexico (Nymeyer 1975 [*in* Hubbard 1977]) could imply maintenance of the pair bond during such a waiting period.

An extended pair bond (or repeat pairing with the same partner), in 'old' mallards is suggested by LaHart (1970), who saw paired Florida Ducks throughout the year, and by Wright (1954: 17), who observed that the female American Black Duck is unpaired only during "hatching...rearing her brood, and moulting." Persistence of the pair bond into middle and late incubation and even into brood rearing has been reported for all species of 'old' mallards (e.g., American Black Duck: Stotts and Davis 1960, Reed 1970; Florida Duck: C. J.

Maynard *in* Bent 1923, LaHart 1970; Mottled Duck: Paulus 1984, Stutzenbaker (unpubl.); Mexican Duck: Bevill and Davis (1969). More recently, Scott and Reynolds "have evidence that the Mexican Duck may form permanent pair bonds, e.g., in all cases where two birds by themselves were shot, one was a female and one a male...and males were taken accompanying females with downy young" (Norman Scott, letter to the author, December 1984). In contrast, Northern Mallard drakes customarily desert their hens soon after or as soon as incubation commences (Sowls 1955; Palmer 1976, vol. 2) and, although certain males may stay into the third week of incubation, they seldom attend the female and her brood (Dzubin 1955, 1957).

LaHart (1970: 12) observed that "the apparent lack of separation [of males and females] during the molt may account for the extended duration of the pair bond [in Florida Ducks]." Weeks (1969 [*in* LaHart 1970]) also found mixed flocks of molting Mottled Ducks in Louisiana. The collection by Scott and Reynolds of both male and female *diazi,* "most [of which] were actively molting" (Scott and Reynolds 1984: 268), from each of six locations in Mexico implies a similar situation for the Mexican Duck, another essentially sedentary species. Possible corollaries of a durable pair bond may be the tendency to remain with flocks of their own species (Huber 1923; Paulus 1984; Stutzenbaker [unpubl.]; re: Mexican and Mottled ducks) and to appear "more wary than [Northern] Mallards" (Coulter and Miller 1968: 6, re: American Black Duck; Scott and Reynolds 1984, re: Mexican Duck). According to Wright (1954), however, the sexes of the migratory American Black Duck are segregated both spatially and temporally during molting.

Under normal conditions, a "...distinctly lower threshold of display response [in] male [American] Black Ducks than in [Northern] Mallard drakes" (Johnsgard 1960d: 154) may contribute to early pair formation and pair bond maintenance in *A. rubripes*, but the availability of suitable food (Brodsky and Weatherhead 1985) and harsh (R. Owen 1982) or unusual wintering conditions may alter pairing chronology. Brodsky and Weatherhead (1984: 851) suggested that the American Black Duck's traditional "behavioral, morphological [and ecological]...mechanisms" of isolation are disrupted when "limited open water and artificial feeding combine to bring wintering populations [of American Black Ducks and Northern Mallards] together." In this case, the provision of food throughout the winter by a local resident encouraged large numbers of "ducks [to] congregrate...in open water [on an Ontario river] nearest to the feeding area [where the daily proximity of] excess [northern] mallard drakes to unmated [American] black duck hens...resulted in interspecific pairing (p. 850)." The presence of year-round water impoundments in the southwest may also facilitate hybridization between 'old' and 'new' mallards by encouraging *A. platyrhynchos* to linger on the breeding grounds of the Mexican Duck, *A. diazi*. Hubbard observed that "spring is usually the driest season [in the SW United States and northern]...mallards [finding] breeding habitat limited usually have vacated the area [whereas]...*diazi* simply waited for the July-August rains, when it could breed—in the absence of *platyrhynchos*" (John Hubbard, letter to the author, October 1983). In the same way, increased use of sewage marshes for breeding waterfowl (Piest and Sowls 1985) could present additional opportunities for hybridization between 'old' and 'new' mallards by extending potential zones of sympatry.

The examination of both live ducklings and downy specimens of all North American mallard taxa disclosed several measureable characters of color and pattern that separate 'old' mallards from 'new'. Unless otherwise stated, only live, newly hatched wild ducklings and very young wild-caught specimens are used in the following comparison (*A. diazi* ducklings [BMNH] were collected in Puebla and Jalisco provinces of Mexico, well south of the zones of intergradation described by Hubbard [1977] and Scott and Reynolds [1984] for *platyrhynchos* and *diazi*). The ear-spots of 'old' mallard ducklings are small, inconspicuous, or even lacking (figs. 5-57, 5-70, 5-80, 5-83); the eye-stripe is thin and often incomplete (fig. 5-72: *fulvigula;* fig. 5-85: *diazi*) or heavy and complete (fig. 5-59: *rubripes*), and the dorsal spots are usually small, rather dull, and inconspicuous (*fulvigula, rubripes*, many *diazi*) or (in some *diazi*) large, pale, and conspicuous. The base color of plumage in 'old' mallards is characteristically orange-yellow, usually with little or none of the 'greener' *hue* of most downy *platyrhynchos.* Base and pattern colors of the feet contrast little or not at all; they are generally dark, almost blackish (*fulvigula, rubripes*), light olive-brown (*diazi;* BMNH), or "uniform dark olive [as in a very young *diazi* duckling]...from Durango" (Norman Scott, letter to the author, December 1984).

'New' mallard ducklings, *A. platyrhynchos*, usually have conspicuous ear-spots (figs. 5-94, 5-100; but note small ear-spots of duckling in fig. 5-92); heavier eye-stripes (figs. 5-96, 5-102); and large, obviously yellow dorsal spots. Base color of the plumage is usually some tint of yellow or greenish yellow, even on the dull undertail region, and the foot colors are recognizeably dull orange or dull orange-yellow, usually with good to fair contrast of the darker pattern color (but note that even large color differences can be reduced to sameness, in older ducklings, by the effects of bleaching [sun, alkali] or by the deposition on the feathers of residue from mineral-rich waters [Hubbard 1977]).

One of the more consistent differences between the two groups lies in the *value* of the gray belly down on Class II ducklings. Belly down in 'old' mallard ducklings is dark (Munsell *value* nearly always lower than 5.0/), that in 'new' mallard ducklings light (Munsell *value* nearly always 5.0/ or higher). Some overlap of all characters of pattern and color does occur in mallard ducklings from areas where species from both groups breed or winter. Such overlap is not surprising in taxa known to be virtually identical genetically (e.g., Kessler and Avise 1984; Ankney et al. 1986), except for the [relatively few?] genes affecting plumage color (Numachi et al. 1983).

Aviary *diazi* ducklings (CESJ) from Hidalgo County, New Mexico, when compared to wild-caught *diazi* specimens from Jalisco and Michoacán provinces of Mexico (BMNH), and to live, wild *platyrhynchos* from Alberta, were clearly intermediate in some ways (see Mexican Duck, pp. 86-87). Hubbard (1977: 5) states, regarding the Mexican Duck and the Northern Mallard, that "their common genetic heritage may well produce similar character states at times," and he cautions against regarding ducklings from the hybrid zones as truly representative of *diazi* [or *platyrhynchos*] (John Hubbard, letter to the author, January 1985). Neither are ducklings from areas of Northern Mallard - American Black Duck sympatry necessarily typical of either *rubripes* or *platyrhynchos.*

Hawaiian Duck, *A. wyvilliana.*

Characters of the downy Hawaiian Duck, *A. wyvilliana*, fall part way between the 'old' mallards and the 'new': foot color and general coloration are more like those of 'old' mallards, but the light-colored belly down of Class II ducklings is clearly a 'new' mallard character. The species is probably less 'old' than ducklings of the Mottled Duck group, because the adult male Hawaiian Duck does seem to be in the process of losing the green head, whereas, according to Palmer (1976, vol. 2), adult males of continental 'old' mallards never acquired it. Weller (1980: 23) suggested that the Hawaiian and Laysan ducks [both of which Weller and others then regarded as subspecies of the Northern Mallard] "evolved from two separate waves of pioneers, with the Laysan Teal having been isolated much earlier."

Laysan Duck, *A. laysanensis.*

Subsequent research on Laysan Island by Moulton and Weller (1984: 115) disclosed that the biology of the Laysan Duck differs in several ways "from [that of] the ancestral and other continental forms of Northern Mallards." Nor does the Laysan Duck hybridize with other species (Ripley 1985). These authors concurred with the A.O.U. (1983) in according the Laysan Duck full species status. Characters of the downy plumage and bill structure, unique among North American Anatini ducklings, also support species recognition for the Laysan Duck (Ripley 1960). The base color of the Laysan duckling is distinctly brownish yellow ("ginger-coloured"; Johnstone 1960: 69), unlike that of almost all other North American *Anas* ducklings, which have clearly yellow or orange-yellow base color. The downy Laysan Duck has either a brownish yellow forehead or, in some individuals, a very thin line of dark down between crown and bill (F. Todd 1979: fig. 1.115 [mislabeled Hawaiian Duck]) or a wider band of dark down narrowing continuously from the crown to a point at or near the top of the bill (*Annual Report of the [Severn] Wildfowl Trust 1960-61* 13, 1962: P. Talbot-Ponsonby photo). All of these pattern characters have their counterparts in ducklings of the blue-winged group, but not in ducklings of the mallard group. Unique to downy Laysan Ducks, a patch of dark brownish gray down suffuses the rictus of most individuals, extending toward and often blending with the dark pre-ocular stripe.

In Class II Laysan ducklings, horizontal body posture and heavy pinkish tarsi combine to give the birds a rather sturdy appearance, in spite of their small size. The Laysan duckling's bill, peculiarly flat-tipped and spatulate in the live birds that I examined, has a narrow, triangular nail—quite different from that of mallard-like ducklings (Ripley 1960: figs. 1a, 1b), but much like those of some downy Blue-winged and Cinnamon teal and all downy Green-winged Teal (compare Laysan figs. 5-103 to 5-109 with mallard figs. 5-53 to 5-102 and teal figs. 5-15 to 5-25, 5-110 to 5-129). The duckling's dusky face, dark yellowish brown back, and grayish yellow underparts recall the Northern Shoveler duckling, its often poorly marked face-stripes the downy American Wigeon. Ripley (1959, 1960) found certain bill and plumage characters of immature and adult Laysan Ducks similar to those of Cape Shoveler, *A. smithii*, and Cinnamon Teal, *A. cyanoptera*, ducklings.

The blue-winged ducks: Blue-winged Teal, *A. discors;* Northern Cinnamon Teal, *A. cyanoptera septentrionalium;* Northern Shoveler, *A. clypeata.*

The small downies of the blue-winged ducks form the last group in the Anatini. Ducklings of all three North American species have quite prominent, dark, elongated ear-spots. On the downy Northern Shoveler, these may extend forward to form a smudgy cheek-stripe that sometimes connects loosely to the dark pre-ocular stripe. A dark forehead further distinguishes the quiet, dusky-faced Shoveler from the two small teal ducklings, which nearly always have a line or stripe of pale base color between dark crown and dark bill. The Blue-winged and Northern Cinnamon teal ducklings are so nearly identical that individuals of one species often can scarcely be separated from those of the other; Kessler and Avise (1984) found the two species also very close genetically. Ducklings of the three blue-winged species have a characteristic resting posture, in which the head rests well back on the shoulders, producing a somewhat hunched-over appearance (pl. 7, teal and Shoveler figs.).

BEHAVIOR. Behavior patterns are rather similar among ducklings of various Anatini species; the ducklings have fewer obvious 'mannerisms' than the young of most other tribes. A subtle upward and forward head movement may accompany distress or pre-distress calls in American Wigeon, Northern Mallard, and

Northern Shoveler ducklings, but I did not observe in North American hatchery ducklings the "chin-lifting" noted by Lorenz ([1941] n.d.: 62) in captive palaearctic Gadwall ducklings. These movements seem neither so developed nor so characteristic as, e.g., Head-bobbing in *Bucephala* ducklings or Chin-lifting in downy Cygnini.

Escape behavior may also differ among ducklings of the tribe. Diving to avoid danger has been reported in many young waterfowl, including some wild downy dabblers (e.g., White-cheeked Pintail: Wetmore 1916; Northern Mallard: Nymeyer 1977), but other Anatini ducklings apparently prefer to seek sheltering vegetation (e.g., Florida Duck: Johnson 1968; Mexican Duck: Nymeyer 1977). Even the loss of ducklings within her Class I brood did not cause an American Black Duck hen and her surviving young to dive or to scatter. Rather, they formed a tight group and paddled rapidly toward emergent vegetation at the side of their pond in the Shubenacadie Provincial Wildlife Park, Nova Scotia, after a captive seal had risen smoothly from the water, seized two of the young ducklings, and submerged, with the feet of one of the victims still protruding from his whiskered jaws.

Perching on the backs of parents or foster-parents is apparently rare among the surface-feeding ducks (Johnsgard and Kear 1968), although reported in wild Alaskan Northern Mallards (Williamson and Peyton 1962). Among captive Anatini ducklings, only downy Laysan Ducks (JPWT captives) perched atop their broody hen.

As in other tribes, some interspecific differences in dominance and 'temperament' may be observed among day-old hatchery young. In most cases, ducklings of larger dabblers (e.g., Northern Mallards) dominate those of smaller species in mixed groups, but in other cases, Gadwalls or downy American Wigeons ('middle-sized' species) will prevail. The agile American Wigeons initiate feeding activity and lead other ducklings on 'expeditions' around the pen, sometimes uttering an insistent, monosyllabic chant. If the chant merges into the whistle of distress, the American Wigeon duckling will raise its head, draw it back, and then thrust it forward, repeating the movement with every few notes. I observed one such noisy malcontent pause on its trek to begin displacement preening: its shrill piping continued, only slightly muffled by the down feathers.

Tiny, newly hatched Blue-winged and Northern Cinnamon teals, skittering about on small, slender feet, chatter constantly. In the water, Northern Cinnamon ducklings dip and preen quickly and repeatedly and, if startled, scoot rapidly across the water's surface. Considering their size—rather like overgrown bumblebees—teals are remarkably aggressive: even day-old young of both species pursue ducklings of their own and other, larger species to 'nip' at bills, heels, and plumage. One group of four Northern Cinnamon Teal ducklings (6 d.) seemed particularly sensitive to outside intrusions: they drew themselves up, thrust their bills forward, and 'hissed' at me as I walked by.

Notes and recordings of the calls of various newly hatched Anatini (10 spp.; by the author, 1966-1980) disclosed only small variations within the group. In general, the soft calls (e.g., conversation calls or pleasure calls) consist of three or four syllables of the same or slightly ascending pitch, lightly accented on the first syllable. Anatini ducklings repeat the soft calls in bouts of three or more, often with scarcely a pause between each. Vocalizations of smaller species are higher pitched than those of larger ones (Kear 1968), more polysyllabic, and more rapidly and frequently reiterated. The high-pitched calls of Northern Cinnamon ducklings have a shrill, squealy quality—lacking in the vocalizations of downy Northern Shovelers and other teal species—that distinguishes them at once from those of other North American Anatini ducklings. The soft calls of American Wigeon, Gadwall and Laysan ducklings also differ from those of most other Anatini in having a rather flat, 'pebbly' timbre.

As in other anatid tribes, vocalizations produced while feeding are recognizeably derived from the conversation calls, but the pitch is a bit lower and the syllables fewer—two or three in most downy Anatini (e.g., the Gadwall's soft "Chid-ip!"), but often monosyllabic in American Wigeon and polysyllabic in teal. The rhythmic structure of the conversation call remains, lending to the feeding calls a certain quiet, 'inexorable' quality that suggests the total concentration of the ducklings upon the matter at hand.

The whistle of distress is much the same in all Anatini. Consisting of a series of six or more well-spaced prefatory notes, it rises in pitch and volume to a level characteristic for the species and is followed by a steady, firmly accented piping (often 2-syllabled in the Northern Cinnamon Teal) of indefinite duration. The call may lose intensity toward the end of the bout, or change to another kind of call if the distress is alleviated (Kear 1968; Kostow 1981).

The short calls (pre-distress) leading up to the whistle of distress also appear to vary interspecifically in pitch, amplitude, and syllabification. For example, Lorenz ([1941] n.d.: 47) described a rapid, low-pitched "tit-tit-tit," that immediately precedes the downy Northern Shoveler's higher-pitched, drawn-out whistle of distress: "teet-teet-teet!" A series of soft, arhythmic, almost syncopated calls recorded from a Laysan duckling may also have signified pre-distress, although the calls were not followed by the characteristic whistle. In contrast, the prefatory distress calls heard from American Wigeons were monosyllabic and steady, rather than rapid, and only a bit lower in pitch and amplitude than the whistle of distress that followed them; the pre-distress notes of other Anatini ducklings had two syllables, accented on the second. The range and source of variation in the pre-distress calls of young anatids is unknown for any tribe.

American Wigeon

Canard siffleur d'Amérique. Pato Chalcuán.
Mareca americana Gmelin

APPEARANCE. The presence of a partial or complete light eye-ring and a secondary base color (yellowish brown) on the head and yoke, together with the absence of an ear-spot and well-marked facial striping—if present, these may be thin or indistinct or both—distinguish the downy American Wigeon from all other Anatini in North America. At a distance, the short, slightly tapered bill and rather trapezoidal head shape in profile also identify the ducklings. In the hand, many buffy down-tips give the back a somewhat mottled look (see Gadwall, pp. 77-78).

VARIATION. A few American Wigeon ducklings have discernible facial striping (e.g., yellow-faced variant on pl. 6; Ridgway 1887), but none that I examined had an eye-stripe as prominent as that portrayed by Hines (*in* Bellrose 1980: pl. 23) and Ridgway (1895: 143-44; "...a distinct blackish olive stripe"). Some very dark-faced specimens lack the eye-ring entirely. The faces of these ducklings are

essentially monochromatic, as in some European Wigeons, *Mareca penelope* (Lorenz [1941] n.d.).

Both primary and seconday base colors may vary. The yellowish brown secondary base color on the duckling's face can appear either brown or rather strongly yellow (see both variants on pl. 6); it does not replace the light yellow primary base color, but seems, rather, superimposed upon it, thereby intensifying the dark color of the crown. The secondary base color lends a buffy tone to the breast and to the pale dorsal down-tips, shoulder-spots, and wing-patches—these last are often quite brownish. Contrast between the pattern color and the two base colors is usually good. Few ducklings have as little contrast of base and pattern colors as does Burton's yellowish-brown American Wigeon duckling (*in* Harrison 1978: pl. 4). The light yellow primary base color usually is much paler and duller on the posterior half of the body than it is on the face and breast. In a few individuals, it is reduced to cream-color or ivory-yellow on the anterior parts of the body, and to near-white on the rump-spots and belly.

Foot color varies from distinctly olive-green (yellower variants) through olive-gray or "olive slate" (dark-faced birds coll. J. A. Munro; ROM, tag data) to grayish brown in other brown-faced birds. Some *M. penelope* ducklings are also dark-footed (e.g., Heinroth and Heinroth 1928, vol. 3: pl. 108; Delacour 1956: Scott pl. 17; Harrison 1975: Burton pl. 4).

DISCUSSION. Plumage color variations of the American and European wigeon ducklings are similar. J. Phillips (1923), Witherby et al. ([1939] 1943, vol. 3), Delacour (1956), Bauer and Glutz von Blotzheim (1968), Harrison (1975), Cramp and Simmons (1977), and Fjeldså (1977) all depict the brown-faced variant; Schiøler (1925: Larsen pl. 54) and Dement'ev and Gladkov ([1952] 1967, vol. 4) describe the yellower ones. J. Phillips (1923: 190), comparing a brown-faced *M. penelope* duckling with a yellower American Wigeon specimen, doubted that the color differences he observed "...would hold in every case for the down color of young ducks is rather variable." He, A. C. Meinertzhagen (*in* Witherby et al. [1939] 1943, vol. 3), and Johnsgard (1965) concluded that European and American wigeon ducklings are morphologically indistinguishable.

J. Phillips (1923) perceived the head and bill of the young European Wigeon as being smaller than those of the young Northern Mallard, whereas Palmer (1976, vol. 2) reported that downy *americana* and *penelope* appeared to be larger-headed than other Anatini ducklings. In a comparison of live, day-old *M. americana* ducklings, (*M. penelope* specimens not available) with day-old young of five species of North American *Anas,* I found the American Wigeon's mean total head length (OBT=back of head to tip of bill) shorter than that of Gadwall, Northern Mallard, and Northern Shoveler ducklings, but longer than that of downy Blue-winged and Northern Cinnamon teals (C. Nelson, unpubl. data). However, both mean culmen length (EC) and mean ratio of culmen length to total head length (EC/OBT) measured smaller in the American Wigeon than in the other five species; compare EC/OBT ratios for *M. americana, A. strepera, A. p. platyrhynchos, A. d. discors, A. cyanoptera septentrionalium*, and *A. clypeata* in Table 1, Appendix A. These data support Phillips's conclusion with respect to 'middle-sized' ducklings, but the short, goose-like bill of the American Wigeon duckling causes the head itself to appear relatively larger, as Palmer observed it to be.

Ducklings of Lesser (and some Greater) Scaup are often misidentified as American Wigeons: the poorly marked face pattern and the 'brown-faced' aspect can be misleading. However, the short, slightly tapered bill; the small, unlobed hallux; and the longer tarsus (TMT) relative to middle toe length (III) readily distinguish American Wigeon ducklings from downy scaup of either species (compare 3 spp. on pls. 6 & 8, in figs. 5-1 to 5-7, 6-25 to 6-42, & in TMT/III ratios in Table 1, Appendix A).

SOURCE OF SPECIMENS. **Alberta:** Caribou Mountains (NMC-1). Driedmeat Lake (ROM-1). Grande Prairie region: Saskatoon Lake (MMMN-5). Red Deer: Camp 4 1/2 (NMC-3), near Nevis Township 38 to 34 (NMC-1). Sinclair Lake (MMMN-1). **British Columbia:** *Cariboo District:* Cummings Lake (PSM-1); Goldpan Lake [=Donnelly Lake] (NMC-1); Williams Lake (OSUFW-1): 149 Mile Road [=Mile 149 -

Plate 6

1 American Wigeon, Mareca americana
Yellow-faced variant. N Old Wives Lake, Saskatchewan (DWWRS).
Brown-faced variant. Delta, Manitoba (DWWRS)

Green-winged Teal, Anas crecca

2 A. c. nimia. Amchitka Island, Alaska (USNM [5-6 d.]: color and pattern) and Delta, Manitoba (DWWRS [A. c. carolinensis]: measurements).

3 A.c. carolinensis. Delta, Manitoba (DWWRS).

4 Northern Pintail, A. acuta
Darker and lighter variants. Delta, Manitoba (DWWRS).

5 White-cheeked Pintail, A. b. bahamensis
Guanica, Puérto Rico (USNM [2-3 d.]).

6 American Black Duck, A. rubripes
Darker variant. JPWT captives.
Lighter variant. Ile aux Pommes, Québec (DWWRS).

Mottled Duck, A. fulvigula

7 Florida Duck, A.f. fulvigula. Merritt Island National Wildlife Refuge, Florida (DWWRS captives).

8 Mottled Duck, A. f. maculosa. Rockefeller National Wildlife Refuge, Louisiana (UFS[DM]), (pursuing mosquito, probably Psorophora spp. or Culiseta spp. [Carpenter and LaCasse 1955]).

9 Mexican Duck, A. diazi
Hidalgo County, New Mexico (CESJ captives [ca. 3 d.]: color and measurements) and Lago de Chapala, Mexico (BMNH [2-3 d.]: pattern).

10 Hawaiian Duck, A. wyvilliana
Kailua, Oahu, Hawaiian Islands (USNM [2-3 d.]).

Mallard, A. platyrhynchos

11 Greenland Mallard, A. p. conboschas. Nanortalik, Greenland (ZMK [2-3 d.]).

12 Northern Mallard, A. p. platyrhynchos. Paler yellow variant. The Pas, Manitoba (DWWRS).
Darker yellow variant. Strathmore, Alberta (UFS[DM]).

Plate 6

Onward—old road now a trail] (NMC-1; RBCM-1). *Lillooet District:* Springhouse: Rush Lake [=shallow slough S Boitano Lake (J. Munro 1945: 99)] PSM-1; ROM-1). *Peace River District:* Tupper Creek (RBCM-3). *Range 4, Coast District:* Nulki Lake: Bradley Slough [unofficial name] (PSM-1). **Manitoba:** Clear Lake (NMC-1). Delta (DWWRS-24 live: figs. 5-1 to 5-3 [*ss:* D-1; UMFBP(DFP)-1]; D-3; ROM-1). Portage la Prairie (DWWRS-2 live). **Northwest Territories:** *District of Keewatin:* James Bay: S end Moar Bay (NMC-6). *District of Mackenzie:* near mouth of Tazin River (NMC-2). **Ontario:** *Kenora District:* Fort Severn (ROM-1); Sutton River near Harvest Lake (ROM-1). *Thunder Bay District:* Geraldton (ROM-1). *York County:* Toronto: Ashbridges Bay (ROM-1: figs. 5-4, 5-5). **Saskatchewan:** Davidson (CM-1), 19.3 km NW Davidson (CM-1: figs. 5-6, 5-7). Dollard: Whitemud Creek (ROM-1). East Trout Lake (ROM-1). Kindersley (PMBRC-5). SW Moose Jaw: 16 km N Old Wives Lake (DWWRS-1 live). South Arm Last Mountain Lake (NMC-2). **Yukon Territory:** Pelly River Valley: Canol Road: Mile 139 (NMC-1). **Minnesota:** *Beltrami County:* Blackduck: Blackduck Lake (BMNH-4). *Nobles County:* (RLWS-2 live captives). **North Dakota:** *Nelson County:* Stump Lake (FMNH-1; ROM-1). **Captive origin** (WT[S]-10 live).

OTHER REFERENCES. Bailey and Niedrach 1965, vol. 1. Bent 1923 (quotes Ridgway 1887). Gollop and Marshall 1954. Grinnell, Bryant, and Storer 1918. Kortright 1942. Roberts 1932, vol. 2. Southwick 1953. Wishart 1983.

Gadwall

Canard chipeau. Pato Friso.
Anas strepera Linnaeus

APPEARANCE. Pale ('creamy') yellow base color, mottled back color, the combination of smaller shoulder-spots and larger rump-spots (often continuous with pale undertail area), and a narrow, high-bridged, 'colorful' bill define the downy Gadwall. The 'bluish' gray or 'bluish' olive-gray upper mandible and pinkish yellow lower mandible, tomia, and sides of bill also characterize juvenal Gadwalls. A wide supraorbital stripe contrasting with the narrow blackish crown gives the duckling a distinctive 'round-faced' aspect.

VARIATION. The pale brilliance of the downy Gadwalls' yellow base color is similar to that of some American Wigeon ducklings. Brightest on head and breast, it varies individually and fades rapidly (Oring 1968). Although Dresser (1871-81, vol. 6) and Heinroth and Heinroth (1928, vol. 3: pl. 108) portrayed distinctly yellow palaearctic Gadwall ducklings, more generally distributed yellow color appears to be less common (Fjeldså 1977). Face and dorsal patterns also vary. The eye-stripe, frequently incomplete behind the eye, is sometimes thin and blackish, at other times wide and grayish. On many ducklings, the pre-orbital stripe blends with a brownish gray 'shadow' extending from the lores across the cheeks, evidently similar to the dark rictal patch described by Dement'ev and Gladkov ([1952] 1967, vol. 4) on palaearctic ducklings. Some North American ducklings have the pale cheeks noted by A. C. Meinertzhagen (*in* Witherby et al. [1939] 1943, vol. 3) and Delacour (1956) on other palaearctic specimens (see pl. 7; also *Wildfowl* 23, 1972: E. E. Jackson photo, pl. 97). As in ducklings of the blue-winged group, a poorly marked light crescent below the eye is somewhat better defined in birds with grayer cheeks. In many ducklings, the thin, grayish, usually elongated ear-spot consists of only two or three pale plumes (see 2 variants on pl. 7, also Fjeldså 1977: fig. 10); it does not join with the grayish cheek wash to form a continuous stripe as in, e.g., Green-winged Teal or Northern Pintail ducklings.

The large, oval or round rump-spots frequently are joined to the light undertail color or are separated from it by just a narrow line of darker pattern color. The somewhat smaller shoulder-spots are usually elongated or broken into a number of smaller spots leading toward the larger rump-spots. Light yellowish brown often tinges the wing-patches.

The pattern color of North American Gadwalls lacks any hint of the 'greenish' olive *hue* found on some European (Percy *in* J. Phillips 1923) and North American Northern Mallard ducklings. The almost blackish crown color is set off on forehead and nape by a sprinkling of creamy down-tips. The mottled effect of the pale down-tips, most pronounced on the yoke and back of the young duckling, becomes more prominent as pale down-plumes fade in older ducklings. The dorsal appearance of downy American Wigeon and Gadwall ducklings is similar except that the Gadwall has larger, usually paler, markings and more conspicuous mottling (compare 2 spp. on pls. 6 & 7).

Newly hatched nearctic Gadwalls have light dull orange and grayish brown tarsi and toes, much like those of some palaearctic ducklings described by Cramp and Simmons (1977) and Fjeldså (1977). None had the greenish or blackish tarsal *hue* noted in other European Gadwall ducklings by Bauer and Glutz von Blotzheim (1968) and Harrison (1975).

SOURCE OF SPECIMENS. **British Columbia:** *Cariboo District:* 149 Mile Road [see *M. americana,* p. 77] (NMC-2). **Manitoba:** Cook's Creek 4.8 km SE Delta (D-2). Delta (62 live: figs. 5-46 to 5-48 [*ss:* D-1; MMMN-1: figs. 5-49, 5-50]; D-6). Minnedosa (DWWRS-1 live). Near Wood Bay (MMMN-1). **Saskatchewan:** Forks of Duncairn Reservoir—17.7 km SSE Webb (MMMN-1: figs. 5-51, 5-52). Kindersley (PMBRC-3). **Idaho:** *Jefferson County:* 3.0 km SW Hamer (UMFBP[DFP]-1). **Minnesota:** *Nobles County:* (RLWS-3 live captives; PSM-1). **Montana:** *Phillips County:* Malta: Lake Bowdoin (USNM-2). **Nebraska:** *Cherry County:* Valentine National Wildlife Refuge (UFS[DM]-14 live). **Oregon:** *Lake County:* Paisley: Chewaucan Marsh (OSUFW-1); Summer Lake (OSUFW-1). **Captive origin** (WT[S]-5 live).

OTHER REFERENCES. Bailey and Niedrach 1965, vol. 1. Bellrose 1976, 1980. Bent 1923. Cogswell 1977. Gollop and Marshall 1954. Grinnell, Bryant, and Storer 1918. Johnsgard 1965. Kortright 1942. Kuroda 1939. Palmer 1976, vol. 2. Ridgway 1895 (quotes Dresser 1871-81, vol. 6). Roberts 1932, vol. 2.

Green-winged Teal

Sarcelle à ailes vertes. Cerceta Alioscura.
Anas crecca Linnaeus

APPEARANCE. The tiny Green-winged Teal duckling has very dark olive-brown pattern color and a variable but usually well-marked cheek-stripe, of which the large ear-spot is the most heavily pigmented part. In the hand, the narrow nail, dark forehead, and gray feet distinguish it from the almost equally small Blue-winged and Northern Cinnamon teal ducklings. In the field, the duckling's near-blackish pattern color, dusky face, rather square head, and characteristically small or linear dorsal spots readily identify it. A light lower eye-ring and a pale lore contrast well, even at some distance, with the dusky, often blackish, cheeks.

VARIATION. At a time when palaearctic *A. crecca* and nearctic *A. carolinensis* were considered separate species, J. Phillips (1923) found no difference between ducklings of the two. Now considered conspecific, together with Aleutian *nimia* Friedmann, ducklings of *crecca* Linnaeus and *carolinensis* Gmelin have a similar range of variation in *value* and extent of pattern color. All three subspecies had very dark, almost blackish individuals (e.g., *crecca:* Heinroth and Heinroth 1928, vol. 3: pl. 108 & Iceland: Hvítavatn [BM(NH)]; *carolinensis:* Ontario: Swan River [NMC]; *nimia:* Alaska: Aleutian Islands [USNM]), but other individuals were lighter over all, with less prominent face-stripes and larger dorsal spots (e.g., Iceland: Mývatn *crecca* [Sutton 1961: 94: half-tone pl.];

most Delta *carolinensis,* incl. fig. on pl. 6 & C. Nelson col. pl. *in* Palmer 1976, vol. 2: 370). The range of variation in *nimia* ducklings is unknown, but the Aleutian specimens were as dark as the darkest *crecca* specimens and darker than any *carolinensis* seen.

The cheek-stripe varies in width and closeness to the eye-stripe. Frequent connections of dark plumes between the two stripes, especially just behind and in front of the eye, leave clear not only the semi-circular area immediately below the eye, but also the lore, which remains quite brightly yellow. The cheek-stripe almost never assumes the straight, linear form shown by Scott (*in* Delacour 1956: pl. 11) and Burton (*in* Harrison 1975, 1978: both pls. 4), nor is the 'white' lore depicted by Hines (*in* Bellrose 1980: pl. 23) typical of young ducklings.

Most dorsal spots are rather small (see dark *nimia* fig. on pl. 6), but others are large or linear. The latter consist either of a series of tiny spots arranged in linear fashion, leading toward very small rump-spots or of long, single, shoulder-spots leading back toward (often) equally linear rump-spots (e.g., Manitoba: SW Thompson [MMMN, Class II duckling]; Ontario: James Bay [CM]).

Colors of bill and feet vary little. The dark, blackish, or blackish gray color ascribed to the 'legs' and feet of teal ducklings by Harrison (1975, 1978), Palmer (1976, vol. 2), and Fjeldså (1977) characterizes museum specimens of all three subspecies, but evidently also represents the dark extreme described by Bauer and Glutz von Blotzheim (1968) in some newly hatched live *crecca.* The feet of live *carolinensis* ducklings were similar to "greenish grey" feet of *crecca* ducklings collected in Iceland by R. Meinertzhagen (BM[NH]; tag data).

DISCUSSION. Variation in the face patterns of *crecca* (see Fjeldså 1977: fig. 10) and palaearctic Northern Mallard ducklings sometimes makes identification of the two species difficult, e.g., A. C. Meinertzhagen (*in* Witherby et al. [1939] 1943, vol. 3: 249) considered it "impossible" to distinguish between Northern Mallard and *crecca* ducklings (see their pls. 83 and 84), whereas Delacour (1956) described cheek-stripes on ducklings of both species. *Carolinensis* and North American Northern Mallard ducklings are seldom confused: *carolinensis* ducklings usually have prominent cheek-stripes with large ear-spots; wild, downy North American Northern Mallards do not. The actual and relative size difference between the two species is also considerable, as are differences in foot color and nail characters.

Portenko ([1972] 1981: 153) found adult *nimia* "much larger" than *crecca.* Presumably, the size difference would also be discernible in the downy young, but I have not confirmed this because I have seen no live, newly-hatched *nimia* ducklings.

SOURCE OF SPECIMENS. **Alberta:** *Slave River:* 30th Base Line (CM-2: fig. 5-18). Tilley (UBC-1). **British Columbia:** *Cariboo District:* 150 Mile House (NMC-1); 149 Mile Road [see *M. americana,* p. 000] (NMC-1). **Manitoba:** Delta (DWWRS-31 live: figs. 5-15 to 5-17 [*ss:* D-2; MMMN-6: fig. 5-19; OSUFW-1; UMFBP(DFP)-1]; UBC-1). Minnedosa (DWWRS-1 live). 20.8 km S, 11.2 km W Thompson (MMMN-1). **Northwest Territories:** *District of Keewatin:* South Twin Island (CM-6: figs. 5-20, 5-21); Rupert Bay: Cabbage Willows Bay (NMC-1). **Ontario:** *Kenora District:* Swan River [=Raft River] (NMC-10). **Québec:** *Lake Saint John West County:* Lac Baillairgé (NMC-2). *Territory of New Quebec:* James Bay: freshwater pond near S end of Moar Bay (NMC-1). **Saskatchewan:** Davidson (CM-1). Kindersley (PMBRC-8). **Yukon Territory:** Rose River: Canol Road: Mile 95 (NMC-1). **Alaska:** Aleutian Islands: Delarof Islands: Ogliuga Island (USNM-1: figs. 5-24, 5-25); Rat Islands: Amchitka Island: Constantine Harbor (USNM-1: figs. 5-22, 5-23). **Minnesota:** *Nobles County* (RLWS-3 live captives). ICELAND: **Arnessýsla:** Hvítavatn (BM[NH]-2). **Captive origin** (FMNH-1).

OTHER REFERENCES. Bailey and Niedrach 1965, vol. 1. Baird, Brewer, and Ridgway 1884, vol. 2 (quoted in Ridgway 1895). Bent 1923. Cogswell 1977. Cramp and Simmons 1977. Dement'ev and Gladkov [1952] 1967, vol. 4. Grinnell, Bryant, and Storer 1918. Johnsgard 1965. Kortright 1942. J. Munro 1937. Roberts 1932, vol. 2.

Northern Pintail
Canard pilet. Pato Golondrino.
Anas acuta Linnaeus

APPEARANCE. White base color faintly tinged with pale yellowish pink, an inconspicuous breast-band, and brownish gray pattern color characterize the Northern Pintail duckling. The pattern color appears more reddish (5YR) than the yellower browns of other downy *Anas* (e.g., 2.5Y, 5Y, 7.5Y). Also characteristic are the blotchy cheek-stripe, linear dorsal spots, and 'bluish' gray or olive-gray bill and foot color; a few ducklings have distinctly olive feet. The upper mandibles of ducklings about two weeks old are quite 'bluish'.

VARIATION. The face pattern and, occasionally, the dorsal spots of the Northern Pintail duckling vary in color and pattern. There are also subtle *hue* differences in the essentially gray feet and bill, i.e., some are 'bluer', a few 'greener'. The faces of most Northern Pintail ducklings are heavily marked with an irregular dark cheek-stripe more or less connected to the dark pre-ocular stripe and ear-spot. In very dark birds, the pre-ocular stripe merges with the dark forehead color as well, giving the area in front of the eye quite a brown appearance (see darker variant on pl. 6). The white "eyebrow" noted by Delacour (1956: 130) remains prominent (sometimes also a light area below the eye), but other light-colored areas of the face are more or less strongly tinged with pale yellowish pink. In downy palaearctic Northern Pintails described by Dement'ev and Gladkov ([1952] 1967, vol. 4), the cheek-stripe is reduced to a small ear-spot (compare light- and dark-faced ducklings on pl. 6 with palaearctic variants shown by Fjeldså [1977: fig. 10]).

Dorsal spots are characteristically narrow and elongated; only J. Phillips (1923) described Northern Mallard-like spots. The shoulder-spots frequently are separated into two or more smaller spots, forming a line to the unbroken, usually larger rump-spots. These are most often elongated but are sometimes also irregularly round or oval. The linear aspect of the dorsal spots—more pronounced in older ducklings—shows up well in the field.

The characteristic subtle contrasts of the downy Northern Pintail's colors have been depicted by Larsen (*in* Schiøler 1925: pl. 23), Heinroth and Heinroth (1928, vol. 3: pl. 108), Kortright (1942: Shortt pl. 33), and Witherby et al. ([1939] 1943, vol. 3: pl. 86). Less common, more contrastingly patterned variants appear in Delacour (1957: Scott pl. 17), Harrison (1975, 1978: both Burton pl. 4), and Bellrose (1980: Hines pl. 23). Bent's (1923) description of a downy Northern Pintail does not match the duckling photographed on plate 30, which has a strongly contrasting pattern much like that of a Blue-winged Teal.

SOURCE OF SPECIMENS. **British Columbia:** *Cariboo District:* Sorenson Lake [=local name for more northerly of the two Westwick Lakes (J. Munro 1945: 99)] (NMC-1). *Lillooet District:* Dog Creek (NMC-1). **Manitoba:** Churchill (NMC-5). Delta (DWWRS-65 live: figs. 5-8 to 5-10 [*ss:* D-1; MMMN-1: figs. 5-11, 5-12]; D-10: figs. 5-13, 5-14). Farnworth Lake [=Landing Lake] (BMNH-2). Oakland (DWWRS-3 live). **Ontario:** *Kenora District:* Hudson Bay: Cape Henrietta Maria (NMC-4); (James Bay): Swan River [=Raft River] (NMC-7). **Québec:** *Territory of New Quebec:* 14.5 km E Schefferville (NMC-1). **California:** *Siskiyou County:* Tule Lake (SDNHM-1). **Minnesota:** *Mahnomen County* (BMNH-1). *Nobles County:* Round Lake (RLWS-14 live captives). *Roseau County:* Ross: Roseau River (BMNH-1). **Oregon:** *Baker County:* 6.4 km W Baker (OSUFW-1). *Lake County:* Paisley: Chewaucan Marsh (OSUFW-1). **Utah:** *Box Elder County:* Bear River Marsh [probably=collective name for complex of marshes along Bear River] (OSUFW-1). ENGLAND: *Norfolk:* Keswick (BM[NH]-1). *Sussex:* Horsham (BM[NH]-1).

OTHER REFERENCES. Bailey and Niedrach 1965, vol. 1. Baird, Brewer, and Ridgway 1884, vol. 2 (quoted in Ridgway 1895). Bauer and Glutz von Blotzheim 1968. Cramp and Simmons 1977. Dresser 1871-81, vol. 6. Gollop and Marshall 1954. Grinnell, Bryant, and Storer 1918. Johnsgard 1965. Roberts 1932, vol. 2. Snyder 1957. Southwick 1953.

White-cheeked Pintail

Canard des Bahamas. Pato Quijada Colorado, Pato de la Orilla (Bond 1971)

Anas bahamensis Linnaeus

APPEARANCE. A combination of characters distinguishes the downy White-cheeked Pintail: a wide post-ocular stripe contrasting with a miniscule pre-ocular stripe (a spot, really); a marked difference in *chroma* of the base color on the anterior and posterior parts of the body (J. Phillips 1923); and the variable—but often strikingly linear—dorsal spots. The downward dip of dark crown color over the eye of the downy *bahamensis* shown in Delacour (1956: Scott pl. 17) may or may not be distinctive for the species: it appeared in both Puerto Rican ducklings, but was poorly marked or absent on all other specimens. Ducklings of all subspecies of White-cheeked Pintail are only a bit larger than those of the Blue-winged Teal; see comparative measurements of adults in Delacour (1956).

VARIATION. Except for the often similar linear arrangement of the paired dorsal spots, the White-cheeked and Northern pintail ducklings have little in common: size, color, and face pattern differ widely (Moffitt 1932). The blurred, brownish eye- and cheek-stripes of the downy Northern Pintail are especially heavy in front of the eye; they do not resemble at all the single eye-stripe of the White-cheeked duckling (compare ducklings of both spp. on pl. 6 & in figs. 5-11 to 5-14, 5-38, 5-39; see also F. Todd 1979: fig. 1.139). Even the dorsal spots are not precisely comparable: those of downy *A. acuta* typically appear as a 'procession' of linear spots (e.g., pl. 6; also Palmer 1976, vol. 2: 370, C. Nelson col. pl.), but dorsal spots of *bahamensis* ducklings, although often resembling those of downy *A. acuta,* are just as often less linear, i.e., more Northern Mallard-like. Sometimes, the broken, linear shoulder-spots contrast sharply with large unbroken rump-spots. Other times, the dorsal spots form a more or less continuous line or band from shoulder to rump to pale undertail area (pl. 6). To my knowledge, the last condition has never been described in Northern Pintail ducklings.

Where the base color of the Northern Pintail duckling is white, that of the White-cheeked Pintail is yellow (Delacour 1956; Palmer 1976, vol. 2). Moreover, the yellow color exhibits individual and age-related variations: a captive Slimbridge specimen (WT[S]) and a wild Puerto Rican duckling (USNM) were quite brightly yellow, an aviary specimen (BM[NH]) and a second Puerto Rican specimen much paler. The color of the very young live birds was like that of the two Puerto Rican specimens. Three partly feathered young from Curaçao (CM) had lost all trace of their presumed yellow natal color, but a Watling Island specimen of similar age (CM) had a wash of exceedingly pale, but still brilliant, yellow on the lores.

Regrettably, because I did not examine the six live White-cheeked ducklings in the hand, I can make only a limited estimate of variation in the colors of the unfeathered parts. However, of the two Puerto Rican specimens, the buffier specimen had rather dull yellow feet, whereas the yellower duckling had much brighter ones (pl. 6).

SOURCE OF SPECIMENS. BAHAMAS: San Salvador Island [=Watling Island] (CM-1). PUERTO RICO: Municipio de Guánica: Laguna de Guánica (USNM-2: figs. 5-38, 5-39). NETHERLANDS ANTILLES: **Curaçao:** Patrick

(CM-3). **Captive origin** (JPWT-6 live; BM[NH]-1; WT[S]-2: fig. 5-37).
OTHER REFERENCES. Bent 1923. Johnsgard 1965. Raffaele 1975. Sorensen 1992.

Mottled Duck
Canard brun. Pato Tejano.
Anas fulvigula Ridgway

APPEARANCE. The downy Mottled Duck gives the impression of an olive-brown and dusky yellow Northern Mallard duckling. However, several characters will usually separate it from the downy Northern Mallard: dark, virtually unpatterned feet; a tiny or inconspicuous ear-spot (often lacking; compare relative size of ear-spots in figs. 5-70, 5-72, 5-94, 5-116, 5-125); a darker, more orange-yellow face; a thinner, browner, eye-stripe (often incomplete); a narrower dark forehead (sometimes appears yellow or even white); a larger, more 'pinkish' area of light color at the base of the bill above the tomia; and (often) very small dorsal spots. Class II Mottled ducklings have medium dark belly-down (Munsell *value* 4.0/); Class II Northern Mallard ducklings have medium to light belly-down (Munsell *value* 4.5/ to 6.5/).

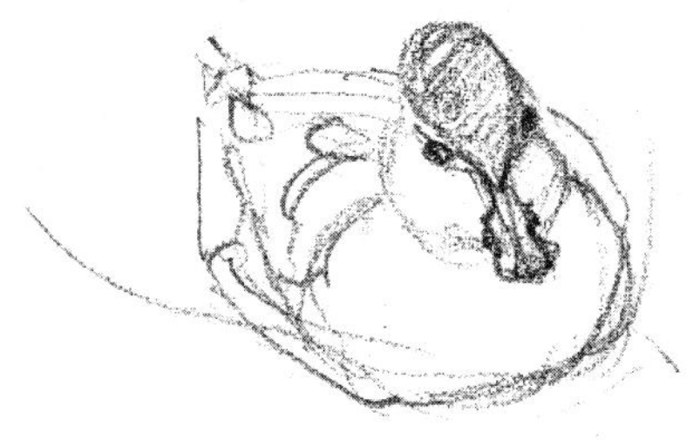

VARIATION. Elements of the face pattern vary in Mottled ducklings; so may *hue* of the base color, forehead color, size of dorsal spots, and (sometimes) foot color. The grayish brown eye-stripe is usually thin and complete (e.g., Florida [*fulvigula*] fig., pl. 6; Delacour 1956; Palmer 1976, vol. 2), but a few Mottled ducklings—e.g., 4 live birds from Louisiana, 2 from Florida—have wide, straight eye-stripes tapering to a point behind the eye (e.g., pl. 6, *maculosa* fig. [pursuing mosquito]; F. Todd 1979: fig. 1.141; Hines [*in* Bellrose 1980: pl. 23]). Baird, Brewer, and Ridgway (1884, vol. 1; quoted in Ridgway 1895), Bent (1923), and J. Phillips (1923) described thin, incomplete eye-stripes, as in some Texas and Florida specimens (figs. 5-69 to 5-77).

The inconspicuous ear-spot, depicted by Delacour (1956), Bellrose (1980: Hines pl. 23), and Stutzenbaker (unpubl.) as a distinguishing character, is nearly always much smaller than that of the Northern Mallard (but see Alberta Northern Mallard duckling, fig. 5-92). When present, it has a distinctive round shape, but often, it is absent (compare Mottled ducklings on pl. 6 & in fig. 5-70 with F. Todd 1979: fig. 1.141).

The dusky rictal 'mustache', depicted by Shortt (*in* Kortright 1942: pl. 33) and Hines (*in* Bellrose 1980: pl. 23), was absent in all downy Mottled Ducks examined, but appeared on some apparently wild *A. p. platyrhynchos* individuals from several areas and on all *A. p. conboschas* specimens (compare *platyrhynchos* ducklings in Delacour [1956: Scott pl. 5] and Fjeldså [1977: fig. 10] with *conboschas* and Mottled figs. on pl. 6 and figs. 5-69 to 5-72, 5-76, 5-77, 5-99 to 5-102). Note that while certain characters of the Mottled and Mexican ducklings are similar (e.g., small ear-spot, dark belly-down in Class II ducklings), other characters are usually distinct (e.g., eye-stripe characters, *chroma* of dorsum, [sometimes] *value* of foot color and size of dorsal spots). The label, "Mottled and Mexican Ducks," which appears on Hines's composite drawing of the two species (*in* Bellrose 1980: pl. 23) is therefore misleading.

The base color of Mottled ducklings ranges from ochraceous or dark yellow on the face and breast (e.g., 1.5Y 6/8, 2.5Y 6.5/8) to a much paler, duller yellow on the belly and undertail (e.g., 2.5Y 7.5/5, 4Y 8/4). Although the base color character has many individual variations, with some overlap between this species and the Northern Mallard (e.g., Alberta Northern Mallard and Louisiana Mottled ducklings on pl. 6), the comparison of a series of well-prepared specimens of each species shows the yellows of the Mottled duckling to be characteristically more 'orange', those of the Northern Mallard more 'greenish' (i.e., toward Munsell 5Y; compare Mottled and Northern Mallard figs. on pl. 6 and color descriptions in Appendix B).

The forehead color also varies: some ducklings have very pale foreheads, others are clearly olive-brown (but often extremely narrow), and most have light 'golden' down-tips which may effectively conceal the dark bases of the forehead down. Lynch found the yellow forehead common in Louisiana ducklings (John Lynch, letter to the author, April 1970), whereas J.Phillips (1923: 61) described a "white" forehead and superciliary stripe from what was evidently an unusually pale (or faded?) specimen.

The pale forehead of the Mottled duckling should not be confused with that of the downy Blue-winged Teal. The much smaller relative size, larger ear-spot, yellower (i.e., less orange) *hue*, light gray belly-down (Class II ducklings), and lighter, more contrastingly patterned, dull orange-yellow feet will distinguish Blue-winged from Mottled ducklings in the parts of Louisiana and Texas where, according to Palmer (1976, vol. 2) and Bellrose (1980), the breeding ranges of the two species sometimes overlap.

Mottled ducklings often have very small shoulder-spots (5-6 mm), with rump-spots somewhat larger (e.g., half of the Florida birds, most of the Louisiana birds). Other times, the sizes of shoulder- and rump-spots are larger and more or less equal (i.e., more Northern Mallard-like).

The dark 'legs' and feet of Mottled ducklings (Palmer 1976, vol. 2), show a range of darkness. Twenty-two of 24 live Louisiana Mottled ducklings had moderate olive-brown feet, similar to those described by Stutzenbaker (unpubl.) in Texas ducklings, but 12 of these measured darker (Munsell *value* ca. 2.5/ to 3.5/) than the other 10 (ca. 3.6/ to 4.5/) and the remaining two paler (i.e., light olive-brown; ca. 4.5/ to 6.5/). The feet of nine Florida birds appeared almost uniformly dark. None of the specimens that I examined had light-colored feet, such as those portrayed by Shortt (*in* Kortright 1942: pl. 33) and Hines (*in* Bellrose 1980: pl. 23).

DISCUSSION. A distinct *hue* difference emerged between the equally dark foot colors of Florida and Louisiana ducklings. Feet of the Florida birds (3 broods) measured Munsell *hue* 5YR [=dark grayish brown] under noon daylight lamps (5000K); those of Louisiana birds examined in north daylight (ca. 7400K) were decidedly yellower: four ducklings (part of 1 brood) measured 2.5Y [=dark olive-brown] and 20 others (3 broods), evaluated without a color standard, were all some variation of grayish or blackish raw umber [=dark yellowish brown]. The gap of two Munsell *hue* charts—7.5YR and 10YR—between Munsell 5YR and 2.5Y suggests a *hue* disparity too great to be accounted for by a difference in colorimetric procedure alone. The Louisiana and Florida populations are apparently well-separated geographically (Palmer 1976, vol. 2) as well as by quantitative plumage differences in the adult birds (Johnsgard 1961a).

Also, a size difference appeared between 15 Texas birds and seven from Florida, all weighed within 24 hours of hatching. Mean weights of Texas ducklings, incubator-hatched from wild eggs, were slightly heavier (32.9 g; Stutzenbaker unpubl.) than those of wild-caught Florida ducklings (30.7 g; Beckwith and Hosford 1957: 467). A similar difference showed up between mean day-old weights of Florida captives and those from Louisiana, including captives weighed by Smart (1965). The captives weighed less as a group, but the Florida birds had longer bills, toes, and tarsi than the Louisiana ducklings did (compare data for two groups in Table 1, Appendix A). Individual variation in hatching-weight or rate of post-hatching weight-loss, or inconsistent weighing techniques, or all three factors, could have caused the differences observed (see Kear 1965 for study of post-hatching weight-loss in closely-related Northern Mallard). Weights (taken from unfed ducklings at precisely 24 hours post-hatching) and color evaluations (made with a color standard under controlled light conditions) from several day-old broods of each population would be necessary to determine whether observed differences were populational or merely the extremes of a continuum of individual variation.

SOURCE OF SPECIMENS. **Florida:** *Alachua County:* Gainesville: Payne's Prairie [State Reserve] (FIMNH-2 adults). *Brevard County:* Merritt Island National Wildlife Refuge (DWWRS-9 live captives: figs. 5-66 to 5-68). Kissimmee River at Lone Cabbage Palm [evidently local name about 1900; unable to verify] (USNM-1: figs. 5-69, 5-70), Kissimmee River at Rattlesnake Bluff [may=Rattlesnake Hammock in *Polk County* at 27° 42' N, 81° 10' W] (USNM-1: figs. 5-71, 5-72). *Collier County:* Everglades (FIMNH-1 adult). *Orange County:* Orlando (PSM-2). **Louisiana:** *Lafayette Parish* (RLWS-20 live captives). *Cameron Parish:* Grand Chenier: Rockefeller [State] Wildlife Refuge (UFS[DM]-4 live: figs. 5-73 to 5-75). **Texas:** *Cameron County:* Brownsville (FMNH-3). *Fort Bend County:* Beasley (TCWC-2: figs. 5-76, 5-77). *Kleberg County:* Laguna Larga (FMNH-1). *Nueces County* (AMNH-2).

OTHER REFERENCES. Johnson 1968. Johnson, Montalbano, and Hines 1984. LaHart and Cornwell n.d.. Lotter 1969. Paulus 1984.

American Black Duck

Canard noir. Pato Oscuro.
Anas rubripes Brewster

APPEARANCE. The downy American Black Duck is a darker version of the Mottled duckling. Comparatively, it has a sometimes larger—but not always darker—ear-spot, a much wider and darker eye-stripe (nearly always complete), and wider dark area on the crown and forehead (often narrowing and shortening the light supraorbital stripe). It has an orange-yellow chin so pale and dull that it is almost 'silvery', a grayish pink base color on the bill, and (nearly always) small dorsal spots, which may be partly concealed by blackish dorsal plumes. It could also be compared to a dark, richly colored Northern Mallard duckling, except that belly and undertail areas are relatively much less yellow, and the feet are dark, even blackish (compare 'old' and 'new' mallard ducklings, pl. 6).

VARIATION. The orange-yellow base color of the American Black duckling (often ochraceous or brownish) frequently becomes deep and bright—almost orange—on the lores, lower cheeks, and sides of the face below the ear-spot, where often there is also a slightly 'greenish' tint. The pale chin contrasts well with the darker or brighter face colors, which are overlaid by faint, dusky down-tips.

Other variations in extent and conspicuousness of plumage pattern seem more or less related to over all darkness of individuals or

broods. Most downy American Black Ducks had heavy, complete eye-stripes, which also encircled the eye on some dark ducklings (e.g., fig. 5-65; Québec duckling on pl. 6); other ducklings had wide but incomplete eye-stripes (fig. 5-61). Blackish ducklings usually also had wide dark crowns and foreheads and narrow supraorbital stripes (fig. 5-59), very small or inconspicuous dorsal spots and wing-patches, and often, a generally dull or brownish yellow base color, unrelieved by any brighter tint. J. Phillips (1923) and Johnsgard (1965) considered [lighter colored?] American Black ducklings quite similar to downy Northern Mallards.

Characteristically inconspicuous on a duckling otherwise strongly marked, the dusky ear-spot described by Baird, Brewer, and Ridgway (1884, vol. 2), Delacour (1956), and Palmer (1976, vol. 2) is virtually lacking in some live ducklings. Grinnell, Bryant, and Storer (1918) and Hines (*in* Bellrose 1980: pl. 23) depicted no ear-spot in their specimens, but Shortt (*in* Kortright 1942: pl. 33) and Scott (*in* Delacour 1956: pl. 5) portrayed American Black ducklings with small, blackish ear-spots. On many darker ducklings, the ear-spot was often elongated as a line or smudge of dusky plumes. In some individuals, it extended in a thin line of dark down-tips forward to the eye or even beyond it, and often curved upward to join the dark pre-ocular stripe (e.g., Wright 1954: pl. 19; Harrison 1978). It was seldom conspicuous (except in certain captives, e.g., JPWT; RLWS) in which it extended forward and was more or less connected to a faint, irregular 'mustache', producing the impression of a cheek-stripe (compare captive American Black duckling on pl. 6 with 'mustached' variants portrayed by Bent [1923] and Hines [*in* Bellrose 1980: pl. 23]).

Bill colors vary little—dark brownish gray pattern colors of the bill contrast well with dull pinkish base colors of the lower mandible, but foot colors have small differences. Some ducklings had feet with dark grayish orange base color (others grayish brown or blackish brown), contrasting poorly with the still darker pattern color (compare American Black ducklings on pl. 6 with Scott's duckling [*in* Delacour 1956: pl. 5], and feet of flightless juveniles [Shortt 1943: frontisp.]). The feet of young ducklings depicted by Shortt (*in* Kortright 1942: pl. 33), Shortt (1943), Hines (*in* Bellrose 1980: pl. 23), and Wright (1954: pl. 22) were paler than those of any live American Black ducklings examined.

Speckled web or "pinto-web"—a condition in which the normally dark brownish gray underside of the webs and toes has patches of paler, reddish yellow hue—was "found in about 11 percent" of adult and immature American Black Ducks resident in Chesapeake Bay (Stotts n.d.: 5) and about 20% of migrating American Black Ducks banded in Labrador (Vernon Stotts, letter to the author, October 1983). Reed reported the condition in "a few" Class II and Class III ducklings in the St. Lawrence estuary (Austin Reed, letter to the author, December 1982), but it did not appear on any of the ducklings that I observed.

DISCUSSION. Pierre Dupuis suggested that the pinkish gray color at the base of the bill and on the tomia and lower mandibles may be diagnostic for young American Black ducklings; he found the tomia of older American Black ducklings "greenish," those of Northern Mallards "yellowish" (Austin Reed, letter to the author, December 1982). Two wild American Black Ducks (Class IIb), showing "very little pinkish yellow" on the tomia developed hybrid (American Black Duck X Northern Mallard) plumage after some weeks in captivity (Pierre Dupuis, letter to the author, February 1983).

The existence of American Black Duck X Northern Mallard adults is well-documented (e.g., Heusmann and Burrell 1974; Brodsky and Weatherhead 1984), but hybrid ducklings are undescribed. Precise descriptions, including Munsell color evaluations, of known wild American Black Duck X Northern Mallard hybrid ducklings would greatly facilitate the detection of suspected hybrids.

SOURCE OF SPECIMENS. **New Brunswick:** *Westmorland County:* Sackville: Coles Island (ROM-1), Midgic Marsh—9.6 km NE Sackville (ROM-1). **Nova Scotia:** *Kings County:* Canard (NMC-1); Wolfville (UMMZ-3: figs. 5-60, 5-61), 4.8 km E Wolfville (UMMZ-1), 6.4 km E

Wolfville (UMMZ-1). **Northwest Territories:** *District of Keewatin:* James Bay: Ship Sands [=shoals] (NMC-4), Strutton Islands (CM-2). **Ontario:** *Algoma District:* Maclennan (ROM-1). *Bruce County:* Boat Lake (ROM-1). *Cochrane District:* Lake Abitibi: Camp 33 (ROM-1: figs. 5-64, 5-65); Fraserdale (ROM-3); (James Bay): Kabiskaubakau River (ROM-1), mouth of Kesagami River [=West River] (CM-7). *Essex County:* Pelee Island (ROM-1); Point Pelee (NMC-2). *Kenora District:* SE Aquatuk Lake (ROM-2: figs. 5-62, 5-63). *Manitoulin District:* Mindemoya Lake (ROM-3). *Middlesex County:* London: Springbank (ROM-1). *Norfolk County:* Turkey Point (ROM-1). *Parry Sound District:* Lake Nipissing: Frank Bay (ROM-2). *Simcoe County:* Willow Creek (ROM-1). *Sudbury County:* Genier (ROM-1). *Wellington County:* Luther Reservoir (ROM-1: figs. 5-56, 5-57). **Québec:** *Abitibi Territory:* Lac du Tast (NMC-1). *Huntingdon County:* Dundee (NMC-2). *Lake Saint John West County:* Saint-Félicien (NMC-3). *Magdalen Islands County:* Grosse Isle: East Point—47° 37' N, 61° 23' W (CM-7). *Québec County:* Québec: Lac Saint-Augustin (NMC-1). *Rivière-du-Loup County:* Trois-Pistoles: Saint Lawrence River: Ile aux Pommes (DWWRS-2 live: figs. 5-53 to 5-55), S shore (DWWRS-5 live captives). **Maryland:** *Worcester County:* South Point (PSM-1). **Michigan:** *Cheboygan County:* Inverness Township: Mud Lake—N Douglas Lake (UMMZ-2). *Schoolcraft County:* Seney National Wildlife Refuge (BMNH-1; UMMZ-1). *Tuscola County:* Fish Point (UMMZ-2: figs. 5-58, 5-59). **New York:** Long Island: *Suffolk* County: Cold Spring Harbor (CM-1 alcoholic). **Captive origin** (JPWT, RLWS-25 live).

OTHER REFERENCES. Clement 1974. Gollop and Marshall 1954. Ridgway 1895. Roberts 1932, vol. 2. Seymour 1977.

Mexican Duck

Canard fauve. Pato Altiplanero.

Anas diazi Ridgway (includes *novae-mexicana* Huber).

APPEARANCE. The Mexican duckling resembles the Mottled duckling except for browner (i.e., brighter) pattern color; often thinner and nearly always incomplete eye-stripe; and (sometimes) larger and more conspicuous dorsal spots (compare ducklings of 2 spp. on pl. 6). The ear-spot is small (CESJ; aviary birds), inconspicuous, or even lacking (all other specimens), and the feet are usually grayish brown (most wild ducklings), but are sometimes dull orange (CESJ; aviary birds). Differences in plumage color and pattern that distinguish Mottled and Florida ducklings from downy Northern Mallards also characterize wild-caught Mexican ducklings from Puebla and Jalisco. Color and pattern characters of Hidalgo County individuals were somewhat intermediate between downy Northern Mallards (e.g., from Alberta & Manitoba) and wild-caught *diazi* from Mexico (BMNH).

VARIATION. There is variation in the width and completeness of the eye-stripe, in the prominence of the dorsal spots, and in the yellow *hue* of the base color. The eye-stripe may be wide and incomplete behind the eye (some aviary ducklings) or thin and incomplete both behind and in front of the eye (most wild-caught Mexican specimens). The dorsal spots, said by Palmer (1976, vol. 2: 310) to be the "largest...among the American Black Duck and [its] allies," appear dull when shaded by darker plumes of pattern color. Sometimes, the shoulder-spots are broken or reduced in size. Of the 14 *diazi* specimens examined, 10 (8 wild-caught specimens from Mexico, 2 from Hidalgo County) had decidedly orange-yellow (i.e., ochraceous) base color; the other four (from Hidalgo County) were yellow, hence more mallard-like.

The light-colored forehead of some downy Mexican Ducks might cause them to be misidentified as Blue-winged or Northern Cinnamon teal ducklings in areas where, according to Palmer (1976, vol. 2) and Bellrose (1976, 1980), their breeding ranges meet or overlap. However, the characters that distin-

(1976, 1980), their breeding ranges meet or overlap. However, the characters that distinguish Mottled from Blue-winged Teal ducklings will also separate Mexican ducklings from those of both blue-winged teal species (note that some Northern Cinnamon Teal ducklings have dusky yellow faces, e.g., pl. 7 and Palmer [1976, vol. 2: 370, C. Nelson col. pl.]).

Delacour's (1956) accurate description of the Mexican duckling does not match the dark-plumaged, dark-footed variant shown by Scott (pl. 5) in the same work. I saw no 'mustache' mark, such as depicted by Hines (*in* Bellrose 1980: pl. 23), on any of the specimens examined.

Bills of the live Mexican ducklings were light yellowish pink on the lower mandible (much as in downy Mottled Ducks), with a yellowish pink wash at the base of the bill above the tomia. In contrast, the base color of downy Northern Mallards' bills was usually light yellowish brown, and did not extend so far up the sides of the bill at the base. Nymeyer (1975 [cited *in* Hubbard 1977: 26]) "reported that in 11 broods each of *diazi*-like and *platyrhynchos*-like ducks [age unknown], the former had bright orange mandibles and the latter dull orange." Somewhat less generally 'dark' than tarsi and toes of Mottled and American Black ducklings, the feet of two live Mexican ducklings were dull orange with fair contrast of the brownish gray pattern color (see pl. 6), whereas the feet of two others were darker, duller, and more evenly colored. Feet of the study specimens were almost uniformly grayish brown, without discernible contrasting pattern.

DISCUSSION. Huey (1961: 429) found the pattern color of live downy Mexican Ducks "lighter or more reddish-brown than in the Northern Mallard [duckling]." Although a comparison of 10 *A. diazi* and 60 *A. p. platyrhynchos* (all study skins, mostly Class I) disclosed few real differences in *hue* and *value* of yoke colors that could not be explained by individual variation or by fading of the specimen either before or after collection, the *chroma* of the yoke color was higher (i.e., brighter) in *A. diazi* specimens than in Northern Mallards (Munsell *chroma* /4.0: 9 *A. diazi*, 10 *A. p. platyrhynchos;* Munsell *chroma* /2.0 to /3.0: 1 *A. diazi,* 50 *A. p. platyrhynchos*). Consequently, the *diazi* ducklings did appear lighter and brighter (i.e., browner) than most of the Northern Mallard specimens.

Both live (CESJ) and prepared (MSB) duckling specimens from New Mexico appeared slightly 'yellower' in *hue* than the wild-caught ducklings collected in Mexico (BMNH). This difference suggests a possible correlation between the color and pattern characters of the downy young and those of adult *diazi* and *platyrhynchos* analyzed by Hubbard (1977) and Scott and Reynolds (1984). However, there is no complete published description known of live, wild downy young from central and southern Mexico, or from any zone of heterogeneity between *platyrhynchos* and *diazi* phenotypes, e.g., Doña Ana County, New Mexico (Hubbard 1977), southeastern Chihuahua, Mexico (Scott and Reynolds 1984). Nor is there a precise description of live, known hybrid *platyrhynchos* X *diazi* ducklings. Even prepared downy specimens of known age and ancestry are rare. The collection and description (including Munsell color evaluations) of both newly hatched and partly grown ducklings would add greatly to our knowledge of this 'old' mallard species.

SOURCE OF SPECIMENS. **New Mexico:** *Hidalgo County:* San Simon Ciénaga [=marshy enlargement of San Simon Creek about 40 km SW Lordsburg] (CESJ-4 live captives; MSB-2). MEXICO: **Jalisco:** Lago de Chapala—6.4 km W Tizapán el Alto (BMNH-5: figs. 5-81 to 5-83). **Michoacán:** 11.2 km W Alvaro Obregón (BMNH-1); Zacapu (BMNH-1). **Puebla:** Laguna del Carmen (BMNH-1: figs. 5-84, 5-85).

OTHER REFERENCES. Bevill and Davis 1969.

Mallard

Canard colvert. Pato de Collar.
Anas platyrhynchos Linnaeus

APPEARANCE. The downy Northern Mallard's yellow and olive-brown plumage, well-marked dark eye-stripe and ear-spot, prominent wing-patches, and four dorsal spots of more or less equal size are the basis for comparison with ducklings of all other species. Clearly yellow base color (often rather 'greenish' on belly and undertail), dull orange feet with contrasting grayish brown pattern, and a well-defined dark forehead are also characteristic. The light area at the base of the bill above the tomium is smaller than that in Mottled or Mexican ducklings and yellower (i.e., less pink) than in any 'old' mallard species. In ducklings Class Ic and older, medium to light belly-down (Munsell *value* 4.6/ or 5.0/ to 6.5/ or 7.0/) separates Northern Mallard ducklings from those of the Mottled Duck group, which have dark belly-down (Munsell *value* range 3.0/ to 4.5/ [rarely 5.0/]).

Downy European *platyrhynchos* Linnaeus are similar to North American Mallard ducklings, except that striking variations from the wild type seem to be fairly common. Some have cheek-stripes (A. C. Meinertzhagen *in* Witherby et al. [1939] 1943, vol. 3; Delacour 1956), 'greenish' olive pattern color (Percy *in* J. Phillips 1923), bills flesh-colored or spotted with black (Bauer and Glutz von Blotzheim 1968; Harrison 1975; Cramp and Simmons 1977), gray or blackish foot color (Dement'ev and Gladkow [1952] 1967, vol. 4; Bauer and Glutz von Blotzheim 1968; Harrison 1975; Cramp and Simmons 1977), a dark rictal 'mustache' (Witherby et al. [1939] 1943, vol. 3: pl. 83; Delacour 1956: Scott pl. 5; Fjeldså 1977: fig. 10) or some combination of all variations. Fjeldså (1977: 64) reports "blackish brown young with yellowish throat and breast...and...nearly uniform buff young with rudimentary markings". Whether such variants are true wild mutants or simply the result of wild individuals interbreeding with sedentary or domestic Northern Mallards is unknown.

Wild-caught, yellow-and-brown *conboschas* (Brehm) specimens are also quite similar to palaearctic *platyrhynchos* (some Greenland *conboschas* paler—"nearly cream-coloured"; Fjeldså 1977: 64): the light base color is equally extensive (Schiøler 1925: Larsen pl. 39), ear-spots are small, and there is no cheek-stripe. The dark eye-stripe may encircle the eye (e.g., Greenland [ZMK]; some American Black ducklings; a few nearctic *platyrhynchos*) and there is usually a small rictal 'mustache'. No *conboschas* had thin, incomplete eye-stripes as in Mottled and Mexican ducklings. The yellow base color of the older *conboschas* duckling (WT[S] captive, Class Ic) had faded to grayish yellow (grayish cream on the dorsal spots), but the pattern color remained very dark grayish olive. The base of the captive's belly-down was darker (Munsell *value* 4.0/) than that of most *platyrhynchos* ducklings, but was consistent with the over all darkness of the pattern color, which may or may not have been typical for the Greenland subspecies.

VARIATION. Although pattern color and general coloration of wild nearctic Northern Mallard ducklings are remarkably constant, there is some variation in *hue* of base and pattern colors; in number, width, and completeness of face stripes; in the presence of a 'mustache'; in size and prominence of the dorsal pattern and ear-spot; and in contrast and *chroma* of foot colors. The yellow base color, recognizeable on ducklings retaining even a little of their natal down, is often more 'orange' on the face and breast (e.g., Munsell *hue* 2.5Y to 4.5Y) and more 'greenish' on the belly and undertail (e.g., Munsell *hue* 6.5Y to 8.5Y). Alternatively, the underparts may show various tints of true yellow (Munsell hue 5Y) from face to undertail. The combination of dark yellow or brownish yellow face and breast with much paler, duller belly and undertail *of the same hue* (characteristic of ducklings of the Mottled Duck group) is not typical of most downy Northern Mallards.

Most wild Northern Mallard ducklings have a single, well-marked stripe, "narrow but usually complete" (Palmer 1976, vol. 2: 279), from bill to occiput. Eye-stripe variations of *platyrhynchos* ducklings from the northern plains (e.g., Alberta, Manitoba, and Minnesota), which I have taken as the standard among North American 'new' mallard ducklings, include: pre-orbital stripe incomplete (uncommon), post-orbital stripe incomplete or thin past ear-level (common), heavy and complete (fairly common), and heavy and incomplete (uncommon). The following normal 'old' mallard characters resemble observed variations of the 'new', e.g., *A. fulvigula:* post-orbital stripe incomplete, either thin (usual) or heavy (fairly common); *A. diazi:* both portions of eye-stripe very thin and incomplete; *A. rubripes:* both portions heavy and complete (see pl. 6 and figs. 5-53 to 5-102 for eye-stripe variations of 'old' and 'new' mallard ducklings).

A small, dark rictal 'mustache' (e.g., Shortt *in* Kortright 1942: pl. 33), appeared on certain Northern Mallard ducklings from British Columbia, Manitoba, Minnesota, Oregon, and Washington. The 'mustache' of most ducklings had only a few dusky plumes, but was fairly heavy on others. In these, the mark tapered backward to eye-level, but stopped well short of the ear-spot.

The downy Northern Mallard's ear-spot is neither so large proportionately as that in Blue-winged Teal ducklings (figs. 5-19, 5-116, 5-123) nor so inconspicuous as that in the otherwise more heavily pigmented American Black duckling (figs. 5-57, 5-63; compare teal and mallard-like ducklings on pls. 6 & 7).

The four yellow dorsal spots of wild Northern Mallard ducklings are of more or less the same size, except for a few ducklings, which had somewhat larger rump-spots. No wild *platyrhynchos* had dorsal spots and wing-patches unusually small, dull, or greatly shaded by dark dorsal down plumes.

Bill colors are essentially invariable, but tarsal colors vary considerably. Most downy Northern Mallards have fair to good contrast of dull orange base color and grayish brown pattern color, but some have brighter (as some downy Blue-winged Teal) or duller colors (as most Mexican ducklings).

DISCUSSION. Aggressive, adaptable, and successful, the Northern Mallard is distributed throughout much of the northern hemisphere and has been introduced extensively elsewhere. Transplantation of 'new' mallards into territories of the 'old'—or of game-farm mallards into wild *A. p. platyrhynchos* populations—can make problems for the resident species. For example, if circumstances are favorable (e.g., normal barriers to interspecific mating are absent), 'new' *A. p. platyrhynchos* may hybridize with 'old' mallards (e.g., Frith 1982 re: Australian Grey Duck; Brodsky and Weatherhead 1984 re: American Black Duck). Moreover, because of deliberate introduction of large numbers of hand-reared Northern Mallards into the wild population (Addy 1964), McKinney (1965: 59) believes that "it has become impossible to distinguish between 'pure' wild Northern Mallards and birds with characteristics produced through artificial selection in captivity." According to Delacour (1964: 161), captive Northern Mallard ducklings show alterations of the wild-type pattern "after a few generations".

Variations in *platyrhynchos* ducklings of ostensibly wild (but more probably mixed) parentage include heavy or added dark facial stripes (Palmer 1976, vol. 2; NPWRC *conboschas* brood had wide cheek-stripes) and narrowed light stripes; dark, 'greenish', or 'khaki' pattern color with pale, greenish yellow base color (ROM; England); 'stubby', blackish bill and shiny, blackish feet (NMC; Connecticut); patchy pigmentation of bill and feet (irregular, virtually unpigmented areas interspersed with those of normal color); marked alteration in size of light-colored plumage areas; and replacement of yellow and olive-brown plumage colors by light, bland pinkish yellow, as in the usual plumage of the Pekin duckling (*A. p. platyrhynchos*, var. *domesticus*). Wild broods having both mutant and 'normal' ducklings are fairly common in some parts of North America (e.g., where sedentary or game-farm Northern Mallards have been introduced), but are unusual in the north central plains (James Bartee, pers. comm., 1966).

SOURCE OF SPECIMENS. **Alberta:** Chipewyan Lake (ROM-1). Clairmont: Bear Lake (MMMN-1). Red Deer: Red Deer River: Camp One (NMC-1). Slave River: 30th Base Line (CM-5: figs. 5-91, 5-92). Strathmore (UFS[DM]-16 live). **British Columbia:** *Cariboo District:* 153 Mile House [=old road house 4.8 km N 150 Mile House on Cariboo Road] (NMC-1); Prince George (NMC-1); Sorenson Lake [J. Munro 1945: 99] (RBCM-1; NMC-1). *Yale District,* Osoyoos Division: Rawlings Lake (ROM-1). **Manitoba:** Delta (DWWRS-15 live: figs. 5-86 to 5-88; MMMN-2). Lake Saint Martin Indian Reserve (ROM-1). Minnedosa (DWWRS-7 live [*ss:* D-1; MMMN-1]). Oakland (DWWRS-4 live). The Pas (DWWRS-3 live). Shoal Lake [village] (NMC-4). Winnipeg: Fort Whyte (NWPW-8 live). Lake Winnipegosis: Dawson Bay: Overflowing River (MMMN-2). **Northwest Territories:** *District of Keewatin:* Rupert Bay: Cabbage Willows Bay (NMC-1). *District of Mackenzie:* Mackenzie Delta: Kendall Island (CM-1). **Ontario:** *Essex County:* Pelee Island (ROM-1). *Prince Edward County:* Hallowell (ROM-1). *Thunder Bay District:* Lake Nipigon: Humboldt Bay (ROM-1). *Wellington County:* Luther Reservoir (ROM-1). *York County:* Toronto Island (ROM-1). **Québec:** *Huntingdon County:* Dundee (NMC-3). **Saskatchewan:** Golden Prairie: Tenaille Lake (USNM-1). Kindersley (PMBRC-35: figs. 5-95 to 5-98). Stalwart (CM-1). **Alaska:** Beaver Creek—6.4 km E Kenai at 60° 32' N, 151° 09' W (USNM-1: figs. 5-89, 5-90). **California:** *Siskiyou County:* Tule Lake (SDNHM-1). **Michigan:** *Washtenaw County:* Ann Arbor (UMMZ-1). **Minnesota:** *Beltrami County:* Blackduck Lake (BMNH-2). *Clearwater County:* Upper Rice Lake (BMNH-1). *Crow Wing County:* Graham Meadows [=local name for small marshy area NE Lake Hubert] (BMNH-1). *Hennepin County:* Minneapolis: Mother Lake [=Cedar Avenue Slough] (BMNH-1). *Kittson County:* Karlstad (BMNH-1). *Marshall County:* Mud Lake (CM-1). *Nobles County* (RLWS-14 live captives). *Roseau County:* S Roseau River (BMNH-1). **New Jersey:** *Bergen County:* Englewood (USNM-1). **North Dakota:** *Golden Valley County:* Beaver Creek (USNM-1). *Logan County:* 9.7 km SW Napoleon (USNM-2: figs. 5-93, 5-94). *McHenry County:* 12.8 km N Towner (USNM-1). *Walsh County:* Grafton (OSUFW-1). **Oregon:** *Baker County:* 6.4 km W Baker (OSUFW-2). *Benton County:* near Adair Air Force Base (OSUFW-1). *Lake County:* Paisley: Chewaucan Marsh (OSUFW-2); Summer Lake (SDNHM-1). **Washington:** *Chelan County:* Kahler Creek about 8 km S S end Lake Wenatchee (UWBM-1). *Grant County:* Black Rock Lake—14.5 km SE Wilson Creek [village] (UWBM-1). *King County:* Lake Sammamish State Park (UWBM-1); Lake Washington (UWBM-1). **Wyoming:** *Uinta County:* Mountain View (ROM-1). GREENLAND: *Holsteinsborg District* [=*Sisimiut kommunia*]: Holsteinsborg [=Sisimiut] (AMNH-1; KUMNH-1). *Nanortalik District* [=*Nanortallip kommunia*]: Nanortalik [=Nanortallip] (ZMK-2: figs. 5-99, 5-100). **Captive origin** (WT[S]-1: figs. 5-101, 5-102).

OTHER REFERENCES. Bailey and Niedrach 1965, vol. 1. Baird, Brewer, and Ridgway 1884, vol. 1 (quoted in Ridgway 1895). Bellrose 1976, 1980. Bent 1923. Cogswell 1977. Gollop and Marshall 1954. Grinnell, Bryant, and Storer 1918. Heinroth and Heinroth 1928, vol. 3. Johnsgard 1965. Kuroda 1939. Roberts 1932, vol. 2. Southwick 1953. F. Todd 1979 ("Gadwall" ducklings, fig. 1.130, appear to be typical Northern Mallards).

Hawaiian Duck
Canard d'Hawaï. Pato Hawaiiense.
Anas wyvilliana Sclater

APPEARANCE. The downy Hawaiian Duck, or Koloa, looks like a tiny Northern Mallard, but is paler and duller on belly and undertail, its yellow base color is "buffier" (Delacour 1956: 45), and its pattern color 'browner'. The forehead is dark to the base of the bill as in the Northern Mallard (compare yellow forehead of Northern Cinnamon and Blue-winged teal ducklings and brownish yellow forehead of downy Laysan Duck [pl. 7] with forehead colors of 'old' and 'new' mallards [pl. 6]). The foot color is darker than that of most downy Northern Mallards (Swedberg 1967).
VARIATION. The Koloa duckling seems to be simply a teal-sized replica of the more widely distributed Northern Mallard, but a closer look at its subtle colors suggests that it may have as many affinities with the 'old' mallards as with the 'new'. 'Old' mallard characters of the newly hatched duckling include the orange-yellow base color (becoming much paler and duller posteriorly), the evenly-colored toes and tarsi, and the 'brown' pattern color. Rothschild (1900: 273) stated that "the olive tint [of downy *A. wyvilliana*] is apparently more variable and generally less intense [than in the Northern Mallard duckling]."

Eye-stripe variations—narrow and complete (USNM; fig. 5-80), moderate and complete (Swedberg 1967: 16), moderate and incomplete (Rothschild 1900; Berger 1981: fig. 52)—are consistent with known variations in ducklings of both 'old' and 'new' mallards (see pl. 6). So are ear-spot variations. I cannot comment on Swedberg's (1967) observation of a possible sex difference in the prominence of the ear-spot. However, Lee found no consistent sex difference in the ear-spot among the many Hawaiian ducklings that he raised, although he noted some individual variation in all pattern elements (Ah Fat Lee, letter to the author, December 1983).

Prepared specimens (USNM; WT[S]) and Swedberg's (1967) and Berger's (1981) ducklings have both dorsal spots and wing-patches, but Keulemans's downy Koloa (*in* Rothschild 1900) has wing-patches only. The absence of dorsal spots could indicate either an individual variation, or an unspotted or inconspicuously spotted condition for the species.

The tarsi and toes of some young Hawaiian ducklings were almost uniformly dull yellowish brown (USNM) or dull orange (Keulemans *in* Rothschild 1900), but others appeared dark (Swedberg 1967) or blackish (Delacour 1956: Scott pl. 5). The range of color is like that of 'old' mallards.

The light belly down of the Class II Hawaiian duckling (WT[S] captive; Munsell *value* 5.6/ to 6.0/) emerged as the most evident 'new' mallard character. The *values* fell within the range of those for the Northern Mallard's belly down (Munsell *value* 5.0/ to 6.5/), well above those of the Mottled Duck group (Munsell *value* 3.0/ to 4.5/, rarely 5.0/) for ducklings Class Ic or older. The Class II Hawaiian duckling had back and rump feathers as dark as those of American Black Ducks, with light-colored edges similar to those of Northern Mallards but narrower and duller. The light buff-pink feathers on throat and malars (Munsell 6YR 6/4)—malars and cheeks finely streaked with brownish gray—resembled those of live Class IIb Mottled Ducks and certain Class IIb Saskatchewan Northern Mallards (other PMBRC Northern Mallards somewhat paler and yellower: Munsell 7.5YR 7/4). However, the color of the Class II 'old' mallard and 'new' mallard ducklings varied enough that it probably cannot be considered distinctive for one species or the other. The colorimetric evaluation of a large series of specimens is needed.
SOURCE OF SPECIMENS. **Hawaiian Islands:** *Honolulu County:* Oahu Island: Kailua (USNM-1: figs. 5-78 to 5-80). **Captive origin** (WT[S]-1).
OTHER REFERENCES. Berger 1972. Johnsgard 1965. G. Munro 1944. J. Phillips 1923. Schwartz and Schwartz 1953. Weller 1980.

Laysan Duck
Canard de Laysan. Pato de Laysan.
Anas laysanensis Rothschild

APPEARANCE. Inconspicuous facial and dorsal patterns, contrasting poorly with brownish yellow base color, and a usually flat-tipped, spatulate bill with narrow, triangular nail characterize the downy Laysan Duck (compare bill of Laysan duckling [figs. 5-103, 5-106] with that of

downy Northern Shoveler [figs. 5-26, 5-29]; see also Ripley [1960: figs. 1a, day-old Laysan Duck, & 1b, day-old Northern Mallard]). A large ear-spot—often paler than the eye-stripe and contrasting poorly with the brownish base color—may extend forward almost to the rictal 'mustache', giving the impression of a cheek-stripe. The dark crown color of many ducklings stops short of the bill, as in downy Blue-winged and Northern Cinnamon teal (compare teal & Laysan figs. on pl. 7 & figs. 5-103 to 5-109, 5-110 to 5-129), but others have a line of dark color between crown and bill (narrow, as in wild Class Ia duckling and F. Todd 1979: fig. 1.115 [mislabeled "Hawaiian Duck"], or wide, as in *Annual Report of the [Severn] Wildfowl Trust 1960-61* 1962, 13: P. Talbot-Ponsonby photo). An olive-gray and dull pink bill (similar to that of 'old' mallard or teal ducklings) and heavy, light-colored tarsi with low-contrast darker pattern also typify the downy Laysan Duck.

VARIATION. I found no major differences among captive Laysan ducklings from Niska and Tunstead, captive Laysan ducklings described by Ripley (1960), and wild ducklings photographed by Moulton on Laysan Island (color transparencies loaned by Daniel Moulton in letter to the author, September 1983; references hereinafter to wild ducklings are based on Moulton's transparencies). Small variations in the length and prominence of the eye-stripe, in the rictal 'mustache', and in other pattern elements were much like differences observed in the same or other characters of many dabbler ducklings. Most Laysan ducklings have a thin eye-stripe similar to that shown by Ripley (1960: 246, fig. 1), but unlike the one described in his text, which had the stripe "only indicated anterior to the eye." J. Phillips (1923) found a streak behind the eye (USNM; coll. W. K. Fisher on Laysan I.) but none in front of it. A few live ducklings had a wide, ill-defined pre-orbital stripe merging with a deep yellowish brown area (almost blackish in study skins) diffused from the rictus nearly to the eye. Other live ducklings, including those from Laysan Island, had quite wide stripes both before and behind the eye, which were complete in some individuals, but incomplete in others (see *Annual Report of the [Severn] Wildfowl Trust 1959-60* 12, 1961; *1960-61* 13, 1962: P. Talbot-Ponsonby photos).

The rictal 'mustache' of wild Class Ia ducklings and most live captives (e.g., P. Talbot-Ponsonby photo, 1961) was absent on other captives (P. Talbot-Ponsonby photo, 1962) and on older wild ducklings. Certain live ducklings (including some from Laysan Island) had light-colored crescents above and below the eye (pl. 7; also Ripley 1960: 246, fig. 1), which were less prominent or virtually absent on other ducklings.

The Laysan duckling's inconspicuous dorsal pattern recalls that of downy Northern Shovelers or Lesser Scaup. Bleaching of the light base color and wearing of overlying dark down-tips made both rump-spots and narrow wing-patches appear quite prominent in Class Ic wild ducklings and in a Class IIa Niska captive (see also P. Talbot-Ponsonby photo, 1961), but the tiny shoulder-spots had all but disappeared. Very young ducklings often show poor

Plate 7

1 Northern Cinnamon Teal, Anas cyanoptera septentrionalium
Darker and lighter variants. Bear River Migratory Bird Refuge, Utah (DWWRS; NWPW).

2 Northern Shoveler, A. clypeata
Darker and lighter variants. Delta Manitoba (DWWRS).

3 Blue-winged Teal, A. d. discors
Delta, Manitoba (DWWRS).

4 Laysan Duck, A. laysanensis
Laysan Island, Hawaiian Islands (NPRC captives; NWPW).

5 Gadwall, A. strepera
Lighter variant. Delta Manitoba (DWWRS).
Darker variant. Valentine National Wildlife Refuge, Nebraska (UFS[DM]).

6 Spectacled Eider, Somateria fischeri
Naskonat Peninsula, Alaska (DWWRS [ca. 2 d.]).

7 King Eider, S. spectabilis
Greenland and Iceland (WT[S] captives: color and measurements) and Seymour Island, Northwest Territories (NMC: pattern).

8 Steller's Eider, Polysticta stelleri
Barrow, Alaska (FMNH [ca. 2d.]).

Common Eider, S. mollissima

9 Icelandic Eider, S. m. islandica. Mývatn, Iceland (BMNH [RLWS captive]).

10 Pacific Eider, S. m. v-nigra. Kashunuk River E Hooper Bay, Alaska (DWWRS [ca. 2d.]).

11 Northern Eider, S. m. borealis. W Coast Baffin Island, Northwest Territories (ROM).

12 Hudson Bay Eider, S. m. sedentaria. Churchill, Manitoba (NWPW; UFS[DM]).

13 Dresser's Eider, S. m. dresseri. Ille aus Pommes, Québec (DWWRS; UFS[DM]).

Plate 7

contrast between the rich brownish yellows of the face and the lighter yellows of chin and throat (e.g., Ripley 1960: 246, fig. 1, & Delacour 1964: Scott pl. 5).

Toes and tarsi of young live ducklings were light, dull yellow ('greenish' on the Niska ducklings, more brownish on the Tunstead captives), whereas the feet of wild Class Ia ducklings appeared somewhat pinker and grayer over all. The small *hue* differences seem within the range of normal variation; the low contrast of web and pattern color was consistent for all.

The bill is distinctly spatulate, but usually flat-tipped and without the marked distal widening and 'droop' characteristic of shovelers' bills. In profile, the bills of wild ducklings Class Ic and older have a square-tipped appearance that is lacking in Hawaiian ducklings (compare profile bills of adult Laysan and Hawaiian ducks in Weller 1980: figs. 1.4 & 1.5).

SOURCE OF SPECIMENS. **Captive origin** (JPWT, NPRC-8 live: figs. 5-103 to 5-105; 2 dead [*ss:* MMMN-4: figs. 5-106 to 5-109]; WT[S]-1).

OTHER REFERENCES. Delacour 1956, 1964. Fisher 1906 (reprinted *in* Bailey 1956 and *in* Berger 1972, 1981). Johnsgard 1965, 1968. Moulton and Weller 1984. G. Munro 1944.

Blue-winged Teal

Sarcelle à ailes bleues. Cerceta Aliazul Clara.
Anas discors Linnaeus

APPEARANCE. A thin, dark, usually complete grayish brown eye-stripe; good contrast between base and pattern colors of plumage, toes, and tarsi; and a quite wide nail distinguish the downy Blue-winged Teal from the closely similar Northern Cinnamon Teal duckling (nails of both species are wider than nail of Green-winged duckling, but narrower than that of the downy Northern Mallard). The narrow yellow forehead separates both Blue-winged and Northern Cinnamon teal ducklings from the smaller Greenwing downies, as well as from most of the larger, but otherwise similar mallard-like ducklings (compare 3 teal spp. [pls. 6 & 7; figs. 5-15 to 5-25, 5-110 to 5-129] with ducklings of Northern Mallard group [pl. 6; figs. 5-53 to 5-102]). The Blue-winged duckling's bill is less gray and pink than that of the Northern Cinnamon duckling, and both are grayer and pinker than the downy Northern Mallard's bill, which is more olive and yellow.

VARIATION. No single physical character can separate Blue-winged and Northern Cinnamon teal ducklings with certainty. Rather, a combination of characters must be used, any and all of which may vary individually and independently. For example, the eye-stripe of the Bluewing duckling is usually thin, grayish brown, and complete and the downy Northern Cinnamon Teal's usually thinner stripe is brownish and incomplete, but sometimes, the characters typical of one species appear on the other. A well-marked, incomplete post-ocular stripe, about 2 mm wide, marked a few individuals of both species, but the wide, ribbon-like, eye-to-nape stripe found on some ducklings of the mallard group did not appear on any teal species.

The Blue-winged duckling's upper mandible is darker and a bit shorter and 'browner' than that of the downy Northern Cinnamon Teal, which is typically gray or olive-gray and "noticeably long" (Palmer 1976, vol. 2: 486). Exposed culmen [EC] measurements of day-old Northern Cinnamon Teal averaged 0.9 mm longer than those of day-old Bluewings (see Table 1, Appendix A). The nail of the downy Blue-winged Teal, fairly wide and somewhat triangular posteriorly, has a longer, more curving anterior edge than the nail of the Northern Cinnamon duckling, which is usually narrower over all, with a sharper posterior angle and a shorter, less deeply curved anterior edge (compare Blue-winged figs. 5-117 and 5-120 with Northern Cinnamon figs. 5-110 and 5-113; note that difference is seldom so clear-cut as in other species pairs—e. g., scaup, goldeneyes—in which the nail characters are diagnostic).

The general color of the duckling is a good distinguishing character, particularly the amount of contrast between pattern and base colors of the plumage and feet. Downy Blue-winged Teals have darker, duller olive-brown pattern color (with dorsal down plumes only moderately conspicuous: 2.5Y 8/5), contrasting well with the yellow (Munsell 5Y) base color, whereas Northern Cinnamon ducklings' olive-brown pattern color appears brighter (i.e., 'browner') and contrasts less well with more greenish yellow (Munsell 7.5Y to 10Y) base color, which is usually pale and bright, if sometimes grayish or dusky on the face. Pale, bright yellow (6Y 8.4/8) down-tips of the yoke and crown enhance the low-contrast plumage color of Northern Cinnamon ducklings, producing what Bent (1923: 125) termed a "golden olivaceous appearance" (compare general coloring of both teal spp. on pl. 7; see Delacour [1956: Scott pl. 23; blackish feet of these ducklings not typical], Bellrose [1980: Hines pl. 23; Northern Cinnamon ducklings unusually dark], and Bailey and Niedrach [1965, vol. 1: Hochbaum pl. 18; downy Bluewing somewhat pale]).

Most Blue-winged ducklings have feet with grayish yellow or dull orange-yellow base color and dark grayish brown pattern color more or less conspicuously distributed on all toe joints, on the webs, and up the backs of the tarsi, whereas the feet of most Northern Cinnamon ducklings are dull yellow or light olive-brown, with the darker pattern areas less well-defined. In many Northern Cinnamon ducklings, only the terminal joints of the toes have any noticeably contrasting pattern color. As a result of these small, comparative differences, the feet of downy Bluewings usually appear rather contrastingly colored, those of Northern Cinnamon ducklings duller and usually more evenly colored.

The long, dark ear-spot reported by Delacour (1956) in teal species is large in proportion to the narrow eye-stripe and the generally small size of the birds. Although somewhat variable, it can be a useful field mark for Class I blue-winged ducklings when considered along with other characters of pattern, color, size, and behavior. A large ear-spot seldom appears in Class I mallard-like ducklings, including the American Black Duck. In Class II ducklings, the ear-spot is one of the first areas to attain juvenal feathers, becoming almost equally conspicuous in both teal and mallard-group ducklings.

DISCUSSION. The occurrence of wild Bluewing X Northern Cinnamon hybrids compounds the difficulties of downy teal identification. Adult male hybrids have been described from Saskatchewan (Lahrman 1971), California (Harris and Wheeler 1965), North Dakota (Lokemoen and Sharp 1981), Oklahoma (Bolen 1979), Texas (Bolen 1978), and Utah (Wilson and van den Akker 1948; Bolen 1978). Adult hybrid females are much more difficult to detect, females of the two species being "essentially indistinguishable" (Bolen 1979: 267) except for the usually longer bill of the Northern Cinnamon Teal. The identification of hybrid ducklings of either sex becomes still more difficult. Detailed descriptions of known or suspected hybrid broods, along with measurements and Munsell color evaluations of positively identified ducklings of both species, are needed.

SOURCE OF SPECIMENS. **Alberta:** Brooks (ROM-1). Demmitt: Updike Lake (MMMN-3). Jasper National Park (NMC-2). Walsh (UMMZ-1). **British Columbia:** *Cariboo District:* Murphy Lake (ROM-1); Williams Lake: Riske Creek (NMC-2). *Lillooet District:* 103 Mile Lake (ROM-1). *Range 4 Coast District:* Nulki Lake: Bradley Slough [unofficial name] (OSUFW-1; ROM-3: figs. 5-122, 5-123). *Yale District,* Osoyoos Division: Okanagan (OSUFW-1). **Manitoba:** Delta (DWWRS-71 live: figs. 5-117 to 5-119 [*ss:* D-1; MMMN-5: figs. 5-120, 5-121; UWBM-2]; D-5; MMMN-1; ROM-2; UMMZ-2). Minnedosa (DWWRS-9 live). Saint Ambroise: Community Pasture (NWPW-8 live). Lake Winnipegosis (AMNH-1). **Ontario:** *Essex*

County: Pelee Island (ROM-3: figs. 5-126, 5-127). **Saskatchewan:** Cherryfield [=School District ca. 1906 near Rock Dell] (AMNH-1). S Flaxcombe (PMBRC-1). Kindersley (PMBRC-1). South Arm Last Mountain Lake (NMC-1: figs. 5-124, 5-125). **Colorado:** *Park County:* Antero Reservoir (USNM-1). **Michigan:** *Chippewa County:* Munuscong Lake (UMMZ-2). **Minnesota:** *Clearwater County:* 6.4 km N Itasca State Park (BMNH-2). *Kittson County:* Twin Lakes (BMNH-1). *Koochiching County:* Ericsburg (BMNH-1). *Mahnomen County:* NW Waubun (BMNH-2). *Meeker County:* 4.8 km W Eden Valley (BMNH-1). *Nobles County* (RLWS-206 live captives). **Montana:** *Rosebud County:* Sumatra (USNM-1: figs. 5-128, 5-129). **Captive origin** (UWGB[RC]-1).

OTHER REFERENCES. Bannerman 1957, vol. 7. Bellrose 1976, 1980. Bennett 1938 (ecology and management; behavior of wild female Bluewings and broods). Cogswell 1977. Gollop and Marshall 1954. Grinnell, Bryant, and Storer 1918. Harrison 1978. Johnsgard 1965. Kortright 1942. J. Munro 1937. J. Phillips 1923. Roberts 1932, vol. 2. Southwick 1953. Witherby et al. (1939) 1943, vol. 3.

Cinnamon Teal

Sarcelle cannelle. Cerceta Aliazul Café.
Anas cyanoptera Vieillot

APPEARANCE. A brownish eye-stripe (usually thin and incomplete); fair contrast between base and pattern colors of plumage, toes, and tarsi; a long bill; and a rather narrow nail characterize Northern Cinnamon Teal ducklings (see Table 1, Appendix A, for EC of Northern Cinnamon, Bluewing, and Northern Shoveler downies). The forehead is yellow as in the Blue-winged Teal, but the Northern Cinnamon duckling's bill is grayer and pinker than that of the downy Bluewing (compare ducklings of 2 spp. on pl. 7).

VARIATION. See Blue-winged Teal, pp. 93-95. Besides the observed overlap in characteristics of pattern, bill structure, and general color between Northern Cinnamon and Blue-winged ducklings, downy Northern Cinnamon Teal have individual variations in face pattern, dorsal spots, and general color. The eye-stripe, usually pale and broken before the eye, is often thin or absent past ear-level. The "prominent brown eye stripe" described by Spencer (1953: 124) appeared complete in two older ducklings but incomplete past ear-level in a duckling two weeks old (his photo p. 129). The ear-spot, if sometimes pale, is always elongated and fairly conspicuous. The "dusky 'shadow' on side of face" (Palmer 1976, vol. 2: 486) appeared on all but a few of the live ducklings. It was darker and grayer in older downies (Classes Ib and IIa), contrasting well with the pinkish tomia at the base of the gray upper mandibles, and often causing a poorly-marked light eye-ring to appear more prominent. A few individuals with unmarked cheeks had yellower, browner coloration, with pale yellow base color. Dorsal spots are large and conspicuous on most ducklings (more so on some others) but partly shaded by overlying darker plumes on ducklings with particularly low-contrast plumage colors.

Most Northern Cinnamon ducklings had the "golden olivaceous appearance" described by Bent (1923: 125), but a brood of five wild ducklings from Utah were unusually dark, although they seemed 'normal' in every other way. The pre-ocular stripe was complete on all; the ear-spot was heavy, distinct, and joined to the pre-ocular strripe by a wide, dusky connection similar to that of many Northern Shoveler ducklings (see pl. 7). Three of the ducklings had partly dark foreheads (a medial light area with dark plumes touching the bill on either side) but two were entirely dark right down to the bill. These more extensive markings may represent a pattern, common to downies of the blue-winged ducks—nearly always present in the downy Northern Shoveler duckling—which requires an extra bit of melanin to be manifested in the two teal species (see also Redhead, dark variant, pl. 8).

Whether there is a correlation between such *value* differences in the downy plumage and the "wide...range of individual variation in [adult] coloring reported by Palmer (1976, vol. 2: 487) is unknown. The plumage and unfeathered parts of the dark ducklings were distinctly 'greener' and more contrastingly colored than those of either Blue-winged or other Northern Cinnamon Teal downies (compare mean culmen measurements [EC] of the dark ducklings—12.9 mm [12.6 - 13.5; n=5, SD=0.36, SE=0.16]—with those of wild-caught, normally colored, Northern Cinnamon Teal brood—13.0 mm [12.2 - 14.1; n=7, SD=0.59, SE=0.22]—and those of Blue-winged Teal and Northern Shoveler ducklings in Table 1, Appendix A; compare also mean weight of 5 newly hatched and dried Northern Cinnamon Teal ducklings [18.2 g; Spencer 1953: 123] with means of author-weighed ducklings).

Although female adult and juvenal Northern Cinnamon Teals can scarcely be distinguished from those of the Blue-winged, live juvenal males (feathered: Class III) can be identified by differences in eye-color: eyes of Blue-winged Teal are brown, those of Northern Cinnamon Teal some shade of red. The transition between natal grayish brown and adult red in Northern Cinnamon Teal occurs between seven and nine or ten weeks (Spencer 1953).

SOURCE OF SPECIMENS. **British Columbia:** *Cariboo District:* 150 Mile House (NMC-1; RBCM-1). *Lillooet District:* Riske Creek (NMC-1). **California:** *Merced County* (MVZ-1: figs. 5-115, 5-116). *Lassen County:* Honey Lake Valley (OSUFW-1): 11.2 km SW Wendel (MVZ-1). **Idaho:** *Jefferson County:* 4.8 km SW Hamer (UMFBP[DFP]-1). **Nevada:** *Elko County:* N end Ruby Lake (MVZ-1). **Oregon:** *Harney County:* Burns: Malheur National Wildlife Refuge (USNM-1); Narrows (LACM-1). *Lake County:* Warner Valley near Adel (OSUFW-1; PSM-2). **Utah:** *Box Elder County:* mouth of Bear River: Black Slough (USNM-1), Brown's Overflow (USNM-2); Bear River Migratory Bird Refuge (DWWRS, NWPW-55 live captives: figs. 5-113, 5-114; UMFBP(DFP)-1]). *Davis County:* New State Gun Club—8 km W Centerville (UMNH-2). MEXICO: **Puebla:** Laguna del Carmen (BMNH-4). **Captive origin** (AMNH-2; MVZ-2; UWGB[RC]-1).

OTHER REFERENCES. Bailey and Niedrach 1965, vol. 1. Bellrose 1976, 1980. Cogswell 1977. Grinnell, Bryant, and Storer 1918. Johnsgard 1965. Kortright 1942. J. Phillips 1923 (descr. from Grinnell, Bryant, and Storer 1918). Ridgway 1895. Snyder and Lumsden 1951.

Northern Shoveler

Canard souchet. Pato Cucharón

Anas clypeata (Linnaeus)

APPEARANCE. Small size, a dusky face with often blotchy cheek-stripe, orange base color on bill and feet, and usually inconspicuous (or absent) wing-patches describe the downy Northern Shoveler. Yellowish white or grayish yellowish white base color, contrasting well with the grayish brown upper parts, marks the belly and undertail regions. Most Northern Shoveler ducklings have discernibly long bills (compare culmen measurements and EC/OBT ratios of various *Anas* ducklings in Table 1, Appendix A).

VARIATION. Most downy Northern Shovelers appear long-billed, dusky-faced, and brown-backed, but face pattern, wing-patches, dorsal spots, and foot color frequently vary. The 'spoon bill' that distinguishes adult shovelers of all species is sometimes not obvious in very young ducklings, e.g., Bent (1923) and Bauer and Glutz von Blotzheim (1968) found bills of newly hatched Northern Shovelers unmistakeably spatulate, but J. Phillips (1925: 12) described the bill of his specimen as "not markedly spatulate" (compare bill development of Northern Shoveler ducklings in figs. 5-26 to 5-36).

Hues of the downy Northern Shoveler's face may be dusky ochraceous yellow, brownish yellow, or grayish yellowish white. The large ear-spot remains constant, but the eye-stripe is sometimes incomplete, and the cheek-stripe often absent (see paler variant, pl. 7). Some 'sculpturing' of the usually heavy eye-stripe before and immediately after the eye seems characteristic, (Fjeldså 1977: fig. 10). The cheek-stripe, when reduced to a grayish wash on the cheeks, brings the poorly-marked subocular crescent into greater prominence (pl. 7; compare 2 Northern Shoveler variants).

Both palaearctic and nearctic Northern Shoveler ducklings may lack wing-patches (Dresser 1871-1881, vol. 6; A. C. Meinertzhagen *in* Witherby et al. [1939] 1943, vol. 3; Cramp and Simmons 1977) or have inconspicuous pale or brownish ones (e.g., Delacour 1956: Scott pl. 23; Bailey and Niedrach 1965, vol. 1: Hochbaum pl. 18; Fjeldså 1977: pl. 6). Evidently not typical of most nearctic Northern Shoveler ducklings are conspicuous wing-patches on the Manitoba duckling shown in Palmer (1976, vol. 2: 370, C. Nelson col. pl.). Many downies from the Delta area (as well as the model for Nelson's drawing) had such light markings, but others were darker, including two entirely dark-winged broods observed in 1977. Two Northern Shoveler specimens from Sheep Creek, Wyoming (CM), also had conspicuous pale wing-patches, but wing-patches on ducklings from other areas were nearly always inconspicuous or lacking. Variation in dorsal spotting is similar. The two Wyoming specimens had large, conspicuous dorsal spots, as did many ducklings from Manitoba, Saskatchewan, and North Dakota, but others from those areas, from British Columbia, and from eastern Canada had small or inconspicuous dorsal spots, virtually lacking in a few specimens. In older ducklings, dorsal spots and wing-patches often are bleached nearly white.

All live nearctic ducklings had tarsi and toes contrastingly patterned in a shade of orange and grayish brown, as in some palaearctic Northern Shovelers (Heinroth and Heinroth 1928, vol. 3: pl. 108; Fjeldså 1977: pl. 6), but none had the dark greenish or olive tint described in other palaearctic ducklings by Bauer and Glutz von Blotzheim (1968), Harrison (1975, 1978), and Cramp and Simmons (1977). A few North American individuals with dull base color appeared generally dark-footed.

SOURCE OF SPECIMENS. **British Columbia:** *Cariboo District:* Williams Lake: 144 Mile Road [=private road E through O. Fletcher ranch] (NMC-2; RBCM-1). *Lillooet District:* Springhouse (PSM-1). **Manitoba:** Churchill (NMC-1: figs. 5-33, 5-34). Clarkleigh (NWPW-7 live [*ss:* MMMN-1]). Delta (DWWRS-66 live: figs. 5-26 to 5-28 [*ss:* D-1; MMMN-2: fig. 5-30; UMFBP(DFP)-1; UWBM-1]; D-8: figs. 5-35, 5-36). Minnedosa (DWWRS-8 live). **Prince Edward Island:** *Queens County:* Mount Stewart (NMC-1). **Québec:** *Huntingdon County:* Dundee (NMC-2). **Saskatchewan:** Davidson (CM-1). Kindersley (PMBRC-5). South Arm Last Mountain Lake (NMC-8: figs. 5-31, 5-32). Stalwart (CM-1: fig. 5-29). **Minnesota:** *Anoka County:* Cedar Creek (BMNH-2). *Nobles County* (RLWS-10 live captives [*ss:* PSM-1]): field near Round Lake (RLWS-7 live). **North Dakota:** *McLean County:* Turtle Lake ((BMNH-6). *Mountrail County:* Parshall (BMNH-2). **Oregon:** *Lake County:* Paisley: Chewaucan Marsh (OSUFW-1). **Wyoming:** *Albany County:* Sheep Creek: 11.3 km SW Toltec (CM-2).

OTHER REFERENCES. Baird, Brewer, and Ridgway 1884, vol. 1 (quoted in Ridgway 1895). Bellrose 1976, 1980. Dement'ev and Gladkov (1952) 1967, vol. 4. Gollop and Marshall 1954. Grinnell, Bryant, and Storer 1918. Kortright 1942. Roberts 1932, vol. 2. Schiøler 1925. Southwick 1953.

Pochards, tribe Aythyini

North American genus: *Aythya* Boie

DISTRIBUTION AND TAXONOMY. Like the dabbling ducks (Anatini), the pochards are found on every continent, but with fewer representative species. As a group, the pochards have a distinctive appearance and structure (Delacour and Mayr 1945; Johnsgard 1961c; 1965); they are believed to be monophyletic (Livezey 1986). Broad-billed pochards (*Aythya* spp.) inhabit mainly the northern hemisphere, narrow-billed pochards (*Netta* spp.) the southern, although neither group is restricted to one hemisphere. Adults of the two genera are well-defined by differences in feather proteins (Brush 1976) and osteology (Livezey 1986); Brush found SCM-proteins of all *Aythya* identical except for those of the Redhead, *A. americana*, which resembled those of *Netta*. Color and pattern of downy Redhead, Ring-necked, Rosybilled, *Netta peposaca* (RLWS live captive; FMNH; Paraguay: Alto Paraguay), and southern pochards, *Netta erythrophthalma* subspp. (FMNH; see also Delacour 1959: Scott pl. 11) are closely similar; bill structure of Redhead and Rosybilled ducklings is virtually identical.

Brush (1976) and Livezey (1986) placed two aberrant species, the Marbled Teal, *Marmaronetta angustirostris*, and the [probably extinct] Pink-headed Duck, *Rhodonessa caryophyllacea*, with the pochards rather than the dabblers—where Delacour and Mayr (1945) and Delacour (1959) had placed them provisionally—and found *Rhodonessa* more closely related to *Netta* than to *Aythya*. Livezey named *Rhodonessa* the sister genus of both *Netta* and *Aythya*, with *Marmaronetta* the sister genus of all three (Livezey 1986: 743, fig. 4), confirming the relationship of Pink-headed Duck, Marbled Teal and pochards suggested earlier by Johnsgard (1961c; 1965; 1978).

Although yellow pochard ducklings have a quite different appearance from the dark scaup and Tufted ducklings, holarctic *Aythya* are very close genetically (Numachi et al. 1983; Patton and Avise 1983). Hollister (1919) believed the Ring-necked Duck to be the nearctic representative of the palaearctic Tufted Duck, but he also considered the Ringneck more closely related to the Canvasback and Redhead than to either scaup species. Kessler and Avise (1984) suggest that the Ring-necked Duck—the appearance of whose downy young places it with the yellow pochard ducklings (Johnsgard 1961b; 1965)—may be intermediate between the Canvasback/Redhead species-pair and the Lesser Scaup.

Close physical resemblance of downy Tufted and scaup ducks suggests common ancestry of the three species at some time in their evolutionary history. Possibly, two groups of scaup became separated during a period of glaciation, the Lesser Scaup evolving in the cool interior grasslands of North America and the Greater Scaup in subarctic wetlands south of the Eurasian glaciers, which were less extensive than those in North America (e.g., Ploeger 1968: fig 1a). During the time of separation, the Greater Scaup gave rise to the Tufted Duck and differentiated into subspecies. Both Greater Scaup and Tufted Duck developed 'blue' eye-color as half-grown ducklings, but the Lesser Scaup, pushed southward by extensive glaciation, developed neither subspecies [that we know of] nor 'blue' eye-color. As the glaciers receded, signaling the beginning of the present interglacial period, the Lesser Scaup followed the wetlands northward, and the Greater Scaup followed them eastward across the Bering Sea and southward down the Mackenzie Valley into northern and eastern Canada. Greater and Lesser scaup now share common nesting areas (e.g., Alaska: Minto Lakes [UAM; Brina Kessel, pers. comm. 1978]; Commander Islands [Stejneger 1885]; Northwest Territories: Great Slave Lake [David Trauger, pers. comm. 1972]; Manitoba: Churchill [CM; NMC], Godfrey 1986)

APPEARANCE. On the basis of general plumage color, ducklings of the five North American *Aythya* species fall into two groups:

the yellow and olive-brown pochards and the dark olive scaup—apparently a vast difference, but in fact only one of degree. The base color in all five species is high chroma yellow or greenish yellow (only the darkest scaup ducklings lack this) and the pattern color is a shade of olive or olive-brown. In the more generally melanic scaup ducklings, the basic *Aythya* pattern is simply more extensive than in the yellow pochard ducklings (as also in dark palaearctic Tufted Duck vs. yellow-and-brown Common Pochard, *Aythya ferina*; Goodwin 1984). The remaining areas of yellow color consequently are dulled by an overlay of dusky or 'sooty' down-tips; only the belly and sometimes the lores remain clearly, often brilliantly, yellow on most downy scaup. In contrast, the dorsal spots and wing-patches of holarctic yellow pochards are more prominent than those on most ducklings of other tribes: both pairs of dorsal spots are often continuous with the base color of the underside.

Similarities among *Aythya* ducklings are most obvious in the face pattern and in what I call the 'Aythyan hood', which extends forward to the bill in downy Canvasback and scaup, but stops short at the wide yellow forehead in Redhead and Ring-necked ducklings. Behind the eye, it dips downward toward the ear (compare Ring-necked fig. 6-17 and profile scaup figs. with Anatini profiles and lighter-colored *Aythya* figs. 6-7, 6-22, 6-24; also yellow pochard and scaup figs. on pl. 8 with Anatini figs. on pls. 6 & 7). Faint, irregular lines near the eyes and on the cheeks of certain Redhead and Ring-necked ducklings are somewhat more prominent on downy Canvasbacks and are much darker on scaup ducklings. The blue-eyed, palaearctic Tufted Duck (RLWS; Iceland: Mývatn) is darkest of all—like a Lesser Scaup lightly dipped in soot.

The eye-stripe is the least prominent element of the face pattern in all downy *Aythya* (in the Red-crested Pochard, *Netta rufina*, it is divided behind the eye [Millais 1913, vol. 1]). In the yellow pochards, it is usually thin, incomplete, or lacking, but in the dark Tufted duckling and in downy scaup of both species, it may be short and thin behind the eye and wide and blotchy in front of it. An irregular cheek-stripe—broken, faint, or lacking on yellow pochard ducklings—is usually prominent on scaup ducklings.

Both posture and structure of tarsus and bill are similar among all North American *Aythya* ducklings. On day-old ducklings, the heavy tarsi, set well back on the body, are about 30% shorter than the middle toe with claw (IIIw). Proportions of goldeneyes are similar, but the tarsi of eiders, scoters, and greater mergansers (*Mergus* spp.) are relatively longer, those of Ruddy ducklings shorter (compare TMT/IIIW ratios of diving spp. in Table 1, Appendix A). Large paddle areas allow day-old *Aythya* ducklings to swim and dive with ease and to balance without difficulty while preening. Scaup ducklings of both species often rest upright on their heels in the manner of scoters and eiders (e.g., female *A. marila* fig., pl. 8).

Bill structure of yellow pochard ducklings differs somewhat from that of the dark scaup. In a dorsal view, the bills of young pochards flare out from the base only slightly (figs. 6-3, 6-11, 6-18) and bills of older ducklings have more or less parallel sides (figs. 6-8, 6-16, 6-23), whereas bills of scaup ducklings widen markedly anterior to the nostrils, then taper evenly to a smooth, rounded point (see bills of very young ducklings in figs. 6-30, 6-32, 6-39, 6-41; note that bills of older Greater Scaup ducklings are heavier at the base and less 'gracefully' curved than those of the Lesser Scaup, e.g., figs. 6-34, 6-36, 6-43, 6-45). The 'horns' (Illustrated Glossary, pp. xviii-xix) of the bill become more prominent on all *Aythya* species as the ducklings mature.

BEHAVIOR. Hatchery-reared downy *Aythya* display all degrees of aggression toward ducklings of their own and other tribes. In a group of mixed *Aythya* species, Redhead ducklings almost invariably emerge as the most aggressive species, pecking all except Ring-necked ducklings, and harassing the Lesser Scaup continually. Collias and Collias (1956) and Mattson (1973) found wild Redhead ducklings also more aggressive than Canvasbacks in mixed (host-parasite) broods. In other groups containing downy *Aythya* as well as dabbler ducklings or other diving species, Redheads and Canvasbacks pecked goldeneyes, and downy Lesser Scaup pecked the tiny Buffleheads. Dabbler ducklings are dominated by all downy *Aythya* except the downy Ring-necked Duck, which seems to give way to ducklings of all species. Aggression usually takes the form of pursuit, with heel-nipping and down-pulling. Often, the aggressor will attack the same individual repeatedly over 10 or 15 minutes' time. In the rare instances where an *Aythya* duckling was attacked by a (usually larger) duckling from another tribe (e.g., eider, scoter), bill-fighting ensued. Redhead and Common Eider (*v-nigra*) ducklings uttered short, 'querulous', monosyllabic calls as they sparred, but I heard no sound from quarreling Lesser Scaup and White-winged Scoter ducklings.

Such antagonistic encounters are not confined solely to ducklings in the artificial, often overcrowded, conditions of captivity. Aggressive ducklings may become aggressive adults, but probably for quite different reasons, e.g., competition for winter feeding areas (Alexander 1980, re: Canvasback; Hepp and Hair 1984, re: dabblers) and loafing sites (Bengtson 1966, re: Harlequin Duck) competitiion among female Canvasbacks over mates (Lovvorn 1989), fighting over nests by Canvasback (host) and Redhead (parasite) hens (McKinney 1954: 149, photos), or defense of brood (Cynthia Bluhm, re: Canvasback, pers. comm., August 1984).

Aside from the overt aggression observed in hatchery-reared birds, there were marked differences in the 'temperament' of *Aythya* ducklings. Canvasback ducklings that I had handled as day-old young—confiding little things that climbed around my neck and nibbled at my hair, twittering all the while with small, 'gravelly' voices—became thoroughly wild at about 10 days of age. The slightest indication of my presence made them draw into a tight group at the far end of their enclosure. They regarded me silently, all eyes fixed as if in one body, their long bills and sloping foreheads already apparent. No amount of coaxing could induce them to move or to make a single sound. Only when I had retreated did they slowly disperse to resume their activity. Redhead ducklings are similar, but less 'wild', whereas Ring-necked ducklings prove to be the 'tamest' of the pochards.

Broods of Greater and Lesser scaup ducklings that I raised at Delta were as lively as goldeneyes. Young Lesser Scaup often leapt out of their enclosure to go on 'expeditions' around the hatchery and even out-of-doors. One afternoon, two such wanderers were found swimming with adult Canvasbacks and Redheads on the Delta Station pond—the biologist who retrieved them was heard to murmur, "Little black devils!" as he put them back into their pen.

These observations suggest a degree of interspecific variation in 'wildness' that may be partly genetic in origin. However, Bluhm found a marked difference in the behavior of hen-reared and hand-reared Canvasback young in Delta's captive flock. She (and also Kostow in subsequent years) found the hand-reared birds easier to catch and easier to handle once caught. Bluhm observed that "natural brooding of ducklings by Canvasback hens appears to have a profound and lasting effect upon the young," an environmental influence that was "evident until the following spring" (Cynthia Bluhm, letter to the author, August 1984).

Aythya hens (and sometimes, Ring-necked drakes; Severinghaus and Benson 1947) give close attention to young broods (Hochbaum 1944; Beard 1964), but most hens of *Aythya* species (possibly excepting Lesser Scaup; J. Munro 1937) pay less attention to older ducklings as the breeding season wanes (J. Munro 1941; Hochbaum 1944). Mixed broods of

Canvasback and Redhead ducklings (the result of parasitic egg-laying by the Redhead; Weller 1959), are common (Hochbaum 1944; Mattson 1973), and the formation of large, communal broods, with or without the presence of attending females, occurs frequently among *Aythya* and other diving species (J. Munro 1941; Hochbaum 1944; Alison 1976).

Aythya ducklings show a gradual transition in food-gathering techniques from exclusive dabbling in ducklings one or two days old (Williams 1956; Collias and Collias 1963; Bartonek and Hickey 1969) to both dabbling and diving in three- to seven-day ducklings (Collias and Collias 1963; Beard 1964; Bartonek and Hickey 1969) to exclusive diving in three- to four-week young (Beard 1964). Food dives are invariably preceded by head-under searching. In Bartonek's glass-fronted aquarium (ca. 1.2 m deep; stocked with various *Daphnia* species), Lesser Scaup (4 d.) searched for food with bill and front of head submerged (as described in young goldeneyes by Myres 1957 and Eriksson 1976), although no very young *Aythya* ducklings appeared to use this as their principal food-gathering technique (compare Aythyini with Somateriini, pp. 111-13, and Mergini, pp. 120-24).

Young *Aythya* ducklings appeared almost reptilian as they dived in Bartonek's aquarium: their down feathers, flattened by the pressure of the water, revealed their slim body shape and caused their eyes, bills, and feet to seem abnormally large in comparison; they held their winglets close to their bodies as their feet propelled them strongly downward. Round bubbles of air, buffeted into shapelessness by the turbulence surrounding the ducklings, escaped to the surface of the water. After a few seconds, they "rose buoyantly as if suddenly released by a spring" (J. Munro 1941: 120, re: adult male Greater Scaup).

Vocalizations of downy *Aythya* are generally similar in form, accent, and syllabification to those of Anatini ducklings, but some are lower-pitched and a bit slower, with more harmonics (compare sonagrams of isolation distress calls of *Anas* and *Aythya* spp. *in* Kear 1968: figs. 10-11). The sum of these small differences is a distinctive, 'husky' timbre, aptly described for the Canvasback duckling as a "rolling peep" (Edward Ward *in* Hochbaum 1944: 101-2). Pleasure calls of the dark scaup ducklings (especially *affinis*) are quieter and more polysyllabic than those of downy yellow pochards. Lesser Scaup (ca. 2 wks) sometimes utter a soft trill similar to the sleepy call of young Canada goslings.

Canvasback

Morillon à dos blanc. Pato Coacoxtle.

Aythya valisineria (Wilson)

APPEARANCE. The downy Canvasback's narrow nail and longer, narrower bill will distinguish it from the paler Redhead and darker Ring-necked ducklings, which have otherwise quite similar color and pattern (compare 3 spp. on pl. 8, and figs. 6-3, 6-6, 6-8, with 6-11, 6-14, 6-16 & 6-18, 6-21, 6-23; see Hochbaum 1944: 101, fig. 5, and Palmer 1976, vol. 3: fig. p. 140). In dorsal view, the pointed apex of the dark mesial feathering meets the bill, and the dark forehead color often goes part way down the sides of the 'horns' as well (figs. 6-6, 6-7). In front view, the combination of long, dark bill and dark forehead gives the downy Canvasback a comically 'horse-faced' appearance. A partial light eye-ring shows up well on many ducklings (Dzubin 1959: 287, photos of Class Ia and IIa ducklings) and the dark 'Aythyan hood' is well-defined. Prominent longitudinal ridges on the 'horns' of the bill, characteristic of adult Canvasbacks, also appear on very young live ducklings (e.g., Bailey and Niedrach 1965, vol. 1: 173, J. H. Stoudt photo of 2 nestlings with female parent in threat posture).

VARIATION. The prominent yellow dorsal spots and wing-patches of Canvasback ducklings usually contrast well with the darker pattern color. As in downy Redheads and

Ringnecks, the large shoulder-spots and rump-spots are often continuous with the light color of the underside (compare ducklings of 3 spp. on pl. 8) or are separated from it by only a thin line of darker down. However, both Bent (1923) and Forbush (1925) found the rump-spots on their specimens inconspicuous, and Roberts (1932) described none at all.

Plumage variation in downy Canvasback consists of differences in darkness of the pattern color, in prominence of the face pattern, and in *chroma* or *hue* of the yellow base color. Of the three yellow-plumaged North American *Aythya* ducklings, downy Ringnecks have the darkest pattern color, Redheads the lightest, and Canvasback intermediate. Dorsal color of ducklings of all three species—but especially those of Canvasback and Redhead—may vary individually: Hochbaum (1944: 100) cited "some Redheads...[that were]...even a shade darker than some Canvasbacks" (e.g., dark Redhead variant on pl. 8; dark Redhead brood seen at NPWRC). A few darker Canvasback ducklings may have a moderately conspicuous face pattern consisting of an irregular, often broken, line extending from the rictus to the region above the ear, and thin pre-ocular or post-ocular lines, or both. These usually consist of a few pale streaks or smudges around or behind the eye; they are seldom connected to more conspicuous patterns.

Most Canvasback ducklings are some tint of bright yellow at hatching (e.g., 5Y to 7.5Y), but the base color of some darker ducklings is duller, less 'greenish', and more orange (e.g., 4Y). The brilliant natal *chroma* fades rapidly to a duller—but still 'greenish'—"straw yellow" (Ridgway 1912) in ducklings about four days old (Dzubin 1959: 286).

Colors of the unfeathered parts usually vary more or less directly with the general darkness or dullness of the plumage colors. Darker ducklings have browner bills and grayer feet; yellower ducklings have 'bluer' bills and yellower feet, which are often quite orange on the sides of the toes and along the webs of the inner toe and hallux.

The face pattern of downies (ca. 10 d. and older) is shadowy at best. Only faint traces of yellow remain in the plumage of four-week-old ducklings. The spotted pattern of the back remains, but in shades of brownish gray and gray-white rather than olive-brown and yellow (e.g., Dzubin 1959: photos & descr. 4 d. to 56 d. ducklings). The adult profile also becomes distinctive at this time (Hochbaum 1944: 102-3; Linduska 1964: 20, Herbert Dill photo of Class IIc ducklings).

SOURCE OF SPECIMENS. **Alberta:** Mirror: Buffalo Lake (NMC-1). La Glace Lake (MMMN-4: figs. 6-8, 6-9). **British Columbia:** *Cariboo District:* 150 Mile House (NMC-1);153 Mile House [see *A. platyrhynchos*, p. 90] (NMC-1). *Lillooet District:* Springhouse (OSUFW-1). **Manitoba:** Clear Lake (NMC-1). Delta (DWWRS, NWPW, UFS[DM]-31 live: figs. 6-3 to 6-5 [*ss:* MMMN-1]; JPWT-3 live captives; CM-1; D-11; MMMN-3). Minnedosa (DWWRS-14 live [*ss:* MMMN-2: figs. 6-6, 6-7; UWDWE-1]). Saint Ambroise (NWPW-1 live). **Saskatchewan:** Kindersley (PMBRC-3). South Arm Last Mountain Lake (NMC-3). **Minnesota:** *Mahnomen County:* 9.6 km SE Mahnomen (BMNH-2). *Marshall County:* Mud Lake (BMNH-2). **North Dakota:** *Steele County:* Hope (FMNH-1).

OTHER REFERENCES. Anderson 1985. Bellrose 1976, 1980. Bluhm 1981. Brooks 1903. Cogswell 1977. Delacour 1959. Gollop and Marshall 1954. Grinnell, Bryant, and Storer 1918. Harrison 1978. Johnsgard 1965. Kortright 1942. Kuroda 1939. Lovvorn 1989. Mendall 1958. J. Munro 1937. J. Phillips 1925. Southwick 1953.

Redhead

Morillon à tête rouge. Pato Cabecirrojo.
Aythya americana (Eyton)

APPEARANCE. The Redhead is typically the lightest-colored of the *Aythya* ducklings as well as the yellowest over all of all wild ducklings

(Weller 1957). Its yellowness is enhanced by the unpatterned face, by the lack of strong contrast between base and pattern colors (pl. 8; Roberts 1932, vol. 2; Southwick 1953), and by prominent dorsal spots often continuous with the base color on the legs and undertail (but J. Phillips [1925: 164] reported "barely visible" dorsal spots and wing-patches; see also Kortright 1942: Shortt pl. 34; Bailey and Niedrach 1965, vol. 1: Hochbaum pl. 19; Bellrose 1980: Hines pl. 24). Rarely, there is a tiny central dorsal spot anterior to the wings. The light olive-brown pattern color has numerous yellow down-tips, the 'Aythyan hood' is less

well-marked than in Canvasback and Ring-necked ducklings, and the round-headed profile is apparent at some distance in ducklings of all ages.

The grayish brown iris of the downy Redhead appears almost blackish against the unpatterned, bright yellow face (Weller 1957: frontispiece), and there is a partial pale eye-ring or crescent behind and below the eye (pl. 8). In the hand, the wide, rounded nail and pointed, light-colored mesial bill feathering are diagnostic, compared to the narrower, oval nail and [usually] rounded bill feathering of the downy Ringneck (W. Todd 1936; compare nail and bill-feathering characters of Canvasback, Redhead, and Ring-necked ducklings in figs. 6-3, 6-6, 6-8; 6-11, 6-14, 6-16 & 6-18, 6-21, 6-23; see also Hochbaum 1944: 101, fig. 5, and Palmer 1976, vol. 3: fig. p. 140). The nostril is shorter and rounder (as in the Ring-necked duckling) and set closer to the base of the bill than in the downy Canvasback (compare figs. 6-5 & 6-20). The 'bluish' gray upper mandible and yellow-orange lower mandible are more brightly colored than those of other *Aythya* ducklings.

Weller (1957: 31) reported a noticeable sex difference in eye-color in Redheads eight or 10 weeks old: "the male's iris is...dull straw yellow [=Munsell 6Y 8.4/6.0; Hamly 1949]...that of the female...dull yellow-lime with a brownish center." In ducklings three to four months old, he found the eyes of males "brighter," those of females "more brown than greenish."

VARIATION. Hochbaum (1944), Weller (1957), and Palmer (1976, vol. 3) noted variation in general darkness of pattern color sufficient to mislead an observer relying solely on color to identify Redhead and Canvasback ducklings (see 2 Redhead variants on pl. 8; also pars. on Canvasback, above).

Presumably darker specimens were described by Brooks (1920: 355), who found "...the colour of the downy young exactly the same in both birds [i.e., Redheads and Ringnecks]", but I saw no downy Redheads as dark as Ringnecks or any Ringnecks as pale as Redheads. Dark-backed Redheads often have inconspicuous face-markings (similar to those of downy Canvasbacks) and 'browner' foreheads (olive-brown bases of yellow down-plumes are longer than those of typically yellow variants). They have also darker bills and feet (Weller 1957).

Colors of bill and feet vary little among bright yellow Redhead ducklings; bills are 'colorful' (unlike the duller, browner bill of the downy Canvasback or the darker, more contrastingly colored bill of the Ring-necked duckling) and the feet are always discernibly yellow, whether dull or bright. I did not find the combination of pale yellow plumage and dark bill and feet (e.g., Delacour 1959: Scott pl. 11; Harrison 1978: Burton pl. 5) on young, wild Redhead ducklings.

As in other *Aythya* ducklings, the brilliant greenish yellow tints of the downy Redhead's natal plumage fade quickly. The processes of fading, pushing out of old feathers by new, and growth of new gray under-down (see Oring 1968 re: downy Gadwall) continue in the Redhead until, after three or four weeks, the olive-brown and yellow natal plumage is almost entirely replaced by shades of brownish gray and yellowish white. The growth of new gray down also has the effect of blurring or softening the pattern color and darkening the base color (e.g., Bailey and Niedrach 1965, vol. 1: 170, photo of Class Ic brood [note pale, still-bright dorsal down tips]).

SOURCE OF SPECIMENS. **Alberta:** La Glace Lake (MMMN-1). Mirror: Buffalo Lake (NMC-1). Edmonton (FMNH-1). **British Columbia:** *Cariboo District:* 150 Mile House (NMC-1); Sorenson Lake [J. Munro 1945: 99] (NMC-1). **Manitoba:** Delta (29 live: figs. 6-18 to 6-20 [*ss:* D-3; MMMN-5; UWBM-1]; D-19: figs. 6-23, 6-24; MMMN-1): Portage Creek (D-2). Minnedosa (DWWRS-14 live [*ss:* MMMN-1: figs. 6-21, 6-22; UWDWE-1; UWBM-1]). Oak Lake (NMC-2). Saint Ambroise (NWPW-3 live). Whitewater Lake (D-1). **Saskatchewan:** Kindersley (PMBRC-5). South Arm Last Mountain Lake (NMC-1). **Kansas:** *Barton County:* Cheyenne Bottoms (UMFBP[DFP]-1). **Minnesota:** *Big Stone County:* NE Ortonville (BMNH-1). *Mahnomen County:* SE Mahnomen (BMNH-1). *Nobles County* (RLWS-16 live captives [*ss:* PSM-1]; BMNH-3). **North Dakota:** *McHenry County:* Upham (UFS[DM]-4 live). **Oregon:** *Baker County:* Upper Baldock Slough—17.7 km NE Baker (OSUFW-1). *Lake County:* Summer Lake (OSUFW-1; PSM-1). **Utah:** *Box Elder County:* Bear River Marsh [probably= collective name for complex of marshes along Bear River] (OSUFW-1).

OTHER REFERENCES. Bent 1923. Brooks 1903. Cogswell 1977. Forbush 1925. Gollop and Marshall 1954. Grinnell, Bryant, and Storer 1918. Johnsgard 1965. Kuroda 1939. Mendall 1958. Ridgway 1895 [1887] 1896, 1900. W. Todd 1936, 1940.

Ring-necked Duck

Morillon à collier. Pato Piquianillado.
Aythya collaris (Donovan)

APPEARANCE. Contrasting colors and bold dorsal markings are the salient characteristics of the newly hatched Ring-necked duckling. Dorsal spots are the most extensive of those on any North American duckling: the large shoulder- and rump-spots are nearly always continuous with yellow color on the legs and undertail (a thin line of dark down enclosing the rump-spots is seldom complete), and there is sometimes a variable central dorsal spot anterior to the wings (pl. 8; also Palmer 1976, 3: 466, col. pl.; Kortright 1942: Shortt pl. 34; Delacour 1959: Scott pl. 11). The 'Aythyan hood' is especially well-marked, and in dorsal view, the apex of the mesial bill feathering is usually rounded (vs. pointed in the downy Redhead [W. Todd 1936]). A relatively narrow oval nail, a wide yellow forehead, and contrastingly patterned feet are also distinctive.

VARIATION. The central dorsal spot described by some authors (e.g., Baird, Brewer, and Ridgway 1884, vol. 2; Bent 1923; Kortright 1942; Mendall 1958) was not recorded by others, including Sennett (1887), J. Phillips (1925: 183-84 & Brooks pl. 59), Delacour (1959), Harrison (1978: 74; shoulder-spots also not recorded), and Bellrose (1980: Hines pl. 24). The spot was highly variable on live birds from Manitoba, Minnesota, and Ontario, and on museum specimens from British Columbia, Minnesota, Ontario, and Saskatchewan. Sometimes, it was a light, dull spot one cm or less in diameter or

consisted of a just a few pale plumes; other times, it was absent. An Ontario duckling (ROM; ca. 15 d.) had the most prominent central spot: it was about two cm long, narrow, and much duller and paler than the larger lateral spots. Even a small spot may become prominent on older ducklings on which the yellow base color has bleached nearly white.

Face pattern elements of the downy Ring-necked Duck vary little. The wide, yellow forehead is nearly always clear and unmarked anterior to the distinctlively rounded dark crown, but in two older ducklings (ROM; ca. 8 d. & ca. 17 d.), the olive-brown bases of the yellow forehead down were unusually long, darkening and dulling the paler base color. Inconspicuous face stripes appear on nearly all newly hatched ducklings. These may consist of a tiny (often absent) pre-ocular spot, a thin post-ocular line or streak (usually incomplete but sometimes thinly connected to the dark occiput), and a faint, thin stripe or small spot on the ear that sometimes extends forward as an irregular line to the pre-ocular spot (as in downy Canvasback). A smudged brownish pre-ocular area (e.g., Mendall 1958: pl. 14) appeared on few specimens, but the "fine eye-ring" (his p. 281) was present to some extent on all downy Ring-necked Ducks. The eye-ring often is eclipsed by the brilliant yellow face colors of newly hatched ducklings, but becomes more prominent in older, faded ducklings, which also have their yellow cheeks darkened and dulled by the growth of new gray under-down (fig. 6-17).

Some downy Ringnecks have yellower tarsal base color and others are grayer (Mendall 1958), but nearly all have good contrast of base and pattern colors, especially between the dark upper mandible and the brighter orange lower mandible of the bill and on the joints of the toes. The contrast in foot color is evident also in many study skins of young ducklings, but is lacking on the feet of older ducklings, which have more uniformly gray feet.

The downy Ring-necked Duck's brilliant natal colors fade to shades of brownish gray and yellowish white or grayish yellow in ducklings three or four weeks old. Usually, the clear forehead, dark crown, and large dorsal spots remain prominent.

DISCUSSION. The nail of the downy Ring-necked Duck is narrower than that of the Redhead duckling (W. Todd 1936; Mendall 1958), but wider than that of the downy Canvasback (compare figs. 6-3, 6-6, 6-8 with 6-11, 6-14, 6-16 & 6-18, 6-21, 6-23; see also Mendall 1958). Although there is some individual variation of nail-shape in all three species, the general form can be classified as narrow or flattened oval (Canvasback), oval (Ringneck), or round (Redhead). The downy Redhead's nail, rounded posteriorly and having a long, curving anterior edge, is nearly as wide as it is long; the Canvasback's narrow nail, either rounded or rather pointed posteriorly with (often) nearly parallel sides, has a short, shallowly curved anterior edge. The downy Ringneck's nail is between the two, either rounded or more or less triangular posteriorly, with the sides of the nail flaring slightly or moderately.

SOURCE OF SPECIMENS. **British Columbia:** *Cariboo District:* Goldpan Lake [=Donnelly Lake] (NMC-1). *Lillooet District:* Lily Pad Lake (ROM-1); 130 Mile Lake [J. Munro 1945: 98] (ROM-1); Tatton Lake (ROM-1). *Range 4, Coast District:* Nulki Lake (PSM-2; ROM-1). **Manitoba:** Clarkleigh: East Meadows Ranch (DWWRS-3 live). Delta (D-1). Minnedosa (DWWRS-9 live). Shoal Lake [village] (D-1). **Ontario:** *Cochrane District:* Lillabelle Lake (ROM-2). *Dufferin County:* Luther Reservoir (ROM-1). *Frontenac County:* Dwyer's Marsh (ROM-1). *Hastings County:* Conroy's Marsh (ROM-5). *Kenora District:* Attawapiskat Lake (ROM-4); Favourable Lake Mine (ROM-5); Lac Seul (NMC-6). *Manitoulin District:* Manitoulin Island: Ice Lake (ROM-2). *Wellington County:* Luther Reservoir (DWWRS-16 live: figs. 6-11 to 6-13 [ss: D-2; MMMN-1: figs. 6-14, 6-15; UMFBP(DFP)-1; UND-2]). **Québec:** *Hunting-*

don County: Dundee (NMC-4). **Saskatchewan:** Stuart Lake (ROM-1). **Minnesota:** *Crow Wing County:* Gateway Slough [=local name for small water area W Minnesota Highway 371 NE Baxter] (BMNH-1); Graham Meadows [see *A. platyrhynchos*, p. 90] (BMNH-1). *Hubbard County:* W edge Itasca State Park: unnamed beaver pond near intersection of Minnesota Highway 200 and U. S. Highway 71 (RLWS-1 live). *Kittson County:* Twin Lakes (BMNH-1). *Mahnomen County:* Mahnomen (BMNH-6: figs. 6-16, 6-17); 8 km W Waubun (BMNH-1). *Otter Tail County:* Pelican Rapids (FMNH-1). *Roseau County:* Ross: Roseau River Wildlife Management Area (DWWRS-3 live). **Pennsylvania:** *Crawford County:* Linesville (CM-1).

OTHER REFERENCES. Bailey and Niedrach 1965, vol. 1. Beard 1964. Bauer and Glutz von Blotzheim 1969. Brooks 1903, 1920. Coues (1872) 1903, vol. 2. Forbush 1925. Gollop and Marshall 1954. Grinnell, Bryant, and Storer 1918. Hochbaum 1944. Hohman 1985. Johnsgard 1965. Ridgway [1887] 1896, 1900. Roberts 1932, vol. 2. Southwick 1953. W. Todd 1940. Witherby et al. (1939) 1943, vol. 3.

Greater Scaup

Grand Morillon. Pato Boludo.
Aythya marila (Linnaeus)

APPEARANCE. Heavier and a bit larger than a newly hatched Northern Mallard, the Greater Scaup duckling is larger and heavier at all ages than the downy Lesser Scaup (Palmer 1976, vol. 3): its bill is wider, higher at the base, and somewhat 'spade-shaped' in dorsal view (older ducklings; figs. 6-34, 6-37, 6-39, 6-41), its nail is often hooked downward less strongly, and the nail 'area' [LNxWN] is about twice as large as that of the Lesser Scaup (W. Todd 1963). The ratio of nail 'area' to height of bill at the base ([LNxWN]/HBB) in live and prepared Greater Scaup ducklings is nearly always 3.0 or greater, regardless of age or sex; that of live and prepared downy Lesser Scaup is nearly always less than 3.0 (compare meas. and ratios of both spp. in Table 1, Appendix A).

Nearctic Greater Scaup (*nearctica;* Banks 1986) ducklings are somewhat darker over all than downy Lesser Scaup, their light-colored dorsal spots and supraorbital stripes smaller and duller. Both species have grayish breast-bands and inconspicuous dorsal patterns: shoulder-spots are usually small or poorly marked [but sometimes yellow and conspicuous in individual *affinis*]; wing-patches and rump-spots are inconspicuous or absent. Despite often overlapping plumage characters, no 'light' Greater Scaup is so contrastingly marked as the lightest Lesser Scaup, and no 'dark' Lesser duckling is so dark as the darkest Greater. Palaearctic ducklings (*marila*; Banks 1986) from Iceland and Siberia (*marila* and "*mariloides*", respectively [AMNH]) were among the darkest downy Greater Scaup examined (the brown cheeks of the two Siberian ducklings appeared "heavily washed with reddish" [Kenneth Parkes, notes in letter to the author, February 1976]). Kuroda (1939 [*from* Sankai 1929, vol. 6 (no other data)]), Dement'ev and Gladkov ([1952] 1967, vol. 4; no subspp.), and Cramp and Simmons (1977) also described very dark palaearctic ducklings.

Most downy Greater Scaup have poor contrast between base and pattern colors of the face (usually, 1.5 or fewer Munsell *value* steps; C. Nelson unpubl. data) and most Lesser Scaup have better contrast (usually, ca. 4.5 Munsell *value* steps; C. Nelson unpubl. data; also Harrison 1978), but some individuals of both species have moderate contrast of base and pattern colors (3 Munsell *value* steps; C. Nelson unpubl. data). Lighter-colored supraorbital areas of some Greater Scaup ducklings may be connected across the forehead by a sprinkling of dark yellow or light olive-brown plumes (fig. 6-38 & Great Slave Lake fig., pl. 8). The lore is recognizeably yellow—dark yellow or light olive-brown in dark individuals—but seldom bright. The eye-stripe may be large in front of the eye and greatly reduced behind it—post-ocular line may consist only of small spot or streak—or it may be absent in some dark-faced specimens. The pale eye-ring present on all but the darkest ducklings may be set off further from the darker yellow face by a thin line of dark down-tips encircling all or part of the eye-ring (figs. 6-29, 6-40, 6-42). Both pale eye-ring and yellow lore can be seen at some distance.

At hatching, the irides of scaup ducklings of both species are usually olive-gray (Munsell 5Y 4/1), moderate grayish olive (5Y 4/3), brownish gray (10YR 4/1), moderate yellowish brown (10YR 4/4), or moderate olive-brown (2.5Y 4/4), becoming paler with age (e.g., 7/ [*nearctica*] to 9/ [*affinis*]). Sex- and species-differences in *hue* and *chroma* of the irides are apparent after two to four weeks: eye-color *hue* of Lesser Scaup males becomes recognizeably yellow (moderate 5Y) or green-yellow (moderate 2.5GY), that of Lesser females grayer (N) or browner (dull 10YR); eye-color *hue* of Greater Scaup males becomes 'bluish' (very dull 5Y, 10Y), that of Greater females blue (dull 2.5B, 5B). Eye-color *hue* of six- or seven-week-old Greater Scaup becomes green-yellow (GY; males) or bluish green (BG; females), but the eyes still appear 'bluish' because the *chroma* of the irides in both sexes is very low (usually less than /2.0). In Lesser Scaup, the *hue* of the irides changes little between two or four and six or seven weeks, but the *chroma* of irides in both sexes is measurably higher than in Greater Scaup of the same age (moderate [/3.0] in females, moderately bright [/4.0] to very bright [/8.0] in males), hence irides of Lesser Scaup appear very pale (*values* 8.0/ to 9.0/) and—in males—distinctly yellow.

Bill and foot colors of the Greater and Lesser scaup are much alike. Base color of the bill in young ducklings of both species is always some *hue* of moderate orange (yellower in Lesser Scaup), fading to grayish pink in two-week-old ducklings, and to pinkish gray in those three weeks or older; light-colored lower mandible and eye-colors lend subtle brightness to an otherwise dark or—in older ducklings—dull appearance. Pattern color of very young Greater Scaup's bills is often 'browner', Lesser Scaup 'grayer'. Tarsal colors of newly hatched *marila* tend to be grayer and 'greener' than those of *affinis,* which are 'yellower', but the difference is often slight. Newly hatched young of both species have good contrast of tarsal colors, and both have quite 'bluish' gray tarsi and feet when half-grown.

VARIATION. Eye-color differences will distinguish between live Greater and Lesser scaup two weeks of age and older (see above), but no single character will identify with certainty either very young live scaup or prepared specimens of any age. Rather, a combination of structural and plumage characters is needed for these groups of specimens (compare Greater and Lesser scaup on pl. 8, in figs. 6-25 to 6-42, and in Table 1, Appendix A). Many small variations of plumage color and pattern are common to young ducklings of both species, especially elements of the face-pattern, size, and over all darkness. In general, eye-lines of downy Greater Scaup are poorly defined, incomplete, or absent, whereas those of Lesser Scaup, if typically thin, are well-marked and often complete (compare scaup figs. on pl. 8 & in 6-25 to 6-42). The cheek-stripe, an irregular line between rictus and nape, curves upward under the eye, downward to include the ear-spot, and often connects directly to the eye-stripe under the eye. It is usually broken or incomplete. The supraorbital stripe is often narrower, darker, duller. It is frequently interrupted by a downward dip of dark crown color over the eye in Greater Scaup ducklings (figs. 6-38, 6-40), but is wider, lighter, brighter, and usually uninterrupted in downy Lesser Scaup (but see fig. 6-33). Elements of the face pattern are poorly defined on dark-faced ducklings; the supraorbital stripe may be reduced to a brownish or yellowish spot before and behind the eye, and dark face stripes may be absent. Very young, dark-faced individuals of both species are sometimes misidentified as downy American Wigeon (compare wigeon figs., pl. 6

& 5-1 to 5-7, with scaup figs., pl. 8 & 6-25 to 6-42; compare meas. of 3 spp. in Table 1, Appendix A).

Variation in size and over all darkness is more or less continuous in Lesser Scaup ducklings, but often discontinuous in downy Greater Scaup. For example, *nearctica* ducklings from James Bay, Northwest Territories (ROM); Churchill, Manitoba (CM; 12 live); and Haines Highway, British Columbia (NMC) were smaller than Greater Scaup from other areas (e.g., Lake Winnipeg, Manitoba [13 live]; Great Slave Lake, Northwest Territories [14 live]; Iditarod River, Alaska [UAM]). Both 'light' and 'dark' individuals were found among live newly hatched Greater Scaup from Iceland, Manitoba, and the Northwest Territories. Trauger regarded similar ducklings from the West Mirage Islands (Northwest Territories: Great Slave Lake) as "dark" and "light" color phases (David Trauger, color transparencies loaned in letter to the author, December 1976), but the two variants are here considered to represent the extremes of individual and brood variation encountered in live and prepared specimens of both *marila* and *nearctica*.

DISCUSSION. The increased range (min - max), with age, of the (LNxWN)/HBB ratio in both scaup species (see scaup meas. in Table 1, Appendix A) is probably caused by two factors: one, the inclusion in a single sample of both 'small' and 'large' individuals of each species, and two, the gradual increase of a sex difference in measurements, characteristic of many waterfowl species. All measurements for both species were ultimately affected by the sex difference, but for Greater Scaup, at least, sample sizes were too small to permit analysis of the differences. The increase in range size is particularly apparent in the Greater Scaup, the sample for which includes both 'small' birds from Churchill, Manitoba, and 'large' birds from Great Slave Lake, Northwest Territories.

SOURCE OF SPECIMENS. **British Columbia:** *Cassiar District:* Haines Highway: Mile 85 (NMC-1; ROM-2). **Manitoba:** Churchill (DWWRS; NWPW-12 live: figs. 6-34, 6-36 [*ss:* MMMN-1]; CM-1: figs. 6-41, 6-42; UMMZ-1). Lake Winnipeg: Little George Island (NWPW-13 live [*ss:* MMMN-2]). **Northwest Territories:** *District of Keewatin:* James Bay: Comb Islands (CM-3). *District of Mackenzie:* Great Slave Lake: West Mirage Islands (DWWRS-14 live [*ss:* MMMN-3]); Mackenzie Delta: Aklavik (UBC-1), Richards Island (CM-4); Ptarmigan Lake (NMC-1). **Ontario:** *Kenora District:* Cape Henrietta Maria (ROM-9: figs. 6-39, 6-40). **Québec:** *Territory of New Quebec:* James Bay: Fort George ([Deignan 1947; Manning and Macpherson 1952] USNM-1). Ungava Peninsula: Leaf River 19.3 km above first rapids (NMC-1). **Alaska:** Bering Island (USNM-2). Iditarod River (UAM-1: figs. 6-37, 6-38). Killik River (USNM-1). Kipnuk: Kuguklik River near Kinak Bay (OSUFW-1). Minto Lakes (UAM-7): Little Minto Lake (UAM-3). Saint Michael (PSM-1; USNM-1). ICELAND: **Sudur-Thingeyjarsýsla:** Laxárdal (UMMZ-1); Mývatn (JPWT, RLWS-9 live: fig. 6-35; 2 frozen; AMNH-2; UWGB[RC]-1). RUSSIA**: Siberia:** Magadan: Gizhiga (AMNH-2). **Captive origin** (UWGB[RC]-1).

OTHER REFERENCES. Bauer and Glutz von Blotzheim 1969. Bellrose 1976, 1980. Brown 1945. Dresser 1871-1881, vol. 6 (quoted *in* Ridgway [1887] 1900). Millais 1913, vol. 1. Grinnell, Bryant, and Storer 1918. Fjeldså 1977. Forbush 1925. Harper 1953. Harrison 1975. Johnsgard 1965. Kortright 1942. Kurilovich, Tarkhanova, and Kharitonova 1984. Palmer 1976, vol. 3. J. Phillips 1925. Schiøler 1926. Witherby et al. (1939) 1943, vol. 3.

Lesser Scaup

Petit Morillon. Pato Boludo Chico.
Aythya affinis (Eyton)

APPEARANCE. Smaller than the newly hatched Northern Mallard, the newly hatched Lesser Scaup weighs only a bit less (compare Class Ia Northern Mallard, figs. 5-86 to 5-90, with Class Ia Lesser Scaup, figs. 6-25 to 6-29; see Table 1, Appendix A; also Kear 1970). "Age for age,

Plate 8

1 Harlequin Duck, _H. histrionicus_
Laxá, Iceland (RLWS).

2 Oldsquaw, _Clangula hyemalis_
Churchill, Manitoba (NWPW).

3 Wood Duck, _aix sponsa_
Darker variant. Magee Marsh, Ohio (UFS[DM]).
Lighter variant. Vergennes, Vermont (DWWRS).

4 Muscovy Duck, _Cairina moschata_
Santo Antonio de Guajara, Brazil (AMNH [4-6 d.]: color, pattern, and bill details) and (WT[S] captive: measurements).

5 Ring-necked Duck, _Aythya collaris_
Luther Reservoir, Ontario (DWWRS).

6 Canvasback, _A. valisineria_
Minnedosa, Manitoba (DWWRS).

7 Redhead, _A. americana_
Darker variant. Delta, Manitoba (DWWRS [2d.]).
Lighter variant. Minnedosa, Manitoba (DWWRS).

8 Greater Scaup, _A. marila nearctica_
Darker variant, male. West Mirage Islands, Northwest Territories (DWWRS).
Lighter variant, female. Churchill, Manitoba (NWPW).

9 Lesser Scaup, _A. affinis_
Darker variant, female. Strathmore, Alberta (DWWRS).
Lighter variant, male. Upham, North Dakota (UFS[DM]).

Plate 8

downy Lesser Scaups...are smaller than Greater...with [a] smaller nail on [the] bill" (Palmer 1976, vol. 3: 235). They have dark olive pattern color and good contrast of base and pattern colors (3 to 6 Munsell *value* steps; C. Nelson unpubl. data [see also Harrison 1978]). The dark eye-stripe is usually well-defined anterior to the eye, contrasting with the often bright yellow lores, and the post-ocular stripe and pale eye-ring are nearly always well-marked. The dorsal pattern is usually inconspicuous (but some Lesser Scaup ducklings have moderately bright yellow shoulder-spots): wing-patches, if present, are poorly marked and a few lack rump-spots entirely. Contrast between base and pattern colors of the face is usually good, with the post-ocular stripe and pale eye-ring nearly always present and well-marked. Compared to the bill of the Greater Scaup, that of the Lesser Scaup is smaller, more slender at the base, and more 'gracefully' spatulate in dorsal view (see pl. 8, also figs. 6-25, 6-28, 6-30, 6-32); the nail is often hooked downward more strongly.

VARIATION. See Greater Scaup, pp. 106-8. The range of variation in plumage colors of downy Lesser Scaup includes more brighter, 'yellower' birds and fewer dark ones than are found among Greater Scaup ducklings. Faces of the ducklings are generally lighter and yellower in Lesser Scaup than in Greater, with consequently better-defined pattern and better contrast with the dark crown color (pl. 8; also Trauger and Bartonek 1977: photo p. 145, wild ducklings [parasitized by leeches] with thin, complete eye-stripes). The size of Lesser Scaup ducklings varies considerably between broods; some broods are composed of relatively 'small' ducklings, some of 'large'. As well, sex differences in weight, measurements, and eye-color, first evident at about a week of age in both scaup species, overlap to some extent. For example, one Lesser Scaup female (DWWRS) was larger and heavier, throughout the eight-week study period during which I examined her daily, than most of her male siblings. Most young female Lesser Scaup have duller yellow eye-color than males, usually with a cloudy brownish ring around the pupil, but a few males have brown eyes, some females bright yellow ones. No duckling displays completely the eye-colors characteristic of the opposite sex.

'Blue' eye-color is absent in half-grown Lesser Scaup of both sexes. Also, the progression from the olive-gray or brownish gray natal colors to the more brilliant greenish yellow or yellow-green colors of the feathered (Class III) ducklings occurs more rapidly in Lesser Scaup males than in those of Greater Scaup. At four weeks, *chroma* of the irides of male Lesser Scaup ducklings ranged from about /2.0 to just over /4.0, but *chroma* of the irides of downy male Greater Scaup ranged from /1.0 to about /2.0, rarely /3.0. Irides of both male and female Lesser Scaup assumed a greenish yellow or yellow-green *hue* at about six weeks (precise time of color change varied widely), but only the eyes of males became distinctly brilliant: yellow-green irides of one eight-week male had a *chroma* of /8.0. Except for becoming steadily paler, irides of nearly all Lesser Scaup females remained some shade of gray, olive-gray, grayish olive, or grayish olive-green. Transitional colors occurring between these dull ones and the "brown...[to]...olive-yellow" eye-colors of year-old female Lesser Scaup (Trauger 1974: 245) are unknown.

SOURCE OF SPECIMENS. **Alberta:** Athabasca Delta: Mamawi Lake (ROM-1). Brooks (ROM-1). Cooking Lake (UFS[DM]-8 live [*ss:* MMMN-2]). Indus (UBC-1). McNeil Lake near Beaverlodge (NMC-2). Ministik Lake (ROM-1: figs. 6-28, 6-29). Peace River region: Cardinal Lake (MMMN-1; USNM-1). Strathmore (DWWRS-35 live [*ss:* D-4]). Tilley (ROM-1: figs. 6-30, 6-31). Two Lakes—54° 20' N, 119° 44' W (MMMN-1). **British Columbia:** *Cariboo District:* Carpenter Mountain Indian Reserve No. 15 (USNM-2); Cummings Lake (UBC-1); Goldpan Lake [=Donley Lake] (UBC-4); 150 Mile Lake [=small lake used as irrigation reservoir by 150 Mile Ranch (J. Munro 1945: 98)] (PSM-1); 149 Mile Lake (UBC-1); Westwick Lake—S Sorenson Lake [J. Munro 1945: 99] (NMC-1; UBC-2); Williams Lake (NMC-1). *Lillooet District:* Clinton (UBC-1); Lily Pad Lake (ROM-1); 105 Mile Lake (ROM-1; PSM-1; UBC-2); Springhouse (NMC-1); Tatton Lake (ROM-1); Watson Lake (PSM-1; UBC-1); Watson Meadow Lake [local name; unable to verify]—near Sheridan Lake (ROM-1). *New Westminster District:* Ladner: Westham Island (UBC-1). *Range 3, Coast District:* Anahim Lake (UBC-3); Chezacut: Lake Chilcotin (UBC-2). *Yale District,* Kamloops Division: Brigade Lake (UBC-1). **Manitoba:** Boggy Creek area about 60 km N Roblin (NWPW-1 dead [*ss:* MMMN-1]). Churchill (CM-6). Clarkleigh: East Meadows Ranch (DWWRS-18 live). Delta (DWWRS, UFS[DM]-14 live [*ss:* D-1; MMMN-2]; MMMN-1; ROM-1; UMMZ-2), 6.4 km E Delta (OSUFW-1). East Shoal Lake (DWWRS-22 live [*ss:* D-6]). Glenboro (MMMN-1). Lake Francis (UMMZ-2). Minnedosa (DWWRS-26 live: figs. 6-25 to 6-27 [*ss:* D-1; UND-1; UWDWE-2]): 4 km S Poseheath School on Highway 10 (UMMZ-1). Oak Lake (NMC-1). **Northwest Territories:** *District of Mackenzie:* Boxer's Area: 16 km NE Aklavik (ROM-1). Great Slave Lake: mouth of Taltson River (NMC-1). **Saskatchewan:** Assiniboia Creek about 130 km W Souris Coal Fields (NMC-1). Davidson (CM-3: figs. 6-32, 6-33). Forks of Duncairn Reservoir—17.7 km SSE Webb (MMMN-1). Moose Jaw (DWWRS-3 live). South Arm Last Mountain Lake (NMC-4). **Alaska:** Akmalik Creek (USNM-1). Circle (USNM-1). College: Chena Pump Road (UAM-1). Minto Lakes (UAM-3): Little Minto Lake (UAM-2). **Minnesota:** *Kittson County:* Twin Lakes (MMMN-1). *Roseau County:* Pinecreek Pothole [local name; later Pool No. 1 at Roseau River Wildlife Management Area] (BMNH-1). **North Dakota:** *McHenry County:* Upham (UFS[DM]-5 live [*ss:* MMMN-3]), 4.8 km N Upham (USNM-1).

OTHER REFERENCES. Bailey and Niedrach 1965, vol. 1. Bellrose 1976, 1980. Brooks 1903. Forbush 1925. Gollop and Marshall 1954. Harrison 1978. Johnsgard 1965. Kuroda 1939. J. Munro 1937, 1941. J. Phillips 1925. Ridgway [1887] 1896. Roberts 1932, vol. 2. Sanford, Bishop, and Van Dyke 1903 (quoted in Grinnell, Bryant, and Storer 1918). W. Todd 1963.

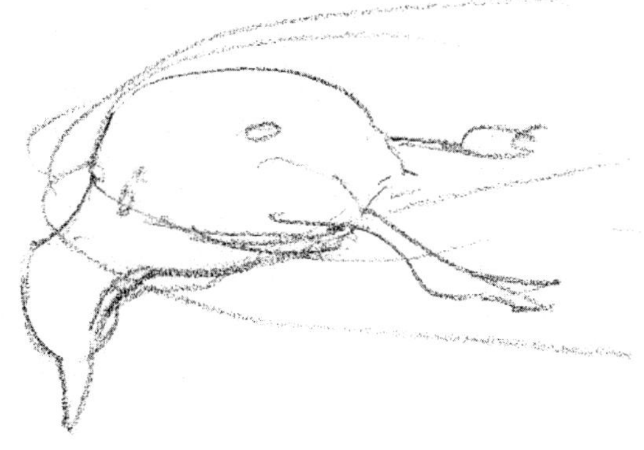

Eiders, tribe Somateriini

North American genera: Somateria Leach, *Polysticta* Eyton

DISTRIBUTION AND TAXONOMY. Eiders breed almost exclusively in arctic and sub-arctic regions; only the Common Eider, *Somateria mollissima,* is represented in more temperate areas, such as the islands in the St. Lawrence River, Québec, and the coastal and off-shore islands of Scotland and Denmark. The breeding ranges of the Spectacled, *S. fischeri,* and Steller's, *Polysticta stelleri,* eiders are relatively restricted compared to the circumpolar distribution of the King and Common eiders (Delacour 1959; Fjeldså 1977). The King Eider, *S. spectabilis,* has no recognizeable subspecies, but the Common Eider has seven, of which five—*borealis, dresseri, islandica, sedentaria, v-nigra*—are found in North America (Palmer 1976, vol. 3; see pl. 7 for downy young of 5 subspp.).

Humphrey ([1955] n.d., 1958a) and Delacour (1959) used downy and female plumages, food habits, and tracheal structure to place the eiders in a separate tribe, Somateriini. Analyses of locomotor mechanisms (Raikow 1973) and feather proteins (Brush 1976), as well as natal characters, support this classification, although Woolfenden (1961), Johnsgard (1960a, 1965, 1978, 1979), and Livezey (1986) retained the eiders in the Mergini on the basis of anatomical and behavioral similarities to the sea-ducks.

APPEARANCE. The dark-backed, brownish gray eiders are unique among downy diving ducks. No other group of ducklings has their combination of dark cheeks, light superciliary area, partly-feathered bills (greater eiders only), and grayish buff or rosy buff base color. The otherwise quite similar Mergini ducklings have a more or less conspicuous light-colored cheek-patch, with heads entirely dark to eye-level or below.

As well as distinctive plumage characters, eider ducklings have also specific adaptations for diving and underwater feeding (Humphrey [1955] n.d.). Their bills are large and high at the base, tapering slightly in *Somateria* but rather square-tipped in *Polysticta.* The nail covers nearly the full width of the bill in all species (figs. G-63 to G-66) and would, presumably, be an effective tool in food-gathering. As in other downy diving ducks, the outer toe (IV) in *Somateria* is nearly always as long as or slightly longer than the middle one (III; characters are reversed in surface-feeding ducks), and the halluxes are deeply lobed. Their tarsi at hatching are just over half the adult length, and the ratio of tarsus to middle toe with claw (TMT/IIIw) is about 0.80 (ratios of scoters, greater mergansers [*Mergus* spp.], American Wigeon, and perching-ducks similar; those of *Aythya, Bucephala, Lophodytes,* and Ruddy ducklings larger: 0.65 to 0.75; *Anas* ducklings ca. 0.85; Table 1, Appendix A, and C. Nelson unpubl. data).

Downy Common Eiders are the heaviest of the North American ducklings (*dresseri:* 67.3 g), newly hatched Spectacled Eiders are a bit smaller (46.2 g), and day-old King Eider weights still smaller (37.0 g)—within the range of some *Aythya,* scoters, and mergansers (but note adult King Eiders are larger than Spectacled adults (Delacour 1959; Palmer 1976, vol. 3). No weight data are known for day-old Steller's Eiders, but the ratio of mean day-old weight (Table 1, Appendix A) to egg size (length x width; meas. from Palmer 1976, vol. 3) in three diving species (Lesser Scaup, King Eider, Ruddy Duck), when compared to egg size of the Steller's Eider, suggests a day-old weight between 31.0 g and 35.0 g for that species.

Bill feathering in *Somateria* ducklings is short, smooth, and flat, with a characteristic 'silvery' appearance along the anterior edge (also in downy White-winged Scoters). The feathers' downward curve at the base of the upper mandible partly conceals the rictus, while its forward extension causes the ducklings' small, dark eyes to appear quite distant from the nostril in a lateral view (e.g., *S. m. v-*

nigra figs. 7-5, 7-7). *Polysticta* downies lack pronounced bill feathering, but some have a tiny 'silvery' area on the dark forehead just above the bill.

BEHAVIOR. Newly hatched *Somateria* ducklings spend much time resting on their bellies: they take a few quick steps, then settle down, then a few steps, and so on. Ducklings two or three days old display a greater variety of resting postures: some quite vertical, others hunched-over and 'hulking'), but seldom the horizontally oriented resting posture of *Aythya* ducklings (compare Spectacled Eider [C. Nelson 1964: fig. 1] and Black Scoter, pl. 9, with *Aythya* figs., pl. 8).

I saw no live lesser eider (*Polysticta*) downies. Observations of these ducklings are rare, but H. M. S. Blair reported (*in* Bannerman 1957, vol. 7: 167) Bolam's account of very young wild broods in Varanger Fjord, Norway: "They were just as prone as young common eiders to herd together, or at least temporarily to follow ducks other than their parents." Broods of ducklings gathered on the sea, "feeding, sometimes diving beneath...drifting weeds." The gathering together of broods or parts of broods into crêches, often attended by one or more females, occurs also in greater eiders, but crêches were "small and...not common" in Spectacled Eiders observed by Dau in Alaska (C. Dau *in* Palmer 1976, vol. 3: 96; see Palmer's pp. 68-69 for summary of Common Eider crêching behavior).

In their survey, Johnsgard and Kear (1968) reported only one instance of eiders carrying their young, an account by Frank McKinney of the Pacific Eider, *S. m. v-nigra*. Driver's (1960a) observation of back-carrying by female *S. m. sedentaria* and a much earlier report of such behavior in *S. m. islandica* (Van Troil *in* Wilson and Bonaparte 1831) suggest that the habit may be more widespread among Common Eiders than is generally believed.

No live young greater eiders used their wings in diving, as Humphrey (1958a) reported for adults, but MacDonald observed that older downy King Eiders (2 - 2 1/2 wk.) on Prince Patrick Island used their wings while diving to escape capture. He said that the ducklings stirred up the debris in their shallow pond by repeated dives and circular movements over the bottom surface, creating turbidity (Stewart MacDonald, pers. comm. 1984); Alison (1976) reported similar behavior among Oldsquaw females and older ducklings [ca. 2 wk.?] in communal broods of that species observed near Churchill, Manitoba.

Unlike pochard ducklings, very young eiders do not feed from the surface of the water, but obtain their food by diving. Common (Driver 1960a) and Spectacled eider ducklings (ca. 3 d.) search for food in the manner of older downy *Aythya* and newly hatched Mergini, with the bill and the forepart of the head submerged; searching is followed by bottom-diving in nominate *mollissima* about two days old (Fabricius 1951). Three-to-six-day Pacific Eiders, *S. m. v-nigra*, swam and dived with ease in Bartonek's aquarium at Delta. After repeated dives of up to five seconds (during which they found and ate most of the daphnids in the tank), the *v-nigra* ducklings remained in the water, resting and preening as Ruddies do.

Downy eiders share with Mergini and Ruddy ducklings the habit of lifting their bodies almost vertically out of the water while treading rapidly just below its surface. Driver (1960a) observed this behavior in wild Hudson Bay Eiders, *S. m. sedentaria*, about a week old; he reported that ducklings followed water-treading with head-under searching and pursuit of food stirred up by the turbulence.

Preening sessions lasting 20 minutes or more invariably follow young eider ducklings' periods of swimming, diving, and feeding. Contentment calls accompany preening—rapid and polysyllabic in downy King Eiders, but slower and less trilling in Common and Spectacled ducklings. Eider and scoter ducklings often remain in the upright position to sleep. A preening posture of the Spectacled

Eider, in which the head is drawn back and the bill moved rapidly from side to side across the breast while the duckling rests upright on its heels (C. Nelson 1964: fig. 2), was observed also in Hudson Bay Eider (UFS[DM]; 2 d.), King Eider (Stewart MacDonald, pers. comm. 1984), White-winged Scoter (DWWRS; 2-3 d.), and (occasionally) *Aythya* ducklings (Michael Anderson, pers. comm. 1987).

Alert and 'confiding', eiders respond to other ducklings—and to humans—with Chin-lifts and, for their size, deep-voiced, two- or three-syllabled greetings that bear a superficial resemblance to goslings' calls (Kear 1968; compare goose and eider calls in her figs. 3 & 10). Feeding calls of Common and Spectacled ducklings are short, sporadic, and more or less evenly accented, but those of downy King Eiders are polysyllabic. The King Eiders (WT[S]; 1-2 d.) had also a sleepy call—a loose trill more or less on one pitch—that I did not hear from other greater eider ducklings.

The deep-voiced prefatory distress call of *Somateria* has a characteristic irregularly spaced (Kear 1968: fig. 10), almost 'angular' quality; Fabricius (1951) also reported polysyllabic distress calls in some Common Eider ducklings. In the two-syllabled call, rising slightly in pitch and accented on the second (higher) note, the 'angularity' results from the pause (equal to or longer than the time value of either of the two sounded notes) following the second, accented note. The ducklings utter this call three or four times, pause, then repeat the series one or more times, sometimes going on to the steady, monosyllabic distress call, sometimes not.

Common Eider
Eider à duvet. Eider.
Somateria mollissima (Linnaeus)

APPEARANCE. A light-colored supraorbital stripe; gray breast-band; the combination of long lateral bill feathering and extremely short mesial feathering; and a broad, brownish gray cheek-stripe (extending from bill to nape and separated from the lighter supraorbital stripe by a thin, dark eye-line) distinguish Common Eider ducklings from those of all other species (compare ducklings of 5 N. A. Common Eider subspp., pl. 7, with those of surface-feeding and diving species, pls. 6-9).

Bills of all Common Eider ducklings are monochromatic, dark 'bluish' gray (a bit lighter in *sedentaria* ducklings), except for the paler, pinkish nail. Feet are also essentially monochromatic: more olive in newly hatched birds, 'bluer' and grayer in older ones.

VARIATION. Downy *islandica* and *dresseri* are the darkest over all, with the darkest pattern color (rump *value* 2.2/, 2.4/) and the shortest, 'brightest' (up to Munsell /3.4) supraorbital stripes (*dresseri's* also the darkest and narrowest). Enhancing the impression of a short, narrow supraorbital stripe in *dresseri* (and a few *islandica*) ducklings are numerous dusky down-tips, blending with the dark pattern color above and below the stripe. Conversely, downy *sedentaria* is the largest and lightest of the Common Eider subspecies, with the widest, palest supraorbital stripe (forehead often nearly white) and the lightest pattern color (rump *value* 2.8/ to 3.8/)—"the only Am[erican eider] subspecies distinguishable on color alone" (Parkes and Palmer *in* Palmer 1976, vol. 3: 33).

Borealis and *v-nigra* ducklings are variously intermediate. *V-nigra* ducklings are paler [and larger] than *borealis* but darker [and smaller] than *sedentaria* (Manning, Höhn, and Macpherson 1956). The long, wide supraorbital stripes; the longer skull; and the extensive, rounded lateral bill feathering, said by Palmer (1976, vol. 3: 31 [figs.], 33) to mark *v-nigra* adults, were also evident in the downy young (compare figs. 7-17 to 7-23 with figs. 7-30 to 7-51; note long skull of older *v-nigra* downy, fig. 7-22). In very young and many older *v-nigra* ducklings, a tightly closed furrow (created by the meeting of lateral and mesial bill featherings over the 'horns') conceals most of the area of the frontal processes, making them consistently the shortest and narrowest among North American eider ducklings (see figs. 7-20, 7-22).

Some downy *borealis* (e.g., Labrador [NMC]) may be almost as dark as *dresseri*—Palmer [1976, vol. 3] considered *borealis* and *dresseri* the darkest of the Common Eider ducklings—and other *borealis* may be nearly as pale as *sedentaria* (e.g., ROM; NWT: SW Baffin I.; Snyder [1957] reported pale *borealis* adults). Color and bill characters of neighboring subspecies often overlap: e.g., *borealis* overlaps with *dresseri* in Labrador (W. Todd 1963), with *sedentaria* N and E of Hudson Bay, and probably with *v-nigra* in the western Canadian Arctic (see Color Descriptions, Appendix B, for details of overlap in downy *mollissima* subspp.).

Supraorbital stripes are usually wide (if sometimes short) in all eider subspecies except *dresseri* (pl. 7). The wide stripes of *sedentaria* and *v-nigra* often curve noticeably upward past ear-level (figs. 7-20, 7-22, 7-33, 7-35), less so in *dresseri* (figs. 7-40, 7-42), *islandica* (fig. 7-45), and some *borealis* ducklings (fig. 7-48; but note fig. 7-50).

Typically, the 'horns' of the bill are long, wide, and rounded in *dresseri* (Gross 1938: pl. 13) and *sedentaria*, short and pointed in *islandica* and *v-nigra*, and intermediate in *borealis* (but sometimes nearly as short as *v-nigra;* compare pattern and bill characters of downy *mollissima*, pl. 7 & figs. 7-17 to 7-51). Variation of bill characters in downy eiders parallels that of adults (e.g., Palmer 1976, 3: 31 [figs.]; see also pl. 7 and figs. 7-17 to 7-51).

Over all darkness of downy eiders varies individually. The pattern color of three nominate *mollissima* (Denmark [CM]; Scotland [ROM]) was as dark as that of *dresseri* (*Wildfowl* 21, 1970: M. L. Gorman photo [pl. 9 (upper)]; Harrison 1975, 1978: Burton pls. 5), but other authors considered *mollissima* variable (Millais 1913, vol. 2; Palmer 1976, vol. 3; Fjeldså 1977) or comparatively light (Cramp and Simmons 1977: Cusa pl. 82). Four newly hatched *islandica* ducklings (BMNH; 2 broods) had even darker pattern color than *dresseri* but were quite light (6.4/) and 'bright' (/3.0) on the supraorbital stripe (Bent 1925: pl. 17, C. Wells photo). Schiøler ([1926] n.d. unpubl. English translation, p. 32), found ducklings from Iceland and Greenland [*islandica*] "greyish, i.e., much lighter than those...[from Spitsbergen, Scandinavia, and the Faeroes]" (see Larsen pls. 46, 47 *in* Schiøler 1926).

SOURCES OF SPECIMENS. **Manitoba:** Cape Churchill (ROM-4). Churchill (UFS[DM])-4 live: figs. 7-30 to 7-32; CM-2; BMNH-1): Stygge Creek—flows N from Stygge Lake to Hudson Bay (UMZM-1). **New Brunswick:** *Charlotte County:* Grand Manan Channel: Kent Island (NMC-2; PSM-1). **Newfoundland:** *Labrador North District:* Nain (NMC-1). *Labrador South District:* Battle Island: Battle Harbour (OSUFW-1); Gannet Islands (NMC-7). **Northwest Territories:** *District of Franklin:* Baffin Island: Cape Dorset (NMC-2): Ihalukpiuk Lake and Tessikakjuak Lake [=Aitken Lakes] (NMC-4); Clearwater Fjord [=Kingwa Fjord] (NMC-4: figs. 7-50, 7-51); Cumberland Gulf: Blacklead Island (NMC-1); Pond Inlet: Erik Harbour (NMC-1); Taverner Bay (ROM-3: figs. 7-47, 7-49). Queen Maud Gulf: Jenny Lind Island (UMFBP[DFP]-1). Victoria Island: Simpson Bay: Read Island (NMC-7). *District of Keewatin:* East Pen Island near mouth of Niskibi River (ROM-1). Eskimo

Point: McConnell River (NWPW-2 live). Hudson Bay: Belcher Islands: Fairweather Sound (CM-3), Kugong Island (ROM-1), Tukarak Island (CM-1: figs. 7-33, 7-34). James Bay: Gasket Shoal (NMC-5), Grey Goose Island (NMC-1), Paint Hills Islands: Walrus Island (CM-4: figs. 7-35, 7-36). Southampton Island: Boas River (NMC-2). **Québec:** *Kamouraska County:* Saint-André-de-Kamouraska: Pilgrim Islands (NMC-2), Long Pilgrim Island (ROM-2). *Rivière-du-Loup County:* Trois-Pistoles: Saint Lawrence River: Ile aux Pommes (DWWRS, UFS[DM]-11 live: figs. 7-37 to 7-39 [*ss:* MMMN-1]). *Saguenay County:* Betchouane (ROM-1: figs. 7-42, 7-43); Etamamu River [=Rivière Etamaniou] (NMC-2); Harrington: Gulf of Saint Lawrence: Boat Islands [=Iles aux Perroquets] (NMC-3); Old Bluff Island—50° 26' N, 60° 13' W [W. Todd 1963: 803] (CM-1: figs. 7-40, 7-41); Petite Romaine (NMC-4); Saint-Augustin—51° 13' N, 58° 39' W (NMC-2). *Territory of New Quebec:* Hudson Bay: Cape Jones [=Pointe Louis-XIV] (CM-1). Ungava Peninsula: island in False River estuary (NMC-1). **Alaska:** mouth of Kashunuk River about 32 km E Hooper Bay [village] (DWWRS-3 live: figs. 7-17 to 7-19 [*ss:* D-1; MMMN-1: figs 7-20, 7-21]). Kipnuk: Kuguklik River near Kinak Bay (OSUFW-2). Nome (ROM-2: figs. 7-22, 7-23). Saint Michael (CM-2). Seward Peninsula: Cape Prince of Wales (UWBM-4). DENMARK: Saltholm Island (CM-1). GREENLAND: *Thule District* [=*Avanersuup kommunia*]: Etah (NMC-1). *Upernavik District* [=*Upernaviup kommunia*]: Duck Island [=Kitsissorsuit] (CM-1: fig. 7-48). ICELAND: **Sudur-Thingeyjarsýsla:** Mývatn (RLWS-3 frozen; BMNH-4: figs. 7-45 to 7-47; OSUFW-1). RUSSIA: **Siberia:** Magadan: Saint Lawrence Bay (NMC-1); Tenkagnei (?) Bay [evidently an inlet of the Chukchi Sea (or Bering Sea?), possibly near the Tenkanij Mountains (=Khrebet Tenkanyy centered at 66° N, 172° 20' W on the Chukchi Peninsula)] (CM-1). SCOTLAND: Shetland Islands: Papa Scalloway Island (ROM-1). *Strathclyde:* Inner Hebrides: Coll Island (ROM-1). **Captive origin** (WT[S]-5 live).

OTHER REFERENCES. Baird, Brewer, and Ridgway 1884, vol. 2. Bauer and Glutz von Blotzheim 1969. Coues (1872) 1903, vol. 2. Dement'ev and Gladkov (1952) 1967, vol. 4. Dresser 1871-81, vol. 6. Forbush 1925. Johnsgard 1965. Kuroda 1939. Latham 1785, vol. 3. Lönnberg 1929, vol. 2. Millais 1913, vol. 2. J. Phillips 1926. Portenko (1972) 1981, vol. 1. Snyder 1941, 1957. Stejneger 1885. Wilson and Bonaparte 1831. Witherby et al. (1939) 1943, vol. 3.

King Eider

Eider à tête grise. Eider Real.
Somateria spectabilis (Linnaeus)

APPEARANCE. A light-colored supraorbital stripe; an inconspicuous breast-band; long, narrow lateral and mesial bill feathering partly enclosing wide, pinkish 'horns' (also distinguishes between adult female King and Common eiders; Harting 1871); and a thin, dark, broken (but well-marked) eye-line and post-orbital streak define the downy King Eider. Dark eyes ("almost black"; Sutton 1932: 78) stand out against the King Eider's light, buffy plumage. The bill, which appears much longer than that of the Common Eider because of the narrower lateral bill feathering, is 'translucent' bluish pink; this color disappears after the first week (Johnstone 1961) and becomes dark bluish olive-gray, like the feet.

VARIATION. Small variations in face pattern and general coloration appeared in King Eider ducklings from all areas. The thin, dusky eye-line is a quite stable character. Sometimes incomplete before the eye, but nearly always interrupting the pale supraorbital stripe to meet the 'horns' of the bill, the line continues behind the eye as the upper border of the brownish cheek-patch; there, it turns downward over the ear, often broken off from the post-orbital portion, and trails away at the side of the nape (figs. 7-13, 7-15). Harrison's (1978: 79) description of the King Eider ducklings's "narrow dark streak" is correct, but a "dark eye-stripe" (caption for downy King Eider, Burton pl. 5) is both inconsistent and misleading, because Harrison uses the same term to describe the wider, more prominent eye-stripes of downy dabbling ducks (p. 65). Defining the posterior border of the supraorbital stripe, a wash of pattern color curves back over the ear from the post-orbital line to the occiput, sometimes linear (Palmer 1976, vol. 2: 370, C. Nelson col., pl.), sometimes poorly defined (*Annual Report of the [Severn] Wildfowl Trust 1960-61* 13, 1962: P. Talbot-Ponsonby photo [uppermost of 3]), and other times appearing as a broad, well-marked connection (fig. 7-15).

The supraorbital stripe—sometimes nearly white, other times with a decidedly yellowish tint—is widest and lightest above and immediately behind the eye, where it rounds off rather abruptly above the ear (figs. 7-12, 7-14). In front of the eye, it becomes narrow and blurred, its pale color often blending with the darker ones of forehead and eye-line.

All three live ducklings had a pale, often grayish, sub-ocular crescent, which was especially prominent on two Koodlotok River, Southampton Island specimens (CM; coll. G. M. Sutton). Only one other duckling (NMC; Cape Henrietta Maria, Ontario) had such an obvious mark, although more than half the museum specimens showed some evidence of a pale, sub-ocular area (as in Millais 1913, vol. 2: Grönvold pl. fac. p. 4). Hines's King Eider duckling (*in* Bellrose 1980: pl. 24), has a large sub-ocular crescent, but a vestigial cheek-patch, a too-prominent post-orbital line, and atypical bill and foot colors. Other birds, including day-old downies from Seymour Island (Stewart MacDonald, color transparencies loaned to the author, August 1968) lacked the crescent entirely (pl. 7; also Brooks [*in* J. Phillips 1926: pl. 80], Shortt [*in* Kortright 1942 & Bellrose 1976: pls. 34], and Scott [*in* Delacour 1959: pl. 11]).

Most downy King Eiders had quite light-colored, low-contrast plumage, with inconspicuous breast-bands and yellowish white or gray-white bellies (e.g., Millais 1913, vol. 2; A. C. Meinertzhagen *in* Witherby et al. [1939] 1943, vol. 3; Johnstone 1961; Cramp and Simmons 1977); Sutton's King Eider duckling (1932: pl. 22, fig. 16), at once paler, yellower, and more distinctly patterned than most downy *spectabilis,* nevertheless shows well the color characters observed in some individuals. Some ducklings were much darker over all, with more contrast of pattern and base colors on breast-band, eye-line, and cheek-patch; and with darker, grayer bills and feet (Fjeldså 1977: pl. 9). Often, the base color of these darker ducklings was quite strongly yellowish (NMC: Baffin Island: Taverner Bay; Southampton Island: Boas River), but in other birds (e.g., certain Seymour Island downies) it seemed nearly as buffy as in some Common Eider ducklings. Manning, Höhn, and Macpherson (1956) concluded that the variation in general darkness and dorsal color among King Eider ducklings of several broods [NMC specimens] was unrelated either to age of the specimens or to the place of collection.

DISCUSSION. Delacour (1959), Palmer (1976, vol. 3), and Johnsgard (1978) report larger weight and linear measuremnts for the King than for the Spectacled Eider; only Cramp and Simmons (1977: 6ll) cite overlap of the Spectacled "with smaller King Eider". Weights of 15 newly hatched King Eiders (35.0 g to 45.0 g; 6 birds est. 1-2 d., 4 est. less than 20 h., 5 precisely 24 h.) were consistently smaller than those of live, day-old Spectacled Eiders (compare weights of 3 greater eider spp. in Table 1, Appendix A). I can think of no reason why the day-old King Eider should be smaller than the day-old Spectacled Eider, when the opposite is true of adult birds. A larger sample of day-old weights from live, wild hatchlings is needed to settle the matter.

SOURCE OF SPECIMENS. **Northwest Territories:** *District of Franklin:* Baffin Island: Foxe Land: Cape Alberta (NMC-3); W coast: Taverner Bay (NMC-1). Banks Island: De Salis Bay (NMC-6). Prince Patrick Island: Mould Bay

(NMC-5), 8 km E Mould Bay (NMC-4). Seymour Island (NMC-2; 9 color transparencies). Somerset Island: Creswell Bay (ROM-2: figs. 7-14, 7-15). Victoria Island: Cambridge Bay (PSM-1; UMFBP[DFP]-4), at sea—about 16 km from bay (UMFBP[DFP]-1). *District of Keewatin:* Adelaide Peninsula: S Barrow Inlet (NMC-3), E side Sherman Basin (NMC-7). Boothia Peninsula: Spence Bay (ROM-1). James Bay: South Twin Island (NMC-1). Southampton Island: Boas River (NMC-10), Coral Harbour (CM-2), Koodlotok River (CM-2: figs. 7-12, 7-13). *District of Mackenzie:* Mackenzie Delta: Richards Island (CM-2). **Ontario:** *Kenora District:* (Hudson Bay): Cape Henrietta Maria (NMC-7). Alaska: Point Barrow (CM-1; OSUFW-1). ICELAND male and GREENLAND female (parents; WT[S]-3 live captives: figs. 7-9 to 7-11). RUSSIA: **Siberia:** Kolyma Bay—W mouth of Kolyma River (NMC-1).

OTHER REFERENCES. Bent 1925. Dement'ev and Gladkov (1952) 1967, vol. 4. Grinnell, Bryant, and Storer 1918. Harrison 1975. Johnsgard 1965. Portenko (1972) 1981, vol. 1. Schiøler 1925. Snyder 1957.

Spectacled Eider

Eider à lunettes. Eider de Fischer.
Somateria fischeri (Brandt)

APPEARANCE. A diagonal line of 'silvery' brownish gray bill feathering—unbroken from rictus to culmen—and a dark 'spectacle' (here considered the round brown eye-patch rather than the light-colored circle of feathers surrounding it) distinguish the newly hatched Spectacled Eider from all other ducklings. The dark crown plumage, puffed out above the paler face (figs. 7-4, 7-6), is short, smooth, and flat on forehead and bill. Bill and foot colors are olive gray or bluish gray—darker in young birds, 'bluer' and grayer in older ones.

VARIATION. The dark area below the 'spectacle', typically most prominent in the ear region, is often narrow, irregularly-shaped, or even lacking (see Palmer 1976, vol. 2: 370, C. Nelson col. pl.). Other times, it is wide and more or less continuous from bill and lores to nape. Most Spectacled ducklings are dark-backed, but occasionally, specimens may have faint but unmistakeable shoulder-spots and wing patches (PSM; Alaska: Cape Simpson; ca. 2 d.)

There are small variations in the *chroma* of the base color. Some Spectacled Eider ducklings are quite pale and dull in the area surrounding the 'spectacle', with 'bluish' bills and olive-gray feet (e.g., 4 live, Kokechik Bay, Alaska; Brandt 1943; C. Nelson 1964). Others have dull orange-yellow faces (2 live, Naskonat Peninsula, Alaska) and darker, almost lead-colored, bills and feet (J. Phillips 1926: Brooks pl. 80; Kortright 1942: Shortt pl. 34; a similar variation occurs in the bill and feet of the Oldsquaw duckling). Such differences do not represent color phases, but appear to reflect rather small differences in the amount of dark pigment present in individuals or broods.

DISCUSSION. Both Bent (1925) and J. Phillips (1926) described (evidently) very young specimens, although Bent portrayed as the 'spectacle' the narrow circle of pale feathers surrounding the brown eye-patch, and Brooks's duckling (*in* J. Phillips 1926: pl. 80) has characters rather different from those described in the text (p. 74). The relationship between the 'spectacle' of the young duckling and that of the adult is correctly portrayed by Dement'ev and Gladkov (1952, vol. 4), Johnsgard (1964), C. Nelson (1964), and Cramp and Simmons (1977: Cusa pl. 83). Descriptions by Kortright (1942: Shortt pl. 34), Delacour (1959: Scott pl. 11), Harrison (1978), and Bellrose (1980: Hines pl. 24) appear to have been done from somewhat older specimens.

The structure of the dark-feathered 'spectacle' accounts for its often bi-colored aspect, as well as for the 'hooded' appearance of the duckling's eye. The upper and lower portions of the 'spectacle' meet in a line that curves down and forward in front of the eye and up and backward behind it. The down of the upper part is fluffed out and appears darker, but the down of the lower part lies flat, appearing paler (pl. 7; see also Cramp and Simmons 1977: Cusa pl. 83).

Color changes in the 'spectacle' occur chiefly during the duckling's third and fourth weeks. A molting Alaskan duckling collected at about 12 days (CM) had entirely new light gray belly down, barred scapular feathers just emerging, and the brown 'spectacle' still largely intact. Two of the Kokechik Bay ducklings (ca. 10 d., 14 d.) showed light buffy down near the center of the 'spectacle', with darker down

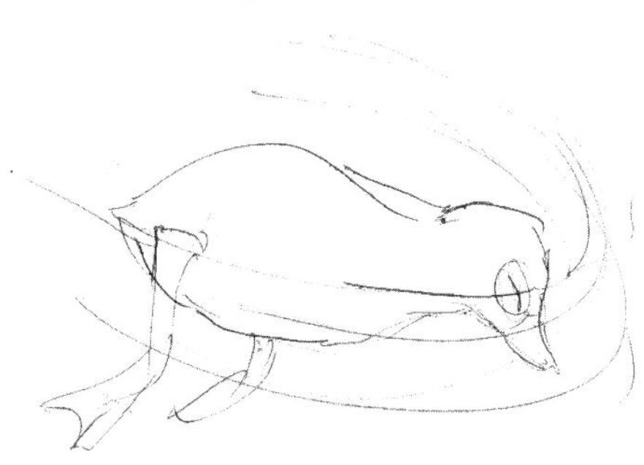

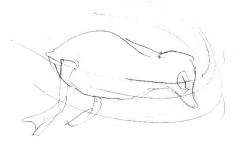

at the periphery and on the post-orbital streak. At this stage, the various streaks and patches of molting dark down and incoming light down define neither the dark natal 'spectacle' nor the pale juvenal one. Illustrations by Brooks (*in* J. Phillips 1926: pl. 80), Scott (*in* Delacour 1959: pl. 11), and Shortt (*in* Kortright 1942: pl. 34) correctly represent this intermediate stage in the first molt.

A 19-day Naskonat Peninsula eider (CM) showed the lower half of the 'spectacle' already unmistakeably molted to the paler juvenal color (fig. 7-7), with barred scapulars and flank feathers (the latter less than 1 cm) and a few sheathed rectrices beginning to appear. A month-old duckling, almost completely feathered, had the 'spectacle' entirely light-colored.

SOURCE OF SPECIMENS. **Alaska:** Aphrewn River SE Bethel (PSM-1). 50 km SE Cape Simpson (PSM-2). Kashunuk River about 48 km SE Hooper Bay (OSUFW-1). Kokechik Bay [=Igiak Bay]: N Hooper Bay [village] (RLWS-4 live). Naskonat Peninsula about 240 km W Bethel (DWWRS-2 live: figs. 7-1 to 7-3 [*ss:* CM-1: figs. 7-6, 7-7]). Nelson Island (BMNH-1). Point Barrow (CM-2: figs. 7-4, 7-5).

OTHER REFERENCES. Gabrielson and Lincoln 1959 (quote Bent 1925). Johnsgard 1965. Kuroda 1939. Portenko (1972) 1981, vol. 1 .

Steller's Eider

Eider de Steller. Eider de Steller.
Polysticta stelleri (Pallas)

APPEARANCE. The downy Steller's Eider's generally dark, blackish brown and brownish gray pattern color, poorly-defined grayish brown breast-band, and buff or rosy buff base color resemble those of downy Black and Surf scoters, but the circumorbital spots and stripes and fleshy bill structure distinguish it not only from downy scoters (J. Phillips 1926), but from ducklings of all other North American species. Steller's Eider ducklings lack the extended bill feathering characteristic of downy greater eiders.

The distinctive face pattern consists of a buff or rosy buff post-ocular stripe of varying width, a buffy supraocular spot (these two light-colored areas always separated by a vertical line of dark pattern color from crown to eye), a buffy spot directly below the eye, and (sometimes) another on the lore. A thin blackish eye-line separates the light markings above the eye from those below it. The anterior portion of the dark eye-line—only a few mm long—is joined to the dark pattern color above the lore; its posterior portion extends back almost to ear level, forming the lower border of the post-orbital stripe (pl. 7; also Shortt *in* Kortright 1942 and *in* Bellrose 1976: pls. 34, and Scott *in* Delacour 1959: pl. 11; older ducklings in F. Todd 1979: fig. 9.49, photo of half-grown brood[s] with 2 females; note pale supraorbital stripe, throat, and neck areas, and rather flat, square head shape).

VARIATION. The stripe and the supraorbital spot are the least variable of the face-pattern components, the subocular and loreal spots the most variable. The subocular spot is consistently the lightest of the markings, but often the post-ocular stripe and the spot over the eye are also pale next to the eye (pl. 7). *Chroma* is highest on the markings above the eye and lowest on the subocular spot (Millais 1913, vol. 2: Grönvold pl. fac. p. 4); the light subocular spot sometimes extends forward to join with the darker loreal spot. The loreal spot, if present, is often dark, dull, and poorly defined. In two specimens from the Alaskan north coast (CM), the entire subocular, loreal, and malar areas were virtually continuous with the grayish throat color (fig. 7-56); the subocular 'spot' may extend as a stripe backward to eye level below the black eye-line, parallel to the post-ocular stripe above it. The eye-ring depicted by J. Phillips (1926: Brooks pl. 80), Delacour (1959: Scott pl. 11), Harrison (1975, 1978), and Fjeldså (1977: pl. 9) did not appear on any ducklings examined (pl. 7; figs. 7-52 to 7-56; see also pl. 8 & figs. 8-5, 8-7, 8-12, 8-14 for similar eye-spot variations in Harlequin & Oldsquaw).

Dorsal spots [four?] described by Johnsgard (1965) and shoulder-spots portrayed by Brooks (*in* J. Phillips 1926: pl. 80; but text, p. 66, states "no white dorsal patches") may be the exception rather than the rule. Only three of 14 wild-caught Alaskan ducklings (CM; FMNH; OSUFW; all from Barrow) had four recognizeable dorsal spots, each of which consisted of, at most, five or six pale plumes. Two specimens (FMNH; Alaska: Kokechik Bay) had inconspicuous spots on the left rump and shoulder and two others (FMNH; Alaska: Chipp River) a barely discernible four-spotted 'shadow pattern'. Such patterns may become more prominent in older, faded ducklings, but they are extremely inconspicuous in young ducklings.

The uniformly light bill color of the Steller's duckling shown by Cusa (*in* Cramp and Simmons 1977: pl. 84) does not agree with the description in the text (p. 617): "black". Upper mandibles of all 14 wild-caught specimens were blackish brown; lower mandibles of young ducklings were noticeably lighter-colored than the upper, denoting, possibly, a tint of grayish pink in life. All specimens had tarsi and toes dark grayish brown, somewhat yellower on the toes adjacent to the webs, with claws mostly dark (a few faintly yellowish). No duckling showed any evidence of the strongly contrasting yellow claws and web-edges depicted by Fjeldså (1977: pl. 9) and F. Todd (1979). The bills of feathered juveniles are "grayish blue", the feet "brownish pearl-gray" (Stejneger 1885: 171).

DISCUSSION. Palmer's (1976, vol. 3: 1) description of the adult's bill as "quite squarish at distal end in a dorsal view" applies also to the bill of the downy young (see figs. 7-35, 7-55). In newly hatched Steller's Eiders identified by George Bolam in Varanger Fjord, Norway, "the bill already resembles that of the adult...tapering evenly from the forehead toward the tip, slightly compressed in the middle, and with the upper mandible overhanging the lower near the base and tip" (H. M. S. Blair *in* Bannerman 1957, vol. 7: 167). Stejneger (1885: 171) wrote that the peculiar "softer lobes formed by the [anterior half of the] tomia of the upper mandible...roll up [when dried] so as to inclose the lower mandible [see fig. 7-52] and become hard, the lateral outline thereby...becoming unduly narrowed towards the tip." The tendency of the duckling's bill to be "hooked over toward the tip" (J. Phillips 1926: 66), may result in part from this enclosure, although the amount of downward curvature of the bill tip seemed in no way unusual in any of the specimens that I examined.

SOURCE OF SPECIMENS. **Alaska:** Barrow (CM-1; FMNH-3). Chipp River (FMNH-2: figs. 7-52 to 7-54). Kokechik Bay [=Igiak Bay]: N Hooper Bay [village] (FMNH-4). Point Barrow (CM-2: figs. 7-55, 7-56; NMC-1; OSUFW-1).

OTHER REFERENCES. Bauer and Glutz von Blotzheim 1969. Bellrose 1976, 1980. Bent 1925. Dement'ev and Gladkov (1952) 1967, vol. 4. Petersen 1981. Portenko (1972) 1981, vol. 1. Witherby et al. (1939) 1943, vol. 3.

Sea-ducks, tribe Mergini

North American genera: *Histrionicus* Lesson, *Clangula* Leach, *Melanitta* Boie, *Bucephala* Baird, *Lophodytes* Reichenbach, *Mergus* Linnaeus

DISTRIBUTION AND TAXONOMY. The Mergini are almost exclusively holarctic; only two species, the Brazilian, *Mergus octosetaceous*, and Auckland Islands, *M. australis*, mergansers are known from the southern hemisphere (J. Phillips 1926). *M. australis*, believed extinct (Delacour 1959; Weller 1980), was thought to be capable of flight (Kear and Scarlett 1970) but incipiently flightless (Livezey 1989).

A large group, diverse in many ways ("...a rather motley assemblage"; Godfrey 1986: 107), members of the Mergini nevertheless share certain structural characters of the trachea and tracheal bulla (Humphrey [1955] n.d.), SCM-proteins (Brush 1976 [Harlequin not examined]), and downy plumages (pls. 8 & 9; Delacour and Mayr 1945; Humphrey [1955] n.d.). Among adults of the tribe, specialization for diving is reflected in similar osteology (Humphrey [1955] n.d.; Woolfenden 1961; Livezey 1986), behavior (Johnsgard 1960a, 1965), and locomotor mechanisms (Raikow 1973, re: paddle index in *Bucephala, Melanitta*).

Delacour and Mayr (1945) proposed monophyly of the sea-ducks, including the eiders, a position reaffirmed by Livezey (1986), but Humphrey ([1955] n.d.) concluded from his study of the tribe that their origins were polyphyletic: the eiders in one group; the scoters, goldeneyes, mergansers, and Oldsquaw in another; and the affinities of the Harlequin unclear. He later (1958a) removed the eiders to a separate tribe, Somateriini. Humphrey proposed four subgenera within *Mergus* (*Mergus, Merganser, Lophodytes, Mergellus*) to describe the structural and behavioral differences that he found among the various merganser species. However, I find that the retention of *Mergellus* as a monotypic genus for the Smew (A.O.U. 1983) and the resurrection of *Lophodytes* as a monotypic genus for the Hooded (lesser) Merganser, as proposed by Woolfenden (1961), Livezey (1986; 1989), and Seeb, Wishard, and Oates (unpubl.), better reflect the differences observed among the downy plumages of the North American merganser species. Intergeneric differences of color and pattern suggest convergence of these character states and possible polyphyletic origin of the tribe, as suggested most recently by Patton and Avise (1983) and Livezey (1986).

APPEARANCE. The large white or gray-white cheek-patch (the chief pattern element of the downy plumage used by Delacour and Mayr [1945] in their analysis of the tribe) appears on all downy Mergini, but takes a slightly different form in each genus. The pattern also varies intragenerically in *Melanitta* and *Bucephala*. It is strikingly and almost identically defined in *Bucephala* (and *Mergellus*) except that the Bufflehead's, *B. albeola*, cheek-patch is quite square at the occiput. The cheek-patch of *Melanitta* is best-defined in the White-winged Scoter, *M. fusca*, but is grayish in the Black Scoter, *M. nigra*, and brownish gray, indistinctly marked by one or two gray-white areas, in the Surf Scoter, *M. perspicillata*. The cheek-patches of Surf and White-winged scoters have the same shape, but that of the Black Scoter is more like a poorly-marked version of the Oldsquaw's, *Clangula hyemalis*, pattern. The newly hatched Harlequin's, *Histrionicus histrionicus*, squared-off cheek-patch—typically ending at eye-level—is well-defined by unmarked white base color and dark grayish pattern color. The Hooded Merganser's, *L. cucullatus*, cheek-patch, entirely suffused with pinkish yellowish gray, shades more or less evenly from light *value* next to the grayish brown crown to extremely pale at the yellowish white throat. In contrast, the greater mergansers (*Mergus merganser, M. serrator*) have white or 'creamy' white cheek-patches contrasting well with the dark yellowish red pattern color and boldly marked by two dark stripes (compare cheek-patches of diving spp. on pls. 8 & 9).

Other pattern elements also vary interspecifically. *Bucephala, Mergellus*, and greater merganser downies invariably have prominent white rump-spots, wing-patches, and (in *Mergus* spp.) tibial patterns, but the lesser merganser, *Lophodytes,* has all light areas smaller and less conspicuous. The Harlequin's characterisic two-spotted dorsal pattern and buffy wing-patches also are inconspicuous, and its tibial pattern is somewhat *Anas*-like. The downy White-winged Scoter, bearing a strong (if superficial) resemblance to the goldeneyes, is usually dark-backed, but sometimes has four small white spots or, more often, a 'shadow pattern' of two or four spots. Black and Surf scoter ducklings rarely display a 'shadow pattern', and the downy Oldsquaw lacks even that. Ducklings of all three scoter species, as well as the Oldsquaw, have the tibial patterns poorly marked. Contrary to Johnsgard's (1965) supposition regarding the downy plumage of the scoters, the gradient in color and definition of pattern proceeds from the Surf Scoter (generally darkest; pattern least distinct) through the Black Scoter to the White-winged Scoter (generally lightest, pattern most distinct). Both Surf and Black scoter ducklings are browner, over all, than the grayer White-winged Scoter. The pattern color is extremely dull and blackish in the downy Surf Scoter, whereas it remains recognizeably brown, albeit still very dull, in the Black Scoter duckling (compare dorsal, wing, and tibial patterns of sea-duck spp., pls. 8 & 9, and eiders, pl. 7).

Except for its white cheek-patch and dark, gray-and-white plumage colors, the downy Harlequin bears little resemblance to other Mergini ducklings or, indeed, to ducklings of any other species. Its combination of characters, e.g., circumorbital pattern (pl. 8; figs. 8-5, 8-7), colors of the unfeathered parts (pl. 8), foot proportions (rather *Anas*-like), and structure of the bill (somewhat laterally compressed; figs. G-78, G-79), is unique. Also distinctive are posture (recalls *Aix*), head-shape (a bit like *Bucephala*), a long undertail area, the tracheal bulla of the adult male (*Anas*-like; Humphrey [1955] n.d.), and (evidently) the microscopic ultrastructure of the iridescent dorsal down feathers (Palmer 1976, vol. 3).

The downy Oldsquaw also differs in some ways from other Mergini ducklings. As in downy *Bucephala,* Harlequins, and White-winged Scoters, the white cheek-patch is prominent, but the pattern color is dark yellowish brown rather than black or dark brownish gray. A few brownish yellow plumes serve as wing-patches. The downy Oldsquaw has a well-marked breast-band similar to that in scoters and goldeneyes (but note breast-band poorly marked in *Lophodytes,* lacking in downy Harlequin and greater mergansers). The Oldsquaw's pointed tail is similar to that of the Harlequin duckling, but its body proportions are shorter and rounder, and the head appears smaller and flatter. Its shorter, wider, less tapered bill is somewhat reminiscent of the scoter ducklings; Seeb, Wishard, and Oates (unpubl.) found the Black Scoter and Oldsquaw also rather similar genetically.

A secondary pattern color on the head and neck (yellowish or 'reddish' brown in *Mergus,* grayish brown in *Lophodytes)* distinguishes downy mergansers from all other North American ducklings. A dark, poorly defined pattern of reddish and brownish hues is described for the Auckland Islands Merganser duckling (J. Phillips 1926; Kear and Scarlett 1970: fig. 1, Scott ink sketch; Weller 1980). In contrast, the plumage pattern of the downy Brazilian Merganser is well-defined, as in *M. merganser,* but lacks yellowish red hue (Partridge 1956: pl. 20, Lunk watercolor sketch and caption). Also characteristic of merganser ducklings are the long, fan-like tail and the puffed-out appearance of the cheek-down (the cheek-down character, most obvious in front view, is seen also in *Bucephala* and stiff-tailed ducklings).

The bills and feet of most Mergini ducklings

are uniformly dark. Among newly hatched birds, only *Histrionicus*, *Lophodytes*, and *M. serrator* have light-colored lower mandibles, and only goldeneyes and *M. merganser* have strongly contrasting toe and tarsal patterns: that of the goldeneyes is similar to *Aythya*, that of *M. merganser* to the Wood Duck, *Aix sponsa*. The feet of the Harlequin duckling are usually gray, but sometimes have low-contrast darker patterns and pale yellowish or pinkish tints on I and on the web of II.

BEHAVIOR: Even day-old Mergini ducklings dive to feed (Beard 1964; Alison 1976) and to escape aerial predators (Alison 1976; Brown and Brown 1981). Specialization for diving is reflected in ducklings' larger paddle areas (C. Nelson unpubl. data) and larger body size relative to those of downy dabbling or perching ducks. For example, in comparing two pairs of species having approximately equal swim-length [CT], mean weight of day-old White-winged Scoters was about 12 g more than that of day-old Muscovy Ducks; mean weight of day-old Common Goldeneyes about 7 g more than Gadwalls (Table 1, Appendix A, and C. Nelson unpubl. data). Brown and Fredrickson (1983) suggested that the large size of day-old White-winged Scoters (among holarctic ducklings, only the Common Eider is heavier), together with their long middle toes (III) and fast-growing tarsi (necessary adaptations for diving), greatly facilitated the ducklings' survival in what is often a harsh environment.

Newly hatched Mergini ducklings (Harlequin, Oldsquaw, White-winged Scoter, *Bucephala*, and mergansers) search for food in the same way as downy *Aythya* and eiders, paddling along with heads part way under water, peering downward (but Nicholson [1930] and Bengtson [1966; 1972] reported surface-feeding in newly hatched Harlequins). At times, the Mergini ducklings immerse the forepart of their bodies as well, paddling and splashing vigorously at the surface, as did White-winged Scoter and Ruddy ducklings seen at Delta and wild goldeneye ducklings observed by Myres (1957). In Bartonek's aquarium, well-stocked with minnows and freshwater invertebrates, Oldsquaw, White-winged Scoter, and *Bucephala* ducklings [all 2-4 d.] searched, sighted their prey, and dived after them, often to the bottom of the aquarium. They seized the wriggling animals, surfaced, then swallowed them, all within a few seconds.

Beard (1964: 497) observed that "young [wild] Hooded Mergansers...swam with just their heads under water or, frequently, with their entire bodies completely submerged with only the rippling of the water above to indicate their presence. Other times they resorted to diving." Harper (1953: 26) reported that wild downy Red-breasted Mergansers engaged in head-under searching "...would dash forward and partly under the surface in pursuit of [prey]." Driver (1960a) also found diving for food well-developed in Red-breasted ducklings only a few days old. He observed one duckling catch and eat more than three dozen small fish in just under 20 minutes. Broods of Common and Red-breasted merganser ducklings, which had no live food in the tiny pool of my observation pen, nevertheless searched actively whenever they entered the water (ca. 20 cm deep; NWPW). They were eventually satisfied with live earthworms and frozen minnows. The sight of a silvery minnow, dangled over the edge of the pen, aroused intense interest and provoked a fierce struggle for the prize. At last, one of the ducklings would seize it, maneuver it quickly into a head-first position, and swallow it with a few rapid gulps.

Nicholson (1930: 397) found "lately hatched" Harlequins picking up food from the surface of a "...roaring torrent of icy water" in Greenland. Moody (*in* Delacour 1959) described head-under-water searching behavior in a captive Harlequin about six weeks old. Bengtson (1966, 1972: 13), observing wild Harlequin broods in Iceland, confirmed that newly hatched birds, although able to dive, took most of their food from the surface of the water, and often snatched insects clinging to vegetation along the stream banks. He reported that "ducklings, hg [=half-grown] and older, fed in the same places and manner as adults: 1) skimming of the surface and dipping of the head under water, 2) diving...by far the commonest method, and 3) 'up-ending'."

Prolonged, vigorous preening sessions invariably follow feeding and drinking. Day-old Oldsquaws, goldeneyes (Myres 1957), and Buffleheads frequently preen sides, wings, and tail while resting on the water; other times they seek a dry surface. The ducklings may begin to preen while standing up, but later settle back on their heels to belly-preen (the Oldsquaw often lay partly on its side), particularly as they grow sleepy. White- winged Scoters habitually rest upright on the heels, as eiders and other scoters do. In this position, White-winged ducklings (DWWRS) often moved their bills rapidly from side to side across their breasts, almost leaning over backward to do so, in the same way as downy Spectacled and Common eiders. Afterwards, they rested, a few still upright and alert, but most on their bellies with white eyelids closed and feet drawn up (pl. 9, White-winged Scoter fig.).

Each group within the Mergini has its characteristic postures. The Harlequin duckling carries its obliquely pointed tail like a short, folded train. Small, slim, and agile, its movements recall those of downy Wood ducklings. Newly hatched Oldsquaws, equally small but somewhat more heavily built, are swift and graceful in the water, but less well-adapted for getting about on land. They alternate short series of hops (Driver 1960a) with periods of resting on their bellies. Newly hatched White-winged and Black scoter ducklings scoot about—much as eiders—with their bellies scarcely above the surface of their pen. The slight dorsoventral flattening of the body causes even the young downies to appear quite wide when viewed from the rear. However, scoter ducklings a few days old often stand and walk with almost galliform straightness, as greater eider ducklings do.

Although goldeneyes and mergansers are considered by many authors (e.g., Delacour and Mayr 1945; Humphrey [1955] n.d.; Johnsgard 1965) to be very closely related, downy young of the two groups have different lower egg-teeth, different foot proportions (see Table 1, Appendix A), and some small behavioral differences. A slightly different resting posture distinguishes each of the three merganser species: low, nearly horizontal in the Hooded; more upright, but still basically horizontal in the round-bodied Red-breasted duckling; upright, with breast up and tail down, in the long-bodied Common Merganser (compare postures of 3 spp. on pl. 9, and in Palmer 1976, vol. 2: 466, C. Nelson col. pl.). Downy *Bucephala* often settle back on their heels to belly-preen, but they seldom remain in that position to rest or to sleep, as some other divers do (compare postures of diving spp. on pls. 7, 8, & 9). Rather, they assume resting postures similar to those of pochard (except scaup) and Red-breasted Merganser ducklings. Day-old *Bucephala* will climb any perpendicular surface to which they can cling with sharp, strongly decurved claws. Goldeneye ducklings can also leap nearly two feet straight up (Peter Ward, pers. comm. 1962).

Ducklings of some species of sea-ducks are more aggressive than others. Day-old goldeneyes and mergansers engage frequently in bill-fighting and heel-nipping with their own and other species, but I observed little aggression among downies of the smaller species: Harlequins, Oldsquaws, and Buffleheads. The lone Black Scoter duckling (RLWS) had been a quiet, 'amiable' little bird, accepted without hostility by its aviary companions. I was therefore quite unprepared for the livelier behavior of the White-winged Scoters. The first brood of newly hatched ducklings that I encountered thrust their heads forward and 'hissed' at me when I approached, then struck my fingers with their bills as I lifted them out of their shipping crate, and continued to 'bite' at my hands as I carried them over to my observation pen. Nor did they settle down once enclosed. Bill-fighting, heel-nips, and wing-pulls were generously inflicted on nearby ducklings of other species as well as on their own siblings.

Soft calls (e.g., conversation, greeting, feeding) of Mergini ducklings are polysyllabic; trilled sleepy calls are close-textured and quiet in the smaller ducklings (e.g., Bufflehead, Oldsquaw), somewhat louder, with the syllables more widely spaced, in ducklings of the larger species. The first syllable of the soft call is lightly accented and, in downy greater mergansers, a bit higher-pitched. In Harlequin, Oldsquaw, and *Bucephala* ducklings, the call ascends slightly and evenly or sounds all on one pitch. The Harlequin duckling's quiet calls (not recorded) have a somewhat 'metallic' quality, whereas the vocalizations of the downy Oldsquaw have the resonance of a small tin trumpet.

Chin-lifts almost invariably accompany the greeting calls of merganser and White-winged Scoter ducklings, but *Bucephala* ducklings replace the Chin-lift with often rhythmic head-bobbing during both conversation and distress calls (pl. 9, Barrow's Goldeneye fig.). Often inconspicuous in day-old birds, the Chin-lift movement develops quickly, e.g., three Hooded Merganser ducklings (ca. 1 wk.) swam toward one another, Chin-lifting repeatedly while voicing five-syllabled soft calls.

Certain vocalizations (evidently distress or pre-distress) of both Harlequin and Oldsquaw ducklings seemed unusual. A Harlequin duckling uttered a series of soft, rapid notes on the same pitch, followed by a louder, higher-pitched note, then repeated the series several times without pause. A watchful Oldsquaw quietly and sporadically reiterated a single 'pebbly' note, then launched into a distress call in which the pitch of the last syllable, a rather 'squealy' note, deflected sharply downward.

Newly hatched White-winged Scoter ducklings, quietest of the downy Mergini (as also the adults: Brooks et al. *in* J. Phillips 1926; Bauer and Glutz von Blotzheim 1969), utter soft, two-syllabled conversation calls, lightly accented on the second syllable. The flat, rather pebbly notes, ascending only slightly in pitch, are sounded very close together. Given at higher pitch and amplitude, with a jerk of the tail, the notes are evidently a call to alertness. The scoter's barely audible, monosyllabic "Tchik!" is accompanied by a small, convulsive body movement. At times, the sound can be perceived only by placing one's fingers gently on the duckling's throat so as to feel the vibration of the trachea. In contrast, the tiny Buffleheads chatter incessantly in quiet, polysyllabic, staccato calls that change to barely audible trills as the ducklings preen and grow sleepy after feeding. The calls of goldeneyes are similar, but lower- pitched and a bit slower.

Harlequin Duck
Canard arlequin. Pato Arlequin.
Histrionicus histrionicus (Linnaeus)

APPEARANCE. The downy Harlequin has one to three white or brownish white spots above and in front of the eye; whitish shoulder-spots; narrow, buffy wing-patches; and a long, rather pointed tail. The upper parts are dark brownish gray with faint greenish blue iridescence, the head down is fluffy, and the underparts are entirely white or gray-white. A well-defined white cheek-patch extends upward behind the eye, turning sharply downward along nape and hindneck. The irregular, 'sculptured' border of the cheek-patch usually meets the lower rim of the eye (but see Colorado [CM] specimen, fig. 8-7, in which cheek-patch starts at rictus; compare white-cheeked ducklings on pls. 8 & 9). Differences among ducklings do not support subspecific distinction for eastern (some palaearctic) and western (Colorado; Pacific Northwest; Siberia) Harlequins.

The bill is high-bridged, narrow, smoothly tapered, and tipped with a wide, oval nail; the nail is brownish pink, the tomium yellowish pink. Base and pattern colors of the bluish olive-gray feet sometimes contrast well, but other times are quite dark and monochromatic.

In partly feathered ducklings, the white

Plate 9

1 Surf Scoter, Melanitta perspicillata
Little Gull Lake, Saskatchewan (URDB).

2 White-winged Scoter, M. fusca deglandi
Miquelon Lakes, Alberta (DWWRS).

3 Black Scoter, M. n. nigra
Mývatn, Iceland (RLWS).

4 Bufflehead, Bucephala albeola
Strathmore, Alberta (DWWRS).

5 Common Goldeneye, B. clangula americana
Delta, Manitoba (DWWRS).

6 Barrow's Goldeneye, B. islandica
Paul Lake, British Columbia (DWWRS).

7 Common Merganser, Mergus merganser americanus
Lake Manitoba near Waterhen River, Manitoba (DWWRS).
Red-breasted Merganser, M. serrator.

8 Red-breasted Merganser, M. serrator. Lake Manitoba near Waterhen River, Manitoba (NWPW: colo
and measurements) and Mackenzie Delta, Northwest Territories (CM: pattern).

9 Greenland Red-breasted Merganser, M. s. schioleri. Strømfjorden, Greenland (ZMK).

10 Hooded Merganser, Lophodytes cucullatus
Vergennes, Vermont (DWWRS).

11 Masked Duck, Nomonyx dominicus
Pinar del Río, Cuba (ANSP [4 d.]).

12 Northern Ruddy Duck, Oxyura jamaicensis rubida
Darker variant. Riske Creek, British Columbia (NMC: color and pattern) and
Delta, Manitoba (DWWRS: measurements).
Lighter variant. Delta, Manitoba (DWWRS).

Plate 9

supraorbital pattern, a white area over top of the bill, and the anterior portion of the cheek-patch (completely dark-feathered behind the eye) form a distinctive round patch in front view; a large white ear-spot is prominent against the dark juvenal contour feathers (Cramp and Simmons 1977: Cusa pl. 85, fig. 5 [juv.]).

VARIATION. The Harlequin Duck's white or brownish white circumorbital spots are "variable but always conspicuous" (Fjeldså 1977: 76). The pre-ocular and supraocular spots may

be separate or connected as in three live ducklings from Yukon Territory (Richard Trethewey color transparencies loaned in letter to the author, August 1977). Sometimes, the supraocular spot is small (Fjeldså 1977: fig. 11 [lower]) or appears as a loreal spot (Dement'ev and Gladkov ([1952] 1967, vol. 4); Cramp and Simmons 1977: Cusa pl. 85, fig. 6 [downy young]). Other times, the spot is long, narrow (PSM), and continuous with the white malar and chin color (Fjeldså 1977: pl. 10), or appears as a whitish or 'silvery' area all around the bill (Schiøler 1926: Larsen pl. 35).

Most Harlequin ducklings have inconspicuous, small, or diffuse paired shoulder-spots; Cramp and Simmons (1977) report inconspicuous paired rump-spots as well (not shown in Cusa pl. 85). Rump-spots on a half-grown duckling from Baffin Island consisted of only two or three tiny plumes. I did not see on any specimen the spot on or above the thigh reported by Dresser (1871-91, vol. 6), Sanford, Bishop, and Van Dyke (1903), Millais (1913, vol. 1), Forbush (1925), A. C. Meinertzhagen (*in* Witherby et al. [1939] 1943, vol. 3), Delacour (1959; not shown in Scott pl. 19), and Harrison (1975, 1978). However, the two younger live Yukon ducklings had, behind each wing and across the tibiotarsus, an inconspicuous, transverse bar of pale brownish gray continuous with the whitish underparts.

DISCUSSION. The underparts of newly hatched Harlequin ducklings appear snowy white, but as the white down-tips wear off, the long, gray bases of the down become more conspicuous. Feather wear on the cheeks, throat, breast, sides, and undertail of older ducklings may be responsible for the "dabble" [=dappled?] effect noted by Fjeldså (1977: 75) or, in ducklings swimming in turbulent water, also for the "striated" appearance reported by Nicholson (1930: 397). Grayish bases of the down form the poorly-marked breast-band described by Snyder (1957), a pattern not seen on newly hatched ducklings.

The "delicate, almost iridescent sheen" of the pattern color described by Palmer (1976, vol. 3: 325; see also pl. 8 & Schiøler 1926: Larsen pl. 35) appeared not only in newly hatched live Icelandic ducklings but also in older dried specimens (4 d. to 3 1/2 wk.) from Washington, Oregon, Colorado, and Baffin Island. The color, a rather dark greenish blue (5B 4/1) on newly hatched birds, became lighter, bluer, and more iridescent on some older ducklings.

The wide, brownish pink nail of the live, young Harlequin duckling occupies almost the entire anterior half of the bill, where it contrasts rather poorly with the 'pinkish', 'bluish', and olive-gray colors of the posterior half of the bill, being somewhat less eye-catching than the pale yellowish pink tomia of the upper mandible. In prepared specimens, the dried, yellowish nail tissue contrasts well with the darker color of the dried upper mandible, but the pale tomium color is entirely lost. Portrayals by Kortright (1942: Shortt pl. 35), Dement'ev and Gladkov ([1952] 1967, vol. 4), Cogswell (1977) and others are evidently based on such prepared specimens.

Often lighter-colored than those of some

other diving species (e.g., eiders, scoters), with good to fair contrast of the darker pattern and webs, the tarsi of Harlequin ducklings may appear somewhat *Anas*-like. Colors described by Millais (1913, vol. 1: 133; "stone-grey") and Delacour (1959: 164; "grey") are similar to pattern colors that I observed; the yellowish colors depicted *in* Schiøler (1926: Larsen pl. 35) matched those of the hallux (I), inner web (II), and sides of toes III and IV on the live Icelandic ducklings.

SOURCE OF SPECIMENS. **Alberta:** Jasper National Park (NMC-1). **British Columbia:** *Peace River District*: Alaska Highway 19.3 km N Summit Lake (NMC-1). **Northwest Territories:** *District of Franklin:* Baffin Island: Cumberland Gulf: Blacklead Island (NMC-6). **Québec:** *Territory of New Quebec*: Ungava Peninsula: Swampy Bay River below Lake Minowean (CM-1). **Yukon Territory:** Lapie Lakes: about 40 km SW Ross River (MMMN-3 frozen). **Colorado:** *La Plata County:* Vallecito Creek (CM-1: figs. 8-6, 8-7). **Oregon:** *Tillamook County:* Jackson Creek: N side Cape Lookout at head of Netarts Bay (OSUFW-1). **Washington:** Cascade and Olympic mountains (UWBM-1: figs. 8-4, 8-5). *Chelan County:* Little Wenatchee River: U. S. Forest Service Riverside Campground—about 11.3 km W Lake Wenatchee near Soda Springs (PSM-1). *King County:* Tacoma Watershed (PSM-2). *Yakima County:* 57.9 km NW Yakima: Lost Creek [=a tributary of the Naches River about 3.2 km S Cliffdell (Wenatchee National Forest Visitors Map, 1980)] (PSM-1). GREENLAND: *Godhavn District* [=*Qeqertarssuup kommunia*]: Godhavn [=Qeqertarssuup] (USNM-1). *Holsteinsborg District* [=*Sisimiut kommunia*]: Holsteinsborg [=Sisimiut] (ROM-1). ICELAND: **Sudur-Thingeyjarsýsla:** Húsavík (FMNH-1); island in Laxá (RLWS-4 live: figs. 8-1 to 8-3).

OTHER REFERENCES. *Annual Report of the [Severn] Wildfowl Trust 1960-61* 13, 1962. Bauer and Glutz von Blotzheim 1969. Bellrose 1976, 1980. Bengtson 1966, 1972. Bent 1925. Grinnell, Bryant, and Storer 1918. Johnsgard 1965. J. Phillips 1925. Portenko (1972) 1981, vol. 1. Stejneger 1885.

Oldsquaw

Canard kakawi. Pato Golondrino Artico.
Clangula hyemalis (Linnaeus)

APPEARANCE. The downy Oldsquaw is the only North American duckling with the combination of white underparts and dark, unpatterned dorsal plumage, white cheek-patch, white or brownish white circumorbital spots, and a well-marked dark breast-band. The dark, yellowish brown crown and back have lighter yellowish brown or (sometimes) buffy down-tips (Bauer and Glutz von Blotzheim 1969); there are narrow, inconspicuous yellowish brown wing-patches; there is a "whitish [mark] around the ankle joint" (Snyder 1957: 79) which appears as a tiny spot above the 'heel' on prepared specimens, and some ducklings have random white plumes in the short, rather pointed tail. There is often an obscure, dark, purplish or greenish iridescence on the lower back and rump.

The bill is short, with a wide, tapered nail, much like those of downy scoters (pl. 8; compare Oldsquaw figs. 8-8 to 8-14 with scoter figs. 8-15 to 8-33). Colors of bill and feet are monochromatic and usually dark, but in some young and all older ducklings, are a quite 'bluish' gray.

VARIATION. Three or four white circumorbital spots, often tinted with pale rosy brown or pale yellowish brown, are typical for the Oldsquaw, but the spots may vary considerably. Often, two spots are joined; sometimes, all spots are connected to form a ring (Palmer 1976, vol. 3); other times, one of the anterior spots is joined to a loreal spot (e.g., [NMC] Manitoba; Northwest Territories; [ROM] Ontario: figs. 8-13, 8-14) or a posterior spot extends backward as a stripe to the nape (e.g., Schiøler 1926: Larsen pl. 30; A. C. Meinertzhagen *in* Witherby et al. [1939] 1943, vol. 3; Dement'ev and Gladkov [1952] 1967, vol. 4; Delacour 1959; Cramp and Simmons 1977). Other variations occur, including no spots at all (Alison 1975: fig. 7; Fjeldså 1977: fig. 11).

Foot and bill colors also vary. Bill and feet of most newly hatched Oldsquaws are dark olive-gray, dark grayish olive ([NMC] Churchill, Manitoba; Audubon 1856, vol. 6: pl. 410), or dark bluish gray (Alaska: Kashunuk River, 2 dead). Ducklings 10 d. or older have lighter bluish gray feet (Stejneger 1885; Sutton 1932), but some very young downy Oldsquaws also have distinctly 'bluish' feet (Iceland: Mývatn, 1 live; Manitoba: Churchill: Palmer 1967, unpubl. color sketch).

DISCUSSION. Stejneger's (1885) synoptical comparison between adult *Clangula* ("*Harelda*") and *Histrionicus* specimens also applies to the structural characters of nail, bill, and lamellae in the downy young. Even in very young downy Oldsquaws, the well-spaced, grayish pink lamellae are clearly visible below the tomia of the upper mandibles (compare Harlequin figs. 8-5 & 8-7 with Oldsquaw figs. 8-12 & 8-14).

SOURCE OF SPECIMENS. **Manitoba:** Churchill (DWWRS, NWPW-6 live: figs. 8-8 to 8-10 [*ss:* MMMN-2; UND-1]; CM-4: fig. 8-12; NMC-19). **Northwest Territories:** *District of Franklin:* Axel Heiberg Island: Schei Peninsula (NMC-3; UMFBP[DFP]-2). Baffin Island: Foxe Peninsula: Dorset: Ihalukpiuk Lake and Tessikakjuak Lake [=Aitken Lakes] (NMC-1); Nuwata (NMC-1). Devon Island: Dundas Harbour (NMC-4). Queen Maud Gulf: Jenny Lind Island (UMFBP[DFP]-1). Victoria Island: Cambridge Bay (UMFBP[DFP]-1). *District of Keewatin:* Adelaide Peninsula near E side Sherman Basin (NMC-9). Hudson Bay: Belcher Islands: Tukarak Island (CM-10); Povungnituk Bay (CM-5). James Bay: Bear Island (NMC-4), island off Kakakischuan Point (CM-5), South Twin Island (CM-3; BMNH-1). Southampton Island (NMC-7): Coral Harbour (CM-1), Seal Point (CM-5). *District of Mackenzie:* Bernard Harbour (NMC-1). [Probably at Franklin Bay NE Fort Anderson (MacFarlane 1890: 9)] (USNM-1). Great Bear Lake (NMC-1). **Ontario:** *Kenora District:* Cape Henrietta Maria (ROM-1: figs. 8-13, 8-14). **Québec:** *Territory of New Quebec:* Hudson Bay: coast adjacent to Long Island (NMC-3); Richmond Gulf [=Lac Guillaume-Delisle] (CM-1). **Alaska:** mouth of Kashunuk River about 32 km E Hooper Bay [village] (DWWRS-2 dead [ss: D-1; MMMN-1: fig. 8-11]). Kipnuk: Kuguklik River near Kinak Bay (OSUFW-4; PSM-2). Point Barrow (CM-1; BMNH-1). ICELAND: **Sudur-Thingeyjarsýsla:** Mývatn (RLWS-1 live; 1 frozen; BMNH-5). **Captive origin** (DWWRS-1 frozen [*ss:* D-1]).

OTHER REFERENCES. Alison 1976. Baird, Brewer, and Ridgway 1884, vol. 2. Bellrose 1976, 1980. Coues (1872) 1903, vol. 2. Forbush 1925. Grinnell, Bryant, and Storer 1918. Johnsgard 1965. Kortright 1942. Millais 1913, vol. 2. Nicholson 1930. J. Phillips 1925. Ridgway [1887] 1896. Roberts 1932, vol. 2.

Black Scoter

Macreuse à bec jaune. Pato Negrón Negro.
Melanitta nigra (Linnaeus)

APPEARANCE. The downy Black Scoter is the smallest of the three scoter species; it is 'browner' than the larger, grayer White-winged duckling, and less generally 'blackish' than the downy Surf Scoter (compare 3 spp. on pl. 9). Next to the Surf Scoter, *M. nigra* is the most plainly colored of the scoter ducklings, but its cheek-patch is between that of the other two species in distinctness: it may be quite white next to the occiput and hindneck, but is light grayish brown at the side of the bill and upward to the eye. Bill-feathering is absent, giving the Black Scoter duckling a round-headed appearance quite different from that of the other two species (compare 3 scoter spp. on pl. 9 and in figs. 8-15 to 8-33).

The dark bill of nominate *nigra* Linnaeus has yellow-orange tomia and nostril-rims [White-winged and Surf scoters lack these bright bill colors] and the posterior edge of the nail curves slightly forward mesially. The feet are almost uniform dark olive-brown or dark grayish olive.

VARIATION. Most downy Black Scoters lack dorsal spots (pl. 9), but some have a 'shadow pattern'. Some Alaskan Black Scoter ducklings had a small white sub-ocular spot (J. Phillips 1926; A. C. Meinertzhagen *in* Witherby et al. [1939] 1943, vol. 3; Dement'ev and Gladkov [1952] 1967, vol. 4; Fjeldså 1977), but none had the small white spot above the eye portrayed by Delacour (1959; not shown in Scott pl. 19), Fjeldså (1977), and Burton (*in* Harrison 1975, 1978: both pl. 5); Harrison's (1978) use of this mark to distinguish Black Scoter ducklings from downy Surf Scoters is unjustified.

Colors of the unfeathered parts of nearctic *americana* Philllips annotated by Conover (FMNH) were similar to those of palaearctic *nigra* (Iceland: Mývatn, 1 live; Dresser 1871-81,

vol. 6; Millais 1913, vol. 2; Cramp and Simmons 1977; Fjeldså 1977; Harrison 1978). No Black Scoter had contrasting yellow-green web edges and dark gray irides (Cramp and Simmons 1977; Fjeldså 1977: pl. 10) or light-colored feet (Bellrose 1976, 1980: Hines pl. 24).

SOURCE OF SPECIMENS. **Newfoundland:** *Ferryland District:* (Avalon Peninsula): 25.7 km SW Cape Broyle (NMC-2: figs. 8-32, 8-33). *Alaska:* Kokechik Bay [=Igiak Bay] near Hooper Bay [village] (FMNH-6). Saint Michael [E. Nelson 1887: 80] (USNM-1: figs. 8-30, 8-31). ICELAND: **Sudur-Thingeyjarsýsla:** Laxárdal (FMNH-1); Mývatn (RLWS-1 live: figs. 8-27 to 8-29; 1 frozen).

OTHER REFERENCES. Bent 1925. Coues (1872) 1903, vol. 2. Johnsgard 1965. Kortright 1942. Palmer 1976, vol. 3. Roberts 1932, vol. 2. Sanford, Bishop, and Van Dyke 1903 (quoted *in* Grinnell, Bryant, and Storer 1918).

Surf Scoter

Macreuse à front blanc. Pato Negrón Nuquiblanco

Melanitta perspicillata (Linnaeus)

APPEARANCE. The general appearance of the downy Surf Scoter is that of a sooty brown duckling with an indistinct grayish white cheek-patch and no prominent white markings of any kind. It is the darkest, most conservatively patterned duckling of all North American waterfowl species. Brownish gray cheeks and throat contrast poorly with the blackish head—much less strongly black and white than suggested by Johnsgard (1965), Scott (*in* Delacour 1959: pl. 19), and Hines (*in* Bellrose 1980: pl. 24). Long mesial feathering on the culmen and long, sharply pointed chin feathering—extending nearly to the lower nail on the underbill—distinguish the downy Surf Scoter from ducklings of all other species. The bill and feet are more or less uniformly blackish brown (pl. 9).

VARIATION. Low contrast of base and pattern colors and poor definition of pattern in the downy Surf Scoter's plumage change little until the bird is two to three weeks old, when the grayish white cheek-patch becomes more prominent and the dark area behind and below the ear enlarges upward and forward, partly separating the anterior and posterior areas of the cheek-patch and causing it to appear somewhat kidney-shaped (e.g., Class Ic brood with 'bluish' bills, near Yellowknife, Northwest Territories; Ray Murdy color transparencies loaned in letter to the author, October 1964). Bills of Harper's partly grown ducklings were "dark, glossy slate"; the feet had "very pale, dull brownish" base color and "slaty brown...fuscous" pattern color (J. Phillips 1926: 47). Grayish, contrasting foot colors and a white mark in front of the eye (Hines *in* Bellrose 1980: pl. 24) do not typify young ducklings.

Conspicuous dorsal spots and wing-patches are invariably absent. One downy Surf Scoter (PSM; Alaska: Cache Lake) had a single indistinct spot on the right shoulder and a second had faint, narrow wing-patches, but none of the other Surf Scoter ducklings had even the shadow of a dorsal pattern.

DISCUSSION. The downy plumage of the Surf Scoter remains one of the least known among holarctic waterfowl species; even museum specimens are rare. Representative drawings by Brooks (*in* J. Phillips 1926) and Shortt (*in* Kortright 1942) were eventually published. Descriptions by Bent (1925) and J. Phillips (1926) were apparently based on two partly grown downy Surf Scoters, collected in 1920 by Francis Harper at Lake Athabaska, Northwest Territories. Unknown to these researchers, W. E. C. Todd, in 1912, had collected a downy Surf Scoter (CM 40080; ca. 12 d.) on Charlton Island, James Bay. Mr. Todd related that the duckling dove repeatedly in its attempts to escape, but after stalking it on several trips around the pond, he was at last able to secure it (W. E. C. Todd, pers. comm. 1967). This specimen apparently remained the youngest known until 1962, when R. W. Nero collected a duckling one or two days old from a brood of eight at Little Gull Lake, Saskatchewan.

SOURCE OF SPECIMENS. **Northwest Territories:** *District of Keewatin:* James Bay: Charlton Island (CM-1: figs. 8-25, 8-26), Sheppard Island (CM-2). *District of Mackenzie:* Campbell Lake (CM-1). Great Slave Lake: Union Island (CM-1). **Québec:** *Territory of New Quebec:* Ungava Peninsula: Swampy Bay River: small lake on portage route between Lake Otelnuk and Lake Minowean (CM-1 [head only]). **Saskatchewan:** Little Gull Lake—59° 02' N, 109° W (URDB-1: figs. 8-22 to 8-24). **Alaska:** Brooks Range: Cache Lake—6.4 km N Anaktuvuk Pass (PSM-2).

OTHER REFERENCES. Palmer 1976, vol. 3. Witherby et al. (1939) 1943, vol. 3 (cites J. Phillips 1926).

White-winged Scoter

Macreuse à ailes blanches. Pato Negrón Aliblanco.

Melanitta fusca (Linnaeus)

APPEARANCE. White cheeks and underparts with dark, brownish gray upper parts and breast-band characterize downy nearctic *deglandi* Peters; a small gray ear-spot becomes more prominent as the duckling grows older. The White-winged Scoter duckling is the most strongly patterned of the three scoters; the degree of contrast is about the same as that in Harlequin and Oldsquaw ducklings (compare these 2 spp., pl. 8, with 3 scoter spp., pl. 9). In the hand, in dorsal view, the apices of the lateral and mesial bill featherings appear about

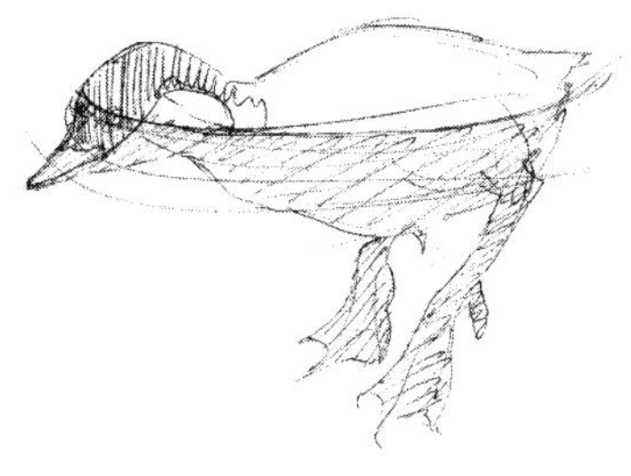

equally spaced (figs. 8-15, 8-18, 8-20; "M shaped" [Palmer 1976, vol. 3: 282]). In the field, the shape of the white cheek-patch, curving up from the angle of the bill to a level above the ear, will distinguish the downy White-winged Scoter from similarly colored but more boldly patterned goldeneye ducklings, in which the white cheek-patch never reaches ear-level (compare goldeneye & scoter figs., pl. 9). Bill and feet are monochromatic 'bluish' gray; with the feet usually somewhat darker than the bill.

VARIATION. The dorsal pattern varies individually among downy White-winged Scoters. Sometimes, the ducklings have no dorsal spots (J. Phillips 1926), but other times, there are inconspicuous dorsal spots and wing-patches, which are almost never so large and conspicuous as those of goldeneyes (or of nearctic scoters depicted by Bent 1925: pl. 24 [lower], H. K. Job photo; Kortright 1942: Shortt pl. 35; and Harrison 1978: Burton pl. 5). Of 46 *deglandi* specimens examined, 31 had wing-patches and 35 had shoulder-spots, but only 14 had rump-spots, some of which consisted of only three or four down plumes. Spotted individuals were found in all broods from all areas, but only six individuals had noticeably 'white' markings.

Either because of small size or gray color or both, all light markings remained inconspicuous (see Scott pl. 19 *in* Delacour 1959), constituting a 'shadow pattern' discernible only under excellent illumination. Spots of older downies with worn or faded plumage were often more prominent than those of newly hatched ducklings.

Similar variations occur in palaearctic *fusca* Linnaeus ducklings. Gould (1873), Blaauw (1909), Dement'ev and Gladkov ([1952] 1967, vol. 4), and Cramp and Simmons (1977) all depicted dark-backed ducklings. Kear described study skins of two Velvet Scoter ducklings from Finland (WT[S]) as "dark brown and white

rather than black and white [as in goldeneye ducklings], have no back spots at all and no spots on the wings" (Janet Kear, letter to the author, August 1969). However, individuals having light-colored rump-spots or whitish wing-patches or both were described by Dresser (1871-81, vol. 6), Millais (1913, vol. 2), Delacour (1959: Scott pl. 19), Bauer and Glutz von Blotzheim (1969), Harrison (1975, 1978: Burton pls. 5), and Fjeldså (1977).

The small white spot on the lores, noted on certain palaearctic *fusca* specimens by A. C. Meinertzhagen (*in* Witherby et al. [1939] 1943, vol. 3), Bauer and Glutz von Bloztheim (1969), Cramp and Simmons (1977), and Fjeldså (1977),

was found on only one nearctic *deglandi* specimen. No *deglandi* specimen had white spots below, around, or above the eye, as described by Bent (1925), Dement'ev and Gladkov ([1952] 1967, vol. 4), and Harrison (1978: Burton pl. 5), although the pale eyelid might be interpreted as a 'spot' in some prepared specimens.

Colors of the plumage and unfeathered parts also display small individual variations. The backs of some ducklings appeared 'grayer', others 'browner'. Either color often had a faint 'bloom' of silvery mauve that faded quickly as the duckling grew and was lost entirely in study skins. These usually acquired a rather brownish color. Bill color of very young ducklings varied from "pale blue-grey" (NMC; British Columbia; coll. S. D. Macdonald) through "dark neutral grey" to "dark slate" (PSM; ROM; coll. J. A. Munro), similar to 21 live Alberta ducklings in which tarsal colors ranged from medium to dark bluish gray. Lighter bill and foot colors of the live ducklings often correlated with a lighter shade of gray in the plumage, but no live duckling had feet so pale and so contrastingly patterned as those shown by Hines (*in* Bellrose 1980: pl. 24) or so dark as the "lead-black" tarsi described by Millais (1913, vol. 2: 65) in *fusca* ducklings. Reddish foot color shown in a Norwegian *fusca* duckling (Millais 1913, vol. 2: Grönvold col. pl. fac. p. 4) is not typical of live *deglandi* ducklings.

DISCUSSION. At first glance, the resemblance between goldeneye and White-winged Scoter ducklings is striking, if superficial. A closer scrutiny discloses many differences: shape and color of the bill (the scoter's bluish gray bill is wider and flatter than the goldeneye's blackish bill, which is narrower and higher); shape of nail and lower egg-tooth (compare scoter figs. 8-15 to 8-17 with goldeneye figs. 8-44 to 8-46, 8-52 to 8-55; eye-colors (C. Nelson 1983); form of the white cheek-patch; color and pattern of plumage and unfeathered parts; and shape of head, body and feet; (compare again scoter and goldeneye figs., pl. 9). The smaller differences are easily discerned in specimens examined in the hand; the larger differences of cheek-patch shape and dorsal pattern can also be seen in the field.

SOURCE OF SPECIMENS. **Alberta:** Cooking Lake (UFS[DM]-8 live). Grande Prairie region: Wembley: Saskatoon Lake (NMC-1). Miquelon Lakes (DWWRS-13 live: figs. 8-15 to 8-17 [*ss:* D-3; MMMN-1: fig. 8-19; UMFBP(DFP)-2; UND-2];

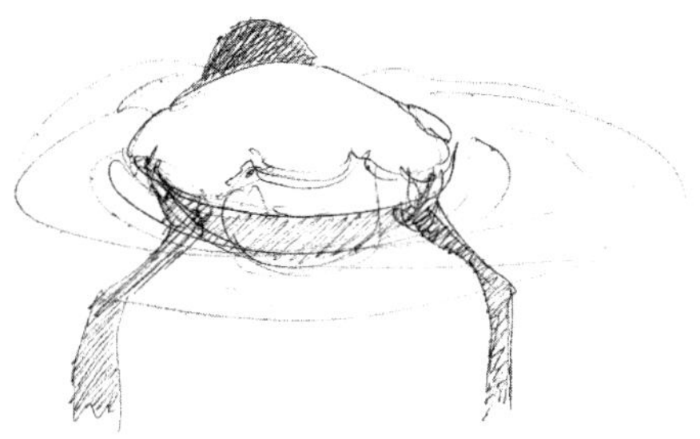

ROM-2. Peace River: Cardinal Lake MMMN-2; USNM-1). **British Columbia:** *Cariboo District:* Williams Lake: 153 Mile House [see *A. platyrhynchos*, p. 90] (NMC-2). *Cassiar District:* Atlin (RBCM-2); Dease Lake (NMC-1). *Lilloet District:* 105 Mile Lake (ROM-1); Watson Lake (PSM-1). **Northwest Territories:** *District of Mackenzie:* Mackenzie Delta: Richards Island (CM-2), Tuktoyaktuk (CM-5: fig. 8-18). **Saskatchewan:** South Arm Last Mountain Lake (NMC-3). **Alaska:** Akmalik Creek (USNM-2: figs. 8-20, 8-21).

OTHER REFERENCES. Baird, Brewer, and Ridgway 1884, vol. 2 (quoted *in* Grinnell, Bryant, and Storer 1918). Bellrose 1976, 1980. Delacour and Mayr 1945. Johnsgard 1965. J. Munro 1937. Roberts 1932, vol. 2. Schiøler 1926.

Bufflehead

Petit Garrot. Patito Crestiblanco.
Bucephala albeola (Linnaeus)

APPEARANCE. See Barrow's and Common goldeneyes, pp. 133-36. Compared to ducklings of either goldeneye species, the rear edge of the downy Bufflehead's nostril falls within the posterior half of the bill (compare figs. 8-34 & 8-39), the underbill in live ducklings usually appears longer than the culmen, and the area of the nail is very small. The Bufflehead's bill tapers nearly as much as that of Barrow's Goldeneye, but the nail area remains comparatively even smaller than that of the Common Goldeneye (compare fig. 8-35 with 8-44, 8-53; compare dorsal views of older ducklings, figs. 8-40, 8-42 with 8-49, 8-51 & 8-58, 8-60; see also Linsdale 1933). The white cheek-patch, extending upward over the ear and turning abruptly downward at the nape, usually has a squared-off or 'eared' effect that is lacking in goldeneye ducklings (pl. 9; also Palmer 1976, vol. 2: 466, C. Nelson col. pl.; note reversal of Bufflehead/goldeneye cheek-patch characters *in* Bailey and Niedrach (1965, vol. 1: Hochbaum pl. 19). Bill and feet are monochromatic, dark gray.

VARIATION. Except for small, apparently individual variations, size and shape of tibial, dorsal and wing patterns were quite consistent among all specimens. Like J. Phillips (1925), I found no difference between Bufflehead and golden-eye ducklings in the spotted pattern of the "sides" (see Millais 1913, vol. 1: 106), nor did I observe the three pairs of dorsal spots or the "irregular stripe" noted by Harrison (1978: 82).

Erskine (1972) reported the pattern color of partly downy and partly feathered juveniles originating west of the Rockies as brownish, that of young birds from east of the Rockies (to

Alberta) as grayish. He suggested that the brownish appearance of western birds might be induced by the alkaline quality of many western lakes.

DISCUSSION. In no other genus of waterfowl (except *Olor*) do the downy young of member species resemble one another so closely as in *Bucephala:* colors of feet and eyes are often diagnostic for live ducklings, but plumages of the three species are virtually identical. Clearly smaller than the downy goldeneyes, the relative size of the Bufflehead duckling may not be useful as a distinguishing character unless the age of the duckling is known. For birds in the hand, bill structure will identify Bufflehead and goldeneye ducklings of unknown age. Linsdale (1933) found the Bufflehead's nail proportionately smaller at all ages than that of Barrow's Goldeneye. He reported (p. 39) [length of] nail-to-culmen ratios of "0.35 - 0.45" and "0.23 - 0.28" in Barrow's and Bufflehead specimens, respectively. Nail-to-culmen ratios of *Bucephala* study skins, Class Ia - IIb, were as follows: Barrow's (n=5), 0.38 - 0.46; Common (n=5), 0.35 - 0.47; and Bufflehead (n=4), 0.23 - 0.32. As with Linsdale's ratios, there was no overlap between the highest Bufflehead ratio and the lowest goldeneye ratio. However, the method should probably be used with caution in live, newly hatched ducklings, in which the nail appears large in proportion to the rest of the bill and the nail-to-culmen ratios consequently also are larger.

In the field, the squared-off 'eared' cheek-patch identifies ducklings newly hatched to about two and one-half weeks of age. According to Erskine (1972: 110-11, photo series), the cheek-patch loses its square appearance and becomes more rounded when the first contour feathers appear, remaining that way until the juvenile's gray-white, oval, ear-to-cheek patch begins to form at about five weeks. Although the preparation technique obscured the 'eared' cheek-patch character in some prepared specimens, it could be seen clearly in other specimens as well as in all live birds.

SOURCE OF SPECIMENS. **Alberta:** Alix (NMC-2). Lower Therien Lake (ROM-1). Red Deer: Red Deer River (NMC-3). Sinclair Lake (MMMN-2). Strathmore (DWWRS, UFS[DM]-12 live: figs. 8-35 to 8-37 [*ss:* D-1; MMMN-2: fig. 8-38; UND-1]). **British Columbia:** *Cariboo District:* Carpenter Mountain Indian Reserve No. 15 (FMNH-1); Williams Lake: 150 Mile House (NMC-2), Riske Creek [creek] (RLWS-4 frozen). *Lillooet District:* 105 Mile House (ROM-1); 105 Mile Lake (OSUFW-1; UBC-1); Tatton Lake (ROM-1: fig. 8-39); Watson Lake (UBC-1). *Peace River District:* Tupper Creek (RBCM-2). *Range 3, Coast District*: Anahim Lake (UBC-1). **Manitoba:** Inglis: near Bluewing Lake (NWPW-2 dead). **Saskatchewan:** Emma Lake (ROM-1: figs. 8-42, 8-43). **Yukon Territory:** Burwash Landing: Kluane Lake (ROM-1: figs. 8-40, 8-41). **Captive origin** (UWBM-3).

OTHER REFERENCES. Bellrose 1976, 1980. Bent 1925. Brooks 1903. Cogswell 1977. Delacour 1959. Dement'ev and Gladkov (1952) 1967, vol. 4. Johnsgard 1965. Kortright 1942. Witherby et al. (1939) 1943, vol. 3.

Barrow's Goldeneye
Garrot de Barrow. Porron Islandico.
Bucephala islandica (Gmelin)

APPEARANCE. Black and white plumage with prominent cheek-patch, wing-patches, and four dorsal spots; dark, monochromatic bills; and gray breast-band (often inconspicuous in Bufflehead) characterize all *Bucephala* ducklings. Compared to the downy Common Goldeneye, the Barrow's duckling has a shorter, more tapering bill with a much wider nail, curving above the surface of the bill in older downies (J. Munro 1918, 1939). The large, round or irregularly triangular nostril (vs. small, flattened oval in Common Goldeneye) is raised above the surface of the bill at all ages (shape best seen in live ducklings, but can also be observed in study skins in which nostrils have not been tied to close bill). The large-appearing head and more abruptly-rising forehead also distinguish young Barrow's ducklings from downy Common Goldeneyes, in which the head in profile appears tall rather than deep, and the forehead slopes backward more gradually from the bill (Palmer 1976, vol. 3; see pl. 9; compare goldeneye figs. 8-44 to 8-52 with 8-53 to 8-61; see also Bellrose 1976, 1980: Hines pl. 24). The same differences in head shape and bill structure also usually distinguish between older ducklings of the two goldeneye species (J. Munro 1918, 1939; Brooks 1920).

Irides of very young Barrow's ducklings are brown, grayish brown, or brownish gray (e.g., OSUFW; PSM; USNM), but irides of ducklings 10 d or older become purple-blue (C. Nelson 1983). Tarsal colors of both palaearctic and nearctic individuals are olive, grayish olive, or yellowish olive (e.g., BM[NH]; OSUFW; UBC; also J. Phillips 1925; Delacour 1959; Bauer and Glutz von Blotzheim 1969).

VARIATION. Ducklings of both goldeneye species had only small individual variations in dorsal, wing, and tibial patterns. A few Barrow's ducklings (2 Icelandic; 5 British Columbian) had a small or diffuse gray-white spot at center back behind the paired dorsal spots. More common were randomly distributed white tail plumes which sometimes formed a compete terminal band (also in some downy mergansers). The prominent gray breast-band typical of all goldeneye and many Bufflehead specimens is absent on Hines's goldeneye ducklings (Bellrose 1976, 1980: pl. 24).

According to Fjeldså (1977), the small gray chin-spot of many Barrow's ducklings appears less frequently on downy Common Goldeneyes. Examination of more than 50 specimens of each species disclosed the spot to be about equally common on individuals of both species, but where the chin feathers of Barrow's ducklings were often entirely gray, those of the downy Common Goldeneye were usually gray only at the base.

DISCUSSION. Downy plumages of the two goldeneye species are virtually identical. Colors of the unfeathered parts vary with the age of the duckling—older ducklings' colors generally lighter and grayer—and overlap to some extent between the two species, but structural bill ratios will identify both adult goldeneyes (e.g., Brooks 1920; Schiøler 1926: fig. 66 [also bills of ducklings]; J. Munro 1939; Kortright 1942: fig. 49) and live or prepared ducklings of any age.

Fjeldså's (1977: 77) method for distinguishing between [live?] ducklings of the two species is virtually infallible for newly hatched young. His ratio, width of nail (WN) to distance between anterior corners of nostrils (DACN), averaged 1.03 in 31 live Barrow's ducklings [1-2 d.] and 0.64 in 4 live Common ducklings of the same age (see Table 1, Appendix A, for statistical details; note that the range of Fjeldså's [1977: 77] ratio was "0.9-1.0" for Barrow's ducklings, "0.6-0.7" for Common ducklings). Tested on Class Ia study skins, the ratio again sorted the two species, with little or no overlap (mean ratio of WN/DACN for 11 Barrow's specimens=1.1 [1.0-1.2], S.D.=0.04, S.E.=0.01; for 25 Common specimens=0.8 [0.7-1.0], S.D.=0.09, S.E.=0.02). However, measurements of live, known-age young of both species, as well as measurements of a series of study skins of closely estimated age, showed that Fjeldså's ratios for both species decreased with age, in parallel fashion, thereby lessening the usefulness of the ratio for the identification of older ducklings of unknown age.

A second ratio, devised after analysis of a series of measurements of both live ducklings and study skins, works well for ducklings older than two or three days, but is somewhat less reliable for newly hatched birds. This ratio, nail area (LN x WN) to the width of the bill at the posterior of the nail (WBPN), is usually 4.0 or greater in Barrow's ducklings but in Common Goldeneye ducklings, is nearly always less than 4.0 (see Table 1, Appendix A, for (LN x WN)/WBPN ratios of goldeneye ducklings 1-28 d.).

Gilpin (1878), Brooks (1920), Kortright (1942; fig. 8), Johnsgard (1961c), Bellrose (1976, 1980), and others described and illustrated the tracheal characters that distinguish between adult males of the two goldeneye species: simple in *B. islandica*, but with an irregular, 'bony' enlargement in *B. c. americana*. J. Munro (1939) believed that the same characters would hold for downies and partly feathered juveniles, although Taverner (1919) had found no enlargement on the tracheas of half grown Common Goldeneyes that he examined. Taverner (1919: 58) illustrated both the bulbous tracheal enlargement of a first-winter male Common Goldeneye and the simple trachea of an adult male Barrow's Goldeneye. Jackson (1959) described an adult male hybrid goldeneye (*B. islandica* X *B. c. americana*) with intermediate characters of plumage, bill, and trachea.

Dissection of the tracheas (as in Johnsgard 1961c) of a 42 d. male Barrow's and a 51 d. male Common goldeneye showed similar tracheal development in both: a slight, gentle swelling over the lower half of the trachea. These findings suggest first, that the bulbous tracheal enlargement, such as found by Taverner (1919) in a first-winter Common Goldeneye male, is not present in downy and juvenal males of the Common Goldeneye; and second, that the use of tracheal examination to distinguish between Class I to Class III males of the two species will result in the misidentification of some species.

SOURCE OF SPECIMENS. **Alberta:** Jasper National Park: Talbot Lake—53° 06' N, 118° W (UBC-2). Red Deer (NMC-1). Waterton Lakes National Park (NMC-5: fig. 8-48). **British Columbia:** *Cariboo District:* Barkerville (RBCM-1); Murphy Lake (ROM-1; UBC-1); Carpenter Mountain Indian Reserve No. 15 (USNM-1); Westwick Lake—S Sorenson Lake [J. Munro 1945: 99] (UBC-5); Williams Lake: 150 Mile House (RBCM-1; NMC-1), 149 Mile Lake [J. Munro 1945: 98] (UBC-1), Riske Creek [creek] (RLWS-5 frozen; BMNH-9; NMC-1; UWGB[RC]-1). *Cassiar District:* Atlin (CM-1): Como Lake (RBCM-1); Dease Lake (NMC-1); Tetana Lake (RBCM-1). *Lillooet District:* 105 Mile Lake (ROM-1; UBC-1); Riske Creek [post office] (DWWRS-16 live [*ss:* MMMN-4]): 6.4 km N junction Chilcotin and Frazer rivers (MMMN-2 frozen). *New Westminster District:* Westham Island—mouth of Frazer River (UBC-1). *Range 3, Coast District:* Abuntlet Lake—6.4 km N Anahim Lake (UBC-1). *Range 5, Coast District:* François Lake (ROM-2: figs. 8-51, 8-52). *Yale District,* Kamloops Division: Curry Lake (DWWRS-6 live [*ss:* MMMN-1]); near Kamloops (DWWRS, NWPW-13 live: figs. 8-44 to 8-46 [*ss:* D-1; DEN-1; MMMN-1]); Paul Lake (DWWRS-26 live [*ss:* MMMN-7]). *Yale District,* Osoyoos

Division: Okanagan (RBCM-2; ROM-2); Okanagan Landing (NMC-3; OSUFW-1); Summerland (FMNH-1); Swan Lake—N end Okanagan Lake (PSM-1). **Alaska:** Russell Fjord at head of Yakutat Bay (ROM-1: figs. 8-49, 8-50). **Montana:** *Gallatin County:* Madison River near West Yellowstone (CM-1: fig. 8-47). **Washington:** *King County:* Tsuga Lakes—about 32 km SE North Bend (PSM-2). ICELAND (BM[NH]-1): **Sudur-Thingeyjarsýsla:** Mývatn (BM[NH]-1). **Captive origin** (DWWRS-1 frozen [*ss:* UND-1]).
OTHER REFERENCES. Bellrose 1976, 1980. Bent 1925. Brooks 1903. Cogswell 1977. Sutton 1961.

Common Goldeneye
Garrot à oeil d'or. Pato Ojiamarillo.
Bucephala clangula (Linnaeus)

APPEARANCE. See Barrow's Goldeneye, pp. 133-35. Compared to the Barrow's duckling, the downy Common Goldeneye has a longer, squarer bill with a narrower nail that is level with the rest of the bill at the ages (J. Munro 1918, 1939). The oval, somewhat flattened nostril can be seen in all live ducklings; usually elevated above the surface of the bill in young downies, it rises only slightly, if at all, in older birds (compare figs. 8-53 to 8-61 [*B. clangula americana*] with 8-44 to 8-52 [*B. islandica*], 8-35 to 8-43 [*B. albeola*]).

VARIATION. Unfeathered parts of most young Common Goldeneyes were similar in color to those of young Barrow's ducklings (e.g., ROM; NMC; USNM), but those of many live Delta specimens were paler, with a distinctly 'bluish' *hue*. The small central dorsal spot of some Barrow's ducklings did not appear on any *clangula* duckling, but many of these had white tail-plumes.
DISCUSSION. See Barrow's Goldeneye, pp. 133-35. Except for the (often) grayer or 'bluer' *hues* of the unfeathered parts of certain ducklings, no consistent color differences distinguish between Barrow's and Common goldeneye ducklings.

The striking eye-color changes observed in both goldeneye species (C. Nelson 1983) may be less pronounced in the palaearctic subspecies of the Common Goldeneye, *clangula* Linnaeus. Lack of descriptions of such changes in the literature provides negative evidence for this view. Positive evidence can be found in "chocolate-brown" irides of hand-reared, feathered but flightless (Class III) Common Goldeneyes (Blaauw 1909: 189), and in "dark" eyes of juvenal ducklings (Dement'ev and Gladkov [1952] 1967, vol. 4: 640). Cramp and Simmons (1977: 665) and Bauer and Glutz von Blotzheim (1969: 371), found paler eye-colors—"light brown," "brownish white"—in [feathered] juvenal females and yellow eye-color in juvenal males (age in days unknown).
SOURCE OF SPECIMENS. **Alberta:** Lake Athabasca: Egg Lake—about 24 km NW Fort Chipewyan (USNM-1). Red Deer: Red Deer River (NMC-4). Slave River about 24 km N 30th Base Line (CM-8: figs. 8-56, 8-57). **British Columbia:** *Kootenay District:* Creston (ROM-2): Duck Creek Channel (ROM-1), Duck Lake—W Sirdar (ROM-2); Golden (NMC-1); Parson (NMC-2). *Lillooet District:* Horse Lake—51° 36' N, 121° 10' W (ROM-1). *Peace River District:* Tupper Creek (RBCM-2). *Range 4, Coast District:* Nulki Lake (ROM-4). *Yale District:* Osoyoos Division: Okanagan: Swan Lake (ROM-1); Rawlings Lake (ROM-1), 4.8 km from Rawlings Lake (ROM-1). **Manitoba:** Clandeboye Bay (DWWRS-5 live [*ss*: MMMN-1]).

Delta (DWWRS-31 live: figs. 8-53 to 8-55 [*ss:* D-1; MMMN-6]): Portage Creek (DWWRS-6 live). Gypsumville: Lake Saint Martin Indian Reserve (ROM-1). Waterhen River 48.2 km N Sainte Rose du Lac (NWPW-10 live [*ss:* MMMN-2]). **Newfoundland:** *Gander District:* Glenwood: Gander River (USNM-1). *Humber East District:* Hinds' Plains: 9.6 km S Howley (CM-3). *Humber West District:* Bay of Islands (CM-1). **Northwest Territories:** *District of Keewatin:* NW corner Nueltin Lake at mouth of Windy River (USNM-1). *District of Mackenzie:* Fort McPherson (USNM-1). **Nova Scotia:** *Inverness County:* upper Margaree River: Long Intervale—S Big Intervale between Old Bridge Pool and Black Rock Pool [unpubl. fisheries map of NE Margaree River] (ROM-2). **Ontario:** *Algoma District:* Amyot (ROM-1); 4 km W Bruce Mines (ROM-2); Laird (ROM-5: figs. 8-58, 8-59). *Cochrane District:* Lake Abitibi: Ghost River (ROM-9). *Hastings County* or *Renfrew County:* Conroy's Marsh (ROM-4). *Thunder Bay District:* Fairloch: long lake E Five Rangers Tower (ROM-1); Lake Nipigon: Aviator's Bay [=Orient Bay] (ROM-1: figs. 8-60, 8-61), small lake across Aviator's Bay from MacDiarmid (ROM-3), SW shore Chief Bay (ROM-3), Humboldt Bay (ROM-1). **Québec:** *Abitibi County:* Boundary Bay 6.4 km W Roquemaure (NMC-1). *Bonaventure County:* Réserve de Port Daniel: Lac Marguerite [=Lac au Brulé] (NMC-1). *Montmorency No. 1 County:* Stoneham: Lac à l'Epaule—47° 15' N, 71° 14' W (NMC-1). *Saguenay County:* Anticosti Island: Chaloupe Creek (NMC-2); Grand Lac aux Cédres—52° 06' N, 67° 10'. W (CM-8). *Lake Saint John West County:* Lac Half Moon [=Lac Demi]: Lac de la Pie—48° 47' N, 74° 05' W (NMC-3); Saint-Méthode (NMC-3). **Saskatchewan:** Kamsack: Lake Madge (ROM-1). Prince Albert National Park: S end Crean Lake (MMMN-1). **Alaska:** Circle (USNM-1). **Minnesota:** *Beltrami County:* Blackduck: Blackduck Lake (RLWS-9 live; BMNH-3; PSM-1; UWGB[RC]-1); Chippewa National Forest: Tenstrike: Gull Lake (NPWRC-4 live). *Cook County:* Gunflint Trail (BMNH-1). *Koochiching County:* Ericsburg (BMNH-2).

OTHER REFERENCES. Bailey and Niedrach 1965, vol. 1. Bellrose 1976, 1980. Bent 1925. Coues (1872) 1903, vol. 2. Delacour 1959. Eaton 1910, vol. 1. Forbush 1925. Grinnell, Bryant, and Storer 1918. Harper 1953. Harrison 1975, 1978. Heinroth and Heinroth 1928, vol. 3. Johnsgard 1965. Kortright 1942. Kuroda 1939. Millais 1913, vol. 1. Myres 1957. Palmer 1976, vol. 3. J. Phillips 1925. Ridgway 1895, [1887] 1896. Roberts 1932, vol. 2. Schiøler 1926. Witherby et al. (1939) 1943, vol. 3.

Hooded Merganser

Bec-scie couronné. Pato Mergo Copeton.
Lophodytes cucullatus (Linnaeus)

APPEARANCE. Compared with Red-breasted and Common merganser ducklings, the downy Hooded Merganser is darker and more subtly colored over all; it has a dingy, pinkish gray breast-band, but it lacks well-marked face stripes, dorsal spots, and tibial pattern. It has a shorter, heavier, lighter-colored bill; rather 'square' head-shape; low, almost horizontal body posture; and (often) a 'silvery' forehead. Its irides are yellowish brown (vs. gray in *Mergus* spp.) and its feet are dark, with poor

contrast of base and pattern colors (vs. light-colored with good to fair contrast in *Mergus* spp.; compare *Lophodytes* and *Mergus* figs. on pl. 9). Bill colors of juvenal birds are distinctively light and 'bright', contrasting well with their dark plumage (Bauer and Glutz von Blotzheim 1969).

VARIATION. A few *Lophodytes* ducklings have fairly conspicuous dorsal spots and wing-patches, but the tibial pattern is seldom so conspicuous as that of goldeneyes, much less the boldly scalloped leg pattern of greater mergansers (compare ducklings of 3 genera on pl. 9). The *Mergus* duckling's bold face-stripes and prominent, light-colored circumorbital areas are either absent in the *Lophodytes* duckling or defined as extremely low-contrast patterns only. The eye-stripe may appear in front of the eye as an *Anas*-like smudge, or behind it, as a thin line fading quickly into the dark crown color. Light areas around the eye are either entirely absent or represented only by an obscure crescent below the eye or a poorly-marked spot above and in front of it. A few ducklings have dark

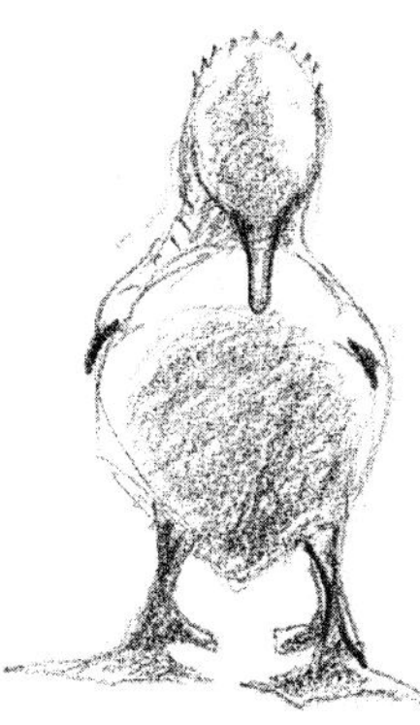

foreheads rather than 'silvery' ones, but none has any indication of a cheek-stripe.

Colors of the unfeathered parts vary little. Tarsi and toes of most live ducklings are grayish olive, with low-contrast pattern and webs of darker, grayer olive. A few ducklings had somewhat paler, 'greener' feet, but none had gray (e.g., J. Phillips 1926: Brooks pl. 96; Delacour 1959: Scott pl. 19), reddish (Millais 1913, vol. 2: Grönvold col. pl. fac. p. 4), or contrastingly colored feet (Bellrose 1976, 1980: Hines pl. 23). Gray or bluish eye-colors and gray feet were evident only in some older ducklings (e.g., partly-feathered female [CM: Adirondack Mountains]; Parkes 1954).

SOURCE OF SPECIMENS. **British Columbia:** *Cariboo District:* Stuart River about 64 km below Stuart Lake (ROM-2). *Comox District:* Vancouver Island: Comox (RBCM-1). **Manitoba:** Assiniboine River (ROM-1). Swan River (NMC-1). **Ontario:** Algonquin Park (ROM-1). *Parry Sound District:* Pickerel Lake: E Burk's Falls (ROM-1). *Rainy River District:* Off Lake (ROM-1). *Renfrew County:* Conroy's Marsh (ROM-1). *Sudbury District:* Biscotasing (ROM-1: figs. 8-67, 8-68). *Thunder Bay District:* Thunder Bay (ROM-1). **Minnesota:** *Cass County:* Hackensack: Baby Lake (BMNH-1). **Missouri:** *Stoddard County:* Puxico: Duck Creek (RLWS-1 live). **New York:** *Essex County:* Newcomb: Adjidaumo Swamp (CM-1). **Oregon:** *Benton County:* Corvallis (OSUFW-1). *Clatsop County:* Hammond (OSUFW-2; PSM-2). **Vermont:** *Addison County:* Vergennes (DWWRS, WT[S]-23 live: figs. 8-62 to 8-64 [*ss:* MMMN-2: fig. 8-66; UMFBP[DFP]-1; UND-1]). **Washington:** *Pierce County:* McChord Air Force Base (UWBM-2). **Captive origin** (MMS-5 frozen [*ss:* D-1; MMMN-1: fig. 8-65; UND-1]; UWBM-1).

OTHER REFERENCES. Baird, Brewer, and Ridgway 1884, vol. 2; quoted *in* Ridgway 1895). Bauer and Glutz von Blotzheim 1969. Bellrose 1976, 1980. Bent 1923. Coues [1872] 1903, vol. 2. Eaton 1910, vol. 1. Grinnell, Bryant, and Storer 1918. Harrison 1978. Johnsgard 1965. Kortright 1942. Palmer 1976, vol. 3. Ridgway 1895, [1887] 1896. Thorburn 1923. Witherby et al. (1939) 1943, vol. 3.

Red-breasted Merganser

Bec-scie à poitrine rousse. Pato Mergo Pechicastano.
Mergus serrator Linnaeus

APPEARANCE. Ducklings of both *Mergus* species have dark, brownish gray upper parts and white or 'creamy' underparts, 'reddish' heads, and two prominent reddish or blackish face-stripes that begin at the bill and continue past the eye. Rump-spots, wing-patches, and tibial pattern are also prominent, but shoulder-spots are small or absent.

The downy Red-breasted is smaller, a bit 'rounder', and more generally 'reddish' (light areas slightly yellowish; dark areas grayish) than the Common Merganser; the face stripes 'bleed' pale yellowish pink onto adjacent areas of white base color; and there is a white or 'creamy' sub-ocular crescent (pl. 9; figs. 8-73, 8-75, 8-77). The crown is high and somewhat triangular rather than long and rounded as in *M. merganser*, and the lower mandible is light-colored (*Mergus* figs., pl. 9). Also distinctive are the position of the nostril in the posterior third of the bill (Taverner 1945; Palmer 1976, vol. 3) and the projection of the lateral bill feathering beyond the mesial (compare *serrator* figs. 8-73 & 8-79 with *merganser* figs. 8-84 & 8-86; see Roberts 1932, vol. 2: 510, W. J. Breckenridge drawing; also Schiøler [1926: fig. 70] and Fjeldså [1977: fig. 12] for differences between *M. s. serrator* and Goosander, *M. m. merganser*, note virtually identical bill feathering of 2 spp. *in* Witherby et al. [(1939) 1943, vol. 3: fig. p. 366]).

Both lower mandible and feet are light yellowish brown. The light-colored lower mandible contrasts with the dark upper; and the feet have often a "lavender" *hue* (Palmer 1976, vol. 3: 464).

Three Greenland specimens of *schioleri* Salomonsen and *serrator* ducklings from continental North America shared quite similar characters of plumage and unfeathered parts. The small sample of Greenland ducklings seemed more 'reddish', with fewer and smaller pale or whitish areas.

VARIATION. Variation in the downy Red-breasted Merganser was most evident in the head markings. A light-colored sub-ocular crescent and light brown loreal stripes—formed by 'bleeding' of the secondary base color between the darker stripes in front of and behind the eye—typified all but a few Red-breasted ducklings, but the marks were absent in nearly all downy *M. m. americanus*. In these, the white loreal stripes remained clear. Palaearctic *serrator* ducklings depicted by D. Farrell (*Annual Report of the [Severn] Wildfowl Trust 1949-50*, 3, 1951: photo), Gould (1873: pl. 35), and Heinroth and Heinroth (1928, vol. 3: pl. 116) also displayed the subocular crescent, but Dement'ev and Gladkov ([1952] 1967, vol. 4), Bauer and Glutz von Blotzheim (1969: fig. 65), and Fjeldså (1977: fig. 12) show opposite crescent and clear-stripe characters in *M. serrator* and *M. m. merganser* ducklings. Light-colored areas above the eye, sometimes white or 'creamy' and quite prominent (e.g., Mackenzie Delta duckling, fig. 8-72; also Curth 1954: fig. 49), at other times contrasted poorly with the dark grayish brown crown color. A wash of light yellowish brown suffuses the sides of the *serrator* duckling's head and neck, sometimes forming a nearly complete neck-band.

Wing-patches and rump-spots are large, shoulder-spots small—often two or three plumes—or absent (contrary to Delacour [1959: Scott pl. 19] and Harrison [1978: Burton pl. 5]). The secondaries have large white patches, with smaller ones on the fronts of alulae and primaries. Millais's (1913, vol. 2: 100) description of the wing pattern ("outer edges white") has a rather misleading illustrative counterpart by Burton (*in* Harrison 1978: pl. 5).

The distinctive black and white tibial pattern, present on all specimens, was especially prominent on two ducklings from the Mackenzie Delta (CM), on the two younger Greenland specimens (ZMK), and on the five live Manitoba specimens. Randomly distributed white plumes, common in live ducklings, sometimes formed a complete terminal band on the tail (CM; NWT: Mackenzie Delta; sibling on pl. 9 & fig. 8-72).

DISCUSSION. The "bristly" appearance of the Red-breasted Merganser's natal down is not peculiar to that species, as Strong (1912: 483) supposed, but is common to all newly hatched ducklings (Palmer 1976, vol. 3; Grice and Rogers 1965). Kear (1972: 104) described "waxy sheaths" on the down of newly hatched cygnets; the delicate sheaths break open and slough off as the down becomes dry and fluffy in the first hours after hatching; usually, only tiny fragments remain on the plumage of day-old birds.

One of the 'blue-eyed' ducklings (others: Common Merganser, goldeneyes, Greater Scaup, and palaearctic Tufted Duck), downy Red-breasted Mergansers usually have gray or bluish gray irides at hatching (see also J. Phillips 1926: Brooks pl. 96; Schiøler 1926: Larsen pl. 83; Heinroth and Heinroth 1928, vol. 3: pl. 116; Fjeldså 1977: 78; and Harrison 1978: Burton pl. 5). A thin, brownish ring around the pupil (e.g., Stejneger 1885 re: young Bering I. specimen), present on all gray-eyed merganser ducklings, was less conspicuous in blue-eyed downies from Manitoba and Iceland. Brownish eye-colors (e.g., Gould 1873: pl. 35; Millais 1913, vol. 2: Grönvold col. pl. fac. p. 4; Fjeldså 1977: pl. 11) are not typical of very young ducklings, but gray eye-colors (Cramp and Simmons 1977) characterize some older ducklings.

Bill colors of downy Red-breasted Mergansers are virtually invariable. Light-colored lower mandibles, distinguishing very young Red-breasted ducklings from those of the Common Merganser, are present on older, half-grown ducklings of both species, as are diffuse face-stripes. Position of the nostril relative to bill length (similar to that in adults described by Taverner 1945: 111, figs. 168-69), and a small color difference in the upper mandible (Common Merganser's bill quite blackish, that of Red-breasted ducklings dark grayish and 'redder') separated older ducklings of the two species. Erskine also reported a somewhat "shaggier" appearance in Class II Red-breasted Mergansers than in Common ducklings of the same age (Anthony Erskine, letter to the author, February 1983).

Feet of the ducklings display many individual differences in base color and general darkness, but no downy Red-breasted Merganser had feet either so dark and greenish as those of Hooded Merganser ducklings or so contrastingly patterned as those of downy Common Mergansers. In a few ducklings, the overlying brownish gray pattern color considerably dulls the lighter base color.

SOURCE OF SPECIMENS. **Manitoba:** Churchill (NMC-7). Lake Manitoba near Waterhen River (NWPW-6 live: figs. 8-69 to 8-71 [*ss:* MMMN-4]). **Newfoundland:** *Humber East District:* Grand Lake (CM-14; BMNH-2: fig. 8-73); Sandy Lake (CM-10). *Labrador North District:* Makkovik (NMC-1); mainland opposite Winsor Harbour Island (CM-2). *Labrador West District:* Churchill River [=Hamilton River] 9.5 km above Churchill Falls [=Grand Falls] (CM-2). **Northwest Territories:** *District of Keewatin:* Boat Opening on Manitounuk Sound (NMC-1). James Bay: Paul Bay (NMC-6). *District of Mackenzie:* Mackenzie Delta: Richards Island: Reindeer Camp (CM-2: fig. 8-72). Taltson River: about 1.6 km above junction with Tazin River (NMC-1), several km below Tsu Lake below Shethko Falls (NMC-1). **Nova Scotia:** *Inverness County:* Margaree River below Margaree Forks: Marples Cove [unpubl. fisheries map of NE Margaree River] (ROM-1). Sable Island (NMC-1). **Ontario:** *Algoma District:* Pancake Bay at mouth of Pancake River (NMC-2). *Nipissing District:* Lake Nipissing: Goose Islands (ROM-1). **Québec:** *Mistassini Territory:* Lac Albanel (NMC-5: figs. 8-74, 8-75). *Territory of New Quebec:* Hudson Bay: Great Whale River (CM-2). **Saskatchewan:** Cochrane River (NMC-1). **Yukon Territory:** Teslin Lake (NMC-1). **Alaska:** Seward Peninsula: Pilgrim River (CM-4). GREENLAND: [Probably=*Holsteinsborg District* (=*Sisimiutkommunia*)]: Strømfjorden [=collective name for Nordre Strømfjord (=Nassuttoq) and Søndre Strømfjord (=Kangerlussuaq) which form, respectively, the northern and southern borders of the Holsteinsborg District] (ZMK-2: figs. 8-76, 8-77). R. E. Peary Expedition [location unknown] (AMNH-1: 8-78, 8-79). ICELAND: **Sudur-Thingeyjarsýsla:** Mývatn (RLWS-11 live [*ss:* PSM-2]).

OTHER REFERENCES. Baird, Brewer, and Ridgway 1884, vol. 2. Bellrose 1976, 1980. Bent 1923. Coues (1872) 1903, vol. 2. Eaton

1910, vol. 1. Forbush 1925. Grinnell, Bryant, and Storer 1918. Harper 1953. Harrison 1975. Johnsgard 1965. Kortright 1942. Ridgway 1895, [1887] 1896. Snyder 1957.

Common Merganser
Grand bec-scie. Pato Mergo Pechiblanco.
Mergus merganser Linnaeus

APPEARANCE: See Red-breasted Merganser, pp. 137-40. The Common Merganser duckling has a long, arrow-like body; the brown head down is puffy and loose, (yet has a 'combed-back' look), and the mesial bill feathering and low-crowned head are longer than comparable plumage and structural characters in the Red-breasted duckling. The position of *merganser's* nostril is more distal relative to that of *serrator* (Taverner 1945: figs. 168, 169; "in the center third of the mandible" [Palmer 1976, Vol. 3: 482]).

An entirely dark bill contrasts with whitish nail-tip and egg-teeth, but the dark lower mandible becomes light yellowish brown in half-grown ducklings—much like that of Red-breasted Mergansers. Tarsi and toes usually have good contrast of base and pattern colors, with dark web color often forming a triangle in the center front third of the web.

Palaearctic *merganser* Linnaeus is like nearctic *americanus* Cassin, except that the white loreal stripe is often clouded with pale brownish color (Bauer and Glutz von Blotzheim 1969: fig. 65; Fjeldså 1977: fig. 12) and the nail is more strongly hooked (*Wildfowl Trust Bulletin* 68 [January 1974]: 2, B. A. Crosby photo).

VARIATION. The larger (but not always heavier; see Table 1, Appendix A, and Smart 1965) downy Common Merganser is less generally 'reddish', with more distinctly marked and less variable head pattern, than is the slightly smaller Red-breasted duckling. The dark head is unmistakeably brown (i.e., not grayish, hence appears *more* 'reddish'), and the side of the head—between dark crown and white throat—clear brownish orange (also quite 'reddish' [but somewhat yellowish in *M. serrator*]). On nearly all ducklings, the white or 'creamy' loreal stripe is clear, with little or no marked 'bleeding' of the secondary pattern color anterior to the eye and ear (but see par. on palaearctic *merganser* Linnaeus, above); it meets the dark crown color rather abruptly just behind the eye. The area of light reddish color between 'reddish' head and white throat of *M. merganser americanus* is narrower than that in *M. serrator* (also in some palaearctic *merganser* ducklings, e.g., A. C. Meinertzhagen *in* Witherby et al. [1939] 1943, vol. 3). In a few individuals, this area is nearly as wide as that in Red-breasted Merganser ducklings, although it does not extend all across the throat in either species; sometimes, the reddish area ends abruptly short of the midline, as if cleanly erased (compare ducklings of 2 *Mergus* spp. on pl. 9).

Areas of light color are comparable in both species of downy *Mergus*. Circumorbital light areas, found most often in front of the eye, are smaller and usually whiter than those in *M. serrator* ducklings. Only a few *M. m. americanus* ducklings had areas of light brown above the eye resembling those in *M. s. schioleri* specimen, pl. 9. The dark rictal stripe is set off by the white or 'creamy' throat and the (usually) much lighter loreal stripe, whereas the dark eye-stripe often contrasts poorly with the somewhat lighter crown color. Both stripes lose definition in the dark crown color behind the eye. Variation in the striking dorsal and tibial patterns is similar to that in downy Red-breasted Mergansers, although shoulder-spots were evidently much larger in live Common Merganser ducklings described by Erskine (1971: 46) who found both pairs of dorsal spots "confluent with the white of the underparts."

Colors of the unfeathered parts vary little. Iris colors at hatching are neither so 'blue' as those of some downy *M. serrator*, nor so grayish brown as those of most goldeneye ducklings. Yellowish juvenal irides (*americanus:* Palmer 1976, vol. 3: 483; *merganser:* Cramp and Simmons 1977) resemble those of some feathered, immature Barrow's Goldeneyes (C. Nelson 1983).

Tarsal and toe colors exhibit a small range of values. Yellowish gray or 'bluish' feet with markedly contrasting pattern areas characterize most downy Common Mergansers. Dark pattern color is more extensive in darker-footed birds in which other yellowish or 'bluish' base colors are also dulled and darkened. Reddish feet (Millais 1913, vol. 2: Grönvold col. pl. fac. p. 4) and gray toes with yellow webs (J. Phillips 1926: Brooks pl. 96; Kortright [1942] and Bellrose [1976, 1980]: Shortt pl. 35 in both) are not typical of young ducklings.

According to Erskine (1971), the ducklings' bellies are almost completely feathered at about four weeks of age, but the upper parts still appear largely downy. The formerly well-marked rictal and eye-stripes also become diffuse and faded at this age, and the dark lower mandible becomes light-colored, both characters then resembling those of the Red-breasted Merganser.

SOURCE OF SPECIMENS. **British Columbia:** *Cariboo District:* Spanish Lake (NMC-2). *Cowichan Lake District:* Robertson River (NMC-1). *Kootenay District:* Kootenay Lake (UMZM-1). *Yale District*, Similkameen Division: Okanagan Valley: Vaseux Lake (NMC-5). **Manitoba:** Cormorant Lake (NMC-1). Lake Manitoba near Waterhen River (DWWRS, NWPW-27 live: figs. 8-80 to 8-82 [*ss:* D-4; MMMN-6; OSUFW-1]). **Newfoundland:** *Labrador North District:* Churchill River [=Hamilton River] 27.3 km above Minipi River (CM-1). **Nova Scotia:** *Inverness County:* Margaree River below Margaree Forks (NMC-1): Big McDaniel Pool (NMC-1); NE Margaree River: Big Intervale (ROM-4), First Fork Brook (NMC-1), Hatchery Pool (NMC-1), Marsh Pool [=Hay Pool]—1.6 km above First Fork Brook (NMC-1), Old Bridge Pool (NMC-1) [unpubl. fisheries map of NE Margaree River]. **Ontario:** *Algoma District:* Pancake Bay (NMC-4). *Bruce County:* Red Bay (NMC-1). *Cochrane District:* Missinaibi River W mouth of Opazatika River (CM-1: figs. 8-85, 8-86). **Québec:** *Portneuf County:* Jacques-Cartier River (NMC-1). **Saskatchewan:** Prince Albert National Park: Kingsmere Lake (D-1). **California:** *Placer County:* Lake Tahoe: 0.8 km S Tahoe Tavern (FMNH-1: fig. 8-83). **Minnesota:** *Cass County:* 6.4 km N Whipholt (UMFBP[DFP]-1). *Cook County:* Caribou Lake—NNE Lutsen (BMNH-1). *Koochiching County:* S shore Rainy Lake between Ranier and Island View (BMNH-2). *Lake County:* Kawishiwi River (BMNH-2). *Saint Louis County:* Ely: White Iron Lake: Burley Resort (BMNH-1: fig. 8-84). **Montana:** *Madison County:* Madison River Canyon above Earthquake Lake (CM-1). **Oregon:** *Klamath County:* Crescent Lake: about 32 km W Crescent (UOMNH-2). *Tillamook County:* Foley Creek area: 4.8 km SE Mohler (PSM-1). **Washington:** *Snohomish County:* North Fork Stillaguamish River (UWBM-1). *Yakima County:* Nache Ranger Station area about 53 km N Yakima (PSM-1).

OTHER REFERENCES. *Annual Report of the [Severn] Wildfowl Trust 1952-53* 6, 1954. Bailey and Niedrach 1965, vol. 1. Baird, Brewer, and Ridgway 1884, vol. 2. Bellrose 1976, 1980. Bent 1923. Cogswell 1977. Coues (1872) 1903, vol. 2. Delacour 1959. Eaton 1910, vol. 1. Forbush 1925. Grinnell, Bryant, and Storer 1918. Harrison 1975, 1978. Heinroth and Heinroth 1928, vol. 3. Johnsgard 1965. Kuroda 1939. Ridgway 1895, [1887] 1896. Roberts 1932, vol. 1 (p. 288: fig. 99); vol. 2.

Stiff-tailed ducks, tribe Oxyurini

North American genera: *Oxyura* Bonaparte, *Nomonyx* Ridgway

DISTRIBUTION AND TAXONOMY. The stiff-tailed ducks are confined to the southern hemisphere, except for the rare White-headed Duck, *Oxyura leucocephala,* whose discontinuous breeding range is restricted to the western and central palaearctic, and the Ruddy Duck, *O. jamaicensis,* subspecies of which are distributed from north central Canada to Tierra del Fuego (J. Phillips 1926; Delacour 1959; Blake 1977; Godfrey 1986). Many authors (e.g., Delacour and Mayr 1945; Delacour 1959; Johnsgard 1965, 1979) recognize two monotypic genera in the Oxyurini (*Biziura,* Musk Duck; *Heteronetta,* Black-headed Duck) and one polytypic genus, *Oxyura,* for all other stiff-tailed species. However, osteological (Woolfenden 1961; Livezey 1986) and behavioral and structural (Weller 1968b) studies of adult ducks, as well as distinctive pattern and structural characters of the downy young, favor the resurrection of *Nomonyx* for the Masked Duck (compare Masked and Northern Ruddy ducklings on pl. 9; compare also figs. 9-2, 9-3 with 9-7, 9-8).

Ducklings of two Australian endemics, the Blue-billed Duck, *O. australis* (ANWC: Australia: New S Wales) and the Musk Duck, *Biziura lobata* (ANWC: Australia: New S Wales), have blackish or dark gray plumage. The Blue-billed duckling has a dark, poorly defined pattern much like that of some downy Northern Ruddy Ducks (e.g., dark variant, pl. 9). Neither species has strongly contrasting face stripes as have downy Masked Ducks, *N. dominicus,* the paler Northern Ruddy ducklings (pl. 9) or the downy White-headed Duck (ROM; Russia: Volga River delta; see also Matthews and Evans 1974: fig. 6, M. Evans photo); the Musk duckling is without strongly contrasting markings of any kind (compare ducklings of 2 stiff-tailed spp. *in* Frith 1982: Watts pl. 5, and see older Musk ducklings *in* Lubbock 1980: photo facing p. 82 [mislabeled "Pink-eared Ducklings"]; note distinctive large bill in *Biziura*). In contrast, downy Black-headed and Masked ducks have consistently well-defined pattern elements and—alone among the stiff-tails—yellow base color. The relationship of the Masked Duck to other stiff-tails is clearly indicated in the similarity of both pattern elements and head structure (pl. 9; compare also figs. 9-3, 9-8), but downy *Heteronetta's* feather proteins (Brush 1976), plumage pattern, and bill characters are somewhat *Anas*-like (Weller 1968a: figs. 13-15; note wide nail), the duckling forages by "sifting" rather than diving (Rees and Hillgarth 1984: 247), and its bill is "narrower at the head end and flatter than those of other Oxyurini so that it does not have a typical stiff-tail shape (Eileen Rees, letter to the author, October 1984). Very young Northern Ruddy ducklings also forage by sifting or straining (Collias and Collias 1963), but their bills are roundly spatulate and heavy

at the base (figs. 9-4 to 9-10), and they can dive vigorously.

APPEARANCE. Downy young Oxyurini are distinguished from those of all other waterfowl tribes by round, heavy bodies; thick tarsi set far back and rather high on the body; long, stiff rectrices; long, coarse down; and ink-dark plumage. The pattern color is inky black in

Northern Ruddy ducklings, but appeared inky brown in the downy Masked Duck specimen that I examined (ANSP; 4 d.), possibly because of color changes after preparation and storage. Shiny black feet with characteristic thick tarsi, an irregular but usually well-marked cheek-stripe, and small eyes in a narrow-crowned skull characterize both *Nomonyx* and *Oxyura* species; in front view, the down on the lower cheeks puffs out much as it does in mergansers and goldeneyes. Descriptions of the plumage patterns of downy and adult Ruddy Ducks (Lehmann 1946 [downy *O. j. andina*]; Delacour 1959 [downy *O. j. ferruginea*]; Adams and Slavid 1984; Fjeldså 1986 [cheek pattern in adult *O. j. andina*]) suggest that variation in general darkness and definition of pattern color in Northern Ruddy ducklings (*O. j. rubida*; pl. 9) may also characterize ducklings of South American subspecies.

BEHAVIOR. I have seen no live downy Masked Ducks. Useful accounts of the habits of adult Masked Ducks appear in Savage English (1916), Barbour (1923), J. Phillips (1926), Scott (1960), Slud (1964), Wetmore (1965), Weller (1968b), and Johnsgard and Hagemeyer (1969), but the vocalizations and behavioral characters of young Masked ducklings are entirely unknown. The following remarks, therefore, pertain only to wild-caught Northern Ruddy ducklings observed in Manitoba and Minnesota. Palmer reports (1976, vol. 3: 503) that newly hatched Ruddies "cannot walk and must scoot along on their bellies", using their feet in the manner of oars (scooting behavior also described in downy *Heteronetta;* Weller 1968a). Sometimes, the simultaneous thrusts of both feet propel them forward in a series of hops. The ducklings' short necks and the extreme posterior position of their legs often make it difficult for them to maintain their balance during preening: day-old young seem about to roll over completely when using the oil gland, but two-day-old birds, by placing their legs and feet almost straight out on either side, are able to stand upright to belly-preen. Evidently, their heavy bellies and large paddle areas are sufficient to balance them, for they seldom tumble backward. At this age, they rest with feet drawn up on either side (Palmer 1976, vol. 2: 466, C. Nelson col. pl.). Awkward on land, Northern Ruddy ducklings are supremely skillful in the water; they seem to prefer it to any other surface. They preen, scratch, and even sleep on the water, heads turned to rest at the side of their breasts, small stiff tails pointed upward, and feet stretched out idly on either side.

Feeding is an intensely active affair. I observed a brood of four two-day-old Northern Ruddies (RLWS) as they swam in a water-filled tank, their bill-tips just below the surface, snapping their mandibles with small rapid movements as they devoured all of the duckweed with which the tank had been stocked. They dived repeatedly, bobbing up and down like little corks, even swimming strongly backward on the surface of the water while keeping heads and necks submerged. Occasionally, a duckling rose almost straight up and trod the water rapidly with its feet, creating turbulence and, perhaps, bringing potential food items to the surface or at least within view. However, these young captive ducklings did not follow the water-treading with head-under searching and pursuit of prey, behavior that Driver (1960a) observed in week-old, wild Common Eiders.

Diving by gradual submersion (i.e., sinking without a ripple) is reported in various adult stiff-tails, e.g., Ruddy Duck (Rich 1907; quoted *in* Bent 1925), Musk Duck (Stewart Holohan, pers. comm. 1983), and Masked Duck (Savage English 1916). According to Bond (James Bond, letter to the author, September 1983), this behavior is the basis for the Masked Duck's Haitian name, 'le zombie capon' [=coward zombie] or "canard zombie" (Bond [1961] 1971: 52). Sinking behavior was not observed in hatchery-reared Northern Ruddy ducklings of any age. Nor was it noted in captive White-headed ducklings (1 d.-7 wk.) or adults observed by Matthews and Evans (1974: 64-65), who related the development of diving skills in the species to "changes in body proportion as well as feather development."

Northern Ruddy ducklings can be quite pugnacious. Ward, who has successfully raised many such ducklings at Delta, observed: "[Northern] Ruddies are on yolk-sac for three or four days and don't do much until they start eating—then they bite" (Peter Ward, pers. comm. 1962). I found that even day-old Northern Ruddies opened their pink mouths in a soundless 'hiss' at my approach. Nice (1962: 51) reported that Frank McKinney and a companion were threatened by a "[Northern] Ruddy duckling [1 d. or less]...in the nest." She noted that a day-old [Northern] Ruddy Duck bit Redheads and [Northern] Mallards (4 d.) when they came near it, and further, that a "three-day-old [Northern] Ruddy duckling [chased] a brood of two-week-old [Northern] Mallards ...and ...threatened and bit them [when] they attacked him." Intraspecific aggression also occurs: a

brood of two-day-old birds engaged in persistent tail-pulling as they swam in the study pool, and continued hostilities even into their preening and resting session.

Day-old Northern Ruddy ducklings have a variety of calls. There are at least two polysyllabic calls: one a softly reiterated, fairly high-pitched, four-syllabled call ascending in whole tones; the other an alternation of descending disyllabic and polysyllabic notes, rapidly repeated during preening. The whistle of distress (Kear 1968: fig. 13c) consists of a sequence of husky, evenly accented notes rising slightly in pitch and volume. There is also a variable short trill. Usually descending in pitch and repeated rapidly in bouts of three or four, the trill sometimes rises in pitch as it decreases in amplitude, so that the end of it is scarcely audible. At other times, it is firmly uttered all on one pitch. The long, soft, low-pitched, 'purring' trill heard occasionally from ducklings 10 days and older may be a kind of greeting or warning call. A

quiet, monosyllabic note also is added to their repertoire at this time.

Ruddy Duck
Canard roux. Pato Rojizo Alioscuro.
Oxyura jamaicensis (Gmelin)

APPEARANCE. A roundly spatulate, high-bridged bill; short neck; thick tarsi; stiff, spiny tail; and short, round body characterize the blackish Ruddy duckling. The nail, hooked sharply downward and "angled somewhat backward" (Palmer 1976, vol. 3: 503) is the narrowest among all downy waterfowl in North America on the *outside* of the bill (figs. 9-4, 9-7, 9-9), although it widens markedly on the *inside* of the upper mandible where it overlaps the tip of the premaxillary bone (=anterior terminal dorsal bone of the avian skull; Van Tyne and Berger 1959).

VARIATION. Both the intensity of the yellow base color and the general darkness of the pattern color vary considerably. These, in turn, affect the extent and definition of the basic pattern. Nearly all previously published descriptions (e.g., Coues [1872] 1903, vol. 2; J. Phillips 1926; Delacour 1959; Cramp and Simmons 1977) refer to the base color of Ruddy ducklings as white, whitish, or pale gray. Although all yellow color had virtually disappeared after a few days' exposure to sunlight, more than 30 live, newly hatched ducklings had unmistakeably—if often faintly—yellow faces, one had a yellowish gray face, and only six were 'white'. Faint, dusky down-tips overlying areas of light base color often obscure perception of any underlying yellow pigment. In some very dark individuals, nearly all pale base color is thus concealed, leaving only the chin and (often) the lores as areas of clear color. In very young ducklings, the pale brilliance of these areas, along with the pink gape, contrasts well, even at some distance, with the otherwise sooty plumage colors.

Dark-plumaged variants, with dark bellies and throats, inconspicuous dorsal patterns (see also Bailey and Niedrach 1965, vol. 1: Hochbaum pl. 19; no dorsal spots and wing-patches), and barely discernible facial stripes, have been photographed by Bailey and Niedrach (1965, vol. 1: 184), F. Todd (1979: fig. 13.8), and J. V. Beer (*Annual Report of the [Severn] Wildfowl Trust 1954-56* 8, 1957: 7 older downies with female parent). See dark and pale variants (pl. 9, this work) and intermediate form (Palmer 1976, vol. 3: 466, C. Nelson col. pl.).

The cheek-stripe varies considerably in definition and completeness, but is almost never so straight and linear as those depicted by Delacour (1959), Cramp and Simmons (1977), and Harrison (1978). Customarily, the cheek-stripe begins as a thin, often indistinct stripe at the rictus. Directly below the eye, the stripe becomes thinner—sometimes consisting of just a few dark plumes and often broken entirely in light-colored individuals—then larger again at the ear. Occasionally, the dark stripe extends to the dark occiput as a thin dusky line. The shape of the stripe is much like that on the ANSP Masked duckling, but is generally less well-marked (compare 2 spp. on pl. 9).

All live downy Northern Ruddy Ducks examined had unmarked winglets and two shoulder-spots. Wing-patches on ducklings depicted by Harrison (1978: Burton pl. 5) and Bellrose (1980: Hines pl. 24) cannot be considered typical. Nor can Bent's duckling (1925: pl. 28 [upper], H. K. Job photo), which appears to have white wing-patches as well as unusually conspicuous dorsal spots. Both Bent (1925) and Roberts (1932, vol. 2) reported rump-spots but no shoulder-spots on their specimens.

The freckled effect on the cheeks and throats of downy Ruddies (e.g., Delacour 1959; Harrison 1978) results from the growth of new gray underdown beneath the paler natal down in ducklings, the contrast of short, *pale* gray tips against the darker bases and shafts of the breast down produces a freckled effect on the breast-band.

Bill and tarsal colors were glossy and essentially 'black' on all but a few specimens. These, being lighter in *value*, appeared also brighter, when in fact both were almost equally dull; greenish feet (Kortright 1942: Shortt pl. 35) are unusual.

The inky blackness typical of young ducklings' pattern colors fades gradually to dark gray and then to brownish gray as the barred reddish buff and blackish brown contour feathers begin to emerge at about three weeks of age. The light gray down of the breast-band and belly becomes darker toward the undertail in Class II ducklings.

SOURCE OF SPECIMENS. **Alberta:** Sinclair Lake (MMMN-3: fig. 9-7). **British Columbia:** *Cariboo District:* Cummings Lake (NMC-1), 150 Mile House (NMC-1). *Lillooet District:* near Riske Creek [post office] (NMC-1); Watson Lake (OSUFW-1). **Manitoba:** Clarkleigh (DWWRS-8 live [*ss:* MMMN-3]). Delta (DWWRS-22 live: figs. 9-4 to 9-6 [*ss:* D-9; MMMN-1: fig. 9-8; UWBM-1]). Duck Mountain: 4.8 km W Lake Olive (MMMN-1: figs. 9-9, 9-10). Gypsumville: Pineimuta Marsh (NWPW-4 live [*ss:* MMMN-4]). Minnedosa (UFS[DM]-1 live [*ss:* MMMN-1]), 3.2

km E, 8.0 km S Minnedosa (UWBM-1). Oak Lake (NMC-1). **Québec:** *Yamaska County:* Saint Lawrence River: Lake Saint Peter—near Sorel (NMC-1). **Saskatchewan:** South Arm Last Mountain Lake (NMC-4). **California:** *Santa Cruz County:* Santa Cruz (CM-5). **Minnesota:** *Anoka County:* Fridley: Moore Lake (BMNH-2). *Hennepin County:* Minneapolis: Mother Lake (BMNH-1). *McLeod County:* Hutchinson (BMNH-1). *Nobles County:* marsh N Round Lake Waterfowl Station (RLWS-6 live). *Roseau County:* Ross: Roseau River (BMNH-1). **Oregon:** *Klamath County:* Klamath Falls (OSUFW-1). *Lake County:* Summer Lake (PSM-1). **Washington:** *Okanogan County:* N Big Goose Lake (UWBM-1). MEXICO: **Morelos:** Laguna Coatetelco (BMNH-2).

OTHER REFERENCES. Baird, Brewer, and Ridgway 1884, vol.2. Brooks 1903. Cogswell 1977. Fjeldså 1977. Grinnell, Bryant, and Storer 1918. Harrison 1975. Johnsgard 1965. Kuroda 1939. Ridgway 1895, [1887] 1896. Tome 1991.

Masked Duck

Canard masqué. Pato Agostero (Barbour 1923), Pato Tímido.

Nomonyx dominicus (Linnaeus)

APPEARANCE. The combination of much smaller size, rich yellow-orange base color, dark breast-band, black cap with prominent superciliary stripe, wide black cheek-stripe, four dorsal spots, and wide, mallard-like nail distinguish the downy Masked Duck from the closely-related Ruddy duckling (compare ducklings of 2 spp. on pl. 9). The narrow, low-crowned skull and long, fan-like tail are unique among yellow-plumaged North American ducklings.

VARIATION. Quoted material in this paragraph is from Bond (1961: 9). Although similar in some respects to the Ruddy duckling (e.g., narrow skull, stiff tail, dark cheek-stripe and breast-band, absence of wing-patches) the downy Masked Duck differs in certain details of pattern, color, bill structure, and tail length. The Masked duckling has a broad yellow superciliary stripe, and a dark cheek-stripe "more prominent" than that in the downy Ruddy duckling. The base color—most intense (Munsell 1Y 6/8 [=Ridgway's (1912) Antimony Yellow]) on the superciliary stripe and lores—is generally "yellowish buff" (rather than white or yellowish white as in the Ruddy duckling), and the pattern color blackish brown (vs. essentially black). The wide, *Anas*-like nail is only slightly down-turned (vs. retrorse), the bill wide and somewhat wedge-shaped in dorsal view (vs. roundly spatulate), and "the tail decidedly longer than that of the downy young Ruddy duck." A tiny, medial yellow spot above the bill, present on the ANSP duckling and on an immature (Class III?) bird photographed by D. Hagemeyer (*Audubon Field Notes* 1968, 22 [1]: cover ill.), was absent on a half-grown specimen from Costa Rica.

The Costa Rican specimen (USNM; "close to four weeks old"; Ralph Browning, letter to the author, January 1977) had an abnormal, prognathous bill, with the upper mandibles nearly 3 mm shorter than the lower. The horny ridge around each nostril, similar to that found in half-grown Ruddy ducks, was enlarged proximally. The belly was largely feathered with grayish buff except for a central patch of pale yellow down, the breast feathers were pale reddish buff barred with grayish brown, and the scapulars, shoulders, and flanks reddish buff barred with blackish brown. Four dorsal spots were clearly visible, and the face pattern was like that of a young duckling (see also photos by Hagemeyer in *Audubon Magazine* [1968, 70 (3): 114] and *in* Johnsgard 1968: pl. 145).

SOURCE OF SPECIMENS. COSTA RICA: **Cartago:** Laguna de Coris—10 km W Cartago (USNM-1). CUBA: **Pinar del Río:** Pinar del Río (ANSP-1: figs. 9-1 to 9-3).

OTHER REFERENCES. Bond 1961, 1971. Delacour 1959. Johnsgard 1965. Johnsgard and Hagemeyer 1969. Palmer 1976, vol. 3. Scott 1960. Slud 1964. Weller 1968b. Wetmore 1965.

Discussion

Taxonomy

With some exceptions, the natural groupings suggested by the pattern and color characters of the newly hatched young correlate well with taxonomic arrangements used by other recent authors, such as Delacour and Mayr (1945), A.O.U. (1957, 1983), and Johnsgard (1978, 1979). These characters, most useful at the generic and tribal levels (Moffitt 1932; Fjeldså 1977), support the recognition of two additional tribes, Cygnini (Woolfenden 1961; Frith 1982; Livezey 1986) and Somateriini (Humphrey 1958a; Brush 1976), as well as the resurrection of several genera suppressed by other authors (i.e., *Olor, Philacte, Nesochen, Mareca, Lophodytes, Nomonyx*). The close relationship indicated by previous authors for other groups of species is confirmed by the similarity of their natal characters, as in the Black-bellied and West Indian whistling-ducks (pl. 1; Johnsgard 1965; Bolen and Rylander 1983), the northern swans, *Olor* (pl. 2; Parkes 1958; Johnsgard 1974; C. Nelson 1976b), the white geese, "*Chen*" (pls. 3 & 4; McLandress and McLandress 1979; Seeb, Wishard, and Oates unpubl.), the wigeons, Falcated Duck, and Gadwall (pls. 6 & 7; J. Phillips 1923; Delacour 1956; Patton and Avise 1983, Livezey 1991), the blue-winged ducks (pl. 7; McKinney 1970; Kessler and Avise 1984), the *Aythya* species (pl. 8; Johnsgard 1965; Patton and Avise 1983; Livezey 1986), the greater eiders (pl. 7; Humphrey 1958a), and the greater mergansers (pl. 9; Humphrey 1955 [n.d.]; Livezey 1986, 1989).

Some relationships among species are also clarified. In certain species-pairs having similar adult, juvenal, and downy plumages (e.g., Barrow's and Common goldeneyes, Greater and Lesser scaup), the downy young often can be distinguished only by means of various bill and nail ratios. The downy young of certain other species in which the adult plumages appear similar (or are believed to have been similar at some stage in their evolution) have quite distinct natal characters (e.g., compare scaup and Ring-necked ducklings, pl. 8, and Northern Mallard and Laysan ducklings, pls. 6 & 7). More subtle, yet measurable and consistent, differences in color and pattern separate the downy young of the 'old', monomorphic, dark-headed mallards, *A. fulvigula* group, from those of the 'new', dimorphic, green-headed mallard, *A. platyrhynchos* (pl. 6; see also Appendix B). These differences, paralleling morphological and biological characteristics of adults of the two groups reported by Wright (1954), Dzubin (1957), Scott and Reynolds (1984), Paulus (1984), and others, suggest that the affinities of the mallards in North America could be much as Palmer (1976, vol. 2) proposed.

Phylogeny

The analysis of color, pattern, and structural characters, so obviously useful at tribal, generic, and specific levels, can also be applied to phylogenetic studies. The difficulty in attempting such analysis lies in establishing the direction of change: a given character may develop 'in reverse' as well as 'forward' (Bock 1960) or may even be lost and re-established (e.g., Raikow, Borecky, and Berman 1979) during the course of its evolution within a particular group, thereby complicating the task of the analyst. Nevertheless, if certain assumptions are made, it may be possible to establish which characters are 'older' (i.e., primitive) and which 'newer' (i.e., derived). The first assumption is that the primitive or 'ancestral' pattern of downy Anatidae had diffuse, poorly marked pattern elements, similar to those of certain extant swans and geese, to the Magpie Goose, *Anseranas semipalmata* (Frith 1964b; F. Todd 1979: figs. 1.179, 3.10; now believed not closely related to other waterfowl; Scherer and Sontag 1986), and screamers, *Anhima cornuta* (Luis Naranjo unpubl. photo) and *Chauna* spp. (Belton 1984; *Wildfowl* 20, 1969: pl. 13a,

Philippa Scott photo), and to other taxa considered phylogenetically old, such as penguins (Sphenisciformes; NMC; Antarctica: Ross I.; Baker et al. 1985: photos), loons (Gaviiformes; NMC; Ont.: Algonquin Prov. Park; Fjeldså 1977: pl. 39), and tube-nosed swimmers (Procellariformes; NMC; NWT: Prince Leopold I.; Baker et al. 1985: photos). The second assumption is that the dark pattern elements (e.g., eye-stripe, 'hood', crown-patch, breast-band) are bound inextricably to the eumelanic plumage component. Melanin itself is a very stable compound (e.g., it can be difficult to extract from feathers [M. Tascona and C. Nelson, unpubl.] and it is exceedingly durable over time [H. Fox and Vevers 1960]). In most downy anatids, it shows only small, individual variations which have little or no effect upon the manifestation of pattern elements typical for the species. Furthermore, eumelanic pattern color (hence, pattern definition) often is largely unaffected by striking variations in the *value* or *chroma* of the base color, such as occur in the Black-bellied Whistling-duck, *Dendrocygna autumnalis*. Traces of melanic pattern color remain even in the plumage of leucistic cygnets (C. Nelson 1976a). The third assumption is simply a recognition of the far-reaching effects of the Pleistocene glacial and interglacial periods upon holarctic avian speciation, as proposed by Rand (1948), Johansen (1956, 1963), Ploeger (1968), Mengel (1971), Hubbard (1973), and others.

Traditional phylogenies (e.g., dendrograms by Delacour and Mayr 1945; Johnsgard 1978; Bellrose 1976, 1980) propose monophyly of the family involving genealogical descent from more 'primitive' species, such as swans and geese, to those more 'derived', such as sea-ducks and stiff-tailed ducks. However, my observations of downy waterfowl from North America and other areas suggest a possibly more complex pattern of evolutionary change. For example, pattern types in downy waterfowl vary from simple (few elements, poorly defined) to more complex (several elements, well-defined), but the simpler patterns do not necessarily appear in tribes thought to be more 'primitive', nor the complex patterns in those more 'derived'. Structure of the lower egg-tooth and coloration of the plumage and unfeathered parts follow a similar heterogeneous distribution.

Characters of the downy young confirm the ancient lineage of swans (Mindell and Honeycutt 1989) and geese (Shields and Wilson 1987a). The same characters suggest a lineage almost equally ancient for certain diving ducks and eiders, as well as an evolution more modern than that generally accepted for perching ducks, dabbling ducks, and all pochards. Most ornithologists agree upon the early emergence of the whistling-ducks (e.g., Delacour and Mayr 1945; Howard 1964; Johnsgard 1965, 1978; Brush 1976; and others), but some have found the whistling-ducks much like other anserine waterfowl (blood tissue: 10 loci; Numachi et al 19830, while others have found the two groups not closely related (single-copy DNA; Madsen, McHugh, and de Kloet 1988). However, swans, geese, and whistling-ducks, as well as *Anseranas, Anhima, Chauna* spp., *Thalassornis, Coscoroba,* and *Stictonetta* have reticulate tarsi, which are here considered primitive, contrary to Brush and Wyld (1980).

The 'oldest' of present-day anatids are thought to be the swans, geese, and their allies, particularly certain taxa endemic in Australia, a continent believed to have been attached to Antarctica as recently as 43-60 million years ago (Jones 1971; Jardine and McKenzie 1972; Rich 1975; Derry et al. 1980). Some of these endemics or their antecedents might even have developed in the "profound isolation" sustained by that continent during much of its Cenozoic journey to its present geographical position (Rich 1975: 99). These taxa include several presently monotypic anatid genera (e.g., *Cereopsis, Malacorhynchus, Biziura*), a monotypic subfamily, Stictonettinae (Livezey 1986) [or, a monotypic Anserine tribe, Stictonettini [Brush 1976]), and a monotypic family,

Anseranatidae (Livezey 1986; Scherer and Sontag 1986 [or, a monotypic subfamily, Anseranatinae [Delacour 1954; Johnsgard 1979]).

Cygnets of the Australian Black Swan, *Cygnus atratus*, have the most generalized, poorly defined pattern of all downy Anatidae (Boyd 1972; C. Nelson 1976b): brownish gray pattern color; gray-white base color; diffuse, poorly marked pattern elements; and dark-colored bill and tarsi. The downy Black Swan is the darkest of the cygnets over all as well as the only one to have unfeathered lores at hatching (Cygnini, pp. 28-30; also Scott et al. 1972: pl. 4, H. J. Lavery photo). That downy young of other southern swans may once have been even darker than the Black cygnet may be inferred from the plumage of the downy Black-necked Swan, "outwardly the whitest of all the cygnets [Munsell 8/; Black cygnet 5.5/], but darker than any other species at the *base* of the dorsal down [Munsell 4/]" (C. Nelson 1976b: 8; 11, Table l).

Both the natal characters of the cygnets and the predominantly black plumage of the adults suggest that the Black Swan (or a type similar to it, e.g., *Cygnus lacustris* [Howard 1964]) may have encountered less rigorous environments during the Pleistocene than did the northern swans (genus *Olor*; Ploeger 1968), other *Cygnus* species (i.e., *C. olor*, *C. melanocoryphus*), and *Coscoroba*. According to Gentilli (1961), only Tasmania and parts of SE Australia were glaciated, whereas Flint (1971) described glaciation in the Andean Cordillera from Colombia to Tierra del Fuego. Presumably, the loss of nearly all dark pigment in adult white and Black-necked swans, as well as the pale plumage colors and species-typical feathered lores of all cygnets represent various successful adaptations to the cooling climatic trends resulting from the Pleistocene and earlier glaciations. The southern swans (*Cygnus*) are here considered more "primitive" than the northern (*Olor*), contrary to Delacour and Mayr (1945: 8), and the Black Swan is presumed to have arrived in Australia very early in its evolutionary history, either by way of the Antarctic dispersal routes described by Cracraft (1973) and Rich (1975) or the Indomalaysian route proposed by Mayr (1944a, 1944b, 1972). While present and prehistoric distribution patterns of organisms are not necessarily correlated (Cracraft 1973) and may even be quite different—e.g., *C. olor* [Howard 1964]—the over all distinctiveness of the Australian anatid fauna appears to favor the Antarctic route for at least some Australian endemics.

Except for their feathered lores, cygnets of the holarctic (but 'southern') Mute Swan are simply paler versions of the Black cygnet. The resemblance between the natal characters of the Black and Mute cygnets suggests that they are derived from the same *Cygnus* stock, but the striking differences in the appearance of the adults may imply that they became separated well before the Black Swan colonized Australia.

The throat and head patterns of all cygnets, and the large wing-patches and shoulder-spots of the pale *Olor* cygnets resemble those of some *Branta*, Pink-footed, and Greater White-fronted goslings; Numachi et al. (1983) found Whooper and Tundra swans genetically inseparable from some Canada goslings. Dorsal and head patterns are better-defined in Barnacle and certain other Canada goslings, but shoulder-spots and wing-patches are nearly always lacking in the insular Hawaiian gosling and in the gray goslings of Emperor Goose and Brant—the last two species are believed by Ploeger (1968) to have differentiated during the Last Glacial in low and high Arctic refugia, respectively. The lack of prominent dorsal pattern in goslings of the last three species may reflect adaptation to dark, sparsely vegetated lava slopes (Hawaiian Goose) or to tundra and marine habitats (Emperor Goose, Brant). Their neutral, medium *value* plumage colors, without conspicuous pattern elements, would afford concealment from both aerial and terrestrial predators in all three habitats. The absence of contrasting patterns could also mean early isolation in all three species, i.e., before the appearance of well-marked dorsal patterns and chromatic color in relatives.

Downy young of another anserine tribe, the Dendrocygnini (whistling-ducks), vary widely in color and dorsal pattern (pl. 1; see also Delacour 1954: Scott pl. 4) but are unified by the distinctive dark crown and occipital 'T' stripe. *Dendrocygna* species are known from the Miocene (Howard 1964)—long enough for the downy plumage to have undergone some evolutionary changes. *D. bicolor* and *D. arcuata* (forming a superspecies; Johnsgard 1979) have the most plainly colored downy plumage—gray and white, usually without prominent dorsal and tibial patterns—of all Dendrocygnini, possibly reflecting *D. bicolor's* wide distribution. These two species are followed by *D. guttata* and *D. eytoni*—black and white, with prominent wing-patches, tibial pattern, and dorsolateral bar—and *D. viduata, D. javanica, D. autumnalis,* and *D. arborea,* all with prominent wing-patches, tibial patterns, and dorsal spots. Note that some downy *D. javanica* have white base color (e.g., Delacour 1954: Scott pl. 4) but other individuals of this tiny species have pale yellow in place of white (FMNH; India: Assam: Goalpara).

Dark, aberrant *Thalassornis* ducklings, have calls similar to downy whistling-ducks (Kear 1968) and have a paler nape and hindneck below their blackish crowns (FMNH; Kenya: Lake Naivasha; Kear 1967), but they lack the occipital 'T' stripe. Evidence for the close relationship of certain swans and whistling-ducks is found in the *Dendrocygna*-like head patterns of downy *Coscoroba* (FMNH; Paraguay: Chaco; Delacour and Mayr 1945; Scott et al. 1972: pl. 1) and, to a lesser extent, of juvenal Whistling Swans (H. Hansen et al. 1971: fig. 43).

The anserine Freckled Duck, *Stictonetta naevosa,* was shown by Olson and Feduccia (1980) to have certain anatomical affinities with fossil *Presbyornis,* which they proposed as a possible anseriform ancestor. Frith (1982) believed *Stictonetta* to be the most primitive of living anatids. He observed (1964a, 1964b) that the brownish gray and gray-white natal plumage and dark bill and feet of the Freckled duckling are most like those of two groups relatively unallied to each other within the Anatidae: the Black Swan and the two Australian stiff-tails, the Blue-billed Duck, *Oxyura australis,* and the Musk Duck, *Biziura lobata.* All of these species have quite dark, low-contrast plumage with few or no discernible pattern elements, (see Frith 1982: Watts pl. 5; also Delacour 1959: Scott pl. 19). Similar monochromatic patterns—if somewhat better defined—are found in certain dark-billed, dark-footed holarctic diving ducklings, i.e., the Oldsquaw, eiders, and scoters. The downy Harlequin's cleanly marked gray and white plumage, and the black and white patterns of *Bucephala* and some greater merganser ducklings may be seen as more boldly marked versions of these. Delacour and Mayr (1945) proposed monophyletic origin for the Mergini (in which they also included the eiders), a view based largely upon the possession of a white cheek-patch by most downy Mergini. Polyphyletic origin of the Mergini was suggested by Humphrey ([1955] n.d.) on the basis of differences in the tracheal bulla among adult males of the tribe. Livezey (1986) later confirmed the possibility of convergence in diving adaptations among adult Mergini. I suggest further the possibility of convergence in the cheek-patch of the downy young, because the form of this patch differs slightly among the various species. Regardless of its form, however, the cheek-patch could be considered a useful adjunct in head-under 'searching', a food-gathering technique practised by all downy Mergini.

However, there is no apparent 'progression' between patterns of downy anserines and certain diving ducklings and those of all perching, dabbling, and pochard ducklings. For the most part, dark pattern colors of the latter groups contrast well with often brilliant yellow base colors—among North American species, only the downy Northern Pintail lacks obviously chromatic base color. Pattern elements such as dorsal spots and eye-stripes are usually well-marked, and there is no evidence among most species of extensive pigment loss such as evidently occurred in the melanic pattern colors of cygnets and many goslings.

The structure of a possibly conservative taxonomic character, the lower egg-tooth, parallels rather closely the pattern characters of the downy young as presented here. Eiders and sea-ducklings—excepting *Bucephala* ducklings but including the downy Smew, *Mergellus albellus* (UWBM; aviary captives), with *Bucephala*-like plumage—share with whistling-ducks, swans, and geese a type of thin, scale-like lower egg-tooth (e.g., figs. 1-21, 3-130, 7-44, 8-16).

Bucephala ducklings are intermediate in some ways between other Mergini ducklings and those of the Aythyini and Anatini (as defined by Livezey 1986). The bi-lobed lower egg-tooth of goldeneyes is sometimes flatter than it is in dabbling, perching, and stiff-tailed ducklings. Strongly contrasting patterns of the dorsal plumage (all downy *Bucephala*) and tarsi (goldeneyes only) are more similar to those of *Aythya* ducklings than to those of any other group. Foot proportions of ducklings of both genera are almost identical (TMT/IIIw ratios ca. 70%; Table 1, Appendix A). The possibility that these characters are not convergent is supported by Patton and Avise (1983), who found shared hypothesized synapomorphs between *Aythya* and *Bucephala* species.

The lower egg-tooth is apparently much more transitory in the Anserinae than in ducklings. If present at all, it is usually fragmentary in downy goslings, cygnets, and whistling-ducks (see Introduction, pp. 1-20). The remnant of an evidently similar structure appeared also on a two-day-old Magpie Goose (WT[S] 1881). On the other hand, *Thalassornis,* all *Bucephala,* pochard, dabbling, perching, and Ruddy ducklings have a bi-lobed lower egg-tooth which is raised above the surface of the lower nail. The character of the lower egg-tooth is unknown in *Nomonyx, Heteronetta,* and the Australian stiff-tails, but is presumed to be like that of the Ruddy duckling. Newly hatched *Thalassornis,* morphologically similar to both whistling- and stiff-tailed ducklings, has also a raised, bi-lobed lower egg-tooth. The occurrence of a lower egg-tooth in several other avian groups (e.g., hornbills: Shelford 1899; doves: Hanson and Kossack 1957; woodpeckers: Wetherbee 1959) suggests that its appearance, ontogeny, and function might reasonably be investigated to determine its homology and possible use in both avian and reptilian systematics.

Neutral plumage colors and dark-colored bills and feet are associated with downy *Cygnus,* some other anserine downies, and nearly all downy eiders and sea-ducks. The occurrence of chromatic pigment among the various tribes is a good deal less orderly. Dull yellowish red tints appear on stiff-tailed, eider, and Northern Pintail ducklings, stronger ones on Radjah shelducklings, some southern teal, and holarctic mergansers. Even cygnets have measurable amounts of exceedingly pale, dull yellow-red in their grayish pattern colors (C. Nelson 1976a, 1976b). A much stronger yellow-red appears in the downy Southern Screamer, *Chauna torquata* (Van Bocxstaele 1986: P. Heyrman photo). The downy Northern Screamer, *C. chavaria,* is almost totally unpatterned (Vigil 1973) or appears like goslings (Hudson 1926). A strong yellow-red appears also in downy *Anhima cornuta* (VIREO photo by Luis Naranjo), but not in its second, dark brown coat of down (Jeffrey Black photos loaned in letter to author, 1986). The color appears again in the plumage and unfeathered parts of the otherwise dark gray and white downy Magpie Goose, *Anseranas.* A live, day-old Magpie gosling described by Davies (1957: 355) had the bill, feet [and fleshy pre-ocular line] "dull claret coloured...fading to yellow after 3-5 days," and the plumage of a Slimbridge captive (2 d.) had a splash of light [bright reddish] brown to brownish pink (Munsell 5YR 6/4 to 5YR 7.5/2) over its head, breast, and upper back (Delacour 1964: Scott pl. 5).

Yellow plumage color is distributed widely among the downy young of holarctic species, sparingly among endemics in the southern hemisphere (e.g., compare downy *Cereopsis,* shelducklings, and sheldgoslings *in* Delacour [1954: Scott pl. 15] with northern goslings on Scott pl. 10, and with pls. 1 & 3-5 this vol.; compare also ducklings of shovelers and torrent ducks *in* Delacour [1956: Scott pl. 23]). In downy *Heteronetta* (Weller 1967), *Nomonyx,* screamers, yellow pochards, nearctic dabblers (except Northern and Georgian pintails), as well as in certain goslings, whistling-ducks, and perching ducks, yellow base colors usually contrast strongly with dark, well-marked dorsal and head patterns. In other newly hatched *Anser* and *Branta* goslings, the brilliant yellow base colors dominate the 'faded' gray pattern colors.

Although there is no way of knowing what were the colors of prehistoric downy waterfowl, I suggest that dark, melanic pigments probably came first. Dark bases of the down on all young anatids, regardless of the color of down-tips, also support the idea of dark ancestral plumage. Melanic pigments evidently underwent considerable fading in cygnets and holarctic goslings and in downy flamingos whose chicks are gray or gray-white. Loss of melanic pigment is also reflected in colors of the unfeathered parts of some species, e.g., *Olor* cygnets, whose pink bills and feet are colored almost entirely by blood pigment beneath the translucent yellowish skin (Parmelee, Stephens and Schmidt 1967). Yellowish red colors may have appeared next, followed by yellow ones. With the acquisition of chromatic plumage color came lighter, brighter hues of the bill and feet (e.g., whistling-ducks, pl. 1), often with strongly contrasting melanic pattern colors (e.g., dabbling ducks, pls. 6 & 7; perching ducks and yellow pochards, pl. 8; Common Merganser, pl. 9).

With the exceptions noted previously, the pattern, structural, and—to a lesser extent—color characters of the downy young of North American anatids separate into three groups: first, the swans and their allies; second, the sea-ducks, eiders, and stiff-tailed ducks; and third, the pochards, dabblers, and perching ducks. Livezey's (1986: 7) analysis shows ducks of the third group to be members of "a poorly-resolved grade". Numachi et al. (1983) suggested comparatively recent evolution of the Anatini, based on the close similarity of all tribal members at 10 loci tested. The parallel between pattern type and the two forms of anatid egg-teeth thus far described could imply that the anserines emerged first and the Mergini and Oxyurini next, followed closely by the pochards and surface-feeding ducks. Phylogenies proposed by Patton and Avise (1983) and Kessler and Avise (1984) support this view to some extent, but the paucity of pre-Pleistocene records for sea-ducks and eiders vs. the relative wealth of such records for pochards and surface-feeding ducks (Brodkorb 1964) does not. However, this disparity could mean simply that the species of sea-ducks and eiders were fewer than those of surface-feeding ducks in pre-Pleistocene time, as they are in Recent time.

The appearance of achromatic colors and simple plumage patterns in the downy young of taxa as widely separated within the family as the 'primitive' swans and the 'derived' sea-ducks, eiders, and stiff-tailed ducks suggests the persistence of elements having survival value. As in the plumage of adult and juvenal birds analyzed by Baker and Parker (1979), color and pattern in downy waterfowl may have evolved primarily in response to predation pressures. For example, in the large areas of open water frequented by downy eiders, scoters, and Oldsquaws, their dark, unspotted dorsal plumage would effect concealment from aerial predators ("procryptic" coloration; Cott 1985: 97); the Harlequin duckling's delicate, pale eye- and shoulder-spots resemble flecks of foam on the rushing rivers of their habitat, and the strongly contrasting cheek-patches, stripes, and dorsal patterns on downies of some species from all tribes (except swans and eiders; but note downy *Coscoroba*) may also function as cryptic coloration by disguising the form of the individual nestling ("disruption;" Cott 1985: 97). The effect of disruptive coloration may be to surprise and, perhaps, confuse (even momentarily) a predator coming upon the nest (Baker and Parker 1979) although such coloration may have greater value when the young have left the nest. However, the relation of pattern types to specific habitats, if any, is poorly understood. Jehl's (1968b: 7-8) conclusion regarding the "conservative" nature of the patterns of shorebird chicks seems to apply also to those of downy waterfowl, namely, "that different patterns may be adaptive in similar habitats, and that some patterns may be adaptive in a variety of habitats" (compare patterns of hole-nesting *Lophodytes* and *Bucephala* spp., pl. 9, and marsh-dwelling Canvasback and Lesser Scaup, pl. 8).

The emergence of strong pattern elements in downy pochards and surface-feeding ducks, *Coscoroba* cygnets, Tadornini (as delimited by Johnsgard 1978, 1979 [Tadorninae]; Livezey 1986), and certain downy whistling-ducks (e.g., *D. autumnalis, D. guttata*) and sea-ducks (i.e., *Bucephala - Mergus* group); the occurrence of yellow color in a variety of *hues, values,* and *chromas* in nearly all North American anatid tribes (cygnets, eider and sea-ducklings excepted); and the appearance of a bi-lobed egg-tooth in both 'derived' Ruddy and 'primitive' *Thalassornis* ducklings suggests an overlapping of this possibly advantageous character in several tribes during the relatively rapid evolution and proliferation of existing species that evidently occurred during the Pleistocene (Livezey 1986; Brodkorb 1964, re: fossil Anseriformes; Ploeger 1968, re: Arctic Anatidae). There is, in any case, little evidence of actual pattern loss among downy anatids such as proposed by Delacour and Mayr (1945), Livezey (1986), and others. However, the eumelanic color component is obviously much faded in most cygnets and in certain goslings.

I suggest that the evolution of pattern in downy waterfowl can be viewed as a progression from simple, diffuse patterns to those complex and well-defined, and further, that this progression can be demonstrated within tribes. For example, poorly defined *Cygnus* patterns grade to better defined (but greatly faded) *Olor;* unpatterned, achromatic *Philacte* to patterned, strongly chromatic *Anser albifrons;* gray-backed *Dendrocygna bicolor/D. arcuata* to strongly patterned, strongly chromatic *D. autumnalis/D. arborea*; dark southern teals (e.g., *Anas aucklandica* [Delacour 1964: Scott pl. 5], *A. castanea* [ANWC], and *A. gibberifrons* [FMNH]) to lighter, yellower Northern Green-winged Teals; dark-footed 'old' mallards to paler-footed 'new'; gray-backed eiders and scoters to spotted mergansers and goldeneyes; and the black-crowned, two-spotted downy Ruddy Duck to the yellow-striped, four-spotted Masked duckling.

Certain monotypic species that appear intermediate in some ways between other groups have yielded important behavioral, anatomical, and biochemical clues to their true affinities, e.g., *Heteronetta* (Weller 1968a, 1968b; Raikow 1970; Brush 1976; Rees and Hillgarth 1984; Livezey 1986) and *Thalassornis* (Johnsgard 1967; Kear 1967, 1968; Raikow 1971; Livezey 1986). Observations of the downy young suggest that further diverse studies are needed for other species, e.g., *Stictonetta, Coscoroba,* the large complex of northern and southern teals and pintails, the cosmopolitan mallards (a study of their parasites alone would be instructive), the Laysan Duck, *Netta* species, Steller's Eider, the Hooded Merganser, and the Harlequin and Masked ducks. Presumably, genetic investigations will eventually clarify these relationships as well as the origin of certain tribes represented in North America (e.g., whistling-ducks, perching ducks, stiff-tailed ducks, and swans), the color and pattern attributes of whose downy young indicate that they may have arisen in the southern hemisphere rather than in the northern, as generally supposed. The efficacy of such studies will depend not only upon the consistency of the methods used (e.g., Matson 1984; Johnson et al. 1984; Raikow 1985a; Scherer and Sontag 1986), but also upon the determination of the investigators to obtain adequate samples of all taxa relevant to their study, including subspecies, species, and genera 'lumped' or suppressed under many current classifications.

Other considerations

Genetic puzzles abound in the waterfowl family. Few have been solved. Notable exceptions are the color phases of the Lesser Snow Goose, *A. c. caerulescens* (Cooke and Cooch 1968), and the Mute Swan, *C. olor* (Munro, Smith, and Kupa 1968). The dominant character of the gray pattern color in polymorphic Ross' goslings, *A. rossii,* has also been confirmed by Hanson, Queneau, and Scott (1956), Williamson (1957), and Cooke and Ryder (1971). However, the cause of the extensive *value* variation in the yellow base color of Ross' goslings is unknown. Observed but also unstudied are discontinuous pattern color variations in downy Trumpeter Swans (Banko 1960) and Fulvous Whistling-ducks (Delacour 1954, 1964), the apparently continuous pattern color variations, well-marked even within broods, among downy Pink-footed Geese (Alphéraky [1904] 1905; Scott, Fisher, and Gudmundsson 1953), the striking base color variations in downy Black-bellied Whistling-ducks (pl. 1), and the wide variation in *value* and *chroma* of both base and pattern colors in Greater White-fronted goslings from different areas (Hanson, Queneau, and Scott 1956; Lensink and Timm unpubl.; Thomas Pogson, color transparencies loaned to the author, December 1983).

There is also a dark 'mutation', quite similar to the Class 3 or 4 Snow (='blue') gosling, in two other species: the Muscovy Duck, *Cairina moschata*, and the Northern Mallard, *Anas p. platyrhynchos.* An apparently similar color variant, incompletely described by Schuyl (1937), occurs in the White-winged Wood Duck, *C. scutulata.* As in 'blue' Snow goslings, a single dark color is diffused over the entire body, effectively concealing all pattern elements except for a white or yellow chin-patch; a dull, somewhat paler breast and belly; and, sometimes, light areas around the bill, forehead, and nape. Usually, these individuals have black or blackish (often glossy) feet.

Mutant Muscovy ducklings are dark brownish olive, the Northern Mallards 'greenish' olive or 'khaki', and the 'blue' goslings blackish or dusky olive. Their dark pattern colors appear to derive measurable *hue* and *chroma* from the brilliant base colors which they conceal: yellow in the Lesser Snow gosling, greenish yellow in the Northern Mallard, orange-yellow in the Muscovy duckling. The chin-patch is moderate yellow (5Y 7.4/6) in the 'blue' gosling (UWGB[RC]; considerably brighter in live birds), pale orange-yellow (2.5Y 9/4) in the Muscovy, and yellowish white or greenish white in the Northern Mallard. The dark variants of the downy Lesser Snow Goose, Northern Mallard, Muscovy and [possibly] White-winged Wood ducks appear to represent a pattern type nearly as simple as that of the Black and Mute cygnets, perhaps even an ancestral natal plumage, as Cooke suggested (Fred Cooke, telephone interview, 30 January 1984). Considering that Barrowclough and Corbin (1978: 700) found "the degree of differentiation between genera of birds [to be] of the same order of magnitude as that between subspecies and semispecies of *Drosophila*," the idea of a dominant, trans-specific mutation is not unthinkable.

Close interrelationships among the waterfowl can be demonstrated by interspecific similarities of proteins (e.g., egg-white: Sibley and Ahlquist 1972; blood: Numachi et al. 1983; muscle: Oates et al. 1983; mitochondrial DNA: Kessler and Avise 1984; Shields and Wilson 1987b) and by the occurrence of hybrids (e.g., J. Phillips 1915; Cockrum 1952; Sibley 1957; Gray 1958; Johnsgard 1960c), one-fifth of which are fertile, between species, genera, and even tribes (Scherer and Hilsberg 1982). The genetic relationships among the Anatidae are so close that Scherer and Hilsberg postulated (p. 376) the existence of an original or ancestral duck—"Urente" ('true duck')—and concluded (p. 380) that the entire family (but subsequently excluding the Magpie Goose, *Anseranas;* Scherer and Sontag 1986)—could be regarded as a "Grundtyp" ('fundamental type').

However, Scherer and Hilsberg described only adult hybrids. Nor did Gilham, Harrison, and Harrison (1966: 49) correlate downy plumages with their admirably detailed descriptions and photographs of "six distinct types of drake *Aythya* hybrids found in Britain," some of which look more like a third species than like either parent. Such correlations would be illuminating, particularly where *Aythya* species having very dark downy young (e.g., Tufted Duck, scaup) hybridize with those having yellow ducklings (e.g., Ferruginous Duck, *Aythya ferruginea*, and Canvasback).

The development of vocalizations and behavior patterns in the downy young is incompletely known for most species, despite stimulating research by Nice (1962), Fischer (1965), McKinney (1965), Kear (1968), Caswell (1972), Kostow (1981), and others. Even the extensive roster of species recorded by Kear (1968) lacked several important—albeit hard to find—North American forms: Harlequin Duck, Oldsquaw, scoters, Steller's Eider, and Masked Duck. Of particular interest would be a comparison of Harlequin, Oldsquaw, and scoter calls with those of other Mergini ducklings and the eiders. Calls of Steller's Eider, Surf and Black scoter, and Masked ducklings are entirely unknown.

Further studies of pre- and post-hatching behavior (e.g., Nice 1962) and of the ontogeny of specific behavior patterns (e.g., Myres 1957; McKinney 1965), feeding techniques (e.g., Beard 1964; Bartonek and Hickey 1969; Bengtson 1972), and vocalizations (e.g., Fischer 1965; Kear 1968) are needed. Such studies could help to elucidate the similarities and differences between, for example, eiders and scoters. Posture (including an apparently unique preening posture; C. Nelson 1964) and general appearance of eider and scoter ducklings are similar, but the eiders are noisy and sociable, whereas the scoters, quietest of ducklings, are often very aggressive.

Perhaps the most absorbing problems for me were those involving the colors of the live, newly hatched birds. Color names and colorimetry, interesting in themselves, became objectively useful in direct proportion to the precision of the color standard and illuminants used. The importance of using excellent, consistent illumination and viewing procedures for both field and laboratory work cannot be overemphasized; even the best color standard can be rendered useless by a poor illuminant or a careless observer.

Color evaluation data obtained with the Munsell system have yielded quantitative information on geographic, ecological, and age-related differences in the colors of plumage and unfeathered parts of birds (e.g., Bowers 1956; Wood, 1973; Wood and Wood 1972, 1973; Slagsvold and Lifjeld 1985). Developmental eye-color changes (e.g., Trauger 1974: adult female Lesser Scaup, *A. affinis;* C. Nelson 1983: goldeneye ducklings), have not been precisely documented for many species in which they are known to occur

For the biologist, the techniques of colorimetry may be only the first steps of a fascinating journey. The certainty of knowing that the eye-color of a two-week-old Barrow's Goldeneye will be strong purplish blue (C. Nelson 1983) quickly gives way to other questions: Does the purple-blue color result from Tyndall scattering alone, as in the eyes of some mammals (H. Fox and Vevers 1960; D. Fox 1976)? Or are there other colorants involved, such as melanic or carotenoid pigments? Why and how does the color appear, then change successively to blue, greenish blue, green-yellow, and yellow? Do the developmental eye-colors of other species (e.g., Black Swan, Northern Cinnamon Teal, Greater Scaup, mergansers) arise through a similar process?

Colorants of the yellow plumage present on many downy waterfowl are essentially unknown, but are believed to be a form of melanin (Völker 1934; Brush 1981). The sources of colorants in some avian taxa have been studied extensively (e.g., Völker 1934 [*Serinus; Melopsittacus*]; D. Fox 1955 [*Phoenicopterus ruber*]; Brush and Power 1976 [*Carpodacus mexicanus*]), but the metabolic pathways of color deposition in downy waterfowl are largely unexplored. However, the extensive surveys of animal colors by H. Fox and Vevers (1960) and D. Fox (1976) offer many valuable insights, as well as extensive bibliographies. More recently, De Ritter and Purcell (1981) have provided a useful guide to the analysis of carotenoid pigments.

The intriguing biological and theoretical problems posed by the newly hatched waterfowl are perhaps best explored through interdisciplinary research. The coordination of field, laboratory, and museum studies not only would add greatly to our knowledge of the downy young, but also would assure for their special attributes a well-deserved place of importance within the larger context of the species and the family.

References

Adams, J., and E. R. Slavid. 1984. Cheek plumage pattern in Colombian Ruddy Duck *Oxyura jamaicensis*. *Ibis* 126:405-7.

Addy, C. E. 1964. Atlantic Flyway. In *Waterfowl tomorrow*, ed. J. P. Linduska, 167-84. U. S. Department of the Interior, Fish and Wildlife Service, Washington, D. C.: U. S. Government Printing Office.

Aldrich, J. W. 1946. Speciation in the white-cheeked geese. *Wilson Bulletin* 58:94-103.

Aldrich, J. W., and K. P. Baer. 1970. Status and speciation in the Mexican Duck (*Anas diazi*). *Wilson Bulletin* 82:63-73.

Alexander, W. C. 1980. Aggressive displays in nonbreeding Canvasbacks. *Auk* 97:198-201.

Ali, S. 1964. *The book of Indian birds.* 7th ed. Revised. Bombay: Bombay Natural History Society.

Alison, R. M. 1975. *Breeding biology and behavior of the Oldsquaw (Clangula hyemalis* L.). American Ornithologists' Union, Ornithological Monographs, no. 18. Lawrence, Kans.: Allen Press.

———. 1976. Oldsquaw brood behavior. *Bird-Banding* 47:210-13.

Alphéraky, S. N. 1904. *Gusi Rossii.* Moscow: I. N. Kushnerev and Company. 1905. English translation entitled, The geese of Europe and Asia. London: Rowland Ward.

American Ornithologists' Union Committee on Classification and Nomenclature. 1957. *The A.O.U. check-list of North American birds.* 5th ed. (A. Wetmore, Chairman). Baltimore, Md.: American Ornithologists' Union.

———. 1983. *The A.O.U. check-list of North American birds: the species of birds of North America from the Arctic through Panama, including the West Indies and Hawaiian Islands.* 6th ed. (E. Eisenmann, Chairman). [Washington, D. C.]: American Ornithologists' Union.

Anderson, M. G. 1985. Social behavior of breeding canvasbacks (*Aythya valisineria*): male and female strategies of reproduction. Ph. D. diss., University of Minnesota.

Andrew, R. J. 1964. Vocalization in chicks and the concept of "stimulus contrast." *Animal Behaviour* 12:64-76.

———. 1975. Midbrain mechanisms of calling and their relation to emotional states. In *Neural and endocrine aspects of behaviour in birds*, eds. P. Wright, P. G. Caryl, and D. M. Vowles, 275-304. Amsterdam, Oxford, New York: Elsevier Scientific Publishing Company.

Ankney, C. D., D. G. Dennis, L. N. Wishard, and J. E. Seeb. 1986. Low genic variation between Black Ducks and Mallards. *Auk* 103:701-9.

Annual Report of the [Severn] Wildfowl Trust 1, 1948; 3, 1951; 4, 1952; 5, 1953; 6, 1954; 8, 1957; 12, 1961; 13, 1962; 15, 1964; 16, 1965. After 1967, superseded by *Wildfowl.*

Anon. 1966. Aleutian Geese raised in captivity for the first time. *Gazette:* October 1966: 36-37.

ASTM (American Society for Testing and Materials). 1962. *Standard method for specifying color by the Munsell system.* Revised ed. 1968 (reapproved 1974). Reprinted from the *Annual Book of ASTM Standards.*

Audubon, J. J. 1856. *The birds of America, from drawings made in the United States and their territories.* Vol. 6. New York: V. G. Audubon.

Audubon Field Notes 22, February 1968.

Audubon Magazine 70 (3), May/June 1968.

Bailey, A. M. 1948. *Birds of Arctic Alaska.* Popular series no. 8. Denver: Colorado Museum of Natural History.

———. 1956. *Birds of Midway and Laysan islands.* Denver Museum of Natural History Pictorial no. 12. Denver, Colo.

Bailey, A. M., and R. J. Niedrach. 1965. *The*

birds of Colorado. Vol. l. Denver, Colo.: Denver Museum of Natural History.

Bailey, T., E. Bangs, and V. Berns. 1980. Back carrying of young by Trumpeter Swans. *Wilson Bulletin* 92:413.

Baird, S. F., T. M. Brewer, and R. Ridgway. 1884. *The water birds of North America.* Vol. 2. Memoirs of the Museum of Comparative Zoology at Harvard College, vol. 13. Boston: Little, Brown and Company.

Baker, A. J., H. A. Best, D. H. Braithwaite, B. D. Heather, and others. 1985. Reader's Digest *Complete Book of New Zealand Birds.* Sydney: Reader's Digest.

Baker, R. R., and G. A. Parker. 1979. The evolution of bird coloration. Philosophical Transactions of the Royal Society of London, Series B. *Biological Sciences* 287:63-130.

Baldwin, S. P., H. C. Oberholser, and L. G. Worley. 1931. *Measurements of birds.* Scientific Publications of the Cleveland Museum of Natural History, vol. 2. Contribution no. 17 from the Baldwin Bird Research Laboratory.

Banko, W. E. 1960. *The Trumpeter Swan: its history, habits, and population in the United States.* North American Fauna no. 63. U. S. Fish and Wildlife Service. Washington, D. C.: U. S. Government Printing Office.

Banks, R. C. 1978. Nomenclature of the Black-bellied Whistling-Duck. *Auk* 95:348-52.

———. 1986. Subspecies of the Greater Scaup and their names. *Wilson Bulletin* 98:433-44.

Bannerman, D. A. 1957-58. *The birds of the British Isles.* Vols. 6 and 7. Edinburgh and London: Oliver and Boyd.

Barbour, T. 1923. *Birds of Cuba.* Memoirs of the Nuttall Ornithological Club, no. 6. Cambridge, Mass.: Nuttall Ornithological Club.

Barrett, V. A., and E. R. Vyse. 1982. Comparative genetics of three Trumpeter Swan populations. *Auk* 99:103-8.

Barrowclough, G. F., and K. W. Corbin. 1978. Genetic variation and differentiation in the Parulidae. *Auk* 95:691-702.

Barry, T. W. 1956. Observations of a nesting colony of American Brant. *Auk* 73:193-202.

Barry, T. W., and J. Eisenhart. 1958. Ross' Goose nesting at Southampton Island, N. W. T., Canada. *Auk* 75:89-90.

Bartonek, J. C., and J. J. Hickey. 1969. Selective feeding by juvenile diving ducks in summer. *Auk* 86:443-57.

Bauer, K. M., and U. N. Glutz von Blotzheim. 1968-69. *Handbuch der Vögel Mitteleuropas.* Vols. 2 and 3, *Anseriformes.* Frankfurt am Main: Akademische Verlagsgesellschaft. In German.

Bauer, R. D. 1979. Historical and status report of the Tule White-fronted Goose. In *Management and biology of Pacific Flyway geese: a symposium,* eds. R. L. Jarvis and J. C. Bartonek, 44-55. Corvallis, Ore.: Northwest Section of the Wildlife Society.

Beard, E. B. 1964. Duck brood behavior at the Seney National Wildlife Refuge. *Journal of Wildlife Management* 28:492-521.

Beckwith, S. L., and H. J. Hosford. 1957. A report on seasonal food habits and life history notes of the Florida Duck in the vicinity of Lake Okeechobee, Glades County, Florida. *American Midland Naturalist* 57:461-73.

Bellrose, F. C. 1976. *The ducks, geese, and swans of North America.* 2nd ed. Harrisburg, Pa.: Stackpole Books.

———. 1980. *The ducks, geese, and swans of North America.* 3rd ed. Harrisburg, Pa.: Stackpole Books.

Belton, W. 1984. Birds of Rio Grande do Sul, Brazil. Part 1. Rheidae through Furnariidae. Bulletin of the American Museum of Natural History, vol. 178, art. 4:369-636. New York.

Bengtson, S.-A. 1966. Field studies on the Harlequin Duck in Iceland. *Annual Report of the [Severn] Wildfowl Trust 1964-65* 17:79-94.

———. 1972. Breeding ecology of the Harlequin Duck *Histrionicus histrionicus* (L.) in Iceland. *Ornis Scandinavica* 3:1-19.

Bennett, L. J. 1938. *The Blue-winged Teal: its*

ecology and management. Ames, Iowa: Collegiate Press.

Bent, A. C. 1923-25. *Life histories of North American wildfowl.* Pts. 1 and 2. U. S. National Museum Bulletins 126 and 130. Washington, D. C.: U. S. Government Printing Office. 1962. Reprint. New York: Dover Publications.

Bent, A. C., O. Bangs, and J. L. Peters. 1927. Kennard on Snow Goose (corresp. section). *Auk* 44:471.

Berger, A. J. 1972. *Hawaiian bird life.* Honolulu: University Press of Hawaii.

———. 1981. *Hawaiian bird life.* 2nd ed. Honolulu: University Press of Hawaii.

Bevill, W. V., and C. A. Davis. 1969. Behavior and habitat-use of the Mexican duck in southwest New Mexico and southeast Arizona. Paper read at 8th Annual Meeting, New Mexico - Arizona Section of the Wildlife Society, 7 February 1969, at Silver City, New Mexico. 6 pp. Typed duplicated copy.

Bjärvall, A. 1968. The hatching and nest-exodus behaviour of Mallards. *Wildfowl* 19:70-80.

Blaauw, F. E. 1899. On the breeding of the Weka Rail and Snow-Goose in captivity. *Proceedings of the Zoological Society of London* [69]: 412-15.

———. 1903. Notes on the breeding of Ross's Snow-Goose in captivity. *Ibis,* 8th ser., 3:245-47.

——. 1904. On the breeding of some of the waterfowl at Gooilust in the year 1903. *Ibis,* 8th ser., 4:67-75.

———. 1909. Some account of the breeding of the Golden-eye (*Clangula glaucion*) in captivity (letter to the editor). *Ibis,* 9th ser., 3:188-89.

———. 1912. On the immature dress of *Anser indicus* and *Dendrocygna arborea. Ibis,* 9th ser., 6:657-59.

———. 1916a. On the breeding of the Emperor Goose at Gooilust. *Avicultural Magazine,* 3rd ser., 7:277-79.

———. 1916b. A note on the Emperor Goose (*Philacte canagica*) and on the Australian Teal (*Nettion castaneum*). *Ibis,* 10th ser., 4:252-54.

Black, J. M., and J. H. Barrow, Jr. 1985. Visual signalling in Canada Geese for the coordination of family units. *Wildfowl* 36:35-41.

Blake, E. R. 1977. *Manual of neotropical birds.* Vol. 1, *Spheniscidae to Laridae (gulls and allies).* Chicago and London: University of Chicago Press.

Blakers, M., S. J. J. F. Davies, and P. N. Reilly. 1984. *The atlas of Australian birds.* Royal Australasian Ornithologists Union. Carlton, Victoria: Melbourne University Press.

Bluhm, C. K. 1981. The environmental controls of breeding in captive canvasback ducks (*Aythya valisineria*). Ph. D. diss., University of Minnesota.

Bock, W. J. 1960. The palatine process of the premaxilla in the Passeres. Harvard University, Cambridge, Mass. *Bulletin of the Museum of Comparative Zoology* 122:362-488.

Bolen, E. G. 1973. Breeding whistling ducks (*Dendrocygna* spp.) in captivity. Reprinted from *International Zoo Yearbook* 13 [6pp.]

———. 1978. Blue-winged Teal X Cinnamon Teal hybrids. *Southwestern Naturalist* 23:692-96.

———. 1979. Blue-winged X Cinnamon Teal hybrid from Oklahoma. *Wilson Bulletin* 91:367-70.

Bolen, E. G., and B. J. Forsyth. 1967. Foods of the Black-bellied Tree Duck in south Texas. *Wilson Bulletin* 79:43-49. Contribution no. 103, Rob & Bessie Welder Wildlife Foundation, Sinton, Texas.

Bolen, E. G., and M. K. Rylander. 1983. *Whistling-ducks: zoogeography, ecology, anatomy.* Texas Tech University, Special Publications of the Museum, no. 20. Lubbock, Texas: Texas Tech Press.

Bolen, E. G., B. McDaniel, and C. Cottam. 1964. Natural history of the Black-bellied Tree Duck (*Dendrocygna autumnalis*) in southern Texas. *Southwestern Naturalist* 9:78-88. Welder Wildlife Foundation Contribution no. 77.

Bond, J. 1961. Sixth Supplement to *The checklist of birds of the West Indies* (1956). Philadelphia: Academy of Natural Sciences.

———. 1971. *Birds of the West Indies.* 2nd ed. (3rd American ed.) London: Collins.

Bowers, D. E. 1956. A study of methods of color determination. *Systematic Zoology* 5:147-60, 182.

Boyd, H. J. 1972. Classification. In *The swans,* by P. M. Scott and the Wildfowl Trust, 18-27. London: Michael Joseph.

Boyd, H. J., and E. Fabricius. 1965. Observations on the incidence of following of visual and auditory stimuli in native Mallard ducklings (*Anas platyrhynchos*). *Behaviour* 25:1-15.

Boyd, H. J., and L. S. Maltby. 1979. The Brant of the Western Queen Elizabeth Islands, N. W. T. In *Management and biology of Pacific Flyway geese: a symposium,* eds. R. L. Jarvis and J. C. Bartonek, 5-21. Corvallis, Ore.: Northwest Section of the Wildlife Society.

Brandt, H. 1943. *Alaska bird trails.* Cleveland, Ohio: Bird Research Foundation.

Brodkorb, P. 1964. *Catalogue of fossil birds.* Part 2, *Anseriformes through Galliformes.* Bulletin of the Florida State Museum, Biological Sciences, vol. 8, no. 3. Gainesville, Fla.: University of Florida.

Brodsky, L. M., and P. J. Weatherhead. 1984. Behavioral and ecological factors contributing to American black duck - mallard hybridization. *Journal of Wildlife Management* 48:846-52.

———. 1985. Time and energy constraints on courtship in wintering American Black Ducks. *Condor* 87:33-36.

Brooks, A. 1903. Notes on birds of the Cariboo district, British Columbia. *Auk* 20:277-84.

———. 1920. Notes on some American ducks. *Auk* 37:353-67.

———. 1926. Notes on the geese of the *Branta canadensis* group. *Ibis,* 12th ser., 2:339-46.

Brown, L. H., E. K. Urban, and K. Newman. 1982. *The birds of Africa.* Vol. 1. London and New York: Academic Press.

Brown, P. E. 1945. Observations on a Scaup-duck and brood on the Lincolnshire coast. *British Birds* 38:192-93.

Brown, P. W., and M. A. Brown. 1981. Nesting biology of the White-winged Scoter. *Journal of Wildlife Management* 45:38-45.

Brown, P. W., and L. H. Fredrickson. 1983. Growth and moult progression of White-winged Scoter ducklings. *Wildfowl* 34:115-19.

Brush, A. H. 1976. Waterfowl feather proteins: analysis of use in taxonomic studies. *Journal of Zoology, London* 179:467-98.

———. 1981. Carotenoids in wild and captive birds. In *Carotenoids as colorants and Vitamin A precursors: technological and nutritional applications,* ed. J. C. Bauernfeind, 539-62. Food Services and Technology: a series of monographs. New York and London: Academic Press.

Brush, A. H., and D. M. Power. 1976. House Finch pigmentation: carotenoid metabolism and the effect on diet. *Auk* 93:725-39.

Brush, A. H., and J. A. Wyld. 1980. Molecular correlates of morphological differentiation: avian scutes and scales. *Journal of Experimental Zoology* 212:153-57.

Bureau of Sport Fisheries and Wildlife, Division of Wildlife Research. 1967. *Wildlife research: problems, programs, progress, 1966.* Resource Publication 43. Washington, D. C.: U. S. Government Printing Office.

Cabot, D. (ed.), R. Nairn, S. Newton, M. Viney, H. Miles, and M. Read. 1984. Biological expedition to Jameson Land, Greenland. 1984: expedition report. Dublin: Barnacle Books.

Carpenter, S. J., and W. J. LaCasse. 1955. *Mosquitoes of North America (North of Mexico).* Berkeley: University of California Press.

Caswell, F. D. 1972. The development of acoustical communication in the Mallard (*Anas platyrhynchos*). Master's thesis, University of North Dakota, Grand Forks.

Cheesman, R. E., and W. L. Sclater. 1935. On a collection of birds from north-western Abyssinia. *Ibis,* 13th ser., 5:151-91.

Choate, J. R., and H. H. Genoways. 1975. Collections of recent mammals in North America. *Journal of Mammalogy* 56:452-502.

CIE (Commission International de l'Eclairage) Expert Committee E-l.3.l (Colorimetry). 1971. *Colorimetry: official recommendations of the International Commission on Illumination* (G. Wyszecki, Chairman). Publication CIE no. 15 (E-l.3.l). Paris: Bureau Centrale de la CIE.

Clark, G. A., Jr. 1961. Occurrence and timing of egg-teeth in birds. *Wilson Bulletin* 73:268-78.

———. 1978. *Guide to the young of European precocial birds.* By Jon Fjeldså. Review. *Wilson Bulletin* 90:329-30.

Clement, R. C. 1974. *The living world of Audubon.* New York: Grosset and Dunlap, a Ridge Press Book.

Cockrum, E. L. 1952. A check-list and bibliography of hybrid birds in North America north of Mexico. *Wilson Bulletin* 64:140-59.

Cogswell, H. L. 1977. *Water birds of California.* California Natural History Guides, no. 40. Berkeley: University of California Press.

Collias, N. E. 1952. The development of social behaviour in birds. *Auk* 69:127-59.

———. 1962. The behaviour of ducks. In *The behaviour of domestic animals,* ed. E. S. E. Hafez, 565-85. lst ed. London: Bailliere, Tindall, and Cox.

Collias, N. E., and E. C. Collias. 1956. Some mechanisms of family integration in ducks. *Auk* 73:378-400.

———. 1963. Selective feeding by wild ducklings of different species. *Wilson Bulletin* 75:6-14.

Conover, H. B. 1926. Game birds of the Hooper Bay region, Alaska. *Auk* 43:162-80.

Conservator (Ducks Unlimited Canada) 6(2), Spring 1985.

Cooch, F. G. 1961. Ecological aspects of the Blue-Snow Goose complex. *Auk* 78:72-89.

———. 1958. The breeding biology and management of the Blue Goose *Chen caerulescens.* Ph.D. diss., Cornell University, Ithaca, New York.

Cooke, F., and F. G. Cooch. 1968. The genetics of polymorphism in the goose *Anser caerulescens. Evolution* 22:289-300.

Cooke, F., D. T. Parkin, and R. F. Rockwell. 1988. Evidence of former allopatry of the two color phases of Lesser Snow Geese (*Chen caerulescens caerulescens*). *Auk* 105:467-79.

Cooke, F., and J. P. Ryder. 1971. The genetics of polymorphism in the Ross' Goose (*Anser rossii*). *Evolution* 25:483-96.

Cooper, J. A. 1979. Trumpeter Swan nesting behaviour. *Wildfowl* 30:55-71. Journal Paper 10,358 of the Minnesota Agricultural Experiment Station, St. Paul. Project 90.

Cott, H. B. 1985. Adaptive coloration. In *A dictionary of birds,* ed. B. Campbell and E. Lack, 97-99. Vermillion, S. D.: Buteo Books, and Calton, England: T. and A. D. Poyser for the British Ornithologists' Union.

Cottam, C., J. J. Lynch, and A. L. Nelson. 1944. Food habits and management of American Sea Brant. *Journal of Wildlife Management* 8:36-56.

Coues, E. 1903. *Key to North American birds.* 5th ed. Vol. 2. Boston: Page Company.

Coulter, M. W., and H. L. Mendall. 1968. Habitat and breeding ecology: Northeastern states. In *The Black Duck; evaluation, management, and research: a symposium,* ed. P. Barske, 90-101. Washington, D. C.: Atlantic Waterfowl Council and Wildlife Management Institute.

Coulter, M. W., and W. R. Miller. 1968. *Nesting biology of Black Ducks and Mallards in northern New England.* Vermont Fish and Game Department Bulletin no. 68-2.

Montpelier.

Cracraft, J. 1973. Continental drift, paleoclimatology and the evolution and biogeography of birds. *Journal of Zoology, London* 169:455-545.

Cramp, S., K. E. L. Simmons, I. J. Ferguson-Lees, R. Gillmor, P. A. D. Hollom, R. Hudson, E. M. Nicholson, M. A. Ogilvie, P. J. S. Olney, K. H. Voous, and J. Wattel, eds. 1977. *Handbook of the birds of Europe, the Middle East, and North Africa: the birds of the Western Palaearctic.* Vol. 1, *Ostrich to Ducks.* Oxford, London, New York: Oxford University Press.

Curth, P. 1954. *Der Mittelsäger.* Wittenberg Lutherstadt: A. Ziemsen Verlag. In German.

Davies, S. J. J. F. 1957. The gosling of the Magpie Goose. *Emu* 57:354-55.

Davis, R. A., R. N. Jones, C. D. MacInnes, and A. J. Pakulak. 1985. Molt migration of large Canada Geese on the west coast of Hudson Bay. *Wilson Bulletin* 97:296-305.

D'Eath, J. O. 1967. The Comb Duck (*Sarkidiornis melanotos*) in captivity. *Avicultural Magazine* 73:197-98.

Defensa de la Naturaleza 2 (5), July 1972. In Spanish.

Deignan, H. G. 1947. HBC and the Smithsonian. *The Beaver* 278, June, 3-7.

Delacour, J. T. 1924. Élévage du Dendrocygne veuf. *L'Oiseau* 5:16-20. In French.

———. 1936. Note sur la classification des Anatides. *L'Oiseau et la Revue francaise d'Ornithologie* 6:366-79. In French.

———. 1951. Preliminary note on the taxonomy of Canada Geese, *Branta canadensis.* American Museum Novitates no. 1537. New York.

———. 1954-64. *The waterfowl of the world.* 4 vols. London: Country Life.

Delacour, J. T., and E. Mayr. 1945. The family Anatidae. *Wilson Bulletin* 57:1-55.

Delacour, J. T., and S. D. Ripley. 1975. Description of a new subspecies of the White-fronted Goose *Anser albifrons.* American Museum Novitates no. 2565. New York.

Delacour, J. T., and J. T. Zimmer. 1952. The identity of *Anser nigricans* Lawrence 1846. *Auk* 69:82-84.

Dement'ev, G. P., and N. A. Gladkov, eds. 1952. *Ptitsky Sovetskogo Soyuza* (Birds of the Soviet Union). Vol. 4. Moscow: Izdatel'stvo "Nauka". In Russian. 1967. Translated by A. Birron and Z. S. Cole. Israel Program for Scientific Translations, ed. Z. S. Cole. Jerusalem, Jordan: Israel Program for Scientific Translations, for the U. S. Department of the Interior and the National Science Foundation, Washington, D. C.

De Ritter, E., and A. E. Purcell. 1981. Carotenoid analytical methods. In *Carotenoids as colorants and Vitamin A precursors: technological and nutritional applications,* ed. J. C. Bauernfeind, 815-923. Food Services and Technology: a series of monographs. New York and London: Academic Press.

Derry, D. R., L. Curtis, D. Fisher, S. Marmont, and B. Kwiecien. 1980. *World atlas of geology and mineral deposits.* London: Mining Journal Books, and New York: John Wiley and Sons, Halsted Press Division.

Desfayes, M. unpubl. An international treasury of bird names.

Devillers, P. J. 1976. Projet de nomenclature francaise des oiseaux du monde. 2. Anhimides aux Otidides. *Le Gerfaut* 66:391-421. In French.

De Vis, C. W. 1897. Diagnoses of thirty-six new or little-known birds from British New Guinea. *Ibis,* 7th ser., 3:371-92.

Dickey, D. R., and A. J. Van Rossem. 1923. Fulvous Tree Ducks of Buena Vista Lake. *Condor* 25:39-50.

Dresser, H. E. 1871-81. *A history of the birds of Europe, including all the species inhabiting the western Palaearctic region.* Vol. 6. London: by the author. [Page numbers handstamped after printing in copy examined at Carnegie Museum, Pittsburgh.]

Driver, P. M. 1960a. Behaviour studies in seaducklings. Ph. D. diss., McGill University,

Montreal, Quebec.

———. 1960b. Field studies on the behaviour of sea-ducklings. *Arctic* 13:201-4.

———. 1960c. A possible fundamental in the behaviour of young nidifugous birds. *Nature* (London) 186:416.

———. 1965. 'Clicking' in the egg-young of nidifugous birds. *Nature* (London) 206:315.

Dunbar Brander, A. A. 1926. On the colour of the eye of the Gaur or Indian Bison (*Bibos gaurus*). *Journal of the Bombay Natural History Society* 31:220-22.

Dzubin, A. 1955. Some evidence of home range in waterfowl. *Transactions of the North American Wildlife Conference* 20:278-98.

———. 1957. Pairing display and spring and summer flights of the Mallard. *Blue Jay* 15:10-13.

———. 1959. Growth and plumage development of wild-trapped juvenile Canvasback (*Aythya valisineria*). *Journal of Wildlife Management* 23:279-90.

Eagles, D. 1964. Where the wild goose goes. *Weekend Magazine* no. 21, 23 May, 10-12.

Eaton, E. H. 1910. *Birds of New York.* Vol. 1. Memoir 12 [with Vol. 2] of New York State Museum. Albany: University of the State of New York.

Einarsen, A. S. 1965. *Black Brant: sea goose of the Pacific Coast.* Seattle: University of Washington Press.

Eisenhauer, D. I. 1976. Ecology and behavior of the Emperor Goose (*Anser canagicus* Sewastianov) in Alaska. Master's thesis, Purdue University, West Lafayette, Ind.

Eisenhauer, D. I., and C. M. Kirkpatrick. 1977. *Ecology of the Emperor Goose in Alaska.* The Wildlife Society, Wildlife Monographs, no. 57. Lawrence, Kans.: Allen Press. Journal Paper no. 6153 from Purdue University Agricultural Experiment Station, West Lafayette, Ind.

Elder, W. H. 1954. The oil gland of birds. *Wilson Bulletin* 66:6-31. Contribution from the Delta Waterfowl Research Station, Delta, Manitoba, and the Missouri Cooperative Wildlife Research Unit, University of Missouri, Columbia.

Elgas, R. W. 1970. Breeding populations of Tule White-fronted Geese in northwestern Canada. *Wilson Bulletin* 82:420-26.

Ely, C. R., D. A. Budeau, and V. G. Swain. 1987. Aggressive encounters between Tundra Swans and Greater White-fronted Geese during brood rearing. *Condor* 89:420-22.

Eriksson, O. G. M. 1976. Food and feeding habits of downy Goldeneye *Bucephala clangula* (L.) ducklings. *Ornis Scandinavica* 7:159-69.

Erskine, A. J. 1971. Growth and annual cycles in weights, plumages, and reproductive organs of Goosanders in eastern Canada. *Ibis* 113:42-58.

———. 1972. *Buffleheads.* Canadian Wildlife Service, Monograph Series no. 4. Ottawa: Queen's Printer.

Evans, M. E. 1975. Breeding behaviour of captive Bewick's Swans. *Wildfowl* 26:117-30.

———. 1977. Notes on the breeding behaviour of captive Whistling Swans. *Wildfowl* 28:107-12.

Evans, M. E., and T. Lebret. 1973. Leucistic Bewick's Swan. *Wildfowl* 24:61-62.

Fabricius, E. 1951. *Zur ethologie junger anatiden* (English summary). Acta Zoologica Fennica no. 68. Helsinki: Societas Pro Fauna et Flora Fennica.

Fallis, A. M., and G. F. Bennett. 1966. On the epizootiology of infections caused by *Leucocytozoon simondi* in Algonquin Park, Canada. *Canadian Journal of Zoology* 44:101-12.

Fischer, H. 1965. Das Triumphgeschrei der Graugans (*Anser anser*) *Zeitschrift für Tierpsychologie* 22:247-304. In German. English summary.

Fisher, H. I. 1958. The "hatching muscle" in the chick. *Auk* 75:391-99.

Fisher, W. K. 1906. Birds of Laysan and the Leeward Islands, Hawaiian group. *Bulletin of the U. S. Fisheries Commission*, vol. 23

(1903), pt. 3:769-807. Washington, D. C.: U. S. Government Printing Office.

Fitch, H. A. 1960. *Autoecology of the Copperhead.* University of Kansas Publications, Museum of Natural History, vol. 1, no. 4. Lawrence.

Fjeldså, J. 1977. *Guide to the young of European precocial birds.* Tisvildeleje, Denmark: Skarv Nature Publications.

———. 1986. Color variation in the Ruddy Duck (*Oxyura jamaicensis andina*). *Wilson Bulletin* 98:592-94.

Flint, R. F. 1971. *Glacial and Quaternary geology.* New York, London, Sydney, Toronto: John Wiley and Sons.

Forbush, E. H. 1925. *Birds of Massachusetts and other New England states.* Pt. 1, *Water birds, marsh birds, and shore birds.* Massachusetts Department of Agriculture. [Boston?]: Commonwealth of Massachusetts.

Fox, D. L. 1955. Astaxanthin in the American flamingo. *Nature* (London) 175:942-43.

———. 1971. Factors in the coloration of birds. *Explorer* 13 (2), Summer, 4-7, 31.

———. 1976. *Animal biochromes and structural colours: physical, chemical, distributional and physiological features of coloured bodies in the animal world.* 2nd ed. Berkeley, Los Angeles, London: University of California Press.

Fox, H. M., and G. Vevers. 1960. *The nature of animal colours.* Text-books of animal biology. London: Sidgwick and Jackson.

Frazer, D. A., and C. M. Kirkpatrick. 1979. Parental and brood behaviour of Emperor Geese in Alaska. *Wildfowl* 30:75-85. Journal Paper no. 7165 from Purdue University Agricultural Experiment Station, West Lafayette, Ind.

Friedmann, H. 1947. Geographic variations of the Black-bellied, Fulvous, and White-faced tree ducks. *Condor* 49:189-95.

Frith, H. J. 1964a. The downy young of the Freckled Duck *Stictonetta naevosa. Emu* 64:42-47.

———. 1964b. Taxonomic relationships of *Stictonetta naevosa* (Gould). *Nature* (London) 202:1352-53.

———. 1982. *Waterfowl in Australia.* Australian Natural Science rev. ed. London, Sydney, Melbourne: Angus and Robertson.

Frome, M. 1967. Wilderness ignored: the Aleutian Islands. *Audubon Magazine* 69 (1), January/February, 28-40.

Gabrielson, I. N., and F. C. Lincoln. 1959. *Birds of Alaska.* Washington, D. C.: Wildlife Management Institute.

Gadow, H. 1891. Vogel, I. Anatomischer Theil. In *Klassen und Ordnungen des Tierreiches, wissenschaftlich dargestelt in Wort und Bild,* by H. C. Bronn, 881-1008. Vol. 6, pt. 4. Leipsig and Heidelberg: Winter. In German. Not consulted.

Gaioni, S. J., and C. S. Evans. 1986. Perception of distress calls in Mallard ducklings (*Anas platyrhynchos*). *Behaviour* 99:250-74.

Gavin, A. 1947. Birds of Perry River district, Northwest Territories. *Wilson Bulletin* 59:195-203.

Gelston, W. L. 1970. A preliminary report on the Traverse City Mute Swan flock. Prepared for D. McBeath, District Biologist, Department of Natural Resources, Cadillac, Mich. 40 pp.; 4 suppl. pp. Typed duplicated copy.

Gentilli, J. 1961. Quaternary climates of the Australian Region. Annals of the New York Academy of Sciences 95, art. 1, pt. 5:465-501.

Gibbon, A. K. 1933. Some notes on the birds of North Bornu, Nigeria. *Ibis,* 13th ser., 3:228-40.

Giles, C. H. 1966. The fading of coloring matters. *Curator* 9 (2):95-102.

Gilham, E., J. M. Harrison, and J. G. Harrison. 1966. A study of certain *Aythya* hybrids. *Annual Report of the [Severn] Wildfowl Trust 1964-65* 17:49-65.

Gilpin, J. B. 1878. On the Golden-eyes, or Garrots in Nova Scotia. Proceedings and Transactions of the Nova Scotia Institute of Natural Sciences (1875-1878), vol. 4:390-403.

Godfrey, W. E. 1986. *The birds of Canada.* Revised edition. Ottawa: National Museums of Canada.

Gollop, J. B., and W. H. Marshall. 1954. *A guide for aging duck broods in the field.* Mississippi Flyway Council Technical Section. Typed duplicated copy.

Goodwin, D. 1984. Do chick and duckling down patterns function as recognition marks? *Avicultural Magazine* 90:112-17.

Gottlieb, G. 1965. Components of recognition in ducklings. *Natural History* 74 (2), February, 12-19.

Gottlieb, G., and J. G. Vandenbergh. 1968. Ontogeny of vocalization in duck and chicken embryos. *Journal of Experimental Zoology* 168:307-26.

Gould, J. 1873. *The birds of Great Britain.* Vol. 5. London: by the author.

Gray, A. P. 1958. *Bird hybrids: a check list with bibliography.* Commonwealth Bureau of Animal Breeding and Genetics, Technical Communication no. 13. Farnham Royal, England: Commonwealth Agricultural Bureaux.

Grice, D., and J. P. Rogers. 1965. *The Wood Duck in Massachusetts.* Massachusetts Division of Fisheries and Game. Federal Aid in Wildlife Restoration, Project no. W-19-R.

Grinnell, J. 1900. *Birds of the Kotzebue Sound region, Alaska.* Pacific Coast Avifauna no. 1. Santa Clara, Calif.: Cooper Ornithological Club of California.

———. 1910. *Birds of the 1908 Alexander Alaska Expedition, with a note on the avifaunal relationships of the Prince William Sound district.* University of California Publications in Zoology, vol. 5, no. 12:361-428. Berkeley: University of California Press.

Grinnell, J., H. C. Bryant, and T. I. Storer. 1918. *The game birds of California.* Berkeley: University of California Press. Contribution from the University of California Museum of Vertebrate Zoology.

Gross, A. O. 1938. Eider Ducks of Kent's Island. *Auk* 55:387-400.

Gurney, J. H. 1877. Note on the Polish Swan. *Proceedings of the Zoological Society of London* [47]:579-80.

Halla, B. F. 1966. The Mute Swan in Rhode Island: a progress report. Paper read at Proceedings, Northeast Section of the Wildlife Society, January 16-19, at Boston, Mass. A Contribution of Federal Aid in Wildlife Restoration, Project W-23-R. 15 pp. Typed duplicated copy.

Hamly, D. H. 1949. The Ridgway color standards with a Munsell notation key. *Journal of the Optical Society of America* 39:592-99.

Hammer, D. A. 1970. Trumpeter Swan carrying young. *Wilson Bulletin* 82:324-25.

Handley, C. O., Jr. 1950. The brant of Prince Patrick Island, Northwest Territories. *Wilson Bulletin* 62:128-32.

Hansen, H. A. 1962. Canada Geese of coastal Alaska. *Transactions of the North American Wildlife and Natural Resources Conference* 27:301-20.

———. 1973. Trumpeter Swan management. *Wildfowl* 24:27-32.

Hansen, H. A., P. E. K. Shepherd, J. G. King, and W. A. Troyer. 1971. *The Trumpeter Swan in Alaska.* The Wildlife Society, Wildlife Monographs, no. 26. Lawrence, Kans.: Allen Press.

Hanson, H. C. 1965. *The Giant Canada Goose.* Carbondale and Edwardsville, Ill.: Southern Illinois University Press.

Hanson, H. C., and C. W. Kossack. 1957. Methods and criteria for aging incubated eggs and nestlings of the Mourning Dove. *Wilson Bulletin* 69:91-101.

Hanson, H. C., P. Queneau, and P. M. Scott. 1956. *The geography, birds and mammals of the Perry River region.* Arctic Institute of North America, Special Publication no. 3. [Montreal].

Hansen, S. 1984. *The Trumpeter Swan: a white perfection.* Flagstaff, Ariz.: Northland Press.

Harper, F. 1953. Birds of the Nueltin Lake Expedition, Keewatin, 1947. *American*

Midland Naturalist 49:1-116.

Harris, S. W., and R. J. Wheeler. 1965. Hybrid of Blue-winged Teal X Cinnamon Teal in northwestern California. *Condor* 67:539-40.

Harrison, C. 1975. *A field guide to the nests, eggs, and nestlings of British and European birds*. Quadrangle Field Guide Series. Boston: Demeter Press, and New York: Quadrangle Books and New York Times Book Company.

———. 1978. *A field guide to the nests, eggs, and nestlings of North American birds.* Glasgow: William Collins Sons and Company.

Hartert, E. 1920. *Die Vögel der paläarktischen Fauna*. Vol. 2, pts. 10-12. Berlin: R. Friedlander und Sohn. In German.

Harting, J. E. 1871. Catalogue of an Arctic collection of birds presented by Mr. John Barrow, F. R. S., to the University Museum at Oxford: with notes on the species. *Proceedings of the Zoological Society of London* [41]: 110-23.

Hatch, S. A., and M. A. Hatch. 1983. An isolated population of small Canada Geese on Kaliktagik Island, Alaska. *Wildfowl* 34:130-36.

Heinroth, O., and M. Heinroth. 1928. *Die Vogel Mitteleuropas.* Vol. 3. Berlin-Lichterfelde: Hugo Bermuhler Verlag. In German.

Hellmayr, C. E., and H. B. Conover. 1948. *Catalogue of birds of the Americas and the adjacent islands in the Field Museum of Natural History.* Field Museum of Natural History Zoological Series, Vol. 13, Pt. 1, no. 2, *Spheniscidae to Anatidae.* Chicago.

Hepp, G. R., and J. D. Hair. 1983. Reproductive behavior and pairing chronology in wintering dabbling ducks. *Wilson Bulletin* 95:675-82.

———. 1984. Dominance in wintering waterfowl (Anatini): effects on distribution of sexes. *Condor* 86:251-57.

Heusmann, H. W., and R. G. Burrell. 1974. Studies in urban wildlife park mallards. In *A symposium on wildlife in an urbanizing environment,* ed., 77-86. Amherst, Mass.: University of Massachusetts Cooperative Extension Service.

Hochbaum, H. A. 1944. *The Canvasback on a prairie marsh.* Harrisburg, Pa.: Stackpole Company; Washington, D. C.: Wildlife Management Institute.

Hohman, W. H. 1985. Feeding ecology of Ring-necked Ducks in northwestern Minnesota. *Journal of Wildlife Management* 49:546-57.

Hollister, N. 1919. The systematic position of the Ring-necked Duck. *Auk* 36:460-63.

Howard, H. 1964. Fossil Anseriformes. In *The waterfowl of the world,* by J. T. Delacour, 233-326. Vol. 4. London: Country Life.

Hubbard, J. P. 1973. Avian evolution in the aridlands of North America. Cornell Laboratory of Ornithology, Twelfth Annual *Living Bird*: 155-96. Ithaca, N. Y.

———. 1977. *The biological and taxonomic status of the Mexican Duck.* New Mexico Department of Game and Fish Bulletin no. 16. Federal Aid in Wildlife Restoration, Project FW-17-R.

Huber, W. 1923. New Mexican Duck, *Anas novimexicana* Huber. In *Life histories of North American wildfowl,* pt. 1, by A. C. Bent, 48-50. U. S. National Museum Bulletin 126. Washington, D. C.: U. S. Government Printing Office.

Huey, L. M. 1936. Notes on the summer and fall birds of the White Mountains, Arizona. *Wilson Bulletin* 48:119-30.

Huey, W. S. 1961. Comparison of female Mallard with female New Mexican Duck. *Auk* 78:428-31.

Humphrey, P. S. 1955. The relationships of the sea ducks (Tribe Mergini). Ph. D. diss., University of Michigan, Ann Arbor. n.d. Doctoral Dissertation Series, Publication no. 12,592. Ann Arbor: University Microfilms International.

———. 1958a. Classification and systematic position of the eiders. *Condor* 60:129-35.

———. 1958b. The trachea of the Hawaiian

Goose. *Condor* 60:303-7.

Humphrey, P. S., and B. C. Livezey. 1985. Nest, eggs, and downy young of the White-headed Flightless Steamer-duck. In *Neotropical ornithology*, eds. P. A. Buckley, M. S. Foster, E. S. Morton, R. S. Ridgeley, and F. G. Buckley, 944-53. American Ornithologists' Union, Ornithological Monographs, no. 36. Washington, D. C.

Inverarity, J. D. 1889. The Indian Bison, with some notes on stalking him. *Journal of the Bombay Natural History Society* 4:294-310.

Jackson, M. F. 1959. A hybrid between Barrow's and Common goldeneyes. *Auk* 76:92-94.

Jardine, N., and D. McKenzie. 1972. Continental drift and the dispersal and evolution of organisms. *Nature* (London) 235:20-24.

Jehl, J. R., Jr. 1968a. The egg-tooth of some charadriiform birds. *Wilson Bulletin* 80:328-30.

———. 1968b. *Relationships in the Charadrii (Shorebirds): a taxonomic study based on color patterns of the downy young.* San Diego Society of Natural History, Memoir no. 3. San Diego, California.

Johansen, H. 1945. Om Racer af Saedgaes. *Dansk Ornithologisk Forenings Tidsskrift* 39:106-27. In Danish. n.d. Translated by K. E. Lumsden, under the title The races of Bean Geese. Typed duplicated copy.

———. 1956. *Revision und Entstehung der Arktischen Vogelfauna.* Acta Arctica, vol. 8. Copenhagen: Ejnar Munksgaard. In German. English summary.

———. 1963. Zoogeographical aspects of the birds of the subarctic. *Proceedings of the XIIIth International Ornithological Congress*: 1117-23. Vol. 2. Baton Rouge, La.: American Ornithologists' Union.

Johnsgard, P. A. 1960a. Classification and evolutionary relationships of the sea ducks. *Condor* 62:426-33.

———. 1960b. Comparative behaviour of the Anatidae and its evolutionary implications. *Annual Report of the [Severn] Wildfowl Trust 1958-59* 11:31-45.

———. 1960c. Hybridization in the Anatidae and its taxonomic implications. *Condor* 62:25-33.

———. 1960d. A quantitative study of sexual behavior of Mallards and Black Ducks. *Wilson Bulletin* 72:133-55.

———. 1961a. Evolutionary relationships among the North American mallards. *Auk* 78:3-43.

———. 1961b. The taxonomy of the Anatidae - a behavioural analysis. *Ibis* 103a:71-85.

———. 1961c. Tracheal anatomy of the Anatidae and its taxonomic significance. *Annual Report of the [Severn] Wildfowl Trust 1959-60* 12:58-69.

———. 1963. Behavioral isolating mechanisms in the family Anatidae. *Proceedings of the XIIIth International Ornithological Congress*: 531-43. Vol. 1. Baton Rouge, La.: American Ornithologists' Union. Contribution no. 355 from the Department of Zoology and Physiology, University of Nebraska, Lincoln.

———. 1964. Observations on the biology of the Spectacled Eider. *Annual Report of the [Severn] Wildfowl Trust 1962-63* 15:104-7. Contribution no. 359 from the Department of Zoology and Physiology, University of Nebraska, Lincoln.

———. 1965. *Handbook of waterfowl behavior.* Ithaca, N. Y.: Cornell University Press.

———. 1967a. Observations on the behaviour and relationships of the White-backed Duck and the stiff-tailed ducks. *Annual Report of the [Severn] Wildfowl Trust 1965-66* 18:98-107. Contribution no. 380 from the Department of Zoology and Physiology, University of Nebraska, Lincoln.

———. 1967b. Sympatry changes and hybridization incidence in Mallards and Black Ducks. *American Midland Naturalist* 77:51-63. Study no. 378 from the Department of Zoology and Physiology, University of Nebraska, Lincoln.

———. 1968. *Waterfowl.* Lincoln, Nebr.:

University of Nebraska Press.

———. 1974. The taxonomy and relationships of the northern swans. *Wildfowl* 25:155-61.

———. 1978. *Ducks, geese, and swans of the world.* Lincoln, Nebr.: University of Nebraska Press.

———. 1979. Order Anseriformes. In *Check-list of birds of the world*, vol. 1, eds. E. Mayr and C. W. Cottrell, 425-506. 2nd. ed. Cambridge, Mass.: Museum of Comparative Zoology.

Johnsgard, P. A., and D. Hagemeyer. 1969. The Masked Duck in the United States. *Auk* 86:691-95.

Johnsgard, P. A., and J. Kear. 1968. A review of parental carrying of young by waterfowl. Cornell Laboratory of Ornithology, Seventh Annual *Living Bird*: 89-102. A joint contribution from the Wildfowl Trust, Slimbridge, and the University of Nebraska Department of Zoology, Lincoln (Contribution no. 388).

Johnson, D. H., D. E. Timm, and P. F. Springer. 1979. Morphological characteristics of Canada Geese in the Pacific Flyway. *In Management and biology of Pacific Flyway geese: a symposium*, eds. R. L. Jarvis and J. C. Bartonek, 56-80. Corvallis, Ore.: Northwest Section of the Wildlife Society.

Johnson, F. A., F. Montalbano, III, and T. C. Hines. 1984. Population dynamics and status of the Mottled Duck in Florida. *Journal of Wildlife Management* 48:1137-43.

Johnson, N. K., R. M. Zink, G. F. Barrowclough, and J. A. Marten. 1984. Suggested techniques for modern avian systematics. *Wilson Bulletin* 96:543-60.

Johnson, T. W. 1968. The survival and ecology of Florida Duck, *Anas fulvigula fulvigula* (Ridgway), broods with notes on Florida Duck molting. Master's thesis, Tennessee Technological University, Cookeville.

Johnstone, S. T. 1957a. Breeding of Bewick's Swans. *Avicultural Magazine* 63:27-28.

———. 1957b. On breeding whistling ducks. *Avicultural Magazine* 63:23-25.

———. 1959. Notes from the Wildfowl Trust. *Avicultural Magazine* 65:37-39.

———. 1960. Notes from the New Grounds. *Avicultural Magazine* 66:67-71.

———. 1961. Breeding the King Eider, 1961. *Avicultural Magazine* 67:196-97.

———. 1972. Slimbridge: curator's report for 1971. *Wildfowl* 23:135-36.

———. 1973. Notes from Slimbridge. *Avicultural Magazine* 79:126-30.

Jones, J. G. 1971. Australia's Caenozoic drift. *Nature* (London) 230:237-39.

Judd, D. B., and G. Wyszecki. *Color in Business, Science, and Industry.* 3rd ed. New York: John Wiley & Sons.

Kear, J. 1965. The internal food reserves of hatching Mallard ducklings. *Journal of Wildlife Management* 29:523-28.

———. 1967. Notes of the eggs and downy young of *Thalassornis leuconotus. Ostrich* 38:227-29.

———. 1968. The calls of very young Anatidae. *Beihefte der Vogelwelt* 1:93-113.

———. 1970. Studies on the development of young Tufted Duck. *Wildfowl* 21:123-32.

———. 1972. Reproduction and family life. In *The swans*, by P. M. Scott and the Wildfowl Trust, 80-124. London: Michael Joseph.

———. 1975. Salvadori's Duck of New Guinea. *Wildfowl* 26:104-11.

Kear, J., and A. J. Berger. 1980. *The Hawaiian Goose: an experiment in conservation.* Calton, England: T. and A. D. Poyser.

Kear, J., and R. J. Scarlett. 1970. The Auckland Islands Merganser. *Wildfowl* 21:78-86.

Kelly, K. L., and D. B. Judd. 1976. *Color: universal language and dictionary of names.* National Bureau of Standards (U. S.), Special Publication 440. Washington, D. C.: U. S. Government Printing Office.

Kennard, F. H. 1927. The specific status of the Greater Snow Goose. Proceedings of the New England Zoological Club, vol. 9:85-93.

Kenyon, K. W. 1961. Birds of Amchitka Island. *Auk* 78:305-26.

Kessler, L. G., and J. C. Avise. 1984. Systematic relationships among waterfowl (Anatidae) inferred from restriction endonuclease analysis of mitochondrial DNA. *Systematic Zoology* 33:370-80.

Khan, R. A., and A. M. Fallis. 1968. Comparisons of infections with *Leucocytozoon simondi* in black ducks (*Anas rubripes*), mallards (*Anas platyrhynchos*), and white Pekin ducks (*Anas boschas*). *Canadian Journal of Zoology* 46:773-80.

Kiracofe, J. M. 1964. Aleutian Canada Goose—progress in its survival. *The Game Bird Breeders, Aviculturalists, and Conservationists' Gazette* 13 (2):12-13.

———. 1966. The Aleutian Canada Goose. *Modern Game Breeding* 2 (11), September, 28-29.

Klauber, L. M. 1956. *Rattlesnakes.* Vol. 1. Berkeley and Los Angeles: University of California Press, for the Zoological Society of San Diego.

Knystautas, A. Y., and A. Liutkus. 1984. Sparnuociu pasaulyje (In the world of birds). Vilnius, SSSR: Leidykla "Mokslas". In Lithuanian.

Koenig, A. 1911. *Avifauna Spitzbergensis.* Bonn: [n.p.] Druck von W. Buxenstein. In German. Not consulted.

Kortright, F. H. 1942. *The ducks, geese and swans of North America.* Washington, D. C.: American Wildlife Institute.

Koskimies, J., and L. Lahti. 1964. Cold-hardiness of the newly hatched young in relation to ecology and distribution in ten species of European ducks. *Auk* 81:281-307.

Kostow, K. E. 1981. The role of duckling vocalizations in maintaining the spatial distribution of a foraging brood. Master's thesis, University of Minnesota, Minneapolis.

Krogman, B. D. 1979. A systematic study of *Anser albifrons* in California. In *Management and biology of Pacific Flyway geese: a symposium,* eds. R. L. Jarvis and J. C. Bartonek, 22-43. Corvallis, Ore.: Northwest Section of the Wildlife Society.

Krohn, W. B., and E. G. Bizeau. 1979. Molt migration of the Rocky Mountain population of the Western Canada Goose [*B. c. moffitti*]. In *Management and biology of Pacific Flyway geese: a symposium,* eds. R. L. Jarvis and J. C. Bartonek, 130-41. Corvallis, Ore.: Northwest Section of the Wildlife Society.

Kurhajec, D. J. 1977. Breeding Canada geese of the Port Etches area, Hinchinbrook Island, Alaska. U. S. Fish and Wildlife Service. Unpublished report. Not consulted.

Kurilovich, L. Ya., M. A. Tarkhanova, and I. A. Kharitonova. 1984. Interrelations of females and ducklings in families of the Wigeon [*M. Penelope*], the Goldeneye [*B. clangula*], the Scaup [*A. marila*], and the Red-breasted Merganser [*M. serrator*]. *Ornitologiya* 19:203-4. In Russian.

Kuroda, N. 1939. *Geese and ducks of the world.* Tokyo: Shukyo-shi Shoin. In Japanese.

Lack, D. 1970. The endemic ducks of remote islands. *Wildfowl* 21:5-10.

LaHart, D. E. 1970. The ecology and population parameters of the Florida Duck, *Anas platyrhynchos fulvigula* Ridgway. Master's thesis, University of Florida, Gainesville.

LaHart, D. E., and G. Cornwell. n.d. Habitat preference and survival of Florida Duck broods. Florida Game and Fresh Water Fish Commission and the Florida Agricultural Experiment Stations. 8 pp. Typed duplicated copy.

Lahrman, F. W. 1971. Hybrid Cinnamon Teal X Blue-winged Teal at Regina. *Blue Jay* 29:28.

Latham, J. 1785. *A general synopsis of birds.* Vol. 3, pt. 2. London: Leigh and Sotheby. Not consulted.

Lee, F. B., C. H. Schroeder, T. L. Kuck, L. J. Schoonover, M. A. Johnson, H. K. Nelson, and C. A. Beauduy. 1984. *Rearing and restoring Giant Canada Geese in the Dakotas.* North Dakota Game and Fish Department; South Dakota Department of Game, Fish, and Parks; U. S. Department of the Interior, Fish and Wildlife Service.

Bismarck, N. D.: North Dakota Game and Fish Department.

Lehmann, F. C. 1946. Two new birds from the Andes of Colombia. *Auk* 63:218-23.

Lemieux, L. 1959. The breeding biology of the Greater Snow Goose on Bylot Island, Northwest Territories. *Canadian Field-Naturalist* 73:117-28.

Leopold, F. 1951. A study of nesting Wood Ducks in Iowa. *Condor* 53:209-20.

Lieff, B. C., C. D. MacInnes, and R. K. Misra. 1970. Food selection experiments with young geese. *Journal of Wildlife Management* 34:321-27.

Linduska, J. P., ed. 1964. *Waterfowl tomorrow.* Bureau of Sport Fisheries and Wildlife. U. S. Fish and Wildlife Service. Washington, D. C.: U. S. Government Printing Office.

Linsdale, J. M. 1933. A way to distinguish young Buffle-head ducks from young golden-eye ducks. *Condor* 35:38-39.

Livezey, B. C. 1986. A phylogenetic analysis of Recent anseriform genera using morphological characters. *Auk* 103:737-54.

———. 1989. Phylogenetic relationships and incipient flightlessness of the extinct Auckland Islands Merganser. *Wilson Bulletin* 101:410-35.

———. 1991. A phylogenetic analysis and classification of Recent dabbling ducks (tribe Anatini) based on comparative morphology. *Auk* 108:471-508.

Lokemoen, J. T., and D. E. Sharp. 1981. First documented Cinnamon Teal nesting in North Dakota produced hybrids. *Wilson Bulletin* 93:403-5.

Lönnberg, E. 1929. *Svenska fåglar.* Vol. 2. Stockholm: Ivar Baarsen. In Swedish.

Lorenz, K. 1935. Der Kumpan in der Umwelt des Vögels. *Journal für Ornithologie* 83:137-213, 289-413. In German.

———. 1941. Vergleichende Bewegungsstudien an Anatinen. *Journal für Ornithologie* 89 (supplement 3):194-293. In German. 1951-53. Translated by C. H. D. Clarke, under the title Comparative studies on the behaviour of the Anatinae. *Avicultural Magazine* 57:157-82; 58:8-17, 61-72, 86-93, 172-83; 59:24-33, 80-90. n.d. Reprinted from *Avicultural Magazine.* 87 pp.

Lotter, C. F. 1969. Habitat requirements and procedures for measuring various population parameters of the Florida Duck, *Anas platyrhynchos fulvigula* Ridgway. Master's thesis, University of Florida, Gainesville.

Lovvorn, J. R. 1989. Food defendability and antipredator tactics: implications for dominance and pairing in Canvasbacks. *Condor* 91:826-36.

Lubbock, M. R. 1975. White-winged Wood Ducks at Slimbridge. *Avicultural Magazine* 81:153-54.

———. 1980. The rearing of Pink-eared Ducks *Malacorhynchus membranaceous,* Musk Duck *Biziura lobata* and Blue-billed Ducks *Oxyura australis. Avicultural Magazine* 86:81-84.

Lusk, C. B. 1975. The invisible danger of visible light. *Museum News,* April, 22-23.

Lynch, J. J. 1943. Fulvous Tree Duck in Louisiana. *Auk* 60:100-2.

McCoshen J. A., and R. P. Thompson. 1968. A study of clicking and its source in some avian species. *Canadian Journal of Zoology* 46:169-72.

MacDonald, S. D. 1954. Report on biological investigations at Mould Bay, Prince Patrick Island, N. W. T., in 1952. National Museum of Canada Bulletin 132:214-38. Annual Report of the National Museum of Canada for the fiscal year 1952-53. Ottawa: Queen's Printer and Controller of Stationery.

MacFarlane, R. R. 1890. *Land and sea birds nesting within the Arctic Circle in the Lower Mackenzie River District.* The Historical and Scientific Society of Manitoba, Transaction 39 (1888-89). Winnipeg: Manitoba Free Press.

Mackay, R. H. 1954. Trapping of Trumpeter Swans in British Columbia. *Canadian Field-Naturalist* 68:28-30.

Mackenzie, M. J. S., and J. Kear. 1976. The

White-winged Wood Duck. *Wildfowl* 27:5-17.

McKillop, W. B. 1986. Induced colour fading in entomological specimens. Association of Manitoba Museums, *Dawson and Hind* 12(3), Winter 1986, 17-19.

McKinney, D. F. 1954. An observation on Redhead parasitism. *Wilson Bulletin* 66:146-48.

———. 1965. The comfort movements of Anatidae. *Behaviour* 25:120-220. 1965. Reprint. Leiden: E. J. Brill.

———. 1969. The behaviour of ducks. In *The behaviour of domestic animals*, ed. E. S. E. Hafez, 593-626. 2nd ed. London: Bailliere, Tindall, and Cassell.

———. 1970. Displays of four species of blue-winged ducks. Cornell Laboratory of Ornithology, Ninth Annual *Living Bird:* 29-64. Ithaca, N.Y.

Mackworth-Praed, C. W., and C. H. B. Grant. 1970. *African handbook of birds.* Ser. 3, vol. 1. *Birds of west central and western Africa.* London: Longman.

McLachlan, G. R., and R. Liversidge. 1972. *Roberts Birds of South Africa.* 3rd. ed. Capetown, S. Africa: John Voelcker Bird Book Fund.

McLandress, M. R., and I. McLandress. 1979. Blue-phase Ross' Geese and other blue-phase geese in western North America. *Auk* 96:544-50.

McNicholl, M. K. 1983. Hatching of Forster's Terns. *Condor* 85:50-52.

Macpherson, A. H., and T. H. Manning. 1959. *The birds and mammals of Adelaide Peninsula, N.W.T.* National Museum of Canada Bulletin 161. Biological Series no. 59. Ottawa: Queen's Printer and Controller of Stationery.

Madsen, C. S., K. P. McHugh, and S. R. de Kloet. 1988. A partial classification of waterfowl (Anatidae) based on single-copy DNA. *Auk* 105:452-59.

Manning, T. H., E. O. Höhn, and A. H. Macpherson. 1956. *The birds of Banks Island.* National Museum of Canada Bulletin 143. Biological Series no. 48. Ottawa: Queen's Printer and Controller of Stationery.

Manning, T. H., and A. H. Macpherson. 1952. Birds of the east James Bay coast between Long Point and Cape Jones. *Canadian Field-Naturalist* 66:1-35.

Markum, D. E., and G. A. Baldassarre. 1989. Breeding biology of Muscovy Ducks using nest boxes in Mexico. *Wilson Bulletin* 101:621-26.

Mason, J. R., and L. Clark. 1990. Sarcosporidiosis observed more frequently in hybrids of Mallards and American Black Ducks. *Wilson Bulletin* 102:160-62.

Matson, R. H. 1984. Applications of electrophoretic data in avian systematics. *Auk* 101:717-29.

Matthews, G. V. T., and M. E. Evans. 1974. On the behaviour of the White-headed Duck with special reference to breeding. *Wildfowl* 25:56-66.

Mattson, M. E. 1973. Host-parasite relations of Canvasback and Redhead ducklings. Master's thesis, University of Manitoba, Winnipeg.

Mayr, E. 1944a. *The birds of Timor and Sumba.* Bulletin of the American Museum of Natural History, vol. 83, art. 2:123-94. New York.

———. 1944b. Timor and the colonization of Australia by birds. *Emu* 44:113-30.

———. 1945. The downy plumage of the Australian Dabchick. *Emu* 44:231-33.

———. 1965. *Animal species and evolution.* Cambridge, Mass.: Harvard University Press, Belknap Press.

———. 1972. Continental drift and the history of the Australian bird fauna. *Emu* 72:26-28.

Meanley, B., and A. G. Meanley. 1959. Observations on the Fulvous Tree Duck in Louisiana. *Auk* 71:33-45.

Meinertzhagen, A. C. 1924. A review of the genus *Burhinus. Ibis*, 11th ser., 6:329-56.

Mendall, H. L. 1958. *The Ring-necked Duck in*

the northeast. University of Maine Bulletin, vol. 60, no. 16. University of Maine Studies, 2nd ser., no. 73. Orono, Me.: University Press.

Mendenhall, V. M., and H. Milne. 1985. Factors affecting duckling survival of Eiders *Somateria mollissima* in northeast Scotland. *Ibis* 127:148-58.

Mengel, R. M. 1971. The North American Central Plains as an isolating agent in bird speciation. In *Pleistocene and Recent environments of the Central Great Plains,* eds. W. Dort, Jr., and J. K. Jones, Jr., 279-340. Department of Geology, University of Kansas, Special Publication no. 3. Lawrence, Manhattan, Wichita, Kans.: University of Kansas Press.

Millais, J. G. 1913. *British diving ducks.* 2 vols. London: Longmans, Green, and Company.

Miller, A. H. 1937. *Structural modifications in the Hawaiian Goose* (Nesochen sandwichensis): *a study in adaptive evolution.* University of California Publications in Zoology, vol. 42, no. 1. A contribution of the University of California [Berkeley] Museum of Vertebrate Zoology.

Miller, S. L., M. A. Gregg, A. R. Kuritsubo, S. M. Combs, M. K. Murdock, J. A. Nilsson, B. R. Noon, and R. G. Botzler. 1988. Morphometric variation in Tundra Swans: Relationships among sex and age classes. *Condor* 90:802-15.

Mindell, D. P., and R. L. Honeycutt. 1989. Variability in transcribed regions of ribosomal DNA and early divergencies in birds. *Auk* 106:539-48.

Minton, C. D. T. 1968. Pairing and breeding of Mute Swans. *Wildfowl* 19:41-60.

Moffitt, J. E. 1932. The downy young of some foreign species of ducks and geese. *Auk.* 49:214-15.

Morgan, R. P., II, L. A. Noe, and C. J. Henny. 1976. Biochemical identification of the Mallard, *Anas platyrhynchos,* and Black Duck, *A. rubripes. Comparative Biochemical Physiology* 53B:499-502. Contribution no. 634 from the Center for Environmental and Estuarine Studies, University of Maryland.

Morgan, R. P., II, S. T. Sulkin, and C. J. Henny. 1977. Serum proteins of Canada Goose (*Branta canadensis*) subspecies. *Condor* 79:275-78. Contribution no. 730 from Chesapeake Biological Laboratory, Center for Environmental and Estuarine Studies, University of Maryland.

Moulton, D. W., and M. W. Weller. 1984. Biology and conservation of the Laysan Duck (*Anas laysanensis*). *Condor* 86:105-17. Paper no. 13,086, Scientific Journal Series, Minnesota Agricultural Experiment Station, University of Minnesota, St. Paul.

Munro, D. A. 1962. Trumpeter Swans. *Canadian Audubon* 24 (3), May-June, 64-69.

Munro, G. C. 1944. *Birds of Hawaii.* Honolulu: Tongg Publishing Company.

Munro, J. A. 1918. The Barrow Goldeneye in the Okanagan Valley, British Columbia. *Condor* 20:3-5.

———. 1937. Studies of waterfowl in the Cariboo region, B. C. *Condor* 39:163-73.

———. 1939. Studies of waterfowl in British Columbia, no. 9: Barrow's Golden-eye, American Golden-eye. Transactions of the Royal Canadian Institute, vol. 22, pt. 2:259-318.

———. 1941. Studies of waterfowl in British Columbia. Greater Scaup duck, Lesser Scaup duck. *Canadian Journal of Research* 19D:113-38.

———. 1945. The birds of the Cariboo parklands, B. C. *Canadian Journal of Research* 23D:17-103.

Munro, R. E., L. T. Smith, and J. J. Kupa. 1968. The genetic basis of color differences observed in the Mute Swan (*Cygnus olor*). *Auk* 85:504-5.

Munsell Color Company. 1929. *Munsell book of color.* 2 vols. Matte samples. Baltimore, Md.: Munsell Color Company.

———. 1966. *Munsell book of color.* 2 vols. Glossy samples. Baltimore, Md.: Munsell

Color Company.

———. 1970. *Munsell Neutral Value Scale.* 32-step scale. Matte samples. Baltimore, Md.: Munsell Color Company.

———. 1973. *Munsell soil color charts.* Baltimore, Md.: Munsell Color Company.

Myres, M. T. 1957. An introduction to the behaviour of the goldeneyes: *Bucephala islandica* and *B. clangula* (Class Aves, Family Anatidae). Master's thesis, University of British Columbia, Vancouver.

Nelson, C. H. 1964. Observations on the day-old young of the Spectacled Eider, *Somateria fischeri. Auk* 81:219-21.

———. 1976a. The color phases of downy Mute Swans. *Wilson Bulletin* 88:1-3.

———. 1976b. A key to downy cygnets with analysis of plumage characters. *Wilson Bulletin* 88:4-15.

———. 1982. A lamp-booth for laboratory use. *Wilson Bulletin* 94:225-29.

———. 1983. Eye-color changes in Barrow's Goldeneye and Common Goldeneye ducklings. *Wilson Bulletin* 95:482-88.

Nelson, D. A. 1980. A Mallard X Mottled Duck hybrid. *Wilson Bulletin* 92:527-29.

Nelson, E. W. 1887. *Report upon natural history collections made in Alaska between the years 1877 and 1881.* Pt. 1, *Birds of Alaska, with a partial bibliography of Alaskan ornithology.* U. S. Army Signal Service, Arctic Series of Publications, no. 3. Washington, D. C.: U. S. Government Printing Office.

Nice, M. M. 1962. *Development of behavior in precocial birds.* Transactions of the Linnaean Society of New York, vol. 8. New York: Linnaean Society.

Nicholson, E. M. 1930. Field notes on Greenland birds. Pt. 2. *Ibis,* 12th ser., 6:395-428.

North Dakota Outdoors 33 (1), July 1970.

Numachi, K-i., M. Watada, R. Kakizawa, N. Kuroda, and S. Utida. 1983. Evolutionary genetics of the Anatidae. *Tori* 32:63-74. Japanese summary.

Nymeyer, L. A. 1975. The Mexican Duck in southcentral New Mexico: distribution, abundance, habitat. Unpublished report for New Mexico Department of Game and Fish. Endangered Species Program FW-17-R. Not consulted.

———. 1977. Waterfowl ecology in the Rio Grande and Uvas valleys of southern New Mexico, with empasis on the Mexican Duck. Master's thesis, New Mexico State University, Las Cruces.

Oates, D. W., J. E. Seeb, L. N. Wishard, and P. Abersold. 1983. *Biochemical identification of North American waterfowl.* Nebraska Game and Parks Commission, Nebraska Technical Series no. 13. Lincoln. Federal Aid to Wildlife Restoration, Project W-38-R.

Ogilvie, M. A. 1978. *Wild geese.* Vermillion, S. D.: Buteo Books.

Olson, S. L., and A. Feduccia. 1980. *Presbyornis* and the origin of the Anseriformes (Aves: Charadriomorphae). Smithsonian Contribution to Zoology, no. 323. Washington, D. C.: Smithsonian Institution Press.

Olson, S. L., and H. F. James. 1982. Prodromus of the fossil avifauna of the Hawaiian Islands. Smithsonian Contributions to Zoology, no. 365. Washington, D. C.: Smithsonian Institution Press.

Oring, L. W. 1968. Growth, molts, and plumages of the Gadwall. *Auk* 85:355-80.

Orth, D. J. 1976. *Dictionary of Alaska place names.* (U. S.) Geological Survey Professional Paper 567. Washington, D. C.: U. S. Government Printing Office.

Ouellet, H., and M. Gosselin. 1983. Les noms francais des oiseaux d'Amerique du Nord. National Museums of Canada, Syllogeus series no. 43. Ottawa. In French.

Owen, M. 1980. *Wild geese of the world.* London: B. T. Batsford.

Owen, M., G. L. Atkinson-Willes, and D. G. Salmon. 1983. *Wildfowl in Great Britain.* 2nd. ed. Cambridge, London, New York: Cambridge University Press.

Owen, M., and J. Kear. 1972. Food and feeding habits. In *The swans*, by P. M. Scott and the Wildfowl Trust, 58-77. London: Michael Joseph.

Owen, R. B., Jr. 1982. Behavioral and physiological responses of coastal-wintering black ducks to changing weather in Maine. Paper read at Workshop on the ecology of wintering waterfowl, April 14-16, at Puxico, Mo. Sponsored by the Delta Waterfowl [and Wetlands] Research Station. Not consulted.

Palmer, R. S., ed. 1976. *Handbook of North American birds.* Vols. 2 and 3, *Waterfowl.* New Haven, Conn., and London: Yale University Press.

Palmer, R. S., and E. M. Reilly, Jr. 1956. A concise color standard. [N. p.]: American Ornithologists' Union Handbook Fund.

Parkes, K. C. 1954. Notes on some birds of the Adirondack and Catskill mountains, New York. Annals of the Carnegie Museum, vol. 33, art. 8:149-78.

———. 1958. Systematic notes on North American birds. Annals of the Carnegie Museum, vol. 35, art. 8, pt. 2:117-25.

———. 1970. A revision of the Philippine Trogon (*Harpactes ardens*). *Natural History Bulletin of the Siam Society*, vol. 23:345-52.

Parkes, K. C., and G. A. Clark, Jr. 1964. Additional records of avian egg teeth. *Wilson Bulletin* 76:147-54.

Parkes, K. C., and C. H. Nelson. 1976. A definite Colorado breeding record for the Harlequin Duck. *Auk* 93:846-47.

Parmelee, D. F., H. A. Stephens, and R. H. Schmidt. 1967. *The birds of southeastern Victoria Island and adjacent small islands.* National Museum of Canada Bulletin 222. Biological Series no. 78. Ottawa: Queen's Printer.

Partridge, W. H. 1956. Notes on the Brazilian Merganser in Argentina. *Auk* 73:473-88.

Patton, J. C., and J. C. Avise. 1983. An empirical evaluation of quantitative Hennigian analyses of protein electrophoretic data. *Journal of Molecular Evolution* 19:244-54.

Paulus, S. L. 1984. Behavioral ecology of Mottled Ducks in Louisiana. Ph. D. diss., Auburn University, Auburn, Alabama.

Peters, J. L. 1931, 1934. *Check-list of birds of the world.* Vols. 1 and 2. Cambridge, Mass.: Harvard University Press.

Petersen, M. R. 1981. Populations, feeding ecology and molt of Steller's Eiders. *Condor* 83:256-62.

Phelps, W. H., and W. H. Phelps, Jr. 1950. *Lista de las aves de Venezuela con su distribucion.* Pte. 2, *Passeriformes.* Boletin de la Sociedad Venezolana de Ciencias Naturales, vol. 12, no. 75. Caracas. In Spanish.

Phillips, A. R. 1961. Correspondence. *Auk* 78:670-72.

Phillips, A. R., and W. Rook. 1965. A new race of the Spotted Nightingale-Thrush from Oaxaca, Mexico. *Condor* 67:3-5.

Phillips, J. C. 1915. Experimental studies of hybridization among ducks and pheasants. *Journal of Experimental Zoology* 18:69-144.

———. 1921. A further report on species crosses in birds. *Genetics* 6:366-83.

———. 1922-26. *A natural history of the ducks.* 4 vols. Cambridge, Mass.: Houghton Mifflin, Riverside Press.

Piest, L. A., and L. K. Sowls. 1985. Breeding duck use of a sewage marsh in Arizona. *Journal of Wildlife Management* 49:580-84.

Ploeger, P. L. 1968. Geographical differentiation in arctic Anatidae as a result of isolation during the Last Glacial. *Ardea* 56:1-159,

Poole, E. L. 1929. Ducks and other water birds on the Reading, Pa., reservoir. *Auk* 46:534-36.

Portenko, L. A. 1972. *Ptitsy Chukotskogo poluostrova i ostrova Vrangelya* (Birds of the Chukchi Peninsula and Wrangel Island). Vol. 1. Leningrad: Izdatel'stvo "Nauka" (Leningrad section). In Russian. 1981. Translated by P. M. Rao. New Delhi, India: Amerind Publishing Co. Pvt., for the Smithsonian Institution and the National Science Foundation, Washington, D. C.

Quinn, T. W., G. F. Shields, and A. C. Wilson.

1991. Affinities of the Hawaiian Goose based on two types of mitochondrial DNA data. *Auk* 108:585-593.

Raffaele, H. 1975. Bahama Duck exploiting feeding habits of yellowlegs. *Wilson Bulletin* 87:276-77.

Raikow, R. J. 1970. *Evolution of diving adaptations in the stifftail ducks.* University of California Publications in Zoology, vol. 94. Berkeley, Los Angeles, London: University of California Press.

———. 1971. The osteology and taxonomic position of the White-backed Duck, *Thalassornis leuconotus. Wilson Bulletin* 83:270-77.

———. 1973. Locomotor mechanisms in North American ducks. *Wilson Bulletin* 85:295-307.

———. 1985a. Museum collections, comparative anatomy and the study of phylogeny. No. 9 in *Museum Collections: their roles and future in biological research,* ed. E. H. Miller, 113-21. British Columbia Provincial Museum, Victoria. Occasional Paper no. 25. Reprint.

———. 1985b. Problems in avian classification. *Current Ornithology* 2, ed. R. F. Johnston, 187-212. New York: Plenum Publishing.

Raikow, R. J., S. R. Borecky, and S. L. Berman. 1979. The evolutionary re-establishment of a lost ancestral muscle in the Bowerbird assemblage. *Condor* 81:203-6.

Rand, A. L. 1948. Glaciation, an isolating factor in speciation. *Evolution* 2:314-21.

Reed, A. 1970. The breeding ecology of the Black Duck in the St. Lawrence estuary. Ph. D. diss., Université Laval, Québec.

Rees, E. C., and H. Hillgarth. 1984. The breeding biology of captive Black-headed Ducks and the behavior of their young. *Condor* 86:242-50.

Rich, P. V. 1975. Changing continental arrangements and the origin of Australia's non-passeriform continental avifauna. *Emu* 75:97-112.

Rich, W. H. 1907. *Feathered game of the northeast.* New York: T. Y. Crowell. Not consulted.

Ridgway, R. 1874. Notes upon American water birds. *American Naturalist* 8:108-111.

———. 1887. *A manual of North American birds.* Philadelphia: J. B. Lippincott.

———. 1895. *The ornithology of Illinois.* Pt. l, *A descriptive catalogue of the birds of Illinois.* Natural History Survey of Illinois. State Laboratory of Natural History. [Springfield?]: State Legislature. 1913. Reprint. Bloomington, Ill.: Pantagraph Printing and Stationery Company.

———. 1896. *A manual of North American birds.* 2nd ed. Philadelphia: J. B. Lippincott.

———. 1900. *A manual of North American birds.* 4th ed. Philadelphia: J. B Lippincott.

———. 1912. *Color standards and color nomenclature.* Washington, D. C.: by the author.

Rijnsdorp, A. D. 1986. Winter ecology and food of Wigeon in inland pasture areas in The Netherlands. *Ardea* 74:121-28.

Ripley, S. D. 1959. Laysan Teal at Litchfield. *Avicultural Magazine* 65:172-74.

———. 1960. Laysan Teal in captivity. *Wilson Bulletin* 72:244-47.

———. 1985. The Laysan Teal - recent history and future? *Avicultural Magazine* 91:76-78.

Roberts, T. S. 1932. *The birds of Minnesota.* Vol. 2. Minneapolis, Minn.: University of Minnesota Press.

Rothschild, W. 1900. *The avifauna of Laysan, and the neighbouring islands, with complete history to date of the birds of the Hawaiian possesions.* London: R. H. Porter.

Rutschke, E. 1966. Die submikroscopische Struktur schillernder Federn von Entenvögeln. *Zeitschrift für Zellforschung* 73:432-43. In German.

Ryder, J. P. 1967. *The breeding biology of Ross' goose in the Perry River region, Northwest Territories.* Canadian Wildlife Service Report Series, no. 3. Ottawa: Queen's Printer.

Rylander, M. K., and E. G. Bolen. 1970.

Ecological and anatomical adaptations of North American tree ducks. *Auk* 87:72-90. Welder Wildlife Foundation Contribution no. 124.

Sada, A. M., A. R. Phillips, and M. A. Ramos. 1987. Nombres en Castellano para las aves Mexicanas. Cuadernos de Divulgacion no. 17. Segunda impresion corregida. Xalapa, Mexico: Instituto Nacional de Investigaciones sobre Recursos Bioticos y Ducks Unlimited de Mexico, A. C. In Spanish.

Salomonsen, F. 1933. The status of the Greenland Snow Goose, *Anser caerulescens atlantica* (Kenn.): miscellaneous notes on Greenland ornithology 1. Meddelelser Om Grønland, vol. 92, no. 5. Copenhagen: C. A. Reitzels Forlag.

———. 1958. The present status of the Brent Goose (*Branta bernicla* [L.]), in Western Europe. *Videnskabelige Meddelelser fra Dansk Naturhistorisk Forening* 120:43-80. 1958. Reprint. International Wildfowl Research Bureau Publication no. 4. London.

Salomonsen, F., and J. Gitz-Johansen. 1950. *The birds of Greenland.* Copenhagen: Ejnar Munksgaard.

Sanford, L. D., L. B. Bishop, and T. S. Van Dyke. 1903. *The waterfowl family.* New York: Macmillan Company.

Savage English, T. M. 1916. Notes on some of the birds of Grand Cayman, West Indies. *Ibis,* 10th ser., 4:17-35.

Scherer, S., and T. Hilsberg. 1982. Hybridisierung und Verwandtschaftsgrade innerhalt der Anatidae - eine systematische und evolutientheoretische Betrachtung English summary. *Journal für Ornithologie* 123:357-80. In German.

Scherer, S., and Ch. Sontag. 1986. Zur molekularen Taxonomie und Evolution der Anatidae. *Zeitschrift für zoologische Systematik und Evolutionsforschung* 24:1-19. In German.

Scherner, E. R. 1984. Die *immutabilis*-Mutante als Grundlage populations-genetischer Untersuchungen am Höckerschwan (*Cygnus olor*). *Ökologie der Vögel* 6:175-83. In German. English summary.

Schiøler, E. L. 1925-26. *Danmarks fugle.* Vols. 1 and 2, *Anseriformes.* Copenhagen: Nordisk Forlag. In Danish.

Schjelderup-Ebbe, T. 1922. Bieträge zur Sozialpsychologie des Haushuhns. *Zeitschrift für Psychologie* 88:225-52. In German.

Schleidt, W. M. 1973. Tonic communication: continual effects of discrete signs in animal communication systems. *Journal of Theoretical Biology* 42:359-86.

Schuyl, D.-G. 1937. L'élévage du Canard à ailes blanches *Asarcornis scutulata. L'Oiseau et la Revue Française d'Ornithologie* 7:171-72. In French.

Schwartz, C. W., and E. R. Schwartz. 1953. Notes on the Hawaiian Duck. *Wilson Bulletin* 65:18-25.

Sclater, P. L. 1870. The secretary's report on additions to the Society's menagerie in June, July, August, and September 1870, and description of *Buceros subcylindricus. Proceedings of the Zoological Society of London* [40]: 663-71.

Scott, D., and J. Lubbock. 1974. Preliminary observations on waterfowl of western Madagascar. *Wildfowl* 25:117-20.

Scott, N. J., Jr., and R. P. Reynolds. 1984. Phenotypic variation of the Mexican Duck (*Anas platyrhynchos diazi*) in Mexico. *Condor* 86:266-74.

Scott, P. M. 1948. The bird report. *Annual Report of the [Severn] Wildfowl Trust* 1:13-66.

———. 1951a. Geese in the Canadian Arctic. *Proceedings of the Xth International Ornithological Congress:* 611-12.

———. 1951b. The Perry River Expedition, 1949. *Annual Report of the [Severn] Wildfowl Trust* 1949-50 3:56-64.

———. 1958. Notes on Anatidae seen on world tour. *Annual Report of the [Severn] Wildfowl Trust* 1956-57 9:86-112.

———. 1960. BBC/IUCN Darwin Centenary expedition to the British Virgin Islands,

Trinidad, Panama, Ecuador and the Galapagos Islands, January-March 1959. *Annual Report of the [Severn] Wildfowl Trust 1958-59* 11:61-76.

Scott, P. M., H. J. Boyd, and W. J. L. Sladen. 1955. The Wildfowl Trust's second expedition to central Iceland, 1953. *Annual Report of the [Severn] Wildfowl Trust 1953-54* 7:63-98.

Scott, P. M., J. Fisher, and F. Gudmundsson. 1953. The Severn Wildfowl Trust Expedition to central Iceland, 1951. *Annual Report of the [Severn] Wildfowl Trust 1951-52* 5:79-115.

Scott, P. M., and the Wildfowl Trust. 1972. *The swans.* London: Michael Joseph.

Scoville, R., and G. Gottlieb. 1980. Development of behaviour in Peking ducklings. *Animal Behaviour* 28:1095-1109.

Sealy, S. G. 1970. Egg teeth and hatching methods in some alcids. *Wilson Bulletin* 82:289-93.

Seeb, J. E., L. N. Wishard, and D. W. Oates. unpubl. Genetic variation and differentiation of the North American waterfowl (*Anatidae*). Typed duplicated copy.

Sennett, G. B. 1887. Some undescribed plumages of North American birds. *Auk* 4:24-28.

Severinghaus, C. W., and D. Benson. 1947. Ring-necked Duck broods in New York State. *Auk* 64:626-27.

Seymour, N. R. 1977. Social aspects of reproductive behavior in the black duck (*Anas rubripes*) in eastern Nova Scotia. Ph. D. diss., McGill University, Montreal, Québec.

Sharpe, R. B. 1896. *Catalogue of the birds in the British Museum.* Vol. 24, *Limicolae.* London: Trustees of the British Museum.

Shelford, R. 1899. On some hornbill embryos and nestlings. *Ibis,* 7th ser., 5:538-47.

Shields, G. F., and A. C. Wilson. 1987a. Calibration of mitochondrial DNA evolution in geese. *Journal of Molecular Evolution* 24:212-17.

———. 1987b. Subspecies of the Canada Goose (*Branta canadensis*) have distinct mitochondrial DNA's. *Evolution* 41:662-66.

Shields, G. F. 1989. Analysis of mitochondrial DNA of Pacific Black Brant (*Branta bernicla nigricans*). *Auk* 107:620-23.

Shortt, T. M. 1943. Correlations of bill and foot coloring with age and season in the Black Duck. *Wilson Bulletin* 55:3-7.

Sibley, C. G. 1957. The evolutionary and taxonomic significance of sexual dimorphism and hybridization in birds. *Condor* 59:166-91.

Sibley, C. G., and J. E. Ahlquist. 1972. A comparative study of the egg-white proteins of non-passerine birds. Yale University, Peabody Museum of Natural History Bulletin no. 39. New Haven, Conn.

Sibley, C. G., J. E. Ahlquist, and B. L. Munroe, Jr. 1988. A classification of the living birds of the world, based on DNA-DNA hybridization studies. *Auk* 105:409-23.

Siegfried, W. R. 1977. Notes on the behaviour of Ruddy Ducks during the brood period. *Wildfowl* 28:126-28.

———. 1979. Social behaviour of the African Comb Duck. Cornell Laboratory of Ornithology, Seventeenth Annual *Living Bird:* 85-104. Ithaca, N. Y.

Sinnott, E. W., L. C. Dunn, and T. Dobzhansky. 1950. *Principles of genetics.* 4th ed. New York: McGraw-Hill Book Company.

Slagsvold, T., and J. T. Lifjeld. 1984. Variation in plumage colour of the Great Tit *Parus major* in relation to habitat, season, and food. *Journal of Zoology, London* (A) 206:321-28.

Slud, P. 1964. *The birds of Costa Rica: distribution and ecology.* Bulletin of the American Museum of Natural History, vol. 128. New York.

[Smallwood, S.] 1984. Shubenacadie wildlife pioneer. *Conservator* (Ducks Unlimited Canada) 5 (4), Fall, 8-10.

———. 1985. The Trumpeters of Grande Prairie. *Conservator* (Ducks Unlimited Canada) 6 (2), Spring, 8-10.

Smart, M. G. 1965. Body weights of newly hatched Anatidae. *Auk* 82:645-48.

Smithe, F. B. 1981. *Naturalist's color guide, pt. 3.* New York: American Museum of Natural History.

Snyder, L. L. 1941. *On the Hudson Bay Eider.* Royal Ontario Museum of Zoology Occasional Papers, no. 6. Toronto: University of Toronto Press.

———. 1957. *Arctic birds of Canada.* Toronto: University of Toronto Press.

Snyder, L. L., and H. G. Lumsden. 1951. Variation in *Anas cyanoptera.* Royal Ontario Museum of Zoology Occasional Papers, no. 10. Toronto: University of Toronto Press.

Soper, J. D. 1928. *A faunal investigation of southern Baffin Island.* National Museum of Canada Bulletin 53. Biological Series no. 15. Ottawa: King's Printer.

———. 1930. *The Blue Goose, Chen caerulescens* (Linnaeus). Canada Department of the Interior. Ottawa: King's Printer. Contribution of the National Parks Bureau, Department of Mines and Resources.

———. 1942. Life history of the Blue Goose, *Chen caerulescens* (Linnaeus). Proceedings of the Boston Society of Natural History, vol. 42:121-225.

Sorensen, L. G. 1992. Variable mating system of a sedentary tropical duck: the White-cheeked Pintail (*Anas bahamensis bahamensis*). *Auk* 109:277-92.

Southwick, C. 1953. A system of age classification for field studies of waterfowl broods. *Journal of Wildlife Management* 17:l-8.

Sowls, L. K. 1955. *Prairie ducks: a study of their behavior, ecology, and management.* Harrisburg, Pa.: Stackpole Company, and Washington, D. C.:Wildlife Management Institute.

Spencer, H. E., Jr. 1953. The Cinnamon Teal (*Anas cyanoptera* Vieillot): its life history, ecology, and management. Master's thesis, Utah State Agricultural College, Logan.

Stahlberg, B.-M. 1974. The development of rank order and aggressiveness in a group of juvenile Greylag Geese. *Wildfowl* 25:67-73.

Stejneger, L. 1883. Outlines of a monograph of the Cygninae. Proceedings of the U. S. National Museum (1882), vol. 5:174-221. Washington, D. C.: U. S. Government Printing Office.

———. 1885. *Results of ornithological explorations in the Commander Islands and in Kamtschatka.* United States National Museum Bulletin 29. Washington D. C.: U. S. Government Printing Office.

Stewart, P. A. 1967. Diving Wood Duck ducklings entangle in filamentous algae. *Condor* 69:531.

Stewart, R. E., and J. W. Aldrich. 1956. Distinction of maritime and prairie populations of Blue-winged Teal. Proceedings of the Biological Society of Washington, vol. 69:29-36.

Storer, R. W. 1967. The patterns of downy grebes. *Condor* 69:469-78.

Stotts, V. D. n.d. The Black Duck in the Chesapeake Bay of Maryland: physical characteristics, growth, and development. Maryland Wildlife Administration. Federal Aid in Wildlife Restoration, Project W-30-R-11. Job no. 9. Typed duplicated copy.

Stotts, V. D., and D. E. Davis. 1960. The Black Duck in the Chesapeake Bay of Maryland: breeding behavior and biology. *Chesapeake Science* l:127-54.

Strong, R. M. 1912. Some observations on the life-history of the Red-breasted Merganser, *Mergus serrator*, Linn. *Auk* 29:479-88.

Strutz, C. E. 1966. Aleutian Geese raised in captivity for the first time. *The Game Bird Breeders, Aviculturalists, and Conservationists' Gazette* 15 (10):36-37.

Stutzenbaker, C. D. unpubl. *The Mottled Duck: its life history, ecology, and management.* Texas Parks and Wildlife Department. Federal Aid in Wildlife Restoration, Project W-96-R. Photocopy.

Sutton, G. M. 1932. *The birds of Southampton Island.* Memoirs of the Carnegie Museum, vol. 12, pt. 2 (Zoology), sec. 2. Pittsburgh: Carnegie Institute.

———. 1961. *Iceland summer.* Norman, Okla.: University of Oklahoma Press.

Swarth, H. S. 1923. Unpublished field notebook. University of California Museum of Vertebrate Zoology, Berkeley. Photocopy.

Swarth, H. S., and H. C. Bryant. 1917. *A study of the races of the White-fronted Goose* (Anser albifrons) *occurring in California.* University of California Publications in Zoology, vol. 17, no. 11. Berkeley.

Swedberg, G. E. 1967. *The Koloa: a preliminary report on the life history and status of the Hawaiian duck* (Anas wyvilliana). Prepared as part of the Koloa Restoration Project. Honolulu: Department of Land and Natural Resources.

Szymczak, M. R. 1975. Canada Goose Restoration Along the Foothills of Colorado. Technical Publication Number Thirty-one. State of Colorado, Division of Wildlife Research.

Taverner, P. A. 1919. An important distinction between our two goldeneyes (*Clangula clangula americana* and *Clangula islandica*). *Canadian Field-Naturalist* 33:57-58.

———. 1931. A study of *Branta canadensis* (Linnaeus). National Museum of Canada Bulletin 67:28-40. Annual Report for 1931. Ottawa: King's Printer.

———. 1945. *Birds of Canada.* Rev. ed. Toronto: Musson Book Company.

Thomson, A. L., ed. 1964. *A new dictionary of birds.* New York: McGraw-Hill Book Company.

Thomson, G. 1978. *The museum environment.* Butterworth Series on Conservation in the Arts, Archeology, and Architecture, eds. N. Brommelle, E. Pye, W. T. Chase, and B. M. Feilden. London and Boston: Butterworths.

Thorburn, A. 1923. *Game birds and wild-fowl of Great Britain and Ireland.* London: Longmans, Green, and Company.

Timm, D. E., and C. P. Dau. 1979. Productivity, mortality, distribution and population status of Pacific Flyway White-fronted Geese. In *Management and biology of Pacific Flyway geese: a symposium,* eds. R. L. Jarvis and J. C. Bartonek, 280-98. Corvallis, Ore.: Northwest Section of the Wildlife Society.

Timm, D. E., M. L. Wege, and D. S. Gilmer. 1982. Current status and management challenges for Tule White-fronted Geese. *Transactions of the North American Wildlife and Natural Resources Conference* 47:453-63. Washington, D. C.: Wildlife Management Institute.

Timmermann, G. 1963. Fragen der Anatidensystematik in parasitologischer Sicht. *Proceedings of the XIIIth International Ornithological Congress* 1:189-97. American Ornithologists' Union. Lawrence, Kans.: Allen Press. In German. English summary.

Tinbergen, N. 1939. On the analysis of social organization among vertebrates, with special reference to birds. *American Midland Naturalist* 21:210-34.

Tjeenk Willink, H. D. 1899. Die Zahnleisten und die Eischwiele bie den Vogeln. *Tijdschrift der Nederlandsche Dierkundige Vereeniging* 6:243-54. In German.

Todd, F. S. 1979. *Waterfowl: ducks, geese, and swans of the world.* San Diego, Calif.: Sea World Press.

Todd, W. E. C. 1936. The redhead and ring-necked duck breeding at Pymatuning Lake, Pennsylvania. *Auk* 53:440.

———. 1938. A new eastern race of the Canada Goose. *Auk* 55:661-62.

———. 1940. *Birds of western Pennsylvania.* Pittsburgh: University of Pittsburgh Press.

———. 1963. *Birds of the Labrador Peninsula and adjacent areas: a distributional list.* Toronto: University of Toronto Press.

Tome, M. W. 1991. Diurnal activity budget of female Ruddy Ducks breeding in Manitoba. *Wilson Bulletin* 103:183-89.

Tome, M. W., and D. E. Wrubleski. 1988. Underwater foraging behavior of

Canvasbacks, Lesser Scaups, and Ruddy Ducks. *Condor* 90:168-72.

Tougarinov, A. 1941. *Fauna of the USSR: Aves.* Vol. l, no. 4, *Anseriformes.* Moscow and Leningrad: Academy of Science of the USSR. In Russian. English summary. Not consulted.

Trauger, D. L. 1974. Eye color of female Lesser Scaup in relation to age. *Auk* 91:243-54.

Trauger, D. L., and J. C. Bartonek. 1977. Leech parasitism of waterfowl in North America. *Wildfowl* 28:143-52.

Trautman, M. B. 1947. Courtship behavior of the Black Duck. *Wilson Bulletin* 59:26-35.

Van Bocxstaele, R. 1986. De la part de la famille Kamichi et ses enfants. *Zoo Anvers* 51 (4), April, 19-22. In French.

Van Horn, D., P. Harrington, and J. T. Ratti. 1979. Preliminary results of surveys of the Vancouver Canada Goose (*Branta canadensis fulva*) in southeast Alaska. In *Management and biology of Pacific Flyway geese: a symposium,* eds. R. L. Jarvis and J. C. Bartonek, 310-15. Corvallis, Ore.: Northwest Section of the Wildlife Society.

Van Rossem, A. J. 1927. Eye shine in birds, with notes on the feeding of some goatsuckers. *Condor* 29:25-28.

Van Tyne, J., and A. J. Berger. 1959. *Fundamentals of ornithology.* New York: John Wiley and Sons.

Van Wagner, C. E., and A. J. Baker. 1986. Genetic differentiation in populations of Canada Geese (*Branta canadensis*). *Canadian Journal of Zoology* 64:940-947.

Vevers, G. 1964. Colour. In *A new dictionary of birds,* ed. A. L. Thomson, 142-44. New York: McGraw-Hill Book Company.

———. 1985. Colour. In *A dictionary of birds,* eds. B. Campbell and E. Lack, 99-100. Vermillion, S. D.: Buteo Books, and Calton, England: T. and A. D. Poyser for the British Ornithologists' Union.

Vigil, C. 1973. *Aves Argentinas y Sudamericanas.* Buenos Aires: Editorial Atlantida. In Spanish.

Villalobos-Dominguez, C., and J. Villalobos. 1947. *Atlas de los colores.* Buenos Aires: El Ateneo. In Spanish. English summary.

Vince, M. A. 1964. Social facilitation of hatching in the Bobwhite Quail. *Animal Behaviour* 12:531-34.

Völker, O. 1934. Die Abhängigkeit der Lipochrombildung bie Völgeln von pflanzlichen Carotinoiden. *Journal für Ornithologie* 82:439-50. In German.

Voous, K. H. 1973. List of Recent holarctic bird species, non passerines. *Ibis* 115:612-38.

Walker, E. P. 1939. Eyes that shine at night. Annual Report of the Smithsonian Institution (1938): 349-60. Publication 3491. Washington D. C.: U. S. Government Printing Office.

Ward, P., and B. D. J. Batt. 1973. *Propagation of captive waterfowl: the Delta Waterfowl Research Station system.* Washington D. C.: Delta Waterfowl Research Station of the North American Wildlife Foundation and Wildlife Management Institute.

Webbe, R. 1958. Brent Geese (*Branta bernicla* [L.]) in Denmark and the colour problem. *Dansk Ornithologisk Forenings Tidsskrift* 52:41-47.

Weeks, J. L. 1969. Breeding behavior of Mottled Ducks in Louisiana. Master's thesis, Louisiana State University, Baton Rouge. Not consulted.

Weller, M. W. 1957. Growth, weights, and plumages of the Redhead, *Aythya americana. Wilson Bulletin* 69:5-38.

———. 1959. Parasitic egg laying in the Redhead (*Aythya americana*) and other North American Anatidae. *Ecological Monographs* 29:333-65.

———. 1965. Chronology of pair formaton in some Nearctic *Aythya* (Anatidae). *Auk* 82:227-35. Journal Paper no. J-4843 of the Iowa Agricultural and Home Economics Experiment Station, Ames, Iowa. Project no. 1504.

———. 1967. Notes on plumages and weights of the Black-headed Duck, *Heteronetta atri-*

capilla. *Condor* 69:133-45.

———. 1968a. The breeding biology of the parasitic Black-headed Duck. Cornell Laboratory of Ornithology, Seventh Annual *Living Bird:* 169-207. Journal Paper no. J-5305 of the Iowa Agricultural and Home Economics Experiment Station, Ames, Iowa.

———. 1968b. Notes on some Argentine anatids. *Wilson Bulletin* 80:189-212. Journal Paper no. J-5455 of the Iowa Agricultural and Home Eocnomics Experiment Station, Ames, Iowa. Project no. 1504.

———. 1980. *The island waterfowl*. Ames, Iowa: Iowa State University Press.

Wetherbee, D. K. 1959. Egg teeth and hatched shells of various bird species. *Bird-banding* 30:119-21.

Wetherbee, D. K., and L. M. Bartlett. 1962. Egg teeth and shell rupture of the American Woodcock. *Auk* 79:117.

Wetmore, A. 1916. *Birds of Porto Rico*. U. S. Department of Agriculture Bulletin no. 326. Washington, D. C.: U. S. Government Printing Office.

———. 1951. Observations on the genera of the swans. *Journal of the Washington Academy of Sciences* 41:338-40.

———. 1965. *The birds of the Republic of Panama. Pt. l, Tinamidae to Rynchopidae.* Smithsonian Miscellaneous Collections, no. 150. Washington, D. C.: Smithsonian Institution.

Wetmore, A., et al. 1965. *Water, prey and game birds of North America*. Natural Science Library. Washington, D. C.: National Geographic Society.

White, N. R. 1984. Effects of auditory stimulation on hatch time in the domestic chick. *Bird Behaviour* 5:122-26.

Wildfowl 21, 1970; 23, 1972; 26, 1975; 27, 1976. From 1967, supersedes *Annual Report of the [Severn] Wildfowl Trust.*

Wildlife Trust Bulletin 68, January 1974.

Will, G. C. 1969. Productivity of Canada Geese in Larimer County, Colorado, 1967-1968. Master's thesis, Colorado State University, Fort Collins.

Willey, C. H. 1968. The ecological significance of the Mute Swan in Rhode Island. Transactions of the Northeast Fish and Wildlife Conference, ed. R. D. McDowell, 121-34. A contribution of Federal Aid in Wildlife Restoration, Project W-23-R.

Williams, J. G. 1956. On the downy young of *Aythya erythrophthalma*. *Bulletin of the British Ornithological Club* 76:140-41; ill. 133.

Williamson, F. S. L., and L. J. Peyton. 1962. *Faunal relationships of birds in the Iliamna Lake area, Alaska*. Biological Papers of the University of Alaska. No. 5. [College, Alaska: University of Alaska.]

Williamson, M. H. 1957. Polymorphism in Ross' Goose *Anser rossii*, and the detection of genetic dominance from field data. *Ibis* 99:516-18.

Wilmore, S. B. 1974. *Swans of the world*. New York: Taplinger Publishing Company.

Wilson, A., and C. L. Bonaparte. 1831. *American ornithology, or The natural history of the birds of the United States*. Popular edition. 4 vols. complete in one. Philadelphia: Porter and Coates.

Wilson, V. T., and J. B. van den Akker. 1948. A hybrid Cinnamon Teal - Blue-winged Teal at the Bear River Migratory Bird Refuge, Utah. *Auk* 65:316.

Wishart, R. A. 1983. The behavioral ecology of the American Wigeon (*Anas americana*) over its annual cycle. Ph. D. diss., University of Manitoba, Winnipeg.

Witherby, H. F., F. C. R. Jourdain, N. F. Ticehurst, and B. W. Tucker. 1943. *The handbook of British birds*. Vol. 3. Rev. ed. London: H. F. and G. Witherby.

Wood, C. A. 1917. *The fundus oculi of birds especially as viewed with the ophthalmoscope: a study in comparative anatomy and physiology*. Chicago: Lakeside Press.

Wood, D. L., and D. S. Wood. 1972. Numerical color specification for bird identification: iris color and age in fall migrants. *Bird-band-*

ing 43:182-90.

Wood, D. S. 1973. A numerical criterion for aging by iris color in the Gray Catbird. *EBBA News* 36(3):147-49.

Wood, D. S., and D. L. Wood. 1973. Quantitative iris color change with age in Downy Woodpeckers. *Bird-Banding* 44:100-1.

Woodyard, E. R., and E. G. Bolen. 1984. Ecological studies of Muscovy Ducks in Mexico. *Southwestern Naturalist* 29:453-61.

Woolfenden, G. E. 1961. *Post-cranial osteology of the waterfowl.* Bulletin of the Florida State Museum, Biological Sciences, vol. 6, no. 1. Gainesville, Fla.: University of Florida.

Wright, B. S. 1954. *High tide and an east wind: the story of the Black Duck.* Washington, D.C.: Wildlife Management Institute, and Harrisburg, Pa.: Stackpole Company.

Würdinger, I. 1970. Erzeugung, Ontogenie und Funktion der Lautausserungen bei vier Gansearten. English summary. *Zeitschrift für Tierpsychologie* 27:257-302. In German.

Yarrell, W. 1838. On a new species of swan. *Proceedings of the Zoological Society of London* [8]:19.

Yocom, C. F., and S. W. Harris. 1965. Plumage descriptions and age data for Canada Goose goslings. *Journal of Wildlife Management* 29:874-77.

Appendix A
Table 1 - Weights and Measurements

Appendix A

Morphometric Methods

Weights and measurements used for Table 1 were taken from live birds of known or closely estimated age. For most species, sample size is small because it was difficult to obtain live, newly hatched young even as captives. Nevertheless, because such quantitative data are rare in the literature (e.g., weights of day-old birds in Heinroth and Heinroth 1928, vol. 3; Southwick 1953; Koskimies and Lahti 1964; Smart 1965), data from samples of three or more birds have been analyzed in Table 1, while a simple average, with range, is presented for data from two-bird samples.

Weights (WT), in grams, of known-age, unfed birds were taken with a 100 g or 300 g Pesola balance (accuracy ± 0.2 g), measurements with a 15 cm plastic ruler (before 1966) and a steel caliper (1966 to present). Duplicating several hundred measurements with both ruler and caliper, I found that the two sets seldom differed by more than 0.5 mm, the result obtained by Weller (1957) in a similar test. Measurements follow Baldwin, Oberholser, and Worley (1931) for the most part (see Glossary), but not all measurements taken were included in the data analyzed for Table 1. Only the exposed culmen (EC), the 'long' tarsus (LTMT), and the middle toe with claw (IIIw) were used consistently; the 'short' tarsus measurement (TMT) is lacking for specimens examined in 1962-63. Certain other diagnostic measurements, usually expressed as ratios in Table 1, are cited in the Identification Keys of the species to which they pertain.

Although author-weighed birds were sexed before weighing and measuring, the small sample size for most species and the wide individual variation in post-hatching weight loss and, to a lesser extent, in linear growth, precluded accurate analysis of possible sex differences in weight of the day-old birds. Therefore, data for both sexes were analyzed together.

David Eisenhauer, Janet Kear, and David Parmelee contributed unpublished weights to fill several gaps in my day-old weight data, while certain published weights are taken from Kear and Berger (1980) and Smart (1965). John Ryder provided measurements of four day-old Ross' goslings from his study area in the Northwest Territories.

It was not always practical to measure and weigh the downy birds at precisely 24 hours after hatching; hatching is defined as the time when the bird pushes free of shell and membranes. Therefore, because weight loss, as the yolk reserves of the unfed hatchling are depleted, is measurable hourly (Kear 1965), while linear growth is discernible daily, I assigned each specimen examined to one of the following four age categories in order to tabulate with some degree of brevity and consistency both weight changes and linear growth: Age A (8-36 h.; nearly all Age A birds were 24-30 h.), Age B (37-48 h.), Age C (49-72 h.), Age D (73-96 h.).

Merged in a single sample for the analysis of each parameter measured were all wild-caught downies, all those hatched from wild-gathered eggs, and all those from captive flocks of essentially local origin, e.g., those at the Delta Waterfowl and Wetlands Research Station and the Round Lake Waterfowl Station. Following the sample number, in parentheses, is the number of broods or partial broods from which the sample was drawn. However, individuals of a single species originating in widely-separated geographical areas, those known or believed to be distinct races or subspecies, and those from flocks long-held in captivity were tabulated separately. Minimum geographical origin data appear below the species name in Table 1; more detailed information follows each species account in the section, Source of Specimens.

Appendix A
Table 1
Weights and Measurements of Downy Waterfowl

Species Origin	Age	Parameter	Sample (broods)	Range	Mean	S.D.	S.E.
	Tribe Dendrocygnini						
Dendrocygna bicolor							
Captive	A	WT[a]	24	24.30 - 33.40	27.80	2.29	0.47
RLWS		EC	27 (6)	13.00 - 15.00	13.90	0.53	0.10
WT(S)		TMT	4 (1)	18.00 - 21.00	20.00	1.35	0.68
		LTMT	27 (6)	21.00 - 25.00	23.20	0.86	0.17
		IIIw	"	26.00 - 29.50	27.90	0.84	0.16
	B	WT	6 (1)	23.50 - 31.00	27.20	3.75	1.53
		EC	7 (2)	14.50 - 18.50	16.80	1.22	0.46
		TMT	6 (1)	21.00 - 24.00	22.20	1.08	0.44
		LTMT	7 (2)	23.00 - 28.00	26.00	1.61	0.61
		IIIw	"	28.00 - 31.50	29.80	1.25	0.47
All locations	A & B	Iw/TMT	10 (2)	0.37 - 0.50	0.43	0.040	0.010
D. arborea							
Captive	A	WT[a]	12	31.80 - 37.20	34.50	1.97	0.57
RLWS		EC	6 (1)	14.50 - 16.00	15.30	0.52	0.20
		LTMT	"	26.00 - 28.00	27.50	0.84	0.34
		IIIw	"	28.50 - 31.00	29.90	0.80	0.33
D. autumnalis fulgens							
Texas	A	WT	13 (2)	20.40 - 28.50	23.30	2.18	0.61
		EC	16 (3)	13.00 - 16.80	14.70	1.13	0.28
		TMT	20 (3)	19.80 - 22.50	21.10	0.77	0.17
		LTMT	21 (3)	22.00 - 25.90	23.90	1.06	0.23
		IIIw	16 (3)	25.00 - 29.40	27.30	1.24	0.31
		Iw/TMT	14 (2)	0.39 - 0.61	0.54	0.060	0.020
	Tribe Cygnini						
Cygnus olor							
Michigan	A	WT	6 (2)	205.00 -218.60	210.80	4.75	1.94
Rhode Island		EC	"	23.00 - 25.30	23.90	0.93	0.38
		TMT	"	35.40 - 38.00	36.70	1.08	0.44
		LTMT	"	41.00 - 44.80	43.10	1.58	0.65
		IIIw	"	43.10 - 49.00	45.40	2.04	0.83
All locations		Iw/TMT	"	0.26 - 0.36	0.30	0.035	0.014
		TMT/IIIw	"	0.77 - 0.84	0.80	0.026	0.011
		DT/Iw	"	0.71 - 1.04	0.90	0.120	0.049

[a]Weights of unsexed, day-old captives at Round Lake Waterfowl Station, Round Lake, Minnesota, from Smart (1965:645-48). Reprinted, by permission of the editor, *The Auk*.

Appendix A

Species Origin	Age	Parameter	Sample (broods)	Range	Mean	S.D.	S.E.
Olor c. columbianus							
Alaska	A	WT[a]	8	170.60 -189.30	179.20	6.51	2.30
		EC	5 (1)	18.00 - 21.50	20.30	1.40	0.62
		LTMT	"	43.00 - 47.00	44.80	1.79	0.80
		IIIw	"	43.50 - 45.50	44.80	0.97	0.44
	B	EC	3 (1)	21.30 - 23.50	22.10	1.22	0.70
		LTMT	"	43.00 - 45.00	44.30	1.15	0.67
		IIIw	"	46.00 - 46.00	46.00	—	—
	A & B	DT/Iw	8 (2)	1.21 - 1.50	1.34	0.127	0.045
O. buccinator							
Captive	A	WT	2 (1)	205.00 -215.00	210.00	—	—
(British Columbia)		EC	"	18.50 - 20.50	19.50	—	—
WT(S)		TMT	"	27.50 - 33.00	30.20	—	—
		LTMT	"	36.00 - 39.00	37.50	—	—
		IIIw	"	40.00 - 41.00	40.50	—	—
Captive	A	WT	1	— - —	215.60	—	—
(Montana)		EC	"	— - —	22.70	—	—
DWWRS		TMT	"	— - —	32.10	—	—
		LTMT	"	— - —	42.00	—	—
		IIIw	"	— - —	42.00	—	—
	B	WT	1	— - —	205.40	—	—
		EC	"	— - —	23.00	—	—
		TMT	"	— - —	40.00	—	—
		LTMT	"	— - —	48.00	—	—
		IIIw	"	— - —	47.00	—	—
All locations	A & B	Iw/TMT	4 (2)	0.24 - 0.29	0.26	0.022	0.011
		TMT/IIIw	"	0.69 - 0.85	0.77	0.067	0.034
		DT/Iw	"	1.10 - 1.42	1.26	0.132	0.066
	Tribe Anserini						
Anser albifrons							
Captive *frontalis* WT(S)	A	WT[b]	5	87.50 - 98.50	93.50	4.73	2.12
Alaska	C	EC	2 (1)	15.50 - 16.50	16.00	—	—
Bethel		TMT	"	36.00 - 36.00	36.00	—	—
		LTMT	"	40.00 - 41.50	40.70	—	—
		IIIw	"	36.00 - 36.00	36.00	—	—

[b]Weights of unsexed, day-old captives at the Wildfowl Trust, Slimbridge, Gloucestershire (data from Janet Kear *in* letters to the author, 1966-67).

Appendix A

Species Origin	Age	Parameter	Sample (broods)	Range	Mean	S.D.	S.E.
Captive *flavirostris*							
(Greenland)	A	EC	1	— - —	14.50	—	—
WT(S)		TMT	"	— - —	29.00	—	—
		LTMT	"	— - —	32.00	—	—
		IIIw	"	— - —	30.00	—	—
All locations		TMT/IIIw	3 (2)	0.97 - 1.00	0.99	0.020	0.011
(all ages; 2 subspp.)		DT/Iw	"	0.48 - 0.73	0.57	0.138	0.080
A. caerulescens							
Captive *caerulescens*							
JPWT	A	WT[a]	10[c]	61.40 - 95.00	79.30	11.37	3.60
RLWS			19[d]	71.90 - 96.70	85.80	2.09	0.48
WT(S)		EC	26 (6)	15.00 - 20.00	17.30	1.11	0.22
		LTMT	"	32.00 - 43.00	38.00	2.96	0.58
		IIIw	"	31.00 - 40.00	35.00	1.98	0.39
	B	EC	10 (5)	15.50 - 19.50	17.50	1.24	0.39
		TMT	8 (4)	32.00 - 38.50	34.00	2.03	0.72
		LTMT	10 (5)	37.50 - 40.00	39.40	2.42	0.76
		IIIw	"	28.00 - 35.00	32.00	1.93	0.61
Captive *atlanticus*							
JPWT	A	WT[b]	22	62.50 - 92.00	79.84	6.82	1.45
PWPS		EC	1	— - —	17.50	—	—
WT(S)		TMT	"	— - —	32.50	—	—
		LTMT	"	— - —	36.00	—	—
		IIIw	"	— - —	32.10	—	—
	B	EC	4 (1)	19.00 - 19.50	19.10	0.25	0.13
		TMT	"	33.00 - 36.00	34.20	1.50	0.75
		LTMT	"	37.00 - 41.00	38.90	1.93	0.97
		IIIw	"	30.00 - 35.00	32.20	2.06	1.03
	C	EC	7 (2)	19.00 - 20.00	19.40	0.46	0.17
		TMT	2 (1)	35.00 - 39.00	37.00	—	—
		LTMT	7 (2)	41.00 - 45.00	42.20	1.44	0.54
		IIIw	2 (1)	32.00 - 36.00	34.00	—	—
All locations		TMT/IIIw	15	1.00 - 1.18	1.07	0.048	0.012
(all ages; 2 subspp.)		DT/Iw	35	0.65 - 1.07	0.80	0.092	0.015

[c]Class 0.
[d]Class 4.

Appendix A

Species Origin	Age	Parameter	Sample (broods)	Range	Mean	S.D.	S.E.
A. rossii							
Northwest	A	EC[e]	4 (2)	14.80 - 15.60	15.30	0.39	0.20
Territories		LTMT[e]	"	35.40 - 38.10	37.00	1.22	0.61
		IIIwo[e]	"	24.40 - 26.20	25.00	0.85	0.42
Captive		WT	5 (2)	50.00 - 65.50	59.30	5.93	2.65
(Northwest		EC	11 (4)	13.50 - 15.50	14.20	0.56	0.17
Territories)		TMT	"	26.00 - 33.00	29.90	1.76	0.53
JPWT		LTMT	"	31.00 - 39.00	34.60	2.22	0.67
WT(S)		IIIw	"	25.80 - 29.00	27.40	1.10	0.33
	B	EC	2 (1)	14.50 - 14.50	14.50	—	—
		TMT	"	35.00 - 35.00	35.00	—	—
		LTMT	"	40.00 - 40.00	40.00	—	—
		IIIw	"	28.50 - 29.00	28.70	—	—
All locations	A & B	TMT/IIIw	14	0.96 - 1.23	1.11	0.065	0.017
		DT/Iw	"	0.72 - 1.05	0.83	0.096	0.026
Philacte canagica							
Alaska	A	WT[f]	30	62.00 -128.00	80.00	—	—
Captive		EC	4 (2)	10.50 - 12.00	11.20	0.87	0.43
(Alaska)		LTMT	"	31.00 - 35.00	33.20	2.06	1.03
JPWT		IIIw	"	32.00 - 34.00	33.20	0.96	0.48
RLWS	B	EC	2 (1)	12.50 - 13.00	12.70	—	—
		TMT	"	31.00 - 32.00	31.50	—	—
		LTMT	"	36.00 - 38.00	37.00	—	—
		IIIw	"	31.50 - 32.50	32.00	—	—
	C	EC	3 (1)	12.80 - 13.50	13.10	0.36	0.21
		TMT	"	29.00 - 33.00	31.30	2.08	1.20
		LTMT	"	36.00 - 38.00	37.30	1.15	0.67
		IIIw	"	31.50 - 33.50	32.30	1.04	0.60
All locations	A & B	TMT/IIIw	5	0.92 - 1.03	0.97	0.041	0.018
		DT/Iw	"	0.72 - 0.87	0.78	0.067	0.030
Branta bernicla							
Alaska *nigricans*	A	WT[a]	24	45.10 - 65.60	54.70	4.72	0.96
Kokechik Bay		EC	18 (5)	10.00 - 12.00	11.10	0.56	0.13
		LT	"	30.00 - 34.00	36.60	1.11	0.26
		IIIw	"	26.50 - 33.00	29.60	1.59	0.38
	B	EC	6 (3)	10.50 - 11.00	10.70	0.26	0.11
		LTMT	"	31.00 - 35.00	33.00	1.38	0.56
		IIIw	"	26.00 - 30.00	28.20	1.33	0.54

[e]Weights and measurements of unsexed, day-old goslings wild-caught at Arlone Lake, NWT (data from John P. Ryder *in* letter to the author, July 1964).

[f]Weights of Class Ia goslings, both sexes, wild-caught in Alaska from Eisenhauer (unpubl.). Reprinted by permission of Purdue Research Foundation.

Appendix A

Species Origin	Age	Parameter	Sample (broods)	Range	Mean	S.D.	S.E.
B. bernicla, cont.							
Captive *nigricans*	A	WT	4 (3)	60.00 - 65.00	63.00	2.16	1.08
WT(S)		EC	5 (3)	9.50 - 11.00	10.50	0.71	0.32
		TMT	"	25.00 - 27.50	26.50	1.00	0.45
		LTMT	"	29.00 - 32.00	30.50	1.12	0.50
		IIIw	"	26.00 - 28.50	27.60	1.08	0.48
Captive *hrota*	A	WT	2 (1)	58.60 - 63.60	61.00	—	—
(Northwest		EC	"	11.70 - 11.80	11.70	—	—
Territories		TMT	"	27.90 - 30.00	29.00	—	—
Southampton I.)		LTMT	"	33.20 - 36.00	34.60	—	—
PWPS		IIIw	"	27.90 - 30.10	29.00	—	—
All locations		TMT/IIIw	5	0.95 - 0.96	0.96	0.007	0.003
(all ages; 2 subspp.)		DT/Iw	29 (8)	0.76 - 1.17	0.93	0.090	0.017
B. leucopsis							
Captive	A	WT[a]	12	48.40 - 71.50	63.40	4.67	1.41
RLWS		EC	9 (3)	9.00 - 11.50	10.70	0.87	0.29
		LTMT	"	30.00 - 37.00	33.90	2.76	0.92
		IIIw	"	28.80 - 34.00	31.50	1.42	0.47
		DT/Iw	7	0.83 - 1.00	0.94	0.068	0.026
B. canadensis							
British Columbia	A	WT	3 (1)	89.30 -100.50	96.10	5.97	3.45
Vancouver I.		EC	"	15.00 - 16.00	15.50	0.50	0.29
fulva		TMT	"	33.90 - 34.50	34.10	0.32	0.19
		LTMT	"	37.50 - 39.00	38.40	0.81	0.47
		IIIw	"	34.00 - 36.00	35.30	1.15	0.67
Manitoba							
Churchill	A	WT	7 (2)	77.10 -112.00	92.50	12.64	4.78
interior		EC	"	16.00 - 18.00	17.10	0.63	0.24
		TMT	"	31.00 - 35.50	33.40	1.51	0.57
		LTMT	"	38.00 - 40.20	38.70	1.00	0.38
		IIIw	"	32.60 - 36.00	34.00	1.10	0.42
Delta	A	WT	2 (1)	121.60 -121.60	121.60	—	—
maxima		EC	"	17.50 - 18.00	17.70	—	—
		TMT	"	31.00 - 33.00	32.00	—	—
		LTMT	"	36.00 - 38.00	37.00	—	—
		IIIw	"	35.00 - 35.00	35.00	—	—
Northern	D	EC	5	17.80 - 19.60	18.50	0.68	0.31
Indian Lake		TMT	"	34.10 - 36.20	35.20	0.76	0.34
maxima?		LTMT	"	39.60 - 43.20	41.10	1.33	0.59
		IIIw	"	32.90 - 36.10	34.10	1.30	0.58

Appendix A

Species Origin	Age	Parameter	Sample (broods)	Range	Mean	S.D.	S.E.
B. canadensis, cont.							
Newfoundland	A	WT	2 (1)	104.60 -117.60	111.10	—	—
canadensis		EC	"	14.10 - 15.50	14.70	—	—
		TMT	"	31.00 - 35.00	33.00	—	—
		LTMT	"	37.00 - 41.00	39.00	—	—
		IIIw	"	36.00 - 38.00	37.00	—	—
Northwest Territories							
McConnell R.	A	WT	3 (1)	65.80 - 72.10	68.00	3.55	2.05
parvipes		EC	"	14.70 - 15.50	15.20	0.46	0.27
(NPRC)		TMT	"	30.70 - 31.10	30.90	0.20	0.12
		LTMT	"	35.80 - 36.10	36.00	0.15	0.09
		IIIw	"	30.00 - 31.80	30.90	0.90	0.52
Alaska							
Buldir I.	A	WT	3 (1)	68.80 - 80.20	74.40	5.70	3.29
leucopareia		EC	"	13.50 - 14.90	14.30	0.72	0.42
(CESJ)		TMT	"	32.00 - 33.50	32.80	0.76	0.44
		LTMT	"	36.00 - 38.00	37.20	1.04	0.60
		IIIw	"	31.50 - 34.30	32.80	1.40	0.81
Cordova	C	WT	3 (1)	88.40 -100.90	94.10	6.33	3.66
occidentalis		EC	"	15.70 - 16.60	16.10	0.46	0.26
		TMT	"	33.50 - 34.00	33.80	0.25	0.15
		LTMT	"	39.10 - 40.90	40.00	0.90	0.52
		IIIw	"	33.10 - 33.80	33.50	0.38	0.22
Kokechik Bay	A	WT[a]	23	54.50 - 73.50	67.60	5.60	1.17
minima	(WT sample includes 17 of captive *minima* listed below)						
		EC	2 (1)	10.80 - 11.50	11.10	—	—
		LTMT	"	32.50 - 34.00	33.20	—	—
		IIIw	"	29.00 - 30.00	29.50	—	—
Colorado	A	WT	5 (1)	103.60 - 115.40	109.40	4.46	1.99
Little Snake R.		EC	"	16.00 - 17.80	17.10	0.72	0.32
moffitti		TMT	"	33.70 - 36.10	34.80	0.88	0.39
		LTMT	"	39.50 - 42.50	40.50	1.19	0.53
		IIIw	"	33.50 - 35.80	34.50	0.94	0.42
Montana	A	WT	5 (1)	90.80 - 99.30	95.60	3.62	1.62
Yellowstone R.		EC	3 (1)	14.50 - 16.20	15.60	0.99	0.57
maxima		TMT	5 (1)	32.20 - 33.80	33.10	0.66	0.30
		LTMT	"	37.00 - 40.50	38.80	1.24	0.56
		IIIw	"	32.20 - 34.50	33.50	0.92	0.41

Appendix A

Species Origin	Age	Parameter	Sample (broods)	Range	Mean	S.D.	S.E.
B. canadenis, cont.							
Captive							
occidentalis	A	WT[b]	6	78.00 - 97.50	86.80	8.86	3.62
(British Columbia:		EC	6 (1)	13.00 - 15.00	14.00	0.71	0.29
Prince Rupert)		TMT	"	30.00 - 34.00	32.40	1.36	0.55
JPWT		LTMT	"	35.00 - 39.00	37.50	1.38	0.56
WT(S)		IIIw	"	29.50 - 34.50	33.10	1.83	0.75
maxima	A	WT	11 (3)	101.60 -124.80	113.10	8.95	2.70
(Manitoba		EC	52 (15)	12.50 - 19.00	16.70	1.08	0.15
Saskatchewan		TMT	11 (3)	32.10 - 37.50	35.30	1.62	0.49
Minnesota)		LTMT	52 (15)	35.00 - 43.00	39.10	1.60	0.22
DWWRS		IIIw	"	32.20 - 40.00	35.60	1.86	0.26
RLWS							
hutchinsii	A	WT	2 (1)	64.40 - 75.40	69.90	—	—
(Northwest		EC	"	14.30 - 16.00	15.50	—	—
Territories:		TMT	"	27.90 - 33.20	30.50	—	—
Baffin I.)		LTMT	"	32.20 - 38.60	35.40	—	—
CESJ		IIIw	"	28.20 - 31.80	30.00	—	—
taverneri	A	WT[b]	6	68.50 - 81.50	76.50	5.50	2.25
(W. Alaska)		EC	6 (1)	13.70 - 14.50	14.20	0.41	0.17
JPWT		TMT	"	31.00 - 35.00	32.60	1.32	0.54
WT(S)		LTMT	"	35.00 - 38.00	37.10	1.11	0.46
		IIIw	"	32.00 - 35.00	33.20	1.08	0.44
minima	A	EC	21 (6)	10.50 - 13.00	11.60	0.74	0.16
JPWT		TMT	4 (2)	26.00 - 32.00	29.10	2.46	1.23
RLWS		LTMT	21 (6)	30.00 - 35.00	33.60	1.32	0.29
		IIIw	"	27.00 - 34.00	31.50	2.74	0.60
All locations		TMT/IIIw	64	0.79 - 1.11	0.99	0.047	0.006
(all ages; 9 subspp.)		DT/Iw	96	0.62 - 1.09	0.85	0.122	0.012
Nesochen sandvicensis							
Captive							
Slimbridge	A	WT[g]	310	63.50 -115.50	93.60	—	0.54
(Hawaiian Is.)			87	90.60 -114.40	101.90	—	—
Pohakuloa		EC	3 (2)	15.00 - 15.50	15.20	0.29	0.17
JPWT		TMT	"	32.00 - 34.00	33.30	1.15	0.67
WT(S)		LTMT	"	37.00 - 41.00	39.00	2.00	1.15
		IIIw	"	35.00 - 36.00	35.70	0.58	0.33
	B	EC	2 (2)	14.50 - 14.50	14.50	—	—
		TMT	"	29.00 - 37.00	33.00	—	—
		LTMT	"	33.00 - 41.00	37.00	—	—
		IIIw	"	33.00 - 35.50	34.20	—	—

[g]Weights of unsexed, day-old goslings wild-caught at Pohakuloa, Hawaiian Islands, and of unsexed, day-old captives at the Wildfowl Trust, Slimbridge, Gloucestershire, from Kear and Berger (1980). Reprinted by permission of T. and A. D. Poyser, Ltd.

Appendix A

Species Origin	Age	Parameter	Sample (broods)	Range	Mean	S.D.	S.E.
N. sandvicensis, cont.							
All locations	A & B	TMT/IIIw	5	0.88 - 1.04	0.94	0.067	0.030
		DT/Iw	"	0.90 - 1.00	0.89	0.077	0.034
	Tribe Cairinini						
Cairina moschata							
Captive	A	WT	2 (1)	42.30 - 42.70	42.50	—	—
(Brazil)		EC	"	12.80 - 14.10	13.40	—	—
WT(S)		TMT	"	22.00 - 23.00	22.50	—	—
		LTMT	"	25.80 - 27.00	26.40	—	—
		IIIw	"	28.30 - 28.30	28.30	—	—
	B	WT	9 (1)	32.80 - 46.60	39.00	4.27	1.42
		EC	"	12.60 - 14.70	13.90	0.76	0.25
		TMT	"	20.50 - 23.50	22.00	0.88	0.29
		LTMT	"	24.30 - 28.40	26.00	1.15	0.38
		IIIw	"	26.00 - 29.30	27.30	0.94	0.31
Aix sponsa							
Illinois	A	WT	32 (4)	18.00 - 24.50	22.10	1.44	0.26
Minnesota		EC	45 (6)	10.10 - 12.60	11.30	0.57	0.09
Ohio		TMT	32 (4)	17.10 - 19.90	18.80	0.81	0.14
Vermont		LTMT	45 (6)	19.00 - 24.00	21.50	1.13	0.17
		IIIw	"	21.90 - 26.50	24.40	0.92	0.14
	B	WT	6 (1)	22.70 - 26.80	23.60	1.61	0.66
		EC	13 (3)	10.00 - 12.70	11.50	0.75	0.21
		TMT	7 (2)	18.30 - 20.10	19.50	0.62	0.23
		LTMT	13 (3)	18.50 - 23.10	21.00	1.72	0.48
		IIIw	"	24.00 - 27.90	25.50	0.94	0.26
Captive	A	WT	13 (2)	22.00 - 26.30	24.50	1.16	0.29
JPWT		EC	15 (3)	9.50 - 11.00	10.10	0.41	0.11
WT(S)		TMT	"	17.00 - 20.00	18.50	0.77	0.20
		LTMT	"	20.00 - 23.00	21.40	1.02	0.26
		IIIw	"	22.00 - 24.00	22.90	0.64	0.16
	Tribe Anatini						
Mareca americana							
Manitoba	A	WT[a]	2	24.80 - 26.90	25.90	—	—
Minnesota		EC	12 (3)	11.10 - 13.50	12.40	0.68	0.20
		TMT	6 (1)	22.00 - 23.50	22.80	0.53	0.22
		LTMT	15 (3)	21.00 - 26.50	24.10	1.70	0.44
		IIIw	9 (2)	25.50 - 31.00	28.60	1.62	0.54

Appendix A

Species Origin	Age	Parameter	Sample (broods)	Range	Mean	S.D.	S.E.
M. americana, cont.							
	B	WT	2 (1)	16.90 - 17.00	16.90	—	—
		EC	"	13.80 - 14.30	14.00	—	—
		TMT	"	19.10 - 19.80	19.40	—	—
		LTMT	"	22.50 - 23.80	23.10	—	—
		IIIw	"	22.80 - 23.80	23.30	—	—
Captive	A	WT	4 (1)	22.00 - 25.00	23.10	1.35	0.68
WT(S)		EC	"	11.00 - 12.30	11.60	0.54	0.27
		TMT	"	19.00 - 20.00	19.50	0.41	0.20
		LTMT	"	22.00 - 23.00	22.70	0.50	0.25
		IIIw	"	24.00 - 27.00	25.20	1.26	0.63
	B	WT	6 (1)	24.00 - 26.80	25.60	1.11	0.46
		EC	"	10.90 - 12.50	12.10	0.63	0.26
		TMT	"	21.50 - 22.50	22.00	0.45	0.18
		LTMT	"	24.00 - 27.00	25.80	1.29	0.53
		IIIw	"	26.00 - 27.50	26.80	0.57	0.23
All locations	A & B	EC/OBT	24 (5)	0.26 - 0.31	0.28	0.013	0.003
		TMT/IIIw	10 (2)	0.70 - 0.86	0.80	0.043	0.014
Anas strepera							
Manitoba	A	WT	26 (4)	24.90 - 32.20	29.00	1.93	0.38
Minnesota		EC	46 (9)	11.50 - 15.10	13.30	0.88	0.13
Nebraska		TM	59 (10)	20.00 - 25.00	21.90	0.90	0.12
		LTM	59 (11)	21.00 - 26.70	24.60	1.14	0.15
		IIIw	43 (9)	23.50 - 29.00	26.20	1.32	0.20
	B	WT	7 (1)	23.80 - 31.00	26.80	3.26	1.23
		EC	"	13.50 - 14.70	14.20	0.43	0.16
		TMT	"	21.40 - 23.00	22.30	0.57	0.21
		LTMT	"	24.80 - 26.10	25.40	0.52	0.20
		IIIw	"	25.00 - 27.40	25.70	0.89	0.34
All locations	A & B	EC/OBT	48 (9)	0.26 - 0.33	0.30	0.020	0.003
A. crecca carolinensis							
Manitoba	A	WT	5 (1)	14.60 - 16.00	15.10	0.64	0.29
Minnesota		EC	14 (4)	10.80 - 12.30	11.50	0.49	0.13
		TMT	23 (5)	16.60 - 19.50	18.00	0.70	0.15
		LTMT	31 (7)	18.00 - 22.50	20.00	1.06	0.19
		IIIw	14 (4)	19.40 - 24.00	21.20	1.41	0.38
	B	EC	3 (2)	11.00 - 11.50	11.30	0.29	0.17
		LTMT	"	19.00 - 20.50	19.80	0.76	0.44
		IIIw	"	22.00 - 24.00	23.00	1.00	0.58

Appendix A

Species Origin	Age	Parameter	Sample (broods)	Range	Mean	S.D.	S.E.
A. acuta							
Manitoba	A	WT	23 (4)	19.20 - 26.40	24.10	1.76	0.37
Minnesota		E	46 (12)	12.00 - 15.50	13.70	0.74	0.11
		TMT	29 (5)	19.00 - 24.00	21.50	1.18	0.22
		LTM	52 (14)	20.00 - 28.50	24.00	1.72	0.24
		III	47 (13)	22.00 - 29.00	25.40	1.51	0.22
A. fulvigula							
Captive *fulvigula*	A	WT	6 (2)	23.80 - 30.80	27.50	2.40	0.98
(Florida)		EC	"	13.60 - 15.10	14.40	0.60	0.24
DWWRS		TMT	5 (2)	20.80 - 21.70	21.40	0.37	0.17
		IIIw	6 (2)	23.80 - 26.20	24.90	1.10	0.45
Captive *maculosa*							
(Louisiana)	A	WT	4 (1)	26.50 - 32.00	29.40	2.32	1.16
RNWR		EC	24 (4)	12.90 - 15.40	13.80	0.60	0.12
RLWS		TMT	4 (1)	19.80 - 22.40	20.70	1.19	0.59
		LTMT	24 (4)	21.00 - 27.00	23.50	1.39	0.28
		IIIw	"	23.00 - 28.00	25.50	1.36	0.28
A. rubripes							
Québec	A	WT	4 (1)	29.20 - 36.00	33.20	3.07	1.77
		EC	6 (2)	14.00 - 16.30	15.10	0.87	0.39
		TMT	"	23.50 - 28.50	26.40	2.13	0.95
		LTMT	2 (1)	26.00 - 26.00	26.00	—	—
		IIIw	6 (2)	27.30 - 29.50	28.50	1.04	0.47
Captive		EC	21 (3)	12.50 - 16.50	14.30	1.02	0.22
JPWT		TMT	4 (1)	21.00 - 22.00	21.40	0.48	0.24
RLWS		LTMT	21 (3)	23.00 - 27.00	24.50	1.01	0.22
		IIIw	"	25.00 - 30.00	26.90	1.12	0.24
A. diazi							
Captive							
WT(S)	A	WT[b]	2	27.50 - 30.00	28.70	—	—
(New Mexico)	C	E	3 (1)	18.00 - 19.30	18.60	0.66	0.38
CESJ		TMT	"	23.50 - 24.00	23.70	0.25	0.15
		LTMT	"	27.00 - 28.00	27.60	0.55	0.32
		IIIw	"	27.50 - 28.00	27.80	0.29	0.17
A. p. platyrhynchos							
Alberta	A	WT	27 (5)	27.20 - 40.60	31.80	3.44	0.66
Manitoba		E	45 (14)	12.80 - 16.80	14.40	0.90	0.13
Minnesota		TMT	33 (9)	19.50 - 24.00	22.00	0.98	0.17
		LTM	45 (14)	22.00 - 27.60	25.00	1.20	0.18
		III	46 (15)	25.00 - 29.10	26.90	1.13	0.17

Appendix A

Species Origin	Age	Parameter	Sample (broods)	Range	Mean	S.D.	S.E.
A. p. platyrhynchos, cont.							
	B	EC	2 (1)	14.50 - 15.50	15.00	—	—
		LTMT	"	24.00 - 26.00	25.00	—	—
		IIIw	"	29.00 - 30.00	29.50	—	—
All locations	A & B	EC/OBT	47 (15)	0.28 - 0.38	0.31	0.017	0.002
A. laysanensis							
Captive	A	WT	2 (1)	28.60 - 28.60	28.60	—	—
(Laysan Island)		EC	"	13.20 - 14.20	13.70	—	—
NPRC		TMT	"	17.60 - 19.50	18.50	—	—
		LTMT	"	20.40 - 22.30	21.30	—	—
		IIIw	"	23.20 - 26.00	24.60	—	—
A. d. discors							
Manitoba	A	WT	22 (3)	15.30 - 18.20	17.30	0.77	0.16
Minnesota		E	45 (12)	10.00 - 14.70	12.20	0.98	0.15
		TMT	16 (4)	17.00 - 19.60	18.30	0.67	0.17
		LTMT	39 (13)	15.50 - 22.80	19.30	1.90	0.30
		IIIw	32 (12)	18.50 - 25.00	21.30	1.16	0.20
	B	EC	11 (5)	11.00 - 13.00	11.90	0.73	0.22
		LTMT	"	17.00 - 21.00	19.40	1.38	0.42
		IIIw	"	21.00 - 23.00	21.90	0.58	0.18
All locations	A & B	EC/OBT	55 (12)	0.27 - 0.39	0.31	0.020	0.003
A. cyanoptera septentrionalium							
Utah	A	WT	19 (4)	13.80 - 19.60	17.40	1.76	0.40
		EC	"	11.60 - 14.20	13.10	0.65	0.15
		TMT	"	16.10 - 19.10	17.50	0.79	0.18
		LTMT	"	18.50 - 21.90	20.30	0.96	0.22
		IIIw	"	19.30 - 23.90	21.40	1.27	0.29
	B	WT	6 (1)	16.40 - 19.40	18.10	0.97	0.40
		EC	7 (1)	11.40 - 14.60	13.70	1.05	0.40
		TMT	"	16.30 - 19.50	18.40	1.02	0.38
		LTMT	"	19.00 - 22.10	21.20	1.07	0.40
		IIIw	"	19.00 - 23.90	21.80	1.63	0.62
Captive	A	EC	5 (2)	11.50 - 12.80	11.80	0.58	0.26
(Utah)		LTMT	"	16.50 - 19.80	17.50	1.33	0.59
DWWRS		IIIw	"	20.50 - 23.00	21.30	0.97	0.44
All locations	A & B	EC/OBT	31 (6)	0.28 - 0.36	0.33	0.021	0.004
A. clypeata							
Manitoba	A	WT	11 (2)	21.40 - 25.60	23.20	1.35	0.41
Minnesota		EC	42 (10)	13.50 - 18.00	15.40	1.08	0.17
		TMT	27 (6)	18.10 - 22.50	20.70	1.27	0.24
		LTM	47 (12)	19.00 - 26.00	23.00	1.67	0.24
		III	39 (11)	21.00 - 30.00	25.00	2.22	0.36
All locations		EC/OB	45 (10)	0.31 - 0.41	0.35	0.020	0.004

Appendix A

Species Origin	Age	Parameter	Sample (broods)	Range	Mean	S.D.	S.E.
A. clypeata, cont.							
Manitoba	B	TMT	5 (1)	21.00 - 22.00	21.50	0.50	0.22
		LTMT	"	23.50 - 25.50	24.40	0.82	0.37
	Tribe Aythyini						
Aythya valisineria							
Manitoba	A	WT	8 (4)	34.00 - 40.40	38.80	2.08	0.73
		EC	17 (9)	15.50 - 19.20	17.20	0.99	0.24
		TMT	25 (8)	21.00 - 23.50	22.00	0.57	0.11
		LTM	26 (11)	22.00 - 27.00	25.50	1.07	0.21
		IIIw	17 (9)	27.20 - 35.00	31.00	1.93	0.47
	B	EC	12 (3)	15.80 - 18.30	17.10	0.73	0.21
		TMT	5 (1)	22.20 - 23.30	22.60	0.50	0.22
		LTMT	12 (3)	21.50 - 27.30	25.60	2.01	0.58
		IIIw	"	29.00 - 33.00	31.20	1.17	0.34
Captive	B	EC	3 (1)	18.50 - 20.00	19.20	0.76	0.44
(Manitoba)		TMT	"	21.00 - 22.50	21.50	0.87	0.50
JPWT		LTMT	"	24.00 - 26.00	25.20	1.04	0.60
		IIIw	"	30.00 - 31.00	30.70	0.58	0.33
All locations	A & B	TMT/IIIw	21 (7)	0.66 - 0.80	0.702	0.031	0.007
A. americana							
Manitoba	A	WT	14 (5)	32.50 - 38.40	35.10	2.54	0.68
Minnesota		EC	42 (14)	13.00 - 15.20	14.00	0.55	0.08
North Dakota		TMT	17 (7)	19.20 - 23.20	20.70	0.88	0.21
		LTMT	42 (16)	21.00 - 27.00	23.50	1.41	0.22
		IIIw	38 (14)	26.30 - 34.00	30.60	2.05	0.33
	B	WT	3 (1)	34.80 - 38.90	36.70	2.07	1.19
		EC	12 (4)	14.00 - 16.60	15.10	0.79	0.23
		TMT	3 (1)	21.20 - 22.50	21.90	0.66	0.38
		LTMT	12 (4)	22.00 - 26.80	24.10	1.36	0.39
		IIIw	"	28.60 - 33.00	30.00	1.12	0.32
All locations	A & B	TMT/IIIw	13 (6)	0.64 - 0.77	0.73	0.031	0.009
A. collaris							
Manitoba	A	WT	6 (1)	28.40 - 31.00	29.30	0.92	0.38
Ontario		EC	16 (3)	13.80 - 15.50	14.70	0.48	0.12
		TMT	25 (4)	19.00 - 20.50	19.90	0.38	0.08
		LTMT	19 (3)	22.00 - 23.50	22.60	0.36	0.08
		IIIw	16 (3)	26.50 - 29.80	28.30	0.91	0.23
All locations	A & B	TMT/IIIw	16 (3)	0.67 - 0.74	0.70	0.021	0.005

Appendix A

Species Origin	Age	Parameter	Sample (broods)	Range	Mean	S.D.	S.E.
A. marila nearctica							
Manitoba	A	WT	25 (3)	33.00 - 44.20	39.90	2.40	0.48
		EC	"	14.20 - 16.80	15.50	0.72	0.14
		TMT	"	21.30 - 23.50	22.50	0.55	0.11
		LTMT	"	25.20 - 27.60	26.40	0.66	0.13
		IIIw	"	28.80 - 33.90	31.80	1.16	0.23
	B	EC	8 (1)	15.70 - 17.10	16.50	0.47	0.17
		TMT	"	22.20 - 23.70	23.10	0.52	0.18
		LTMT	"	26.80 - 28.40	27.50	0.56	0.20
		IIIw	"	30.30 - 32.70	32.00	0.76	0.27
All locations	A	TMT/IIIw	31	0.63 - 0.76	0.70	0.028	0.005
Manitoba	7d.	LNxWN/HBB	14	3.07 - 4.17	3.50	0.314	0.084
Northwest	14d.	"	"	2.88 - 4.37	3.42	0.490	0.131
Territories	21d.	"	13	2.85 - 4.26	3.37	0.446	0.124
Great Slave Lake	28d.	"	11	2.97 - 4.47	3.39	0.543	0.164
A. affinis							
Alberta	A	WT	51 (6)	26.00 - 34.20	29.80	1.55	0.22
Manitoba		E	75 (11)	11.50 - 15.20	13.70	0.74	0.09
		TMT	101 (14)	18.00 - 23.00	20.10	0.99	0.10
		LTMT	83 (12)	20.50 - 25.50	23.00	0.99	0.11
		IIIw	75 (11)	24.90 - 31.80	27.90	1.22	0.14
	B	WT	8 (1)	33.20 - 37.80	34.80	1.46	0.52
		EC	24 (5)	13.00 - 15.60	14.40	0.82	0.17
		TMT	16 (4)	18.50 - 21.20	19.80	0.64	0.16
		LTMT	"	21.20 - 25.00	23.20	0.91	0.23
		IIIw	15 (4)	26.00 - 29.30	27.60	0.88	0.23
All locations	A	TMT/IIIw	72	0.63 - 0.76	0.71	0.020	0.003
Manitoba	7d.	LNxWN/HBB	39	2.21 - 3.09	2.68	0.230	0.037
Saskatchewan	14 d.	"	42	2.09 - 3.40	2.69	0.262	0.040
	21d.	"	33	2.12 - 3.26	2.65	0.311	0.054
	28d.	"	28	2.35 - 3.46	2.67	0.296	0.056
Tribe Somateriini							
Somateria mollissima							
Manitoba *sedentaria*	A	WT	2 (1)	68.40 - 70.20	69.30	—	—
Churchill		EC	"	18.40 - 18.80	18.60	—	—
		TMT	"	27.00 - 27.80	27.40	—	—
		LTMT	"	32.50 - 33.20	32.80	—	—
		IIIw	"	32.80 - 33.70	33.20	—	—

Appendix A

Species Origin	Age	Parameter	Sample (broods)	Range	Mean	S.D.	S.E.
S. mollissima, cont.							
	B	WT	4 (1)	54.20 - 59.40	57.20	2.18	1.09
		EC	"	18.50 - 19.80	19.10	0.54	0.27
		TMT	"	27.20 - 28.30	27.50	0.52	0.26
		LTMT	"	32.00 - 33.80	32.80	0.74	0.37
		IIIw	"	31.70 - 34.30	33.20	1.20	0.60
Québec *dresseri*	A	WT	7 (2)	60.80 - 73.20	67.30	4.75	1.80
St. Lawrence R.		EC	10 (3)	15.80 - 18.30	17.20	0.96	0.30
		TMT	"	25.00 - 27.90	26.50	0.88	0.28
		LTMT	"	28.50 - 32.30	31.20	1.15	0.36
		IIIw	"	31.00 - 35.40	33.50	1.59	0.50
Captive *v-nigra*	A	WT[b]	3	47.00 - 57.50	49.70	2.36	1.36
WT(S)							
Alaska	D	EC	1 (1)	— - —	16.00	—	—
Kashunuk River		TMT	3 (1)	28.00 - 30.00	29.00	1.00	0.58
		LTMT	"	32.50 - 33.00	32.80	0.29	0.17
All locations	A & B	TMT/IIIw	17	0.76 - 0.87	0.80	0.033	0.008
(2 subspp.)							
S. spectabilis							
Captive	A	WT[h]	2	35.00 - 39.00	37.00	—	—
(Greenland;		EC	2 (1)	10.00 - 12.00	11.00	—	—
Iceland)		TM	"	21.00 - 23.50	22.20	—	—
WT(S)		LTMT	"	24.50 - 27.00	25.70	—	—
		IIIw	"	26.00 - 29.00	27.50	—	—
		TMT/IIIw	"	0.81 - 0.81	0.81	—	—
S. fischeri							
Alaska	A	WT[a]	4	44.80 - 49.00	46.20	—	—
Naskonat		EC	3 (2)	9.50 - 11.50	10.70	1.04	0.60
Peninsula		LTMT	"	27.00 - 30.00	28.30	1.53	0.88
		IIIw	"	29.00 - 32.00	31.00	1.73	1.00
	B	EC	3 (2)	11.00 - 11.50	11.30	0.29	0.17
		TMT	2 (1)	26.20 - 26.50	26.30	—	—
		LTMT	3 (2)	27.00 - 30.00	28.80	1.61	0.93
		IIIw	"	30.00 - 32.00	30.70	1.15	0.67
		TMT/IIIw	2 (1)	0.83 - 0.87	0.85	—	—

[h]Weights of Class 1a ducklings, both sexes, wild-caught on Victoria I., NWT, from tag data of UMFBP[DFP] uncat, coll. D. F. Parmelee.

Appendix A

Species Origin	Age	Parameter	Sample (broods)	Range	Mean	S.D.	S.E.
	Tribe Mergini						
H. histrionicus							
Iceland	A	WT[a]	4	29.10 - 36.70	33.80	—	—
		EC	3 (1)	9.80 - 10.50	10.10	0.36	0.21
		LTMT	"	23.00 - 25.00	24.00	1.00	0.58
		IIIw	"	25.00 - 27.00	26.20	1.04	0.60
Clangula hyemalis							
Manitoba	A	WT	3 (1)	20.40 - 22.20	21.10	0.99	0.57
Iceland		EC	5 (3)	9.20 - 11.00	9.70	0.77	0.34
		TMT	4 (2)	18.10 - 20.50	19.40	1.07	0.53
		LTMT	5 (3)	21.80 - 23.70	22.90	0.76	0.34
		IIIw	4 (3)	23.00 - 25.00	24.20	0.96	0.48
Manitoba	B	WT	2 (1)	21.20 - 23.60	22.40	—	—
		EC	"	10.40 - 10.90	10.60	—	—
		TMT	"	20.00 - 20.80	20.40	—	—
		LTMT	"	23.20 - 24.30	23.70	—	—
		IIIw	"	25.30 - 25.50	25.40	—	—
Melanitta n. nigra							
Iceland	A	WT[a]	1	— - —	43.20	—	—
		EC	"	— - —	14.00	—	—
		LTMT	"	— - —	28.00	—	—
		IIIw	"	— - —	29.00	—	—
M. fusca deglandi							
Alberta	A	WT	8 (1)	48.00 - 60.90	54.10	5.86	2.07
		EC	10 (2)	11.50 - 13.50	12.50	0.64	0.20
		TMT	15 (2)	23.50 - 26.50	25.20	1.12	0.29
		LTMT	"	27.70 - 31.30	29.50	0.99	0.25
		IIIw	10 (2)	29.60 - 35.10	32.20	1.86	0.59
	B	EC	5 (1)	12.00 - 14.20	13.00	0.79	0.35
		TMT	"	24.90 - 26.50	25.80	0.61	0.27
		LTMT	"	28.20 - 30.00	29.00	0.73	0.33
		IIIw	"	32.00 - 34.50	33.10	0.96	0.43
Bucephala islandica							
British Columbia	A	WT	32 (5)	32.40 - 43.20	37.90	2.77	0.49
		EC	21 (5)	10.80 - 13.10	12.10	0.61	0.13
		TMT	4 (2)	20.80 - 23.90	22.30	1.41	0.70
		LTMT	5 (3)	24.90 - 28.70	26.00	1.63	0.73
		IIIw	"	27.30 - 34.00	30.70	2.67	1.19
	B	WT	5 (1)	28.40 - 32.70	30.10	1.67	0.75
		EC	21 (3)	11.70 - 13.20	12.50	0.48	0.11
		TMT	5 (1)	22.00 - 23.50	22.90	0.67	0.30
		LTMT	"	6.50 - 27.20	26.90	0.34	0.15
		IIIw	"	30.50 - 32.20	31.50	0.72	0.32

Appendix A

Species Origin	Age	Parameter	Sample (broods)	Range	Mean	S.D.	S.E.
B. islandica, cont.							
	A & B	UB/EC	29	0.69 - 1.10	0.85	0.84	0.015
	1d.	LNxWN/WBPN	37 (5)	4.00 - 5.20	4.50	0.28	0.04
	7d.	"	23 (3)	3.70 - 5.00	4.30	0.34	0.07
	14d.	"	20 (3)	3.80 - 5.10	4.50	0.32	0.07
	21d.	"	12 (2)	4.40 - 5.60	4.80	0.39	0.11
	28d.	"	10 (2)	4.40 - 5.80	5.00	0.35	0.11
B. clangula americana							
Manitoba	A	WT	9 (2)	34.60 - 37.40	36.10	0.89	0.30
		EC	42 (9)	11.50 - 14.40	13.00	0.74	0.11
		TMT	18 (3)	20.70 - 22.20	21.70	0.42	0.10
		LTMT	31 (7)	21.00 - 26.10	24.60	1.14	0.21
		IIIw	27 (7)	28.80 - 34.00	30.90	1.58	0.30
	B	EC	18 (5)	13.20 - 15.00	14.10	0.56	0.13
		LTMT	3 (3)	25.00 - 26.80	25.60	1.04	0.60
		IIIw	"	31.50 - 34.00	33.20	1.44	0.83
	A & B	UB/EC	35	0.83 - 1.00	0.89	0.052	0.009
	1d.	LNxWN/WBPN	17 (3)	2.80 - 4.30	3.40	0.35	0.08
	7d.	"	9 (2)	2.50 - 3.40	3.00	0.33	0.11
	14d.	"	5 (2)	2.40 - 3.20	2.80	0.29	0.13
	21d.	"	1	— - —	3.00	—	—
	28d.	"	5 (1)	2.80 - 3.10	2.90	0.11	0.05
B. albeola							
Alberta	A	WT	8 (1)	20.30 - 24.00	22.10	1.24	0.44
		EC	"	10.10 - 11.70	10.70	0.51	0.18
		TMT	"	17.00 - 19.00	18.40	0.65	0.23
		LTMT	"	21.40 - 22.70	22.10	0.49	0.17
		IIIw	"	24.00 - 25.50	24.70	0.57	0.20
	B	WT	1	— - —	18.20	—	—
		EC	"	— - —	10.20	—	—
		TMT	3 (2)	17.50 - 18.50	18.10	0.51	0.30
		LTMT	"	19.80 - 21.60	20.80	0.92	0.53
		IIIw	1	— - —	23.50	—	—
	A & B	UB/EC	9 (3)	0.90 - 1.07	1.00	0.050	0.018
Lophodytes cucullatus							
Missouri	A	WT[a]	1	— - —	31.30	—	—
Vermont		EC	13 (2)	13.00 - 14.30	13.60	0.47	0.13
		LTMT	"	19.00 - 24.00	21.10	1.60	0.44
		IIIw	"	25.50 - 29.00	27.80	0.88	0.24

Appendix A

Species Origin	Age	Parameter	Sample (broods)	Range	Mean	S.D.	S.E.
L. cucullatus, cont.							
Vermont	B	EC	11 (1)	12.50 - 14.00	13.20	0.49	0.15
		TMT	"	17.00 - 19.50	18.40	0.79	0.24
		LTMT	"	20.50 - 23.00	22.00	0.84	0.25
		IIIw	"	27.00 - 29.50	28.10	0.74	0.22
Mergus s. serrator							
Manitoba	A	WT	5 (1)	44.00 - 47.60	46.00	1.36	0.61
		EC	8 (2)	15.50 - 16.60	16.20	0.38	0.13
		TMT	5 (1)	23.00 - 24.70	23.80	0.78	0.35
		LTMT	8 (2)	23.50 - 29.00	26.70	2.13	0.75
		IIIw	"	27.50 - 30.30	28.90	0.95	0.34
	B	WT	1 (1)	— - —	37.80	—	—
		EC	9 (2)	16.20 - 17.80	16.80	0.51	0.17
		TMT	1 (1)	— - —	21.20	—	—
		LTMT	9 (2)	25.20 - 28.50	27.10	1.14	0.38
		IIIw	"	29.20 - 31.00	30.20	0.55	0.18
M. merganser americanus							
Manitoba	A	WT	11 (3)	38.40 - 46.10	42.50	2.55	0.77
		EC	13 (4)	13.80 - 17.20	15.80	0.86	0.24
		TMT	11 (3)	23.00 - 25.80	24.40	0.77	0.23
		LTMT	13 (4)	25.00 - 29.70	28.10	1.22	0.34
		IIIw	"	28.30 - 34.00	31.80	1.74	0.48
	B	WT	2 (1)	35.60 - 40.40	38.00	—	—
		EC	3 (2)	14.30 - 16.30	15.30	1.00	0.58
		TMT	"	23.00 - 25.00	24.00	1.00	0.58
		LTMT	3 (2)	27.00 - 30.20	28.10	1.79	1.03
		IIIw	2 (1)	30.00 - 32.50	31.20	—	—
	Tribe Oxyurini						
Oxyura jamaicensis rubida							
Manitoba	A	WT	12 (4)	38.20 - 45.40	40.80	2.31	0.67
Minnesota		EC	33 (8)	17.00 - 20.30	17.90	1.81	0.31
		TMT	28 (6)	17.60 - 20.30	19.40	0.63	0.12
		LTMT	33 (8)	20.00 - 24.80	22.70	0.82	0.14
		IIIw	"	27.50 - 33.00	30.10	1.22	0.21
	B	WT	2 (1)	38.20 - 40.00	39.40	—	—
		EC	"	18.50 - 18.80	18.60	—	—
		TMT	"	19.90 - 20.00	19.90	—	—
		LTMT	"	23.80 - 24.20	24.00	—	—
		IIIw	"	30.70 - 31.00	30.80	—	—

Appendix B
Color Descriptions

Appendix B

Color Descriptions

Color nomenclature, based on the author's Munsell notations taken mainly from live, newly hatched birds (exceptions noted), is from Kelly and Judd (1976) or employs widely understood terms in general use. Kelly and Judd's nomenclatuure may be visualized exactly using the *Centroid Colors*, 1974 ed. (Munsell Color Company).

Whistling-ducks, tribe Dendrocygnini

Dendrocygna bicolor. Materials examined: 36 live, 1 dead, 14 study skins, 2 alcoholics. **Plumage**. Base color white (N; *normal* and *'silver'* phases): clearest on chin and throat; extremely pale gray on lower breast, belly, cheeks, and occiput; medium gray on 'shadow' dorsal spots (if present) and undertail; light to pale gray on wing-patches (some individuals) and more conspicuous dorsal spots (if present); light gray on fronts of alulae, primaries, and tibiotarsi; yellowish gray ('buffy') on wing-patches (other individuals) and spot above 'horn' of bill (if present). Pattern color brownish gray (2.5Y): *normal:* dark on *crown* and 'T' stripe; deep or medium on yoke, back, rump, and tibiotarsi; medium on breast-band (if present); 'silver': crown and 'T' stripe medium dark, all other parts correspondingly paler. **Unfeathered parts.** Irides dark brown; eyelid rims brownish gray or dark brownish gray. Upper mandible dark or medium bluish gray; lower mandible, tomia, and rim around nostrils pale dull yellow-orange; nail brownish pink, much paler at tip; upper egg-tooth dull yellow or chalky white, lower not seen. Tarsi and toes dull olive-green, dull yellow-green, "olive" (MVZ, tag data; coll. H. C. Bryant), or "light yellowish green" (MVZ, tag data; coll. J. A. Moffitt); yellowish along sides of toes; pattern and webs brownish blue-gray; contrast low.

D. viduata. Materials examined: 5 study skins. Description based on author's translation of Delacour's account (1924: 18-19; in French) of a downy White-faced Whistling-duck hatched and reared at Cléres; author notes from other specimens in brackets [ ]. **Plumage.** Base color yellow (2.5Y): brightest on face, neck, [and uropygial tuft]; much duller on belly and undertail. Pattern color blackish brown [10Y; darkest on head, hindneck, and rump; moderate on diffuse spot at top of breast (3 specimens); a bit lighter on yoke]. **Unfeathered parts.** Bill and feet lead-gray [upper mandible blackish olive-brown; lower mandible, tomia, and narrow rim of nostrils dull orange-yellow; feet dark grayish olive or dull olive-yellow]; colors of irides and egg-teeth undescribed.

D. arborea. Materials examined: 6 live, 5 study skins, 1 color transparency. **Plumage**. Base color pale yellow (6Y): brightest on head and upper breast; pale and a bit duller on dorsal spots, wing-patches, and fronts of alulae and primaries; much paler and 'silvery' on lower breast, belly, and undertail. Pattern color blackish gray (10YR): darkest on head and hindneck; moderate on breast-band (if present); a bit lighter on yoke; darker on rump. **Unfeathered parts**. Irides dark brown, often nearly black; eyelid rims yellowish brownish gray. Upper mandible dark olive-brown, "dark olive-green" (Blaauw 1912: 659), or "slaty blue" (FMNH, tag data; coll. H. A. Beatty); lower mandible pale dull red-orange; tomia and rim of nostrils light dull orange-yellow; nail reddish brown, paler at tip; upper egg- tooth dull yellow, lower not seen. Tarsi and toes olive-green, bluish olive-green, "dark olive-green" (Blaauw 1912: 659), or "slaty blue" (FMNH, tag data; coll. H. A. Beatty); terminal joints and webs dull yellowish brown; contrast low.

D. autumnalis. Materials examined: 21

live, 20 study skins, 3 color transparencies. Description based on live *fulgens* Friedmann [=*lucida* Friedmann 1947; Banks 1978]; southern *autumnalis* Linnaeus [=*discolor* Sclater and Salvin; Banks 1978] similar except yellow supraorbital stripe narrower than black transocular stripe (see Wetmore et al. 1965: 160, P. Schwarz photo; *Annual Report of the [Severn] Wildfowl Trust 1950-51* 4, 1952: P. Talbot-Ponsonby photo). No brilliant yellow individuals seen among six southern specimens examined. **Plumage.** Base color greenish yellow, either extremely pale and bright (1.25GY 9/6) or very light and brilliant (6.25Y 8/12); brightest (bright or vivid greenish yellow or yellow) on head and breast; somewhat duller on belly, dorsal spots, uropygial tuft, and fronts of legs, alulae, and primaries; dullest (pale yellow-green) on undertail. Pattern color black (N): darkest on head; a bit lighter on yoke and breast-spot (if present); darker on rump. **Unfeathered parts.** Irides dark brown; eyelid rims dark gray or brownish gray. Upper mandible dark brownish gray; lower mandible, tomia, and base of upper mandible pale dull yellowish pink; inconspicuous narrow rim around nostrils pale brownish pink; nail light reddish brown, paler and pinkish at tip; upper egg-tooth yellowish white or greenish yellow, lower translucent pale dull yellow. Tarsi and toes olive-yellow, pattern and webs light olive; contrast low.

Swans, tribe Cygnini

Cygnus olor. Materials examined: 6 live, 6 frozen, 8 study skins, 1 color transparency. **Plumage.** *Gray:* Base color white (N): clearest on chin, breast, and belly; slightly grayer on neck, sides of breast and belly, and fronts of alulae, primaries, and undertail. Pattern color brownish gray (10YR): palest and dullest (light gray) on crown and face; a bit brighter (toward yellowish gray) on winglets, lower back, tail, and tibiotarsi; darker and brighter (light brownish gray to light yellowish grayish brown) on hindneck and upper back. *White:* Base color as in *gray* phase, but 'whiter' over all. Pattern color yellowish gray (10YR): palest and dullest (light gray to pale gray) on crown and face; a bit darker (light gray to pinkish gray) on winglets, lower back, tail, and tibiotarsi; palest and brightest (yellowish gray to pale yellowish pink) on hindneck and upper back. **Unfeathered parts.** Irides dark brown or dark grayish brown, eyelid rims light olive-gray (both color phases). Upper and lower mandibles dark gray (*gray*) or grayish yellowish brown (*white*); nail pinkish gray, whitish at tip; upper egg-tooth yellowish white or grayish yellowish white, lower translucent and scale-like (remnant only). Tarsi and toes entirely medium gray or dark gray (*gray*) or light brown (*white*), with narrow band of yellowish gray or light yellowish brown from pad of foot to heel along rear midline of tarsi; pattern lacking, webs light to medium gray (*gray*) or light grayish brown (*white*); contrast very low or absent.

Olor columbianus. Materials examined: 8 live, 16 study skins. Description based on live *O. c. columbianus* from Alaska. **Plumage.** Base color white (N): clearest on chin, throat, and breast; tinged with palest yellowish gray or brownish pink (appears 'silvery') on face, dorsal spots, wing-patches, fronts of alulae and primaries, and belly; slightly grayer on undertail. Pattern color gray (7.5YR): very pale and brownish ('silvery') on crown, face, and hindneck; somewhat darker on back, rump, and fronts of tibiotarsi; darkest (light gray to medium gray) on winglets and on sides and backs of tibiotarsi (pattern color often appears quite 'bluish'; a few individuals somewhat darker over all). **Unfeathered parts.** Irides dark brown, eyelid rims olive-gray or light olive-gray. Upper and lower mandibles light dull pink or light dull yellowish pink, shading to light grayish blue behind nail and along tomia; nail light dull bluish pink; upper egg-tooth yellowish white, pale dull yellow, or pale dull yellowish green, lower whitish, translucent, and scale-like. Tarsi and toes light dull pink; claws pinkish brownish gray; darker pattern color lacking except for pale grayish blue tints along sides of toes and tarsi and on terminal joints; almost no contrast.

O. buccinator. Materials examined: 4 live, 16 study skins, 1 alcoholic, 11 color transparencies. **Plumage.** Base color as *O. c. columbianus*. Pattern color as *O. c. columbianus* except a few darker individuals medium gray on hindneck, back, rump, and fronts of tibiotarsi; darkest (medium gray to light brownish gray) on winglets and on sides and backs of tibiotarsi. Both pattern and base colors of leucistic cygnet may appear entirely white. **Unfeathered parts.** As *O. c. columbianus* except bill and foot colors of leucistic cygnet paler and yellower (Carrol Henderson, letter to the author, October 1982).

Geese, tribe Anserini

Anser brachyrhynchus. Materials examined: 15 study skins. Description of plumage from newly hatched Icelandic specimens (IMNH; RM 334, RM 337-38, RM 347-48, RM 351, RM 410). **Plumage.** Base color greenish yellow (6Y; 7.5Y): lightest and brightest (often brilliant) on breast, belly, and sides of rump; a bit duller on throat, wing-patches, and (sometimes) undertail; dullest on lower cheeks, dorsal spots, and (other times) undertail. Pattern color grayish olive (5Y) or greenish olive-gray (7.5Y): dark, very dark, or blackish on eye-stripe (variable); dark on back of crown, winglets, and rump; lightest on forehead, upper cheeks, and yoke. **Unfeathered parts.** From Fjeldså (1977: 56): "Bill [upper and lower mandibles] dark grey with pinkish buff nail...legs and feet greyish; iris brown; eye-ring grey"; upper egg-tooth pale, dull olive-yellow, lower not seen. Tarsi and toes "slaty flesh," "leaden grey" (BM[NH], tag data; coll. J. D. Brown, F. C. R. Jourdain, R. Meinertzhagen, and B. W. Tucker), "medium to dark grayish" (Palmer 1976, vol. 2: 112), "black" (Cramp and Simmons 1977: 402), or grayish yellowish brown (IMNH specimens); pattern and webs brownish gray: contrast very low.

A. albifrons. Materials examined: 3 live, 44 study skins, 30 color transparencies. Description based on live goslings of *frontalis* Baird and *flavirostris* Dalgety and Scott; *gambelli* Hartlaub and nominate *albifrons* Scopoli similar. **Plumage.** Base color yellow or greenish yellow (5Y; 6Y): brightest (often brilliant) on breast, sides of neck, belly, and sides of rump; slightly duller on forehead, lower cheeks, wing-patches, and dorsal spots; duller still on upper cheeks; palest and dullest (often nearly gray) on chin, throat, and undertail. Pattern color olive (2.5Y) or greenish olive (5Y; 6Y): lightest on yoke, darker on crown, darkest on winglets, rump, and (sometimes) eye-stripe (loreal wash often quite blackish on dark variants). **Unfeathered parts.** Irides dark grayish brown; eyelid rims light yellowish brown. Upper and lower mandibles grayish olive-brown or blackish olive-brown (dark variants); nail light dull yellowish brown, paler at tip, contrasting well with bill; upper egg-tooth as nail, but paler and more yellowish, lower not seen. Tarsi and toes usually light dull yellowish brown (sometimes 'greenish', rarely blackish except on some *flavirostris*), darker on webs, terminal joints, and backs of tarsi; contrast nearly always good.

A. caerulescens. Materials examined: 50 live, 57 study skins. Description of plumage classes 0-4 (Cooke and Cooch 1968; theirs = classes 1-5 of Palmer 1976, vol. 2) based on captive *caerulescens* Linnaeus; *atlanticus* Kennard (Classes 0-1) similar; dark *atlanticus* goslings (Classes 2-4) presumed similar based on dark ('blue' phase) immature and adult wild Greater Snow Geese reported by Palmer (1976, vol. 2). **Plumage**. Base color yellow (5Y) or greenish yellow (7.5Y): Classes 0 and 1: brilliant or vivid on forehead and face (*atlanticus* with pronounced orange-yellow tint), chin, breast, and belly; moderate to grayish on dorsal spots, wing-patches, and undertail. Class 2: brilliant to light yellow on chin; moderate to strong on narrow line around bill, on forehead, and on patch at occiput and nape; moderate or grayish yellow eye-ring (some individuals); dark grayish yellow to light grayish olive on face, breast, belly, dorsal spots, wing-patches, and undertail. Class 3: like 2 except less yellow and lacks yellow line around bill (Cooke and Cooch 1968). Class 4: brilliant to light or moderate yellow only on chin (usually retained as yellowish white area in juvenal plumage; but see dark-chinned juvenal 'blue' *caerulescens* portrayed by Scott *in* Cramp and Simmons 1977: pl. 56). Pattern color olive (2.5Y; 5Y): Classes 0 and 1: light olive to light olive-gray on crown pattern (Class 1: medium gray), yoke, back, and tibiae (Class 1 gosling has numerous dark plumes); grayish olive to olive-gray on rump; dark grayish olive to dark gray or blackish gray on eye-ring (if present) and eye-line (Class 1 gosling has "frizzled or near-agouti appearance" [Cooke and Cooch 1968: 291]). Classes 2 and 3: moderate olive to olive-gray on yoke, back, and tibiae; dark olive-gray on head and rump. Class 4: moderate olive to dark olive on yoke, back, and tibiae; dark grayish olive on rump; dark grayish olive to blackish olive on head ("sooty black" [Cooke and Cooch 1968: 291]). **Unfeathered parts.** Irides light grayish brown to dark grayish brown; eyelid rims olive-gray (Classes 0 and 1) to dark brownish gray (Classes 2-4). Upper and lower mandibles dark 'bluish' gray (Classes 0 and 1), dark gray to blackish gray (Classes 2-4); nail brownish pink, much paler at tip; upper egg-tooth light grayish yellow, lower not seen. Tarsi and toes yellowish olive to moderate or grayish olive, paler on midline from pad of foot to heel, dark bluish gray on terminal joints and claws, with low-contrast webs light grayish olive to grayish olive (Classes 0 and 1); entire foot dark 'bluish' grayish brown (Class 2), blackish (Class 3), or shiny black (Class 4); see goslings of five color classes on plates 3 and 4.

A. rossii. Materials examined: 14 live, 12 study skins, 21 color transparencies. Description of two yellow and two gray morphs from live captive specimens; "dark yellow", "black yellow", and "dark gray" morphs described from prepared day-old specimens, color transparencies, and/or field notes made by J. P. Ryder; "white" morph from J. P. Ryder (pers. comm. 1970) and Scott (1951b; pl. 10 *in* Delacour 1954). **Plumage.** Seven plumage designations "light yellow", "yellow-green", "dark yellow", "black-yellow", "dark gray", "pearly gray", and "white" from Ryder (1967: 36); 'medium gray' designated by author. Base color yellow (5Y) or greenish yellow (7.5Y; 10Y): brilliant on forehead and sides of head and neck (except extremely dull or virtually lacking in "dark gray" morph), often with orange tint (light in "dark yellow" and "black-yellow" morphs; pale in "light yellow" and "yellow-green" morphs; exceedingly pale in all gray morphs, including "white"); progressively paler and duller from breast and head to dorsal spots and wing-patches to undertail (pale yellow to grayish yellow, or yellowish gray to yellowish white [light dorsal pattern extremely dull and inconspicuous on darker gray morphs]), except some bright yellow morphs more or less evenly yellow from chin to undertail. Pattern color light olive (5Y), grayish olive (10Y), olive-gray or dark olive-gray (7.5Y) dark to blackish on eye-stripe (all color morphs); moderate to dark on 'hood' ("dark gray" morph); moderate (darker morphs) to exceedingly pale (light and pale morphs) on 'bonnet'; moderate on back ("dark-gray", "black-yellow") to moderately light or light ("dark yellow", 'medium gray'), greenish ("yellow-green"), pale ("light yellow", "pearly gray"), or exceedingly pale ("white"). **Unfeathered parts.** Irides dark grayish brown; eyelid rims light grayish olive or light olive-gray. Upper and lower mandibles entirely dark 'bluish' gray; nail brownish pink near bill, much paler at tip; upper egg-tooth light dull yellowish pink or light dull greenish yellow, lower not seen. Tarsi and toes grayish olive or olive-gray: darker ('bluish' gray) on terminal joints, paler (yellowish gray) on midline from pad of foot to heel; webs only slightly darker; contrast very low. Note: gray morphs have more uniformly gray or olive-gray tarsi and toes (sometimes with 'greenish' tint); yellow morphs have distinct olive or yellowish olive tint.

Philacte canagica. Materials examined: 9

live, 1 frozen, 18 study skins, 16 color transparencies. **Plumage.** Base color white (N): clearest around bill, very slightly grayer ('silvery') on lower cheeks, chin, throat, and breast; mixed with pale gray on belly, grayer still on undertail. Pattern color gray (N/10YR): some individuals darkest on crown, lighter on hindneck and yoke; paler on upper cheeks, rear edge of wings and (sometimes) front edge of primaries (other individuals lighter, more uniformly colored); eye-stripe and/or pre-ocular blotch may be quite dark, but sometimes faint and poorly marked or blended with lighter crown color. **Unfeathered parts.** Irides grayish brown; eyelid rims grayish olive-brown. Upper and lower mandibles blackish brown; nail dark reddish brown at base, palest grayish brown at tip; upper egg-tooth palest olive-gray, lower translucent and scale-like. Tarsi and toes grayish olive or grayish olive-brown, usually with somewhat lighter line of same hue along rear midline of tarsi; webs and terminal joints 'bluish' gray-brown; contrast fair.

Branta bernicla. Materials examined: 34 live, 45 study skins, 2 color transparencies. Description based on live *hrota* Müller from Southampton Island (PWPS) and live *nigricans* (Lawrence) from Alaska. **Plumage.** Base color white (N/5Y): clearest (but still very slightly grayish) on chin-patch (if present) and on transverse, shallow 'V' between breast-band and belly; pale gray on face, throat, belly and (in a few very pale individuals) on inconspicuous shoulder-spots and wing-patches. Pattern color brownish gray (N/10YR): light on breast-band; progressively darker on yoke, back, rump, and crown-patch; darkest on 'mask' and 'bridle'. **Unfeathered parts.** Irides dark brown or dark grayish brown; eyelid rims olive-gray or dark olive-gray. Upper and lower mandibles blackish gray; nail dark 'reddish' gray at posterior, whitish on anterior third (whitish area very narrow in some specimens); upper egg-tooth white or pinkish white, lower translucent and scale-like. Tarsi entirely gray or dark gray (*hrota* with dull, yellowish olive rear midline from pad of foot to heel; *nigricans* often evenly blackish), toes and pattern color a bit darker (but "slightly paler" in palaearctic *bernicla* (Linnaeus) [Cramp and Simmons 1977: 441]); contrast very low.

B. leucopsis. Materials examined: 14 live, 12 study skins. **Plumage.** Base color yellow (5Y): pale on face, chin, and throat; paler and very dull (yellowish gray or nearly white) on breast, belly, dorsal spots, wing-patches, fronts of alulae and primaries, and undertail. Pattern color olive (N/10YR): lightest (light olive-gray) on breast-band, a bit darker (olive-gray) on 'mask' and 'bridle' (if present) and on crown, yoke, winglets (darkest), and rump. **Unfeathered parts.** Irides dark brown or dark grayish brown: eyelid rims dark or blackish olive-gray. Upper and lower mandibles blackish gray with 'bluish' tint; nail blackish gray with brownish tint; upper egg-tooth yellowish white, lower not seen. Tarsi and toes blackish gray, slightly paler on pad of foot and up rear midline of tarsi; claws dark gray; pattern and webs blackish gray; almost no contrast.

B. canadensis. Materials examined: 144 live, 3 dead, 1 frozen, 10 study skins, 2 color transparencies. Description based on live or newly dead goslings from 16 North American locations; colors of eastern goslings appear first, those of western goslings follow in parentheses ( ) or square brackets [ ]. Nomenclature follows Delacour (1951, 1954). **Plumage.** Base color yellow (5Y-10Y [10Y-2.5GY]): brilliant on face (*interior* with "sulphur yellow" wash on cheeks; W. Todd 1936), breast, and belly [many dusky down-tips]; duller on dorsal spots, wing-patches, and leg pattern; dullest (light, pale or grayish yellow [light, pale or grayish greenish yellow]) on undertail. Pattern color olive (5Y-10Y [2.5GY-5GY]): moderate olive, grayish olive, or moderate olive-gray [grayish olive-green or dark grayish olive-green] on yoke and rump; paler on breast-band, if present [western goslings, certain *parvipes*]; sometimes darker on crown and face pattern; many iridescent golden plumes throughout plumage [iridescent plumes largely absent]. **Unfeathered parts.** Irides brown, dark brown, grayish brown, or (in some pale yellow goslings) a shade of gray or brownish gray (e.g., irides of newly hatched *moffitti* "hazel" [MVZ, tag data; coll. J. A. Moffitt]; irides of *hutchinsii* "pale blue-grey" [Manning *in* Witherby et al. [1939] 1943, vol. 3: 218]); eyelid rims grayish olive or olive-gray (dark grayish olive). Upper and lower mandibles dark gray or 'bluish' gray (some pale individuals grayish olive); nail dark grayish reddish brown, slightly paler at tip; upper egg-tooth grayish yellow or greenish yellow [dark yellowish green, dark grayish yellowish green], lower egg-tooth (if present) translucent and scale-like. Tarsi and toes at hatching grayish orange, dark grayish orange, olive-gray, or grayish olive [dark greenish olive, dark gray, or blackish; a few *interior, canadensis,* and *parvipes* also with dark gray or blackish feet]; tarsi and toes of older goslings (10-12 d.; all subspp.) some shade of gray: light, 'greenish', medium, 'bluish', [dark, 'brownish', or blackish]; midline from pad of foot to heel light yellow, light olive, light olive-gray, grayish yellow, or dark grayish yellow; pattern and webs grayish olive or olive-gray [dark olive-brown, dark gray, blackish]; contrast fair, poor, or lacking (see downy young of 10 subspp. on pl. 5, *hutchinsii* on frontispiece).

Nesochen sandvicensis. Materials examined: 5 live, 1 dead, 5 study skins. **Plumage.** Base color yellowish white (N/2.5Y): extremely pale yellow on malar region (some individuals); 'silvery' (yellowish gray) on malar region (other individuals), chin, supraorbital stripe, eye-ring, forward edge of wing, fronts of alulae and primaries, and belly; darker and slightly duller (near pale grayish yellowish brown) on breast (faint breast-band sometimes present) and on wing-patches (if present); duller (brownish gray) on dorsal spots (if present) and undertail; duller still (medium gray) on throat. Pattern color yellowish brown (10YR): brightest on cheeks and ear-patch (dark yellowish brown); lightest on yoke and hindneck (dark grayish yellowish brown); darkest and dullest on crown and rump (brownish gray/dark grayish yellowish brown). **Unfeathered parts.** Irides dark brown, eyelid rims olive-gray. Upper and lower mandibles olive-gray, dark grayish olive, or 'bluish' brownish gray; yellowish along tomia of lower mandible; nail dark 'bluish' olive-gray; upper egg-tooth pale olive, dark olive-gray, or (sometimes) whitish; lower translucent, scale-like. Tarsi and toes yellowish olive-gray or brownish olive-gray; edges of webs, lobe of hallux, pad of foot, and midline up back of tarsi to heel pale, dull olive-yellow; pattern, webs, and claws dark olive-gray; contrast fair.

Perching ducks, tribe Cairinini

Cairina moschata. Materials examined: 11 live (10 dark mutants, 1 wild type), 7 study skins. **Plumage** (wild type). Base color yellow (3.5Y; 5Y): light and brilliant on forehead, face, and upper breast; a bit paler on chin and throat; moderate and duller on lower breast, belly, dorsal spots, wing-patches, and on fronts of alulae, primaries, and tibiotarsi; paler and much duller ('greenish') on undertail. Pattern color yellowish brown (10YR): dark on crown and yoke (dark yellow down-tips give 'golden' appearance); dark and grayish on face pattern, winglets, lower back, rump, and tail. **Unfeathered parts.** Irides brownish gray; eyelid rims olive-gray. Upper mandible dark grayish brown or dark olive-brown; lower mandible dull pinkish yellow; nail brownish pink, paler at tip; egg-teeth pale dull yellow; lower opaque, raised, bi-lobed. Tarsi and toes dull yellow or dull greenish yellow, paler on sides of toes; pattern and webs grayish brown; contrast good.

Aix sponsa. Materials examined: 82 live, 37 study skins. **Plumage.** Base color greenish yellow (7.5Y; 10Y): pale (or extremely pale) but vivid or brilliant on face, chin, throat, and breast; duller on belly; light (but sometimes dull or buffy) on dorsal spots, wing-patches, and fronts of tibiotarsi (some individuals); pale and dull (yellowish white) along sides, on fronts of tibiotarsi (other individuals), alulae, and primaries, and on undertail. Pattern color olive (7.5Y; 10Y): pale and 'silvery' yellowish white to yellowish gray on forehead, shading into darker crown color; moderate to dark on yoke, winglets, and backs of tibiotarsi; dark and grayish (or blackish) on eye- stripe, crown, rump, and tail. **Unfeathered parts.** Irides brown or grayish brown; eyelid rims dark brownish gray. Upper mandible 'bluish' gray-brown, tomia pale dull yellow; lower mandible pale dull yellowish pink; nail reddish brown, paler and pinkish at tip; egg-teeth yellowish white, pale yellow, pale greenish yellow, or dull yellowish pink; lower opaque, raised, bi-lobed. Tarsi and toes grayish yellow, grayish green-yellow, or grayish yellowish pink, paler and (usually) yellower along sides of toes and on webs adjacent to toes; claws brownish gray; pattern and webs dark olive-gray or dark brownish gray to blackish olive-gray; contrast good to excellent.

Dabbling ducks, tribe Anatini

Mareca americana. Materials examined: 39 live, 58 study skins. **Plumage.** Primary base color yellow (5Y): pale and usually bright on face and throat; a bit duller on breast and eye-ring; duller and much paler (grayish yellow) on belly, fronts of tibiotarsi, wing-patches, and dorsal spots; palest and dullest (yellowish gray to yellowish white) on undertail. Secondary base color strong or moderate yellowish brown (10YR), most prominent on head and face; many yellowish brown down-tips on crown and yoke. Pattern color olive-brown (2.5Y): dark to blackish on crown; dark (grayish olive) on winglets, lower back, and rump; lightest (moderate olive) on yoke; buffy and 'creamy' down-tips give quite mottled look to dark upper parts. **Unfeathered parts.** Irides grayish brown; eyelid rims dark brownish gray. Upper mandible gray, olive-gray, 'bluish' gray-brown, or "slate" (ROM, tag data; coll. J. A. Munro), lower mandible and tomia at base of bill light dull yellowish pink; nail dull brownish red, pinkish at tip; egg-teeth pale, dull orange-yellow, lower opaque and elevated. Tarsi and toes olive-green, light olive-gray, light grayish olive-brown, grayish brown, or "olive-slate" (ROM, tag data: coll. J. A. Munro); pattern and webs grayish olive-brown; contrast fair.

Anas strepera. Materials examined: 85 live, 21 study skins. **Plumage.** Base color greenish yellow (6Y): extremely pale and brilliant on face, throat, and upper breast; paler and duller (='creamy') on dorsal spots, wing-patches (sometimes buffy), belly, and on either side of post-ocular stripe above ear and back to occiput; pale grayish yellow on undertail. Pattern color olive-brown (2.5Y): moderate and fairly bright on yoke; dark (even blackish) and much duller on crown and rump; many buffy and 'creamy' down-tips give mottled appearance to dark back, forehead, forepart of crown, and nape. **Unfeathered parts.** Irides dark grayish brown; eyelid rims dark brownish gray. Upper mandible brownish gray (often slightly 'bluish') except light orange at base almost halfway to nostril; lower mandible and tomia light orange, with tomia becoming darker and duller toward tip of bill; nail dull pinkish orange, paler at tip; egg-teeth dark dull yellow, pale dull yellowish pink, or pale dull cream-color, lower opaque and elevated. Tarsi and toes light yellow or light orange-yellow; pattern and webs grayish brown; contrast good to fair.

A. crecca. Materials examined: 35 live, 42 study skins. Description based on live *carolinensis* Gmelin ducklings and prepared *nimia* Friedmann (USNM 464723 & 366383); nominate *crecca* Linnaeus similar. **Plumage.** Base color orange-yellow (3.5Y); brightest (moderate to strong) on face and breast, duller (pale to grayish) on belly, dorsal spots, and wing-patches; much paler, duller and a bit 'greener' (yellowish gray) on undertail (almost parchment-colored in older downies). Pattern color olive-brown (2.5Y): darkest (dark olive-brown) on crown, winglets, rump, and face pattern; somewhat lighter (moderate olive-brown) on yoke. **Unfeathered parts.** Irides grayish brown; eyelid rims dark brownish gray. Upper mandible dark grayish brown; lower mandible and tomia at base of bill light yellowish brown (often rather 'pinkish'); nail dull brownish red, paler and pinkish at tip; upper egg-tooth light dull greenish yellow, lower not seen. Tarsi and toes gray or olive-gray; webs and pattern brownish gray; contrast low.

A. acuta. Materials examined: 82 live, 53 study skins. **Plumage.** Base color white (N/10YR): clearest over eyes, under chin, and on breast, dorsal spots, wing-patches, and tibiotarsi; a bit grayer on cheeks, throat, belly, and undertail. Pattern color brownish gray to grayish brown (5YR): darkest (dark grayish brown) on crown and rump; lighter on face-pattern (brownish gray); lightest (toward light brownish gray) on yoke; faint brownish pink breast-band usually present; brownish gray face stripes usually 'bleed' pale, dull yellowish pink onto adjacent areas of white base color. **Unfeathered parts.** Irides brown or grayish brown; eyelid rims dark brownish gray. Upper mandible brownish gray or brownish blue-gray; lower mandible and tomia at base of bill brownish pink; nail brownish red, paler and more pinkish at tip; upper and lower egg-teeth white or pale [dull] yellowish pink. Tarsi and toes olive-gray, brownish olive-gray, brownish blue-gray, or brownish gray; webs and pattern brownish gray; contrast low.

A. bahamensis. Materials examined: 6 live (observed), 9 study skins. Description based on two Puerto Rican *bahamensis* Linnaeus (USNM 238298-99); *rubirostris* Vieillot similar but a bit larger; *galapagensis* Ridgway not examined. **Plumage.** Base color orange-yellow (2.5Y): very bright (strong yellow) on face and throat; paler and a bit duller (light yellow) on breast, paler still (pale yellow) on wing-patches, tibiotarsi, and dorsal spots; extremely pale and dull (yellowish white) on belly and undertail. Pattern color olive-brown (2.5Y): moderate on face pattern, crown, and rump; a bit lighter on back and winglets, lightest on yoke. **Unfeathered parts.** Irides presumed grayish brown—those of three partly feathered Curaçao ducklings were "hazel" (CM, tag data; coll. M. A. Carriker). Bill "bluish gray with a pink wash on the sides [of the upper mandible]" (Delacour 1956: 120); lower mandible light, dull yellowish pink; nail reddish brown; egg-teeth not seen. Tarsi and toes dark orange-yellow; pattern and webs brown or grayish brown; contrast fair.

A. fulvigula. Materials examined: 33 live, 12 study skins. Plumage characters apply to both *fulvigula* Ridgway (Florida Duck) and *maculosa* Sennett (Mottled Duck), but foot color of the two subspecies appears to differ slightly. **Plumage.** Base color orange-yellow (Munsell *hue* 2.5Y [1.5Y-5Y]): brightest (moderate or dark yellow to deep or strong yellow) on cheeks, superciliary line, lores, and (sometimes) forehead; a bit darker and duller (light olive-brown) on chin; paler on forehead (other times); dark yellow on breast, wing-patches, and dorsal spots; moderate to grayish yellow on belly; grayish yellow on undertail. Pattern color olive-brown (5Y [2.5Y to 7.5Y]): lightest (moderate) on yoke, slightly darker on crown and face pattern, darkest (dark olive-brown) on rump. Down-tips on yoke and crown light olive- brown. **Unfeathered parts.** Irides dark grayish brown; eyelid rims dark brownish gray. Upper mandible brownish gray, lower mandible and base of upper mandible at tomia brownish pink; nail light reddish brown, paler and pinkish at tip; egg-teeth pale dull yellow. Tarsi and toes dark grayish brown (5YR; 7.5YR; *fulvigula*) or dark olive-brown (10YR; *maculosa*); pattern and webs dark gray or blackish gray; contrast low.

A. rubripes. Materials examined: 32 live, 64 study skins, 1 alcoholic, 12 color transparencies. **Plumage.** Base color orange-yellow (10YR; 2.5Y): general color much as in *A. fulvigula* except bright color (strong yellow) in some individuals confined to lores, other individuals darker (dark yellow or dark orange- yellow to light olive-brown) over entire face and breast; duller (grayish yellow) on dorsal spots and wing-patches; belly and undertail very much paler and duller (grayish yellow to yellowish gray; "dull grayish white" [Bent 1923: 56], "'dirty neutral'" [Palmer 1976, vol. 2: 325]). Pattern color olive-brown (2.5Y): lightest (moderate) on crown, yoke, and face pattern; darkest (dark olive-brown to near blackish gray) on rump; light-colored down-tips sparse or absent. **Unfeathered parts.** Irides grayish brown; eyelid rims very dark brownish gray. Upper mandible dark brownish gray; lower mandible and base of bill near tomia brownish pink, pinkish gray, or light grayish brown; nail dark reddish brown, paler at tip; upper egg-tooth dull yellow, lower not seen. Tarsi and toes grayish brown or (sometimes) dark yellowish brown; pattern and webs dark brownish gray; contrast very low.

A. diazi. Materials examined: 4 live, 10 study skins. Description of plumage based on live aviary ducklings from New Mexico (CESJ; ca. 3 d.) and wild-caught Mexican specimens (BMNH 13302-4, 13391-95); colors of unfeathered parts quoted from tag data of very young duckling ("33 g") collected in Durango, Mexico, by N. J. Scott, Jr., and R. P. Reynolds (Norman Scott, letter to the author, December 1984). **Plumage.** Base color as in *A. fulvigula*, except paler over all, often whitish on wing-patches, rump-spots, forehead, and (less often) shoulder-spots; extremely pale and dull on belly and undertail. Pattern color as in *A. fulvigula*, but may appear lighter and brighter on yoke. **Unfeathered parts.** "Iris brown. Bill [upper mandible] uniform dark olive above, lower mandible tan; nail and [upper] egg tooth tan. Feet uniform dark olive, yellow on each side of digits." Three 72-hour aviary birds had iris, bill, and nail colors as in *A. fulvigula*, but a bit paler on lower mandible (light yellowish pink); egg-teeth not seen. Tarsi and toes medium or dark, dull yellowish brown; pattern and webs grayish brown; contrast fair.

A. platyrhynchos. Materials examined: 67 live, 101 study skins. Description based on nominate *platyrhynchos* Linnaeus; *conboschas* Brehm similar. **Plumage.** Base color yellow (5Y [2.5Y-8.5Y]): brightest (brilliant yellow) on face, throat, and breast; less bright on belly, dorsal spots, and wing-patches; least bright (light greenish yellow) on undertail; but all areas nearly always recognizeably yellow. Pattern color olive or olive-brown (4Y [10YR-7.5Y]); darkest (grayish olive) on crown, rump, and face pattern; moderate on yoke. **Unfeathered parts.** Irides brown; eyelid rims dark brownish gray. Upper mandible dark olive or dark olive-brown; lower mandible light yellowish brown; nail dull brownish red, paler at tip; upper egg- tooth dull yellowish white or pale dull greenish yellow, lower pale dull orange-yellow. Tarsi and toes usually medium or light dull orange, sometimes very dull and brownish but almost never blackish; paler along sides of toes; pattern and webs grayish olive-brown or dark grayish olive-brown; contrast good to fair, seldom poor.

A. wyvilliana. Materials examined: 2 study skins. Description based on very young wild Oahu specimen (USNM uncat.); Swedberg's (1967: 10 & 12) color notes taken from live ducklings quoted. **Plumage.** Base color orange-yellow (2.5Y; "light buffy yellow"): brightest on face, throat, and breast; paler and duller on shoulder-spots, fronts of legs, and undertail. Pattern color olive-brown (1.5Y; "chocolate brown"): darkest on crown, rump, and face pattern, lightest on yoke. **Unfeathered parts.** Iris color undescribed (presumed brown or grayish brown). Upper mandible olive-brown or "dark-gray...[becoming]...yellow-orange at about six weeks"; lower mandible (presumed) light dull yellowish pink; colors of nail and egg-teeth undescribed (presumed similar to those of other Northern Mallard-like ducklings). Tarsi and toes "dark gray [changing] to a pale yellow-orange [after about] six weeks"; feet of USNM specimen light yellowish brown with pale, dull yellow along sides of toes and on inner web of II; pattern and webs brownish gray; contrast poor on toe pattern, good to fair elsewhere.

A. laysanensis. Materials examined: 8 live, 2 dead, 1 study skin, 7 color transparencies. **Plumage.** Base color orange-yellow (1.5Y to 2.5Y): lightest and brightest (deep to dark yellow) on chin; a bit darker (dark orange-yellow) on supraorbital stripe, forehead, lores, and ear region; much darker (deep yellowish brown) at rictus (some ducklings; others only a bit darker); paler and duller (grayish yellow) on lower cheeks, breast, belly, wing-patches, dorsal spots, and (sometimes) around eye; still paler and duller (yellowish gray) on undertail. Pattern color olive-brown (2.5Y): dark on back and winglets; blackish on crown, rump, and face pattern (down plumes tipped with deep yellow); pale and grayish on inconspicuous breast-band. **Unfeathered parts.** Quoted color notes from Ripley (1960: 246). Irides dark grayish brown; eyelid rims brownish gray. Upper mandible brownish gray, lower mandible yellowish pink; nail brownish pink, paler at tip; upper egg-tooth dull yellow, lower not seen. Tarsi and toes "dull greenish yellow" or light olive-brown; pattern and webs "dull greenish brown", brownish gray, or 'bluish' gray; contrast fair.

A. discors. Materials examined: 294 live, 46 study skins. Description based on live *discors* Linnaeus; *órphna* Stewart and Aldrich not examined, but presumed to be somewhat darker over all (as adults; Stewart and Aldrich 1956). **Plumage.** Base color greenish yellow (6.25Y): brightest (strong to vivid yellow) on lores and—in some individuals—on cheeks (others dark or deep yellow): paler and greener (light greenish yellow) on breast and belly; a bit duller (pale yellow) on superciliary line, wing-patches, and dorsal spots; paler and still duller (pale greenish yellow or grayish yellow) on undertail. Pattern color olive-brown (2.5Y-3.5Y): lightest (moderate) on yoke and face pattern, darkest (dark olive-brown) on crown and rump. **Unfeathered parts.** Irides brown; eyelid rims grayish brown. Upper mandible olive-brown or grayish olive-brown; lower mandible and tomia at base of bill orange-yellow; nail light brownish red, paler at tip; egg-teeth light dull yellow or dark yellow. Tarsi and toes grayish yellow or moderate orange-yellow, paler and a bit brighter along sides of toes and on inner web of II; pattern and webs dark brownish gray or dark olive-brown; contrast usually good.

A. cyanoptera. Materials examined: 55 live, 27 study skins. Description based on downies of subspecies *septentrionalium* Snyder and Lumsden, reported by Delacour (1956: 177) to be "paler and yellower than [nominate] *cyanoptera.*" **Plumage.** Base color greenish yellow (7.5Y; 10Y): brightest (vivid) on lores and (in some individuals) on face, forehead, breast, belly, dorsal spots, wing-patches, and tibiotarsi (a bit duller [moderate, light, or brilliant] on other individuals); 'dusky' (moderate toward grayish) on cheeks (some individuals) with somewhat lighter area under or around eye; a bit duller (light) on undertail. Pattern color olive (7.5Y [1Y-10Y]): moderately dark on yoke and entire back ("yellowish olive"; Spencer 1953: 124), much brighter (moderate) on crown adjoining pale forehead (all three areas with many light greenish yellow down-tips), duller (olive-gray) on winglets and rump. **Unfeathered parts.** Irides dark brown, eyelid rims grayish brown. Upper mandible dark reddish gray or brownish gray, lower mandible and tomia at base of bill moderate pink or moderate orange; nail brownish pink, paler at tip; egg-teeth dark yellow or dark pinkish yellow. Tarsi and toes grayish yellow or light grayish brown; claws yellowish gray, light brownish gray, or pinkish gray; pattern and webs brownish gray; contrast fair to poor, seldom good.

A. clypeata. Materials examined: 98 live, 44 study skins. **Plumage.** Base color yellow (2.5Y); moderate to strong on face and breast except usually dusky or ochraceous on cheeks; light and dull (grayish yellow) on wing-patches (if present) and dorsal spots; pale and bright (light yellow) on chin and throat; paler and duller (yellowish gray) on belly and undertail. Pattern color olive-brown (2.5Y): moderate to dark on crown, rump, and eye-stripe; moderate to grayish on yoke and other areas. **Unfeathered parts.** Irides dark grayish brown; eyelid rims dark brownish gray. Upper mandible brownish gray; lower mandible and tomia at base of bill orange; nail dull reddish orange, paler at tip; upper egg-tooth dark yellow, lower not seen. Tarsi and toes strong brownish orange or strong yellowish brown; pattern and webs grayish brown or dark grayish brown; contrast usually good.

Pochards, tribe Aythyini

Aythya valisineria. Materials examined: 49 live, 35 study skins. **Plumage.** Base color greenish yellow (6Y-7.5Y): bright or brilliant on face, throat, and breast; duller and greenish (moderate greenish yellow) on dorsal spots and wing-patches; pale and dull (pale greenish yellow) on chin and (usually) on partial eye-ring or crescent behind and below eye; duller (grayish yellow) on belly; dullest (grayish greenish yellow) on undertail. Pattern color olive (7.5Y-2.5Y): light and grayish on face pattern (if present); moderate on crown and yoke; a bit darker on winglets; moderate and brownish on lower back and rump. **Unfeathered parts.** Irides grayish brown, eyelid rims brownish gray. Upper mandible brownish gray ('bluish' in some individuals); lower mandible and tomia brownish pink to moderate yellowish pink; nail reddish brown, a bit paler and pinker at tip; egg-teeth olive-yellow, dark yellow, or dark greenish yellow, lower opaque, bi-lobed, and elevated. Tarsi and toes light olive-gray to dark grayish yellow, paler and brighter on sides of toes and on inner web of II and I; claws brownish gray; pattern and webs brownish gray to olive-brown; contrast good to fair.

A. americana. Materials examined: 66 live, 46 study skins. **Plumage.** Base color greenish yellow (7.5Y): pale and almost uniformly brilliant on face, throat, breast, belly, and dorsal spots; slightly duller (moderate) on forehead, eye-ring, wing-patches, and tibiotarsi; yellow or pale greenish yellow on undertail. Pattern color olive (5Y): moderate (with many yellow down-tips) on all areas, except slightly darker (toward grayish olive) on crown and rump. **Unfeathered parts.** Irides grayish brown or brownish gray; eyelid rims dark brownish gray. Upper mandible moderate brown, grayish brown, or brownish gray (often 'bluish'); lower mandible, tomia, and base of upper mandible above tomia moderate orange; nail brownish pink (faintly 'bluish' at base), paler and pinker at tip; egg-teeth dull yellow (often pale or chalky), dull greenish yellow, or dark olive-yellow, lower opaque, bi-lobed, and elevated. Tarsi and toes dark yellow, becoming dark orange-yellow along sides of toes and on inner web of II and lobe of I; claws light brownish gray; pattern and webs moderate to grayish yellowish brown; contrast good to fair.

A. collaris. Materials examined: 32 live, 46 study skins, 8 color transparencies. **Plumage.** Base color greenish yellow (7.5Y): brilliant on face, (wash of brilliant yellow [4Y] on cheeks appears 'orange'); a bit duller (light greenish yellow) on breast, eye-ring, and upper belly; slightly darker (moderate) on dorsal spots, wing-patches and tibiotarsi; light yellow (4Y-5Y) on chin; dullest (grayish greenish yellow or pale greenish yellow) on undertail. Pattern color olive-brown (3.5Y): moderate on yoke, winglets, and tibiotarsi; darker (brownish gray to moderately dark olive-brown) on crown and rump. **Unfeathered parts.** Irides dark yellowish brown, eyelid rims dark grayish brown. Upper mandible dark brownish gray; lower mandible and proximal half of tomia of upper mandible moderate orange-yellow to moderate yellowish pink; nail dark brownish pink, paler at tip; egg-teeth orange-yellow, usually dull but sometimes fairly bright, lower opaque, bi-lobed, and elevated. Tarsi and toes dark grayish yellow or "dark gray with faint olive cast" (Mendall 1958: 281), becoming moderate orange-yellow on sides of toes, somewhat paler on inner web of II and lobe of I; claws brownish gray; pattern and webs dark olive-brown; contrast good to excellent.

A. marila. Materials examined: 48 live, 2 frozen, 49 study skins, 6 color transparencies. Description based on Manitoba and Northwest Territories *nearctica* Stejneger; palaearctic *marila* Linnaeus similar, but somewhat darker over all. Nomenclature follows Banks 1986). **Plum-**

age. Base color greenish yellow (7Y; 10Y): generally lightest and brightest on belly or cheeks; paler on malars, throat, and on fronts of alulae and primaries; palest on chin and eye-ring; much duller on dorsal spots (if present) and tibiotarsi; dullest on undertail. Forehead often with many light olive-brown down tips (2.5Y 5/6). Considerable variation in certain areas as follows: cheeks and lores (dark, grayish, dark grayish, moderate, or [rarely] brilliant yellow; light yellow; light or moderate olive; moderate yellowish brown); malars and throat (pale or grayish yellow, pale greenish yellow); chin and eye-ring (pale yellow or whitish yellow); belly (vivid, brilliant, light, or grayish yellow; grayish greenish yellow, light or moderate olive or olive-brown); and undertail (light olive to light grayish olive [near belly], grayish olive [near rectrices]). Pattern color olive: lightest (moderate) on yoke, breast-band, and on sides of undertail between rectrices and tibiae; dark on face pattern (some individuals), winglets, and lower back; darker (dark grayish) on rump; darkest (olive-gray) on face pattern (other individuals) and crown. **Unfeathered parts.** Eye-color description based on eight ducklings from Churchill, Manitoba (6 ducklings from Great Slave Lake, NWT, similar). Irides at hatching light olive-gray, grayish yellowish brown, or (rarely) grayish yellow-green (both sexes: *values* 4.0/-5.0/). Sex difference in eye-color apparent from about two weeks (10 d. in some individuals, 4-7 d. in certain Icelandic ducklings) to four or five weeks: irides of both sexes appear paler (*values* to 6.0/ or 6.5/) and 'bluish' with little or no darker ring around pupil (males: *hue* 5Y-10Y, *chroma* /1.0-/1.5) or blue with [often] brownish ring around pupil (females: *hue* 5B-2.5PB, *chroma* /1.0-/2.5 [David Trauger (pers. comm. 1972) also reported 'blue' eyes in half-grown ducklings from his study area on the West Mirage islands, NWT]); from four or five weeks to six or seven weeks, irides of both sexes become paler (*values* 7.0/ or 8.0/) and greener (males: *hue* 1GY-5GY, *chroma* /0.5-/2.0) or grayer and a bit greener (females: hue 2.5BG-5BG; *chroma* /0.5-/2.0); irides of feathered, flightless [Class III; unsexed] wild *marila* ducklings "rich warm brown" (Brown 1945: 1193); eyelid rims olive-gray. Upper mandible olive-gray or brownish gray, lower mandible and tomia near base of bill moderate orange; nail brownish pink, paler at tip; egg-teeth dull orange-yellow, lower opaque, bi-lobed, and elevated. Tarsi and toes dark yellow, grayish yellow, dark grayish yellow, or grayish greenish yellow; claws grayish olive; pattern and webs olive-gray; contrast fair to good.

A. affinis. Materials examined: 131 live, 1 dead, 81 study skins. **Plumage.** Base color yellow (4Y) to greenish yellow (7.5Y): generally lightest and brightest on face (especially lores); pale on chin; somewhat duller on belly, dorsal spots, fronts of alulae and primaries, and tibiotarsi; dullest on undertail. Considerable variation in certain areas as follows: cheeks (moderate, dark, or grayish yellow; moderate or grayish greenish yellow; light olive-brown); lores (brilliant, light, or pale yellow; grayish yellow); dorsal spots, wing-patches (if present), and tibiotarsi (grayish or dark grayish yellow, light olive [dorsal spots in some individuals moderate yellow]); belly (pale or grayish yellow; light or pale greenish yellow), and undertail (grayish yellow to yellowish gray, darker near rectrices). Pattern color olive (5Y) or olive-brown (2.5Y): lightest (moderate) on yoke, breast-band, and (in some individuals) on sides of undertail between rectrices and tibiotarsi; darker (grayish olive or olive-gray) on face pattern (some individuals), winglets, and back; darkest (dark grayish olive) on face pattern (other individuals), crown, and back. **Unfeathered parts.** Irides at hatching usually brownish gray or moderate olive-brown, sometimes olive-gray or grayish olive (*values* 3.25/-4.5/). Sex difference in eye-color apparent from about two weeks (7-10 d. in some individuals) to three or four weeks: irides of both sexes appear paler (*values* 4.25/-6.0/) and olive (males: *hue* 5Y-2.5GY, *chroma* less than /4.0) or gray with brownish ring around pupil (females: *hues* N, 10YR, *chroma* less than /3.0); irides of both sexes increasingly paler from three or four to six or seven weeks (*values* to 7.5/) and yellower and greener (males: *hue* 5Y-5GY, *chroma* to /4.2) or more or less same as previous group (females); at seven or eight weeks, irides of both sexes still paler (*values* 8.0/-9.0/) and yellower, greener, and more brilliant (males: *hue* 7.5Y-5GY, *chroma* to /8.0) or same as previous group (some females; but others slightly yellower, greener, and brighter: *hue* 10YR-5GY, *chroma* less than /4.0); eyelid rims dark brownish gray. Upper mandible brownish gray (often faintly 'bluish') or dark grayish yellowish brown; lower mandible and tomia at base of bill moderate orange or moderate orange-yellow; nail pinkish brown, paler at tip; egg-teeth dull, pale, or moderate greenish yellow, light or moderate orange-yellow, brownish yellow, or yellowish brown, lower egg-tooth opaque, bi-lobed, and elevated. Tarsi and toes grayish olive or light grayish olive, yellower along sides of toes and on inner webs of II and lobe of hallux (I); claws brownish gray; pattern and webs olive-gray; contrast fair to good.

Eiders, tribe Somateriini

Somateria mollissima. Materials examined: 25 live, 3 frozen, 97 study skins. Description based on North American subspecies *borealis* Brehm (ROM), *islandica* Brehm (BMNH), *dresseri* Sharpe, *sedentaria* Snyder, and *v-nigra* Bonaparte; nominate subspecies *mollissima* Linnaeus similar to *dresseri* Sharpe in general darkness; *faeroensis* Brehm "supposed to be darker" (Delacour 1959: 30). **Plumage.** Base color dull yellow (2.5Y) or dull orange-yellow (10YR): brightest on supraorbital stripe (light yellowish brown [*borealis, islandica, v-nigra*], pale [dull] orange-yellow [*dresseri*], or yellowish gray [*sedentaria*]); usually paler and duller on belly (yellowish gray [*dresseri, v-nigra,* some *borealis,* a few *sedentaria*] or yellowish white [*sedentaria, v-nigra,* other *borealis,* a few *dresseri*), but *islandica* darker (light brownish gray [sometimes also *dresseri,* rarely *v-nigra*]); palest and dullest (yellowish white, white, or 'silvery') on chin, along rami of lower mandible, and on edge of lateral bill feathering (all subspp.); darker and duller on throat (light brownish gray [*borealis, dresseri*] or yellowish gray [*islandica, sedentaria, v-nigra*]). Forehead variable: dark (grayish yellowish brown [some *dresseri*]), dull and light to moderate (light brownish gray [other *dresseri,* some individuals of all subspp.]), pale and dull (yellowish gray [*islandica,* some *sedentaria,* other individuals of all subspp.]), or extremely pale and dull (yellowish white [other *sedentaria*]). Pattern color brownish gray (10YR; 2.5Y): light on breast-band (all subspp.); darker on yoke (grayish yellowish brown [*islandica, dresseri, v-nigra,* most *borealis*] or light olive-brown [*sedentaria,* some *borealis,* possibly some *islandica*]); still darker on crown, rump, and cheek-patch (grayish or dark grayish yellowish brown [*islandica, dresseri, v-nigra,* most *borealis*] or moderate [grayish] olive-brown [*sedentaria,* some *borealis*]); blackish on thin eye-line (all subspp.). **Unfeathered parts.** Live *borealis* and *islandica* ducklings not examined but presumed similar in color to other subspecies. Irides grayish brown, eyelid rims brownish gray (all subspp.). Upper and lower mandibles dark gray (*dresseri, v-nigra*) or medium gray (*sedentaria*); nail pinkish gray (*dresseri, v-nigra*) or brownish pink (*sedentaria*), paler at tip; egg-teeth yellowish gray, yellowish white, or pinkish white; lower translucent and scale-like. Tarsi and toes dark gray (*dresseri, v-nigra*) to moderate [grayish] olive-brown (*sedentaria*), all rather 'bluish' and slightly paler on sides of toes; pattern and webs somewhat darker; contrast poor.

S. spectabilis. Materials examined: 3 live, 67 study skins, 9 color transparencies. **Plumage.** Base color orange-yellow (1.5Y): pale and dull (grayish yellow) on supraorbital stripe and on suborbital crescent (if present); paler and duller (yellowish white) on breast, belly, and undertail; palest (yellowish white to white) on chin and along rami of lower mandibles. Pattern color yellowish brown (10YR): light and grayish on breast-band; moderate on yoke; dark on winglets; dark and grayish on cheek-patch, crown, and rump. **Unfeathered parts.** Irides dark brown or dark grayish brown; eyelid rims brownish gray or "greenish gray" (Sutton 1932: 78). Upper and lower mandibles bluish gray (some darker specimens purplish gray), lower mandible sometimes 'pinker' (=grayish purple), becoming grayish pink or grayish purplish pink on tomia, on swollen frontal processes, and on proximal part of lower mandible; nail grayish pink, paler at tip; upper egg-tooth grayish yellow or pale dull olive, lower grayish yellow, translucent and scale-like. Tarsi and toes brownish gray (often with 'bluish' hue), paler along sides of toes and on inner web of II and I; pattern and webs brownish gray; contrast low.

S. fischeri. Materials examined: 6 live, 7 study skins. **Plumage.** Base color orange-yellow (10YR): lightest and brightest (light yellowish brown or [sometimes] moderate orange-yellow on area surrounding dark 'spectacle'); paler and a little brighter (yellowish gray toward pale orange-yellow) on breast; duller (light yellowish gray) on chin and throat; a bit darker and duller (yellowish gray) on belly; darker (grayish yellowish brown) on undertail; palest and dullest (yellowish gray to yellowish white) along rami of lower mandible and at rictus. Pattern color yellowish brown (10YR): lightest and brightest (moderate yellowish brown) on dark 'spectacle'; very pale and 'silvery' at edge of bill feathering; darker and duller (light yellowish brown) on breast-band; considerably darker and grayer (dark grayish yellowish brown) on crown, yoke, and thin post-orbital streak, also on irregular dark patch from lores to nape below 'spectacle'; still darker (toward dark yellowish brown or blackish brown) on rump. **Unfeathered parts.** Irides dark brown or dark grayish brown; eyelid rims dark brownish gray. Upper and lower mandibles moderate or dark 'bluish' gray, paler and 'bluer' in ducklings one week or older; nail brownish pink or brownish red, paler at tip; upper egg-tooth yellowish white or dull pinkish yellow, lower not seen. Tarsi and toes grayish brown, dark yellowish brown, or moderate 'bluish' gray, paler on sides of toes and on inner web of II; pattern and webs brownish gray; contrast low.

Polysticta stelleri. Materials examined: 14 study skins. Description based on Alaskan specimens (FMNH 3622-25, 14257-58: CM 113641). **Plumage.** Base color orange-yellow (8.5YR; 10YR): dull (light yellowish brown) on post-ocular stripe and on spots around eye, brighter (some individuals toward dark orange-yellow), paler and duller (brownish pink) in others, often paler still (pale yellowish pink) on areas of spots immediately bordering eye; lighter on chin (pale, dull orange-yellow); a bit darker on throat (light grayish yellowish brown); paler and duller on belly and undertail (yellowish gray [some individuals noticeably darker]); 'silvery' at point of mesial bill feathering (some individuals); gray-white on dorsal spots (if present). Pattern color yellowish brown (10YR): dark on winglets; grayish on breast-band; moderate to grayish on yoke; dark and grayish on eye-line, crown, lower back, and rump. **Unfeathered parts.** Quoted color notes from tag data of very young Alaskan specimens (FMNH; coll. H. B. Conover). Irides "brown"; eyelid rims dark brownish gray. Upper mandible blackish brown, "grayish horn [on lower mandible(?); possibly dull yellowish pink or pinkish gray in life]"; lower egg-tooth pale brownish yellow [scale-like posteriorly, slightly elevated anteriorly], upper not seen. "Legs [=tarsi] brownish olive"; pattern and webs dark grayish brown; contrast low.

Sea-ducks, tribe Mergini

H. histrionicus. 4 live, 3 frozen, 19 study skins, 9 color transparencies. Description based on live Icelandic ducklings similar to prepared specimens from E and W North America (e.g., Baffin I. [NMC], Washington [UWBM], and Colorado [CM; Parkes and Nelson 1976]).

Plumage. Base color white (N/10YR): clearest on chin, throat, pre-ocular and (sometimes) supraocular spots, upper cheeks, and belly; gray-white on lower cheeks, wing-patches (some individuals), dorsal spots, undertail, and fronts of alulae, primaries, and tibiotarsi; pale grayish brown on supraocular spot (other times); light grayish buff on narrow wing-patches (most individuals) and on some tail plumes. Pattern color brownish gray (10YR): dark on crown, winglets, and rump (discernible greenish blue iridescence [5B] on crown and back); moderate on yoke, back, and legs. **Unfeathered parts.** Irides moderate brown; eyelid rims brownish gray. Upper and lower mandibles 'pinkish' olive-gray, 'bluish' on narrow area behind nail and above tomia posteriorly to anterior corner of nostril; entire tomia to nail pale dull yellowish pink; nail pinkish brown, much paler and pinker at tip (as in young, wild Greenland ducklings [Nicholson 1930]); upper egg-tooth grayish-white, grayish yellow, or yellowish white; lower translucent and scale-like. Tarsi and toes yellowish gray ('bluish'), paler and yellower along sides of toes, inner web of II, and lobe of I; pattern and webs 'bluish' gray; contrast good to fair.

Clangula hyemalis. Materials examined: 7 live, 2 dead, 2 frozen, 107 study skins. **Plumage.** Base color white (N/2.5Y): clearest on chin and malars; a bit grayer on throat, breast, and belly and on fronts of alulae and primaries; usually brownish on spots around eye, at uneven upper border of cheek-patch, and at rear edge of wing. Pattern color yellowish brown (10YR): moderate on breast-band, dark on yoke and tibiotarsi, dark and grayish on face pattern, crown, winglets, and rump (sometimes a weak, greenish or purplish iridescence on lower back). **Unfeathered parts.** Irides grayish brown or dark brown; eyelid rims brownish gray. Upper and lower mandibles bluish gray or dark bluish gray; nails dark reddish brown, paler and pinkish at tips; upper egg-tooth reddish-brown, dull olive, light yellowish brown, or grayish white; lower pale yellowish brown, translucent and scale-like. Tarsi and toes bluish gray, dark bluish gray, olive-gray, or dark olive-gray; paler and yellower or 'bluer' along sides of toes (some ducklings); pattern and webs dark grayish olive; contrast fair to poor.

Melanitta nigra. Materials examined: 1 live, 1 frozen, 10 study skins. Description based on live *nigra* Linnaeus duckling, and on study skins of *americana* Swainson (USNM). **Plumage.** Base color white (N/10YR): white or grayish white on cheeks, 'silvery' on chin, lower breast, and belly; grayish on dorsal spots (if present) and on undertail. Pattern color grayish brown (10YR): blackish on head; dark on yoke, tibiotarsi, and breast-band; darker on lower back and rump. **Unfeathered parts.** Irides dark olive-brown; eyelid rims dark brownish gray. Upper and lower mandibles blackish olive-brown; tomia (and, in frozen specimen, narrow rim around nostrils) dull orange-yellow; nail reddish brown with dull orange-yellow tip; upper egg-tooth pale dull yellow, lower not seen. Toes and tarsi entirely dark dull olive-brown or greenish brown, webs and pattern a bit darker; contrast low.

M. perspicillata. Materials examined: 9 study skins, 3 color transparencies. Description based on a Saskatchewan specimen (URDB 598; ca. 2 d.). **Plumage.** Base color white (N/10YR): 'silvery' on point of chin feathering, on spot over ear, and on belly; gray on cheeks, throat, and front edges of alulae and primaries. Pattern color blackish brown (10YR): darkest on head and rump; a bit lighter on yoke, breast-band, and undertail; mixed with gray along flanks and on fronts of tibiotarsi. **Unfeathered parts.** Irides "deep olive-brown" (J. Phillips 1926: 47); "bill and feet slaty brown" (Delacour 1959: 151). URDB 598: upper and lower mandibles brownish slate (possibly with 'bluish' tint in live birds); nail reddish brown, paler at tip; upper egg-tooth pale dull yellow, lower not seen. Tarsi and toes blackish olive-brown on outer side, deep olive-brown on inner side, lighter on inner side of toes I, II, and III; webs blackish; contrast very low.

M. fusca. Materials examined: 21 live, 25 study skins. Description based on live nearctic *deglandi* Bonaparte specimens; palaearctic *fusca* Linnaeus similar. **Plumage.** Base color white (N): clearest on chin, throat, and breast; mixed with light brownish gray at rear of cheeks and on sides, flanks, undertail, and front edges of alulae and primaries; dorsal spots and wing-patches (if present) light to pale brownish gray, seldom conspicuously white in young downies. Pattern color brownish gray (10YR): blackish on head except for light brownish gray ('silvery') forehead and medial edges of lateral bill feathering; medium or deep on breast-band and yoke; dark on lower back and rump. **Unfeathered parts.** Irides very dark brown; eyelid rims brownish gray. Upper and lower mandibles very dark bluish gray; nail reddish brown lighter at tip; upper egg-tooth white, lower whitish, translucent, and scale-like. Tarsi and toes dark bluish gray (often with violet tint); webs and pattern a bit darker; contrast low.

Bucephala islandica. Materials examined: 61 live, 8 frozen, 57 study skins. **Plumage.** Base color white (N): clearest on cheeks, throat, breast, and belly; slightly grayish on sides, dorsal spots, wing-patches, and undertail. Pattern color black (N/10YR): purest on 'hood', nape, winglets, and rump; a bit lighter on yoke, gray on breast-band; pale brownish gray ('silvery') on forehead, blending with dark 'hood'. **Unfeathered parts.** Irides in newly hatched birds usually brownish gray, often brown, almost never bluish gray; become strong purple-blue (e.g., 7.5PB 5/12) at about 10-20 days (more so in males) with central brown ring of individually varying width (usually wider in females); gradually duller and 'greener' by seven to nine weeks (C. Nelson 1983); eyelid rims dark gray. Upper and lower mandibles dark gray with faint greenish tint; nail dark reddish gray; egg-teeth chalky white or yellowish white, lower opaque and slightly elevated. Tarsi and toes light olive, yellower on lobe of hallux (I) and inner web of II; pattern and webs olive-gray or dark grayish olive; contrast good.

B. clangula. Materials examined: 65 live, 103 study skins, 3 color transparencies. Description based on ducklings of nearctic *americana* Bonaparte; palaearctic *clangula* Linnaeus similar. **Plumage.** Pattern and color like those of Barrow's Goldeneye, and Bufflehead, both p. 219. **Unfeathered parts.** Irides in newly hatched birds usually brownish gray, often bluish gray or gray, sometimes brown; become light purple-blue (e.g., 7.5PB 6/8—more so in males) at about two to three weeks, with central brown ring of individually varying width—usually wider in females; gradually duller and 'greener' by six or seven weeks (C. Nelson 1983); eyelid rims dark brownish gray. Upper and lower mandibles dark gray with faint bluish tint; nail dark reddish gray, a bit paler at tip; egg-teeth chalky white or yellowish white, lower opaque and slightly elevated. Tarsi and toes light olive, greenish gray, or 'bluish' gray; paler and yellower on inner sides of toes, inner web of II, and lobe of hallux (I); pattern and webs olive, grayish olive, or olive-gray; contrast good.

B. albeola. Materials examined: 12 live, 2 dead, 9 frozen, 24 study skins. **Plumage.** Pattern and color like those of Barrow's and Common goldeneyes, p. 219, but breast-band sometimes poorly defined. **Unfeathered parts.** Irides dark brown; eyelid rims dark gray. Upper and lower mandibles dark gray; nail reddish gray, paler and faintly pinkish at tip, egg-teeth white or dull bluish white, lower opaque and slightly elevated. Tarsi and toes entirely gray, sometimes with pinkish tint on lobe of hallux (I) and webs of inner toe (II); contrast extremely low.

Lophodytes cucullatus. Materials examined: 24 live, 5 frozen, 21 study skins, 1 color transparency. **Plumage.** Base color white (N/2.5Y): clear and often 'creamy' on chin, throat, breast, and belly; clear and slightly grayish on dorsal spots; grayish white or buffy on wing-patches. Primary pattern color yellowish brown (10YR):

grayish on breast-band and along sides of breast and belly; dark and grayish on yoke; darker on winglets, back, and tail; blackish on rump. Secondary pattern color grayish brown (7.5YR): pale yellowish pink to light grayish brown below eye-level, grayish brown on nape and over entire head above eye-level (often a bit of pinkish gray on forehead), dark on eye-stripe (if present). **Unfeathered parts.** Irides moderate yellowish brown; eyelid rims dark grayish brown. Upper mandible brownish slate; lower mandible, lamellae, tomia, and base of bill at commissure yellowish pink to light orange; nail light reddish brown, paler and pinker at tip; upper egg-tooth pale dull yellow, yellowish white, or pinkish white; lower yellowish white, translucent and scale-like. Toes and tarsi grayish olive, paler and yellowish on inner web of II and on lobe of hallux (I); pattern and webs olive-gray or brownish gray; contrast low.

Mergus serrator. Materials examined: 17 live, 60 study skins. Description based on live *serrator* Linnaeus ducklings; specimens of *schiøleri* Salmonsen similar. Colors of closely similar Common Merganser, *M. merganser,* where different from those of *M. serrator,* follow in parentheses or square brackets [ ]. **Plumage.** Base color white (N): clear or faintly 'creamy' on loreal stripe, spots above eye (some *M. serrator,* few *M. merganser*), chin, throat, breast, and belly; grayish white on dorsal spots, wing-patches, tail plumes (some individuals both spp.), undertail, and along sides. Primary pattern color brown (10YR [8.5YR]): dark grayish and yellowish on yoke, back, tibiae, and tail (a bit darker and less yellowish in *M. merganser*); dorsal down has long, light grayish brown down plumes, usually more numerous on rump and tail (sometimes a weak, bluish green iridescence both spp.); a bit darker on winglets and rump (*M. merganser* brownish gray). Secondary pattern color orange (3.5YR to 1.5Y [5YR to 6.5YR]): pale yellowish pink on spots above eye (some individuals both spp.) and along sides of dark eye- and rictal stripes (blended area extensive in *M. serrator,* usually narrow in *M. merganser*); light brown to brownish orange on spots above eye (most *M. serrator,* other *M. merganser*), on cheeks, and from ear region along sides of crown, nape, throat, and neck (lighter area extensive in *M. serrator,* usually more restricted in *M. merganser*); very dark [i.e., brown: grayish and a bit yellowish in *M. serrator,* moderate in *M. merganser*] on crown and nape; darkest [i.e., dark brown: grayish in *M. serrator,* blackish in *M. merganser*] on eye- and rictal stripes. **Unfeathered parts.** Irides light grayish blue, light bluish gray, or light gray; inner ring of iris brownish gray; eyelid rims dark 'bluish' gray. Upper mandible dark grayish yellowish brown; lower mandible light brown; nail light brown, paler and pinkish at tip; upper egg-tooth whitish, light brown, pale yellowish brown, or pale yellowish pink; lower yellowish white, translucent and scale-like. Tarsi and toes grayish yellow or grayish orange-yellow, paler along sides of toes, inner web of II, and lobe of hallux (I); pattern and webs brownish gray to moderate olive-brown; contrast fair.

M. merganser. Materials examined: 27 live, 43 study skins. Description based on live specimens of *americanus* Cassin; *merganser* Linnaeus similar except for loreal stripe variations (Bauer and Glutz von Blotzheim 1969; Fjeldså 1977) and more strongly hooked nail. **Plumage.** See Red-breasted Merganser, p. 220. **Unfeathered parts.** Irides light blue-gray, light brownish blue-gray, or light brownish gray; inner ring of iris brownish gray; eyelid rims dark olive-gray. Upper and lower mandibles dark brownish gray; nail brownish pink or pale purplish pink, darker and browner at base, whitish or 'creamy' at tip; upper egg-tooth white or yellowish white, lower yellowish white, translucent and scale-like. Tarsi and toes yellowish gray, light grayish yellowish brown, or brownish gray (dark individuals); 'bluish' on tarsi and tops of toes, paler and yellower on sides of toes and webs, inner web of II, and lobe of hallux (I); pattern and center part of webs brownish gray or dark brownish gray; contrast good to excellent.

Stiff-tailed ducks, tribe Oxyurini

Oxyura jamaicensis. Materials examined: 41 live, 33 study skins. Description based on ducklings of subspecies *rubida* Wilson; South American subspecies *ferruginea* (Eyton) "darker...cheeks reddish...with no white spots on the back and no whitish line below the eye" (Delacour 1959: 234); *andina* Lehmann more like *rubida* Wilson, with "chin, sides of face and side of neck whitish [and] two white [dorsal] spots [but without dark cheek stripe?]" (Lehmann 1946: 222-23). **Plumage.** Base color orange-yellow (2.5Y; 10YR): extremely pale yellow, yellowish white, or yellowish gray on cheeks and lores; yellowish white ('creamy') or white on chin, belly (some individuals), fronts of alulae and primaries, and dorsal spots; yellowish gray on belly (other individuals); yellowish gray to brownish gray on throat; yellowish white or yellowish gray on undertail. Pattern color dark yellowish brown (10YR): grayish (but very dark) on yoke, cheek-stripe (some individuals), tibiotarsi, breast-band and (sometimes) sides of undertail; blackish on crown, cheek-stripe (other individuals), lower back, rump, and tail. **Unfeathered parts.** Irides dark brown or blackish brown; eyelid rims blackish brown. Upper mandible dark grayish brown; lower mandible and proximal third of upper tomia yellowish pink or light yellowish brown; nail brownish red, paler and pinkish at tip; egg-teeth yellowish white or grayish white, lower opaque and elevated. Tarsi and toes very dark yellowish brown or grayish yellowish brown; pattern and webs brownish black or brownish gray; contrast low.

Nomonyx dominicus. Materials examined: 2 study skins. Description based on Cuban specimen (ANSP 167963; ca. 4 d.). **Plumage.** Base color orange-yellow (1Y; 2.5Y): dark on cheeks, superciliary stripe, and tiny central spot on forehead at bill; moderate yellow on lower cheeks, chin and throat; pale yellow on dorsal spots; grayish yellow on belly, on fronts of alulae and primaries, and on small round spot under tail: light olive-brown on undertail anterior to darker band. Pattern color dark yellowish brown (10YR): grayish on yoke, breast-band, and undertail band; blackish on face-stripes, winglets, tibiae, rump, and tail; 'inky' on crown and on midline from nape to tail. **Unfeathered parts.** Irides undescribed (presumed brown or grayish brown re: adult male's "reddish brown" irides [Wetmore 1965: 151]); eyelid rims dark grayish brown. Upper mandible moderate brown to blackish brown; lower mandible and tomia at base of bill (evidently) dull yellowish pink; nail (evidently) brownish red; egg-teeth not seen. Tarsi and toes moderate brown, yellowish on inner web of II, brownish gray on backs of tarsi and webs; contrast poor.

Appendix C
Identification Keys

How to Use the Identification Keys

In the Key to Genera, characters that separate the whistling-ducks, swans, geese, diving ducks, and surface-feeding ducks are presented first, followed by those that distinguish genera. Except in monotypic genera, the Key to Genera is not meant to work at the species level; each polytypic genus has its own Key to Species.

Within each pair of key choices, the most reliable characters are arranged first and the more equivocal ones last. Likewise, the more easily identifiable species are keyed out first, the more difficult ones last. Characters are chosen, insofar as possible, to emphasize quantitative differences in plumage pattern and bill structure rather than color differences which, although undeniably attractive, are subject not only to fading and 'foxing', but also to a good deal of subjective interpretation. The use of color as a primary diagnostic character has resulted in many specimens being misidentified by banders and collectors. To list but two examples: dark-faced Class Ia American Wigeon ducklings are frequently misidentified as Lesser Scaup, and brownish gray and white Class II Ruddy ducklings have been taken for half-grown Northern Pintails or Ring-necked Ducks. In both cases, similar coloration appears to have distracted the observer from diagnostic hallux, bill, and pattern characters. When it was necessary to use color as a distinguishing character, I described it either by means of Munsell evaluations of the color dimension relevant to a particular key choice or in widely-understood generic terms, with few adjectives. In the same way, I have not used general body size as a primary character unless no other diagnostic criteria were available. In the few cases where its use was unavoidable (e.g., Snow Goose, Hawaiian Duck), comparative measurements of closely related taxa are given.

The figure captions contain known age (in parentheses) or estimated age [in square brackets] of the specimens illustrated, as well as minimum information on geographical origin. More detailed information appears under "Source of Specimens" at the end of each species account, where specimens used as figure models are also listed. Designations of age class (Ia, Ic, IIb, etc.) follow Gollop and Marshall (1954; see also Southwick 1953, Bellrose 1980). Consult the Glossary for definition of terms.

In executing the life-size drawings for the keys, I chose as models specimens that displayed clearly the characters typical for a species. With only a few exceptions, the selection of 'typical' characters was based on the examination of several additional live and prepared specimens. Occasionally, it was necessary to compensate in a drawing for an obvious artifact of preparation. To this end, I straightened feathers that had become bent or twisted in preparation or storage, I closed open bills and smoothed grooves and craters left by preparators, and I straightened some crooked necks and unstuffed a few chins. For the most part, however, the specimens were measured and drawn exactly as the preparators made them.

Finally, some words of caution. Do not leaf quickly through the keys, looking for a 'portrait' of the specimen in your hand: you may find one, but more likely you will not. Instead, begin with the Key to Genera and read each pair of key choices carefully and completely, comparing each separate character with those of your specimen, and make your decisions accordingly. You should arrive at a positive identification with a minimum of difficulty.

Key to Genera

Caution: Key characters do not necessarily apply to non-North American species or to certain aviary or introduced specimens which may represent integrades of subspecies (e.g., Canada Geese, Common Eiders); they do not apply at all to domestic varieties and their hybrids.

1a. Tarsus entirely reticulate, i.e., net-like (figs. G-1, G-2); upper surfaces of all toes reticulate or irregularly scutellate on proximal phalanges, scutellate on distal phalanges. Note: if tarsus is concealed by preparation technique, examination of proximal phalanges of toes III or IV will give needed information. Use hand-lens. Sub-family Anserinae. Go to 2.

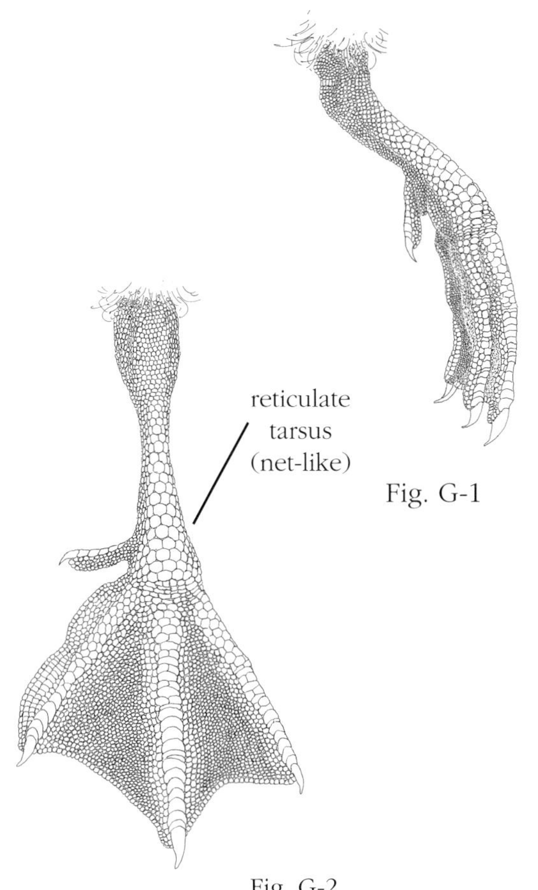

Fig. G-1

Fig. G-2

1b. Front of tarsus and entire upper surface of toes III and (usually) IV scutellate, i.e., scaled (figs. G-3, G-4); proximal phalanges of toes II and (sometimes) IV irregularly scutellate. Sub-family Anatinae. Go to 8. See Note under 1a.

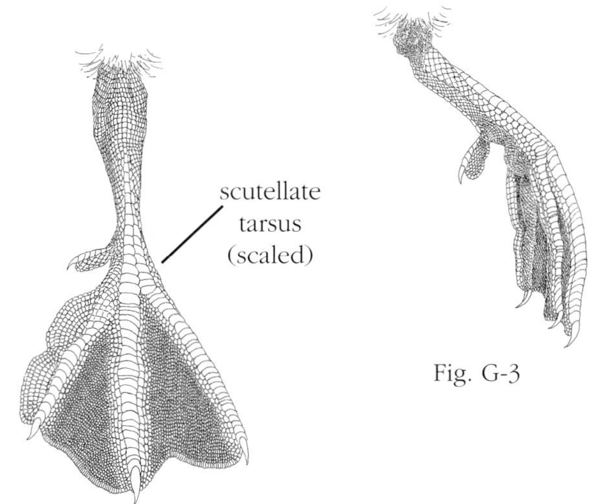

Fig. G-3

Fig. G-4

2a. Tibio-tarsi always partly exposed above 'heel' (figs. G-5); hallux long and well-developed: in live birds, mean ratio of hallux with claw (Iw) to tarsus (TMT)=0.49 (0.37-0.61; n=24, SD=0.081, SE=0.016; fig. G-5, G-6). Whistling-ducks, tribe Dendrocygnini. Genus *Dendrocygna*, pp. 237-39. Note: hallux is attached on proximal (inner) side of tarsus. When measuring hallux, be sure that calipers reach point of attachment on upper side of hallux.

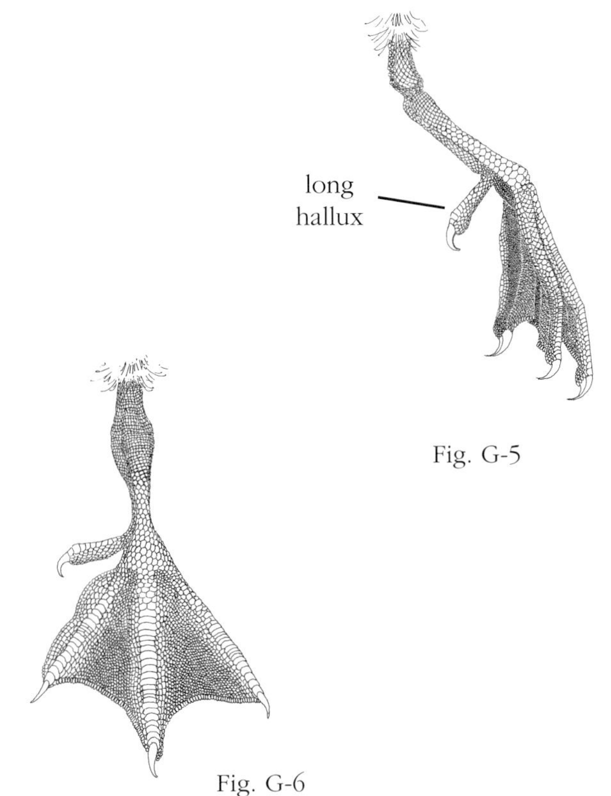

Fig. G-5

Fig. G-6

2b. Tibiotarsi covered to 'heel' by down (figs. G-7, G-8); hallux small or very small: in live birds, mean ratio of hallux with claw (Iw) to tarsus (TMT)=0.26 (0.19-0.36; n=96, SD=0.038, SE=0.004; figs. G-7, G-8). Go to 3. See Note under 2a.

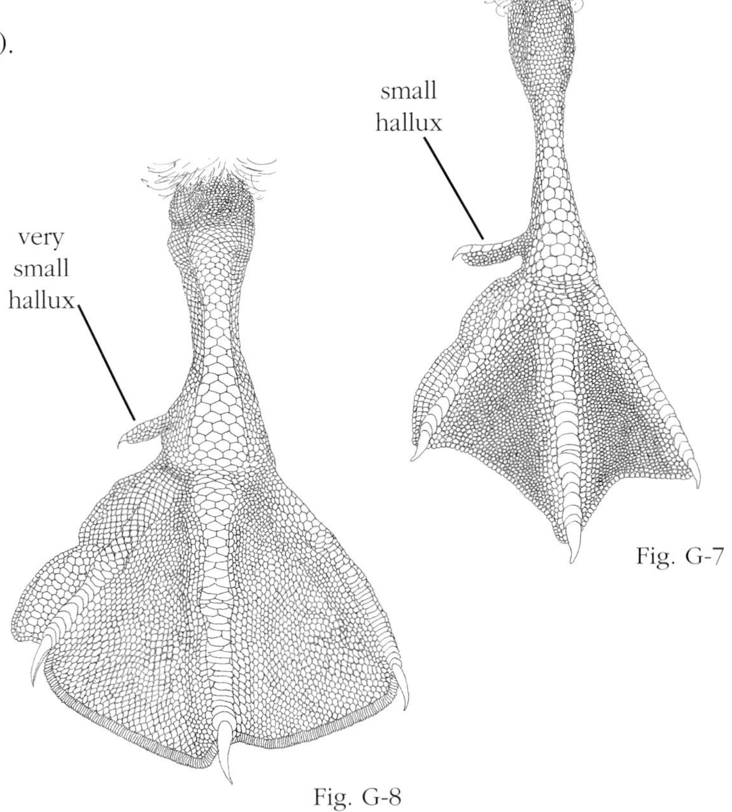

Fig. G-7

Fig. G-8

3a. Tarsus always shorter than middle toe with claw: in live birds, mean ratio of tarsus (TMT) to middle toe with claw (IIIw)=0.79 (0.69-0.85; n=10, SD=0.046, SE=0.015); depth of tarsus at mid-point (DT) exceeds or is more or less equal to Iw: in live birds, mean ratio of DT/Iw= 1.31 (1.10-1.50; n=12, SD=0.129, SE=0.037 [2 spp.]) or 0.90 (0.71-1.04; n=6, SD=0.120, SE=0.049 [1 sp.]) — same proportions found in some museum specimens (e.g., fig. G-9), but ratios usually about 1.00 or smaller in all three species; tarsal skin on live young downies shiny, with pronounced folds and wrinkles; tarsal skin on museum specimens usually flattened to form deep ridge on front and rear of tarsal bone (fig. G-9); plumage always appears almost entirely white, gray-white, or light brownish gray, with poor contrast between pattern and base colors. Swans, tribe Cygnini. Go to 4.

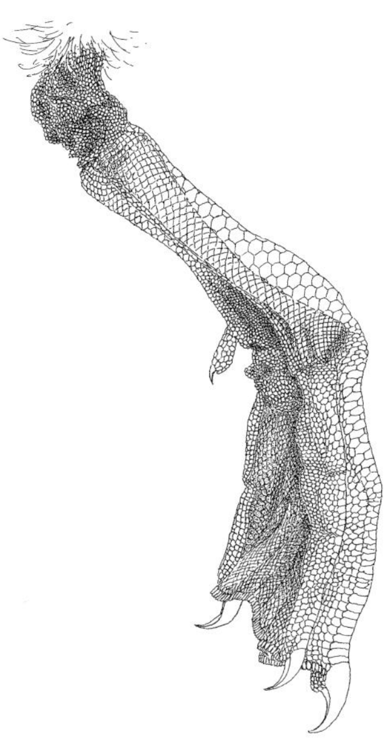

Fig. G-9

3b. Tarsus usually about as long as or longer than middle toe with claw: in live birds, mean ratio of tarsus (TMT) to middle toe with claw (IIIw)=1.01 (0.79-1.23; n=112, SD=0.068, SE=0.006); depth of tarsus at mid-point (DT) nearly always less than or about equal to Iw: in live birds, mean ratio of DT/Iw=0.85 (0.48 - 1.17; n=194, SD=0.122, SE=0.008) — character more pronounced in museum specimens, i.e., ratio averages much lower (see fig. G-10); tarsal skin on live young downies usually shiny (matte in some small, dark-footed species), without pronounced folds and wrinkles as in 3a; tarsal skin on museum specimens shrunken but does not form deep ridges as in 3a (compare figs. G-9, G-10); plumage seldom appears almost entirely white, usually good to fair contrast between pattern and base colors (except 1 sp. sometimes almost entirely dusky olive). Geese, tribe Anserini. Go to 5.

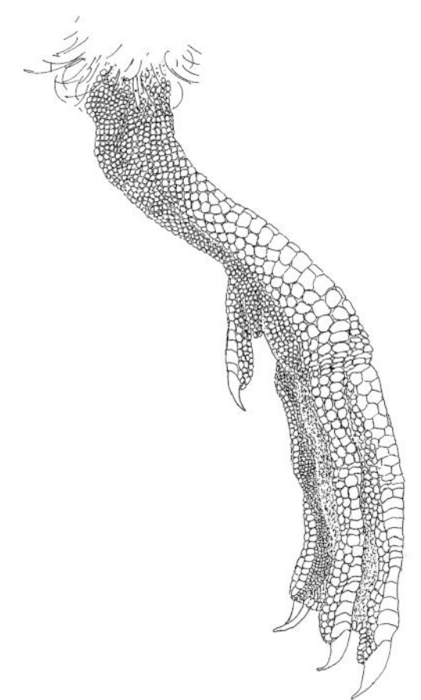

Fig. G-10

4a. Bill blackish (ca. 70% of cygnets) or brownish (ca. 30% of cygnets) with whitish nail; nail of bill with pronounced lateral extensions (fig. G-11); mesial chin-feathering extends well beyond lateral feathering (fig. G-12). Genus *Cygnus*, p. 240.

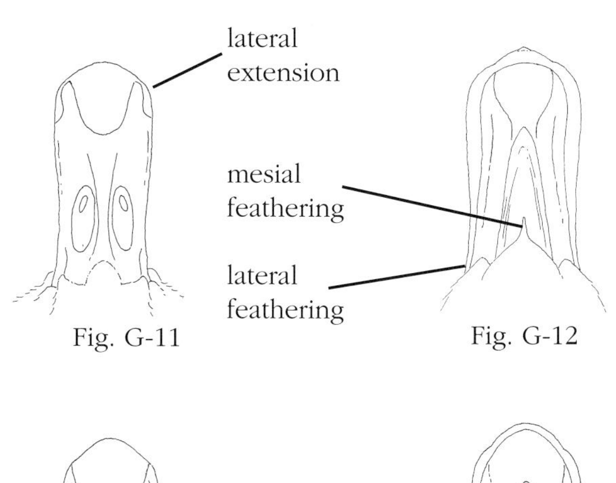

Fig. G-11 Fig. G-12

4b. Bill and nail more or less same pale color; nail of bill without pronounced lateral extensions (fig. G-13) as in 4a; mesial chin-feathering extends little or not at all beyond lateral feathering (fig. G-14). Genus *Olor*, pp. 241-42.

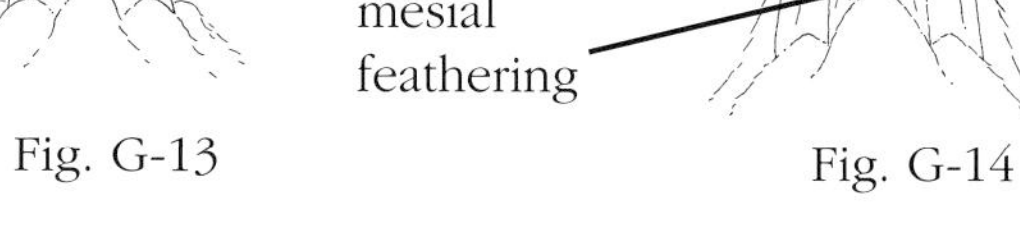

Fig. G-13 Fig. G-14

5a. White area all around bill (fig. G-15); entire base color white from chin to undertail, with no trace of yellow. Genus *Philacte*, p. 249.

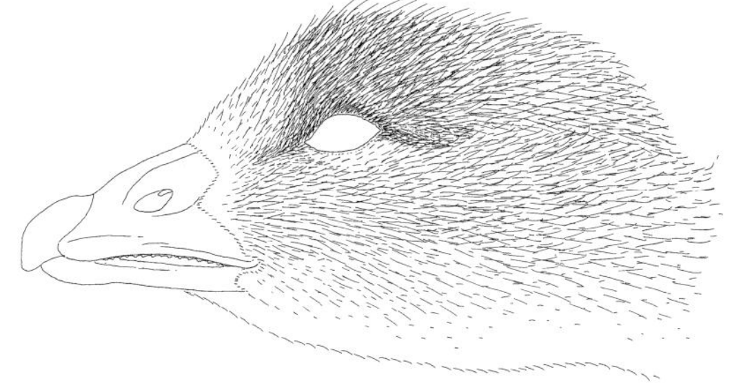
Fig. G-15

5b. Bill without surrounding white area as in 5a; pattern color usually some shade of moderate olive, but sometimes gray, brownish gray, or blackish olive; base color usually yellow, but sometimes creamy, white, gray-white, gray, dusky olive, or pale olive. Go to 6.

6a. Well-marked dark crown-patch always continuous with dark nape, usually also joined to eye-stripe, 'mask', or ear-spot (fig. G-16); large ear-spot nearly always dark and conspicuous (fig. G-17); pattern color brownish gray or grayish brown; base color yellowish white or grayish white, often 'silvery'. Genus *Nesochen*, p. 259.

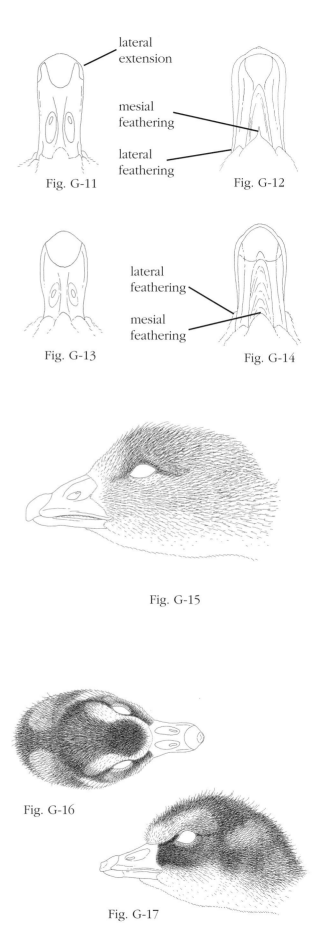

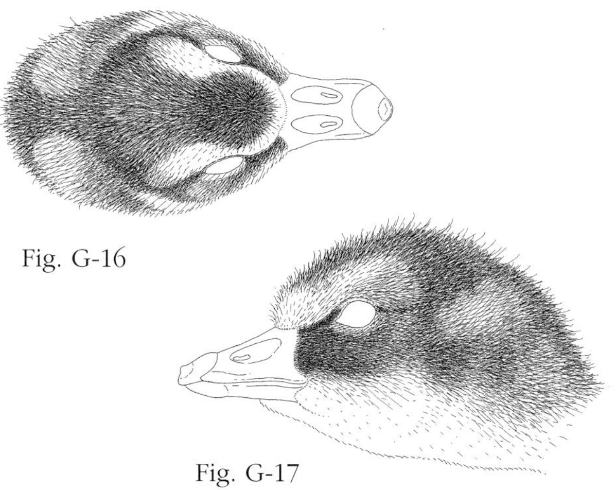
Fig. G-16

Fig. G-17

6b. Usually well-marked dark crown-patch clearly separated from pale nape (except 1 sp. sometimes with darker connecting band on hind-neck), does not join with eye-stripe, 'mask', or ear-spot as in 6a. (figs. G-18, G-19); small ear-spot almost never dark and conspicuous, sometimes virtually lacking (fig. G-19); pattern color usually some shade of olive (1 sp. sometimes blackish), but sometimes gray; base color usually yellow, but sometimes creamy, white, gray-white, gray, pale olive, or dusky olive. Go to 7.

7a. Entire nail area lighter than rest of bill; breast and belly never patterned; in dorsal view, head pattern crescentic (often very pale) behind eye-level (figs. G-20, G-21), diffuse—covering all or nearly all of crown and blending gradually into a paler forehead (figs. G-22, G-23), or totally concealed by dark down (fig. G-24); small eye-stripe usually present (fig. G-25), sometimes poorly marked (fig. G-26); grinning patch or prominent lamellae evident in profile (fig. G-25), more so in older downies (fig. G-27). Genus *Anser,* pp. 243-48.

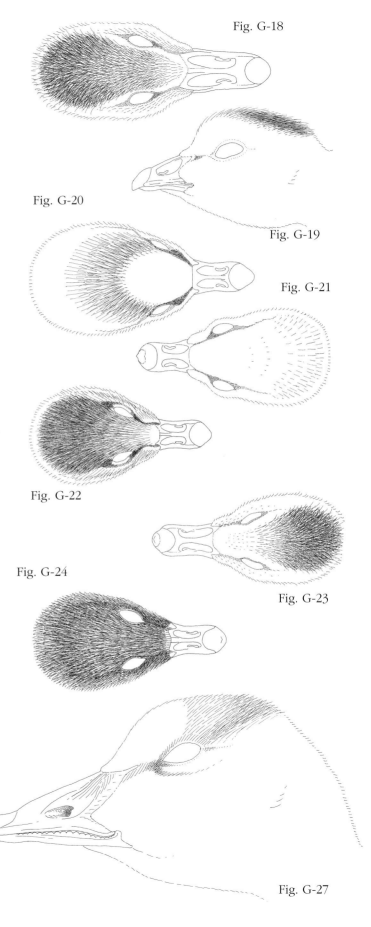

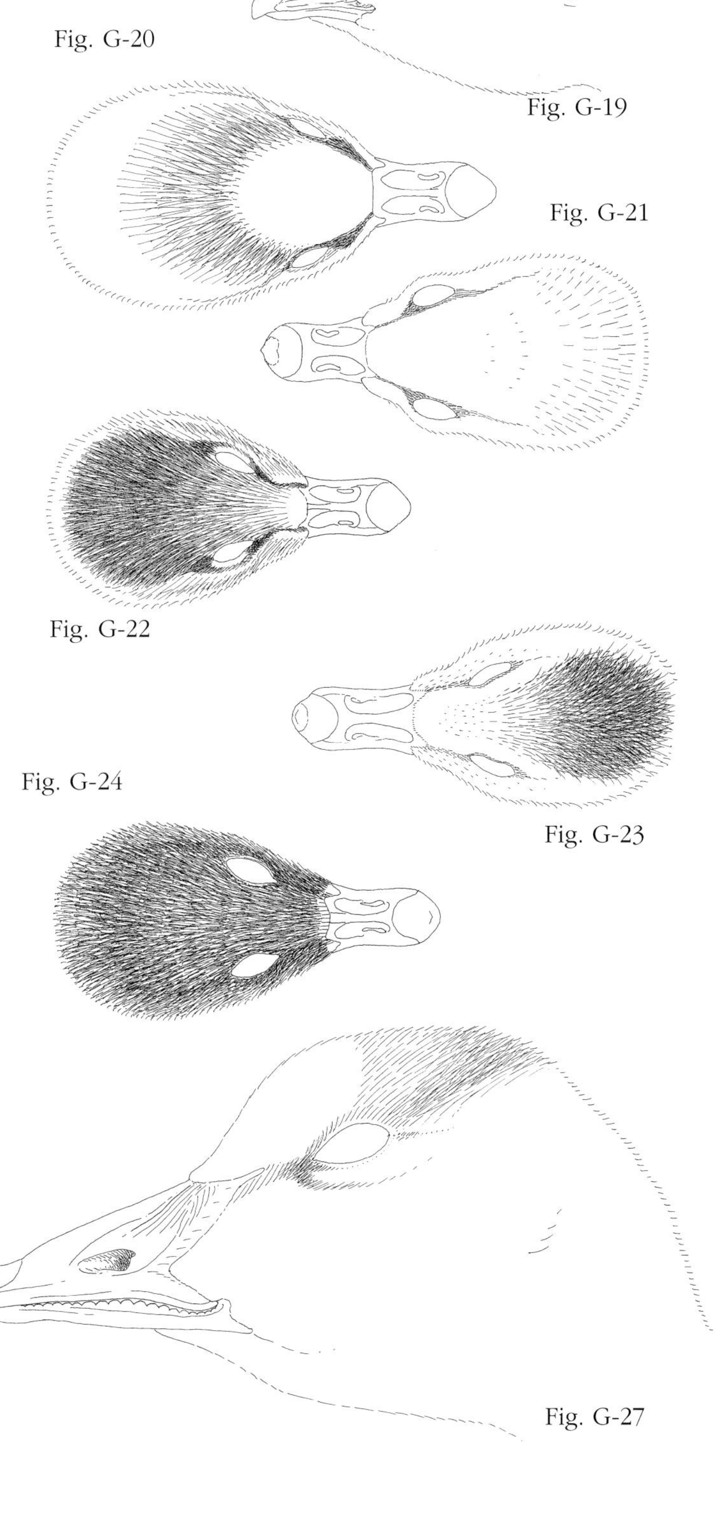

Fig. G-18

Fig. G-20

Fig. G-19

Fig. G-21

Fig. G-22

Fig. G-24

Fig. G-23

Fig. G-25

Fig. G-27

Fig. G-26

7b. Entire nail area nearly as dark as rest of bill (except 1 gray-plumaged sp. with whitish nail-tip); breast or belly often with transverse contrasting band; in dorsal view, head pattern always some variation of a more or less round, dark cap, usually clearly separated from pale forehead (figs. G-28, G-29) but sometimes with line of dark down from crown to forehead (figs. G-30, G-31, also fig. 3-125, Key to *Branta* spp.); dark cap sometimes extends to forehead and below eye-level to lore (fig. G-32); eyestripe, if present, usually combined with small 'bridle' or 'mask' (figs. G-33, G-34) or (1 sp.) merged with dark crown color to form 'hood' (figs. G-32, G-35); grinning patch never present, lamellae seldom prominent (fig. G-36), even in older downies (fig. G-37). Genus *Branta*, pp. 250-58.

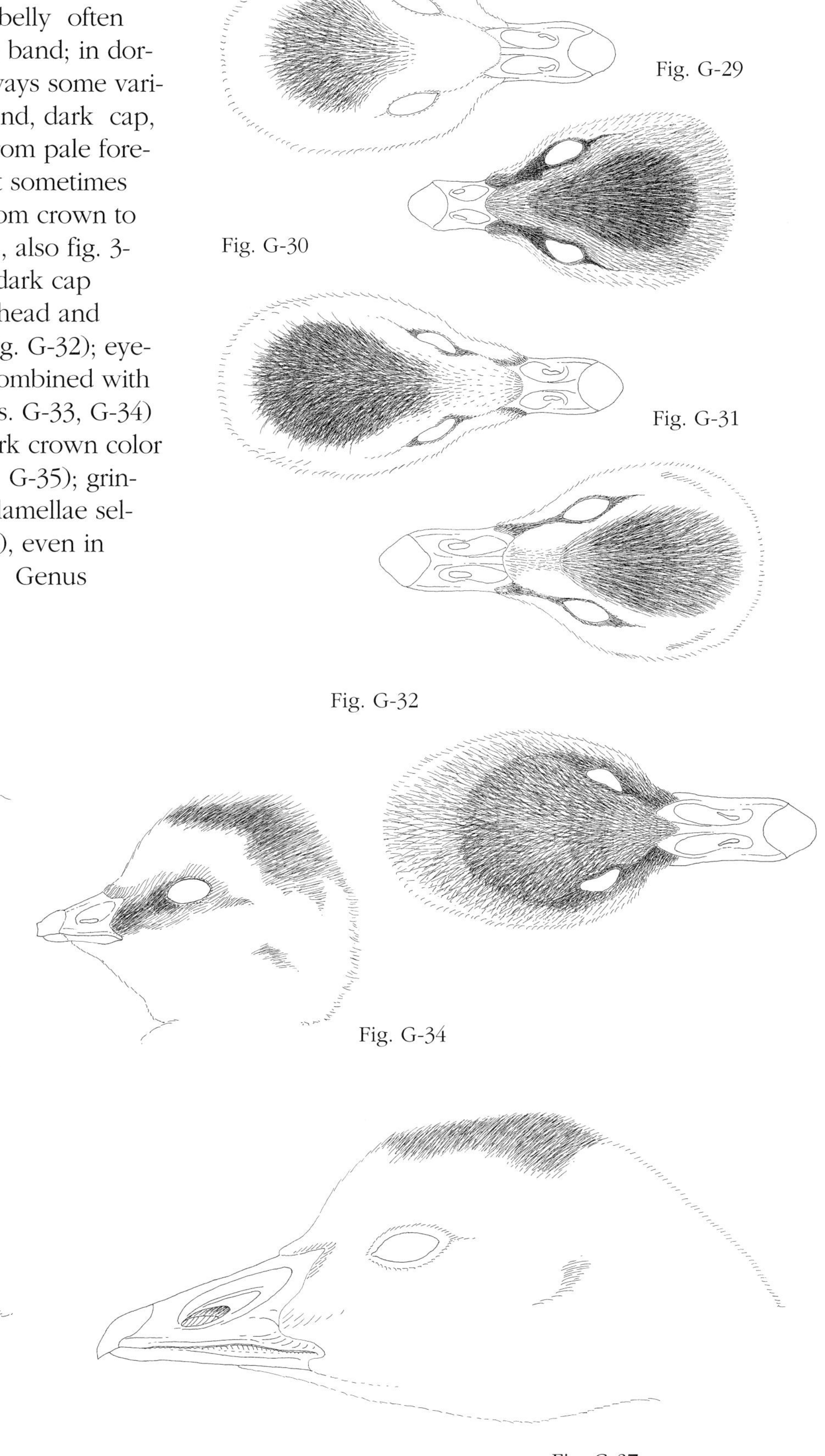

Fig. G-28

Fig. G-29

Fig. G-30

Fig. G-31

Fig. G-32

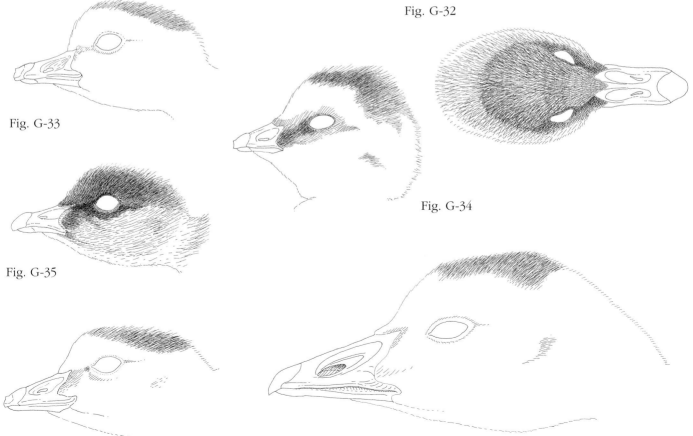

Fig. G-33

Fig. G-34

Fig. G-35

Fig. G-36

Fig. G-37

8a. Hind edge of hallux forms prominent notch at juncture with tarsus; flattened lobe of hallux deepest near notch: about 4 x (or more) deeper than hallux bone; tip of hallux usually extends nearly to end of claw, following closely beneath it to form a more or less continuous visual curve, as indicated by dotted line (....); length of middle (III) and outer (IV) toes with claw nearly always more or less equal, IIIw often shorter than IVw. Compare carefully figs. G-38, G-39 with figs. G-40, G-41. Diving ducks. Go to 12. ***Caution:*** in some prepared specimens, hallux may be shrunken or folded back against tarsus. Examine with hand-lens in good light; a strip of white paper slipped carefully under the hallux will display it for easier examination.

8b. Hind edge of hallux does not form prominent notch at juncture with tarsus; flattened lobe of hallux deepest near claw or more or less same depth from claw to notch: about 2 to 2½x deeper (rarely more) than hallux bone; tip of hallux usually does not extend nearly to end of claw, or follow closely beneath it, or form visual curve as in 8a; length of middle (III) and outer (IV) toes with claw almost never more or less equal, IIIw almost never shorter than IVw. Compare carefully figs. G-38, G-39 with figs. G-40, G-41. Surface-feeding ducks. Go to 9. Observe ***Caution*** as in 8a.

9a. Distinct eye-stripe begins at eye (fig. G-42), nearly always contrasts well with lighter base color, but may be extremely thin or lacking in some specimens. Perching ducks, tribe Cairinini. Go to 10.

9b. Distinct eye-stripe begins at bill (figs. G-43, G-44 [diffuse pre-ocularly], G-45 [incomplete pre-ocularly]) or is absent as a distinct pattern (fig. G-46). Dabbling ducks, tribe Anatini. Go to 11.

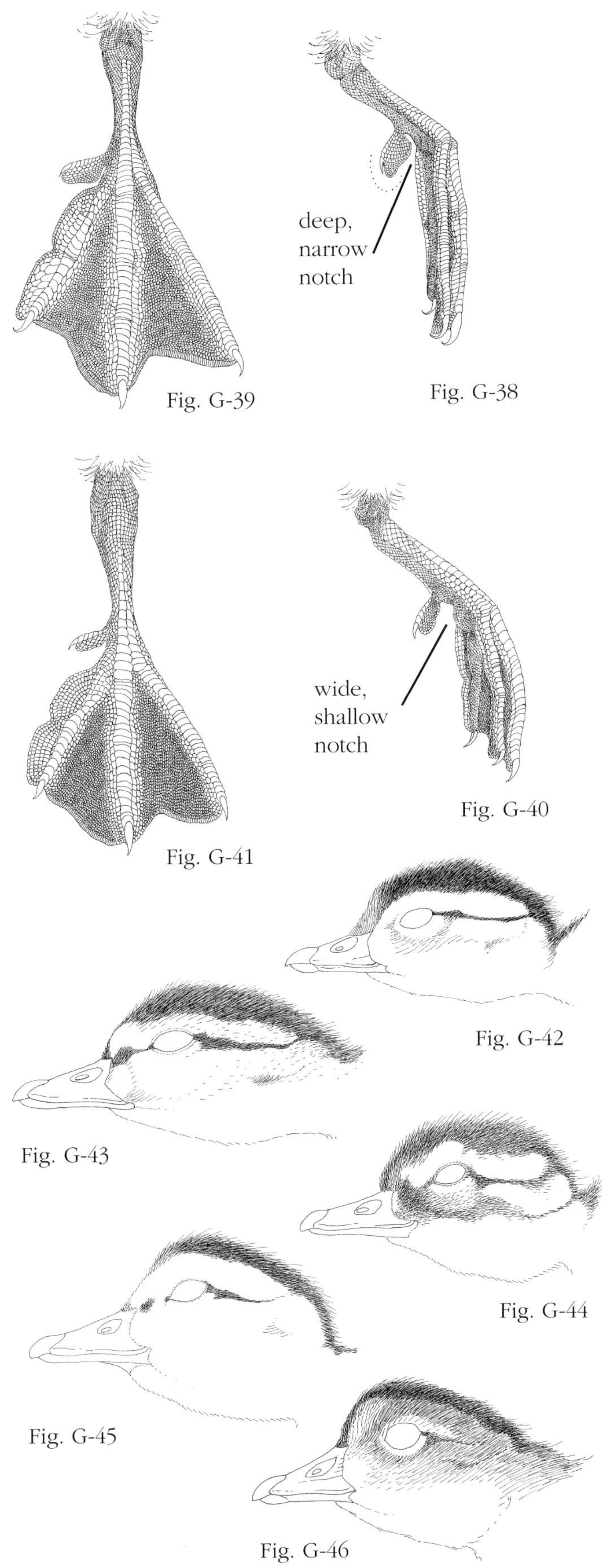

Fig. G-39

Fig. G-38

Fig. G-41

Fig. G-40

Fig. G-42

Fig. G-43

Fig. G-44

Fig. G-45

Fig. G-46

10a. Dark color of crown stops well short of bill (fig. G-47). Genus Cairina, p. 259.

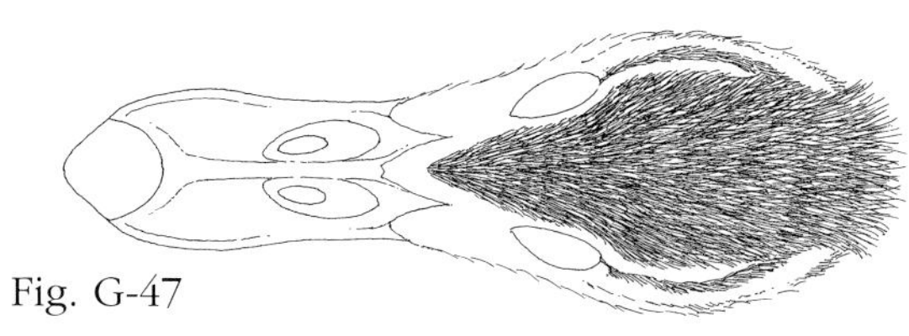
Fig. G-47

10b. Dark color of crown extends all the way to bill (fig. G-48). Genus *Aix*, p. 260.

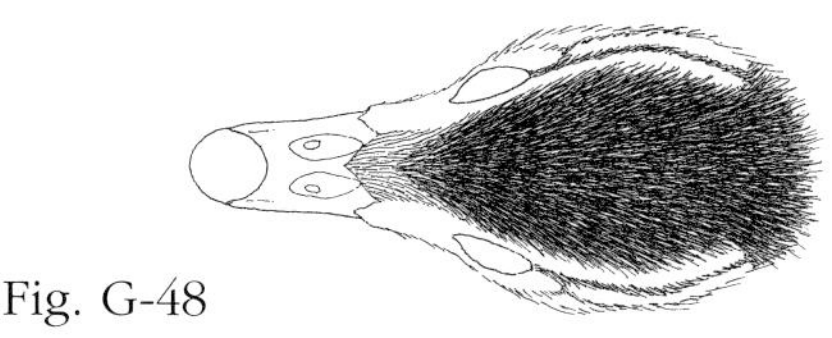
Fig. G-48

11a. Eye-stripe indistinct or incomplete or both, contrasting poorly with lighter base color, or virtually lacking (fig. G-49). Genus *Mareca,* p. 260. ***Caution:*** Check hallux; if flattened lobe is more than 3 x wider than hallux bone, and if tarsus (TMT) is about 70% length of middle toe with claw (IIIw), specimen may be a scaup of either species (compare TMT/IIIw ratios of *M. americana* [TMT/IIIw=ca. 80%], *A. affinis*, and *A. marila* in Table 1, Appendix A). If suspected misidentification, return to 8a and 8b and re-examine specimen.

Fig. G-49

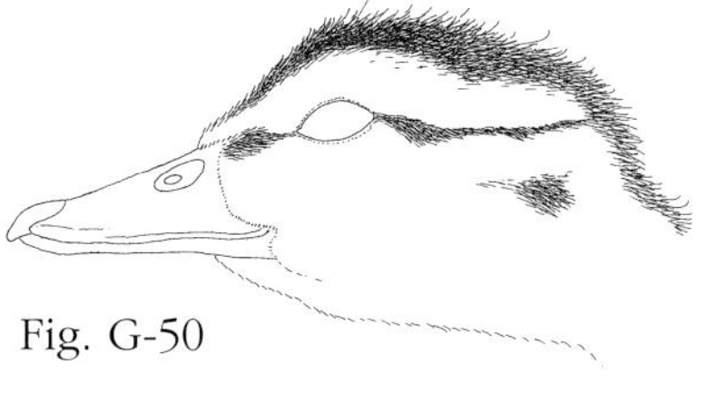
Fig. G-50

11b. Eye-stripe, whether complete or incomplete, contrasts well (fig. G-50) or fairly well (fig. G-51) with lighter base color. Genus *Anas,* pp. 261-70.

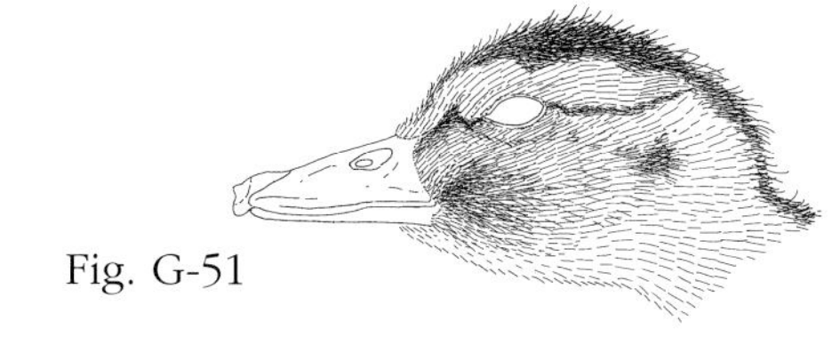
Fig. G-51

12a. Entire upper head dark (black, blackish brown, or reddish brown) to eye-level or below (figs. G-52, G-53, G-54) except one species with yellow base color has prominent light superciliary line and well-marked blackish cheek-stripe extending from near bill to past ear-level (fig. G-55). Go to 15.

Fig. G-52

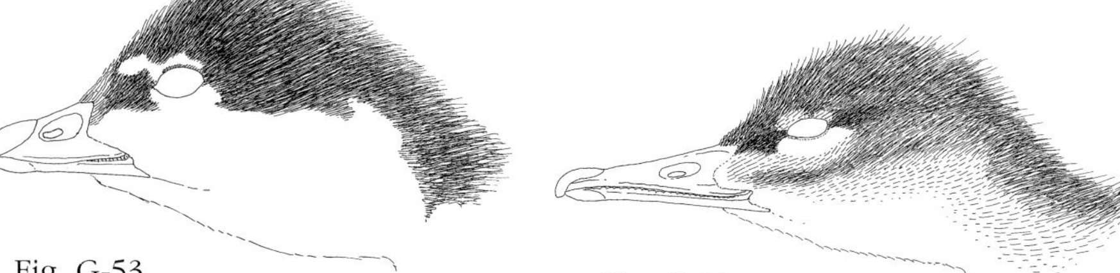
Fig. G-53

Fig. G-54

Fig. G-55

12b. Light supraorbital line or area always present, usually extensive and continuous (figs. G-56, G-57), but sometimes interrupted immediately over eye by blotch or bar of dark pattern color continuous with crown (figs. G-58, G-59; 3 spp.) or by disc or half-disc of dark feathers around or above eye (fig. G-60; 1 sp.). Go to 13.

Fig. G-56

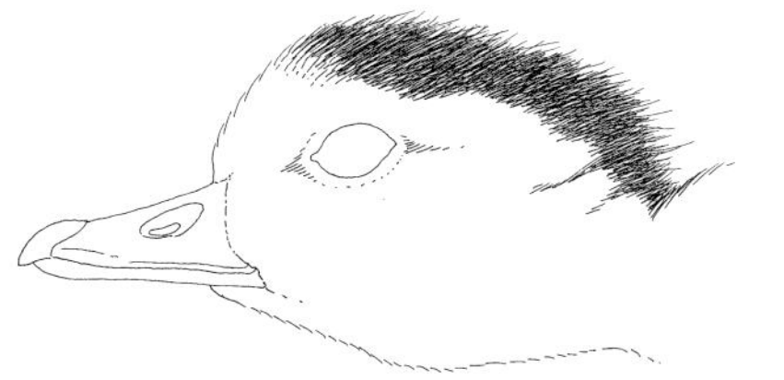
Fig. G-57

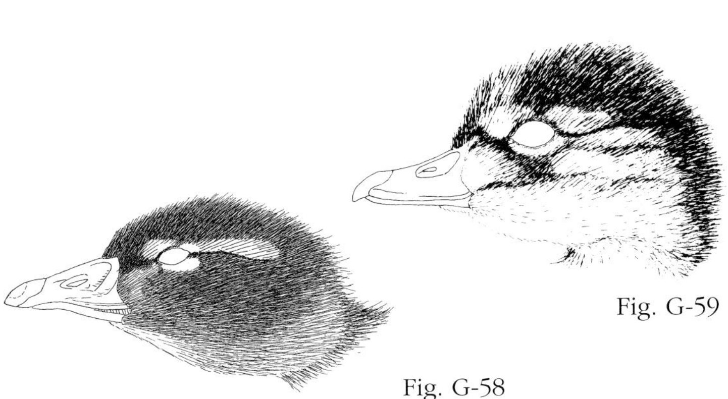
Fig. G-59

Fig. G-58

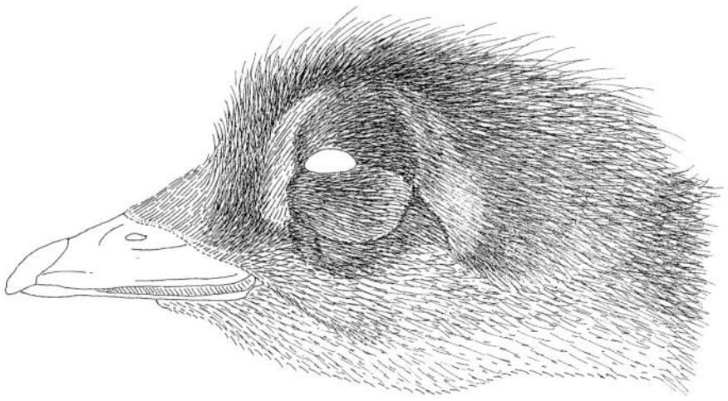

Fig. G-60

13a. Base color of plumage always some tint of yellow (bright or brilliant and greenish in young downies, grayish in older ducklings); pattern color always some shade of olive-brown, brownish olive, or (in older downies) olive-gray or grayish olive; cheeks usually clear (fig. G-57), but irregular, poorly marked stripes sometimes present (fig. G-61); dorsal spots and wing-patches nearly always present, usually conspicuous (but 2 dark-plumaged spp. may have wing-patches and rump-spots inconspicuous or lacking); tarsus (TMT) about 70% length of middle toe with claw (IIIw): in live downies, mean ratio of TMT/IIIw=0.71 (0.63-0.80; n=151, SD=0.027, SE=0.002; see TMT/IIIw ratios of *Aythya* spp. in Table 1, Appendix A). Broad-billed pochards, tribe Aythyini. Genus *Aythya*, pp. 271-74.

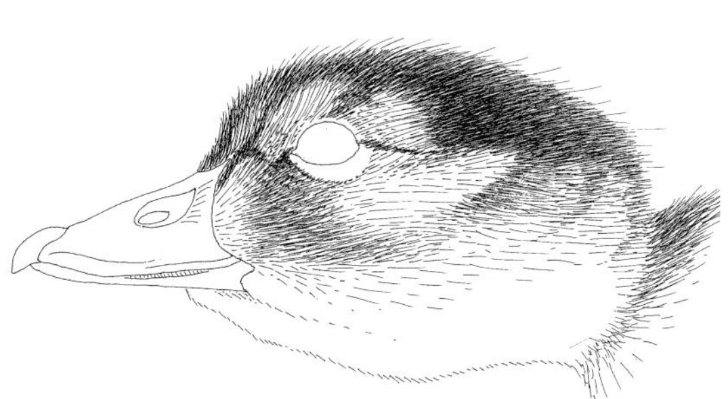
Fig. G-61

13b. Base color of plumage light or grayish yellowish brown (dull buff); pattern color always some shade of grayish brown, fading to brownish gray in older downies; cheeks always some shade of gray or brownish gray (figs. G-60, G-62); dorsal spots and wing-patches nearly always absent (except 1 sp. occasionally has extremely small or inconspicuous dorsal spots — a 'shadow pattern'); tarsus (TMT) about 80% length of middle toe with claw (IIIw): in live downies, mean ratio of TMT/IIIw=0.81 (0.76-0.87; n=21, SD=0.033, SE=0.007; see TMT/IIIw ratios of *Somateria* spp. in Table 1, Appendix A. TMT/IIIw ratios of 5 very young *Polysticta* study skins averaged 0.83 [0.81 - 0.85]). Eiders, tribe *Somateriini*. Go to 14.

Fig. G-62

14a. Bill well-feathered laterally or mesially or both (figs. G-63 to G-65). Genus *Somateria*, pp. 275-79.

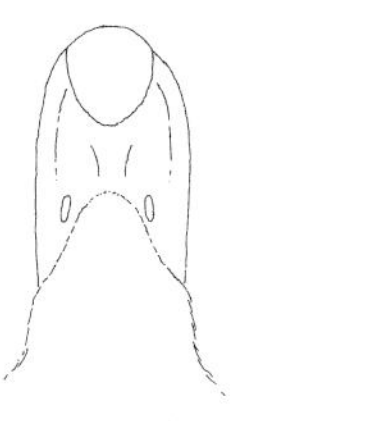

Fig. G-63

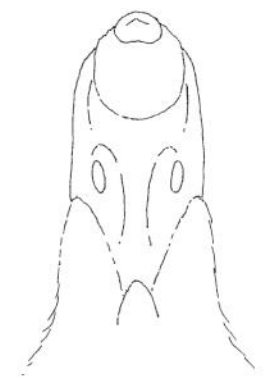

Fig. G-64

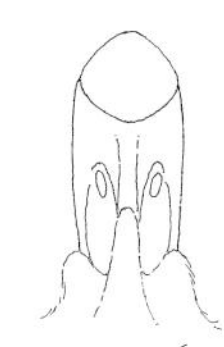

Fig. G-65

14b. Bill unfeathered (fig. G-66). Genus *Polysticta*, p. 279.

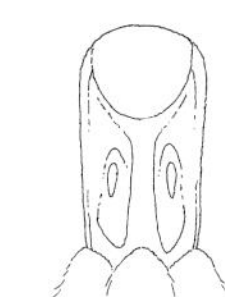

Fig. G-66

15a. 'Cheek' with wide black or blackish stripe of uneven width contrasting well with base color, but sometimes obscure in dark individuals (fig. G-67). Stiff-tailed ducks, tribe Oxyurini. Go to 21.

Fig. G-67

15b. 'Cheek' without wide black or blackish stripe as in 15a. Sea-ducks, tribe Mergini. Go to 16.

16a. Bill narrow and attenuated (fig. G-68), with saw-like lamellae exposed along edges of upper and lower mandibles in side view, especially in older downies (fig. G-69); upper head distinctly reddish brown. Mergansers. Go to 17.

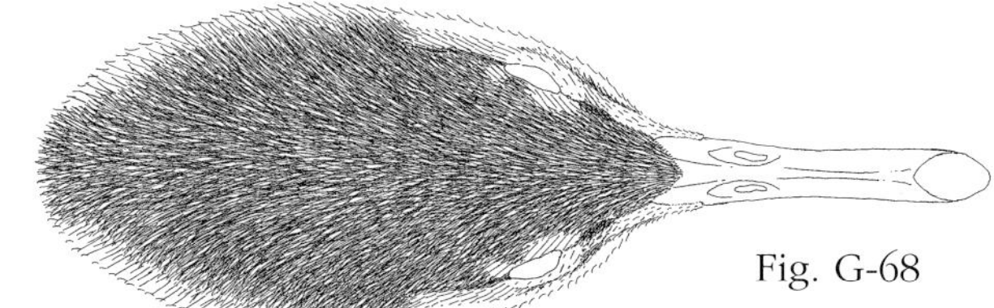

Fig. G-68

16b. Bill more or less wide and spatulate (if narrow, not attenuated as in 12a); upper head black, brown, or brownish gray, without distinct reddish tint. Go to 18.

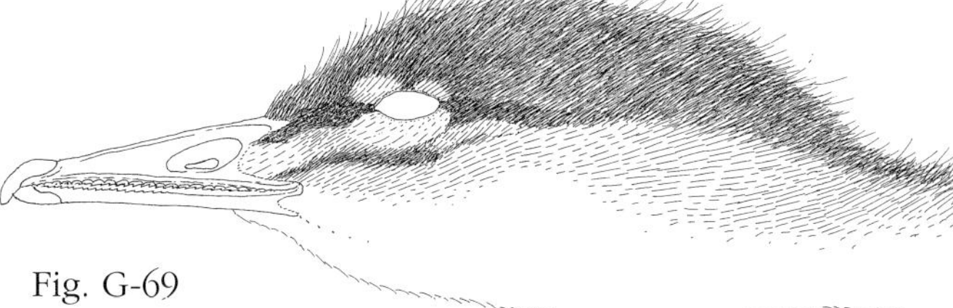

Fig. G-69

17a. Face without strongly contrasting striped pattern (fig. G-70). Genus *Lophodytes*, p. 286.

Fig. G-70

17b. Face with strongly contrasting striped pattern (fig. G-71). Genus *Mergus*, pp. 287-288.

Fig. G-71

18a. Back with four prominent white spots, wings with prominent white patches (fig. G-72). Genus *Bucephala*, pp. 283-85.

Fig. G-72

18b. Back and wings unspotted or inconspicuously spotted (1 sp. sometimes with 4 spots, 1 sp. with shoulder-spots only). Go to 19.

Fig. G-73

19a. One to four small, light-colored spots above and around eye (figs. G-73, G-74); white or gray-white base color on chin, throat, and sides of head forms large 'cheek-patch', contrasting well with dark upper head. Go to 20.

Fig. G-74

19b. Area around eye unspotted or with single small spot below eye (***caution:*** do not confuse 'spots' with light-colored lower eyelid which may be exposed in certain prepared or frozen specimens); white or gray base color on chin, throat, and sides of head forms large 'cheek-patch', contrasting well (fig. G-75), fairly well (fig. G-76), or poorly (fig. G-77) with dark upper head. Note contour of bill feathering in all three figures. Genus *Melanitta,* pp. 281-82.

Fig. G-75

Fig. G-76

Fig. G-77

20a. Bill narrow, laterally compressed; nail oval (figs. G-78, G-79). Genus *Histrionicus,* p. 280.

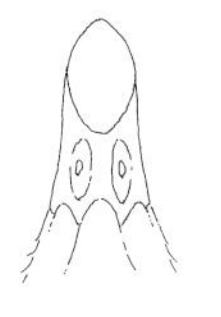
Fig. G-78

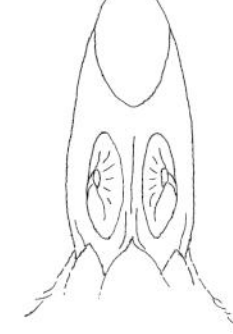

Fig. G-79

20b. Bill wide, not laterally compressed; nail round (figs. G-80, G-81). Genus *Clangula,* p. 280.

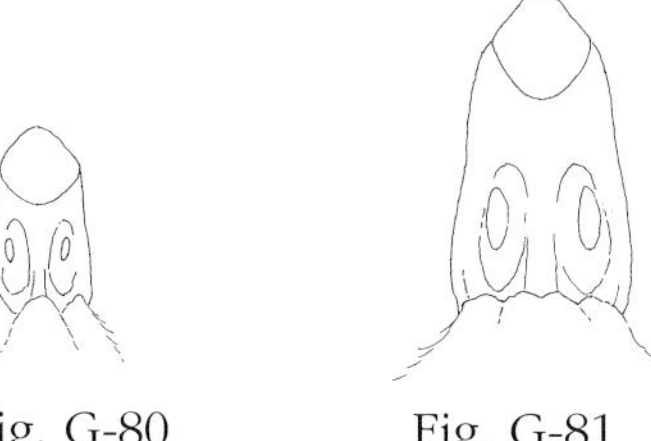
Fig. G-80

Fig. G-81

21a. Broad, pale supraorbital stripe (fig. G-82); nail of bill wide and Mallard-like. Genus *Nomonyx,* p. 289.

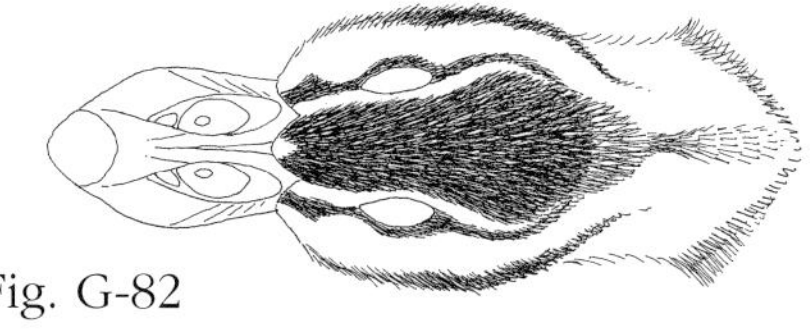
Fig. G-82

21b. Supraorbital stripe lacking; nail of bill extremely narrow (fig. G-83). Genus *Oxyura,* p. 289.

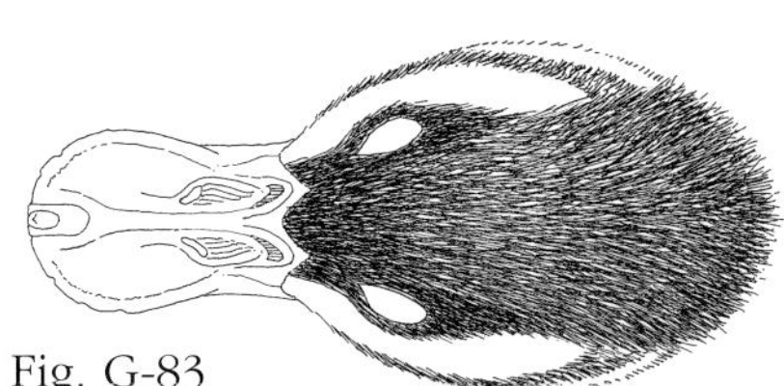
Fig. G-83

Tribe Dendrocygnini
Key to *Dendrocygna* species

1a. Wide, light-colored supraorbital stripe (fig. 1-1). Go to 2.

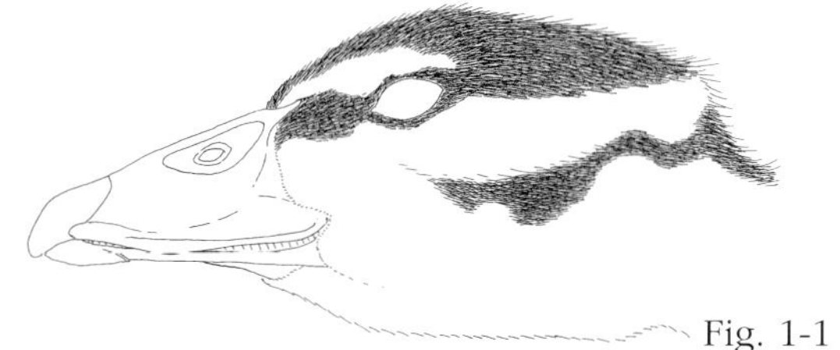
Fig. 1-1

1b. Supraorbital stripe lacking (figs. 1-6, 1-8). Fulvous Whistling-duck, *Dendrocygna bicolor,* figs. 1-2 to 1-8.

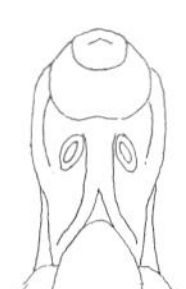
Fig. 1-2

Fig. 1-3

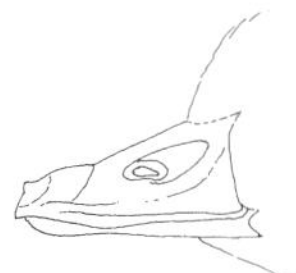
Fig. 1-4

Figs. 1-2 to 1-4 (1 day): captive (Africa and India); figs. 1-5, 1-6 [1-2 days]: California; figs. 1-7, 1-8 [12-14 days]: Louisiana.

Fig. 1-5

Fig. 1-6

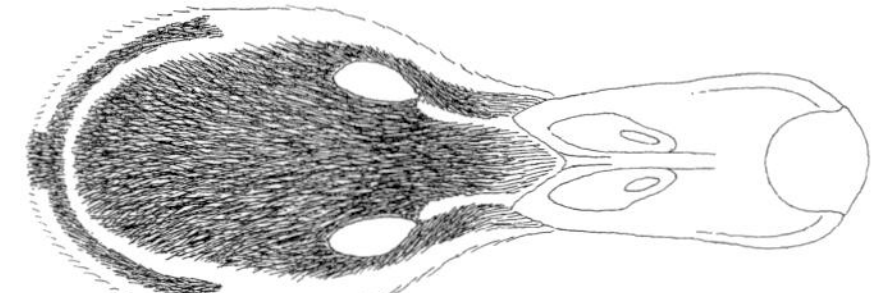
Fig. 1-7

Fig. 1-8

2a. Long, dark face-stripe extends clearly and unmistakeably from median occipital stripe forward across ear at least to level below eye, paralleling horizontal dark crown (fig. 1-1), forms straight-armed 'T' at back of head, as partly seen in dorsal view (fig. 1-9). Go to 3.

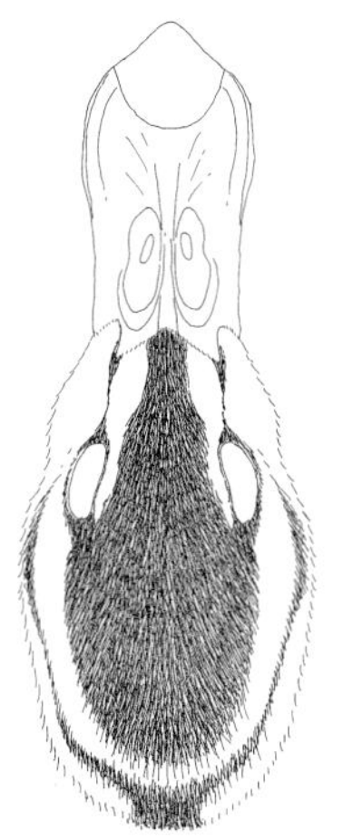
Fig. 1-9

2b. Short, dark face-stripe connected either thinly or not at all to median occipital stripe, does not extend forward to level below eye, does not parallel horizontal line of dark crown, but droops downward over ear (often appears as a well-marked diagonal ear-spot; fig. 1-12), does not form straight-armed 'T' at back of head, as partly seen in dorsal view (fig. 1-11). White-faced Whistling-duck, *Dendrocygna viduata,* figs. 1-10 to 1-12.

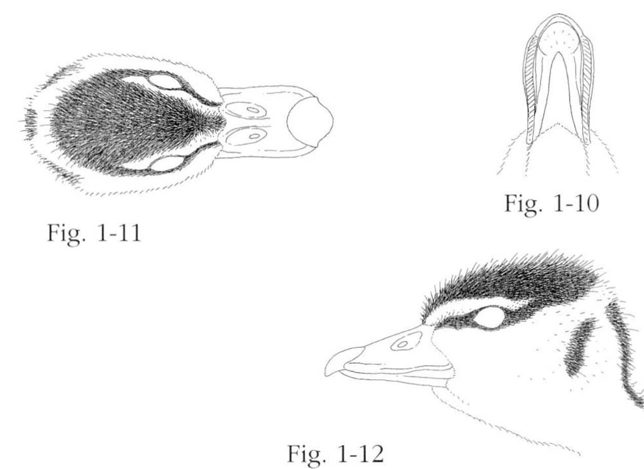

Fig. 1-11

Fig. 1-10

Fig. 1-12

3a. Dark crown nearly always separated from dark bill by conspicuous line or stripe of light-colored down; base color of plumage of very young downies nearly always exceedingly pale (Munsell *value* 9/ or more) but fairly bright on face (Munsell *chroma* /4 or higher), 'silvery' on belly. West Indian Whistling-duck, *Dendrocygna arborea,* figs. 1-13 to 1-19.

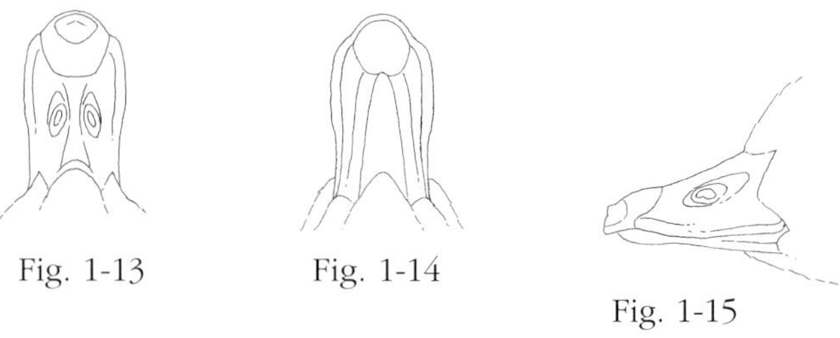

Fig. 1-13

Fig. 1-14

Fig. 1-15

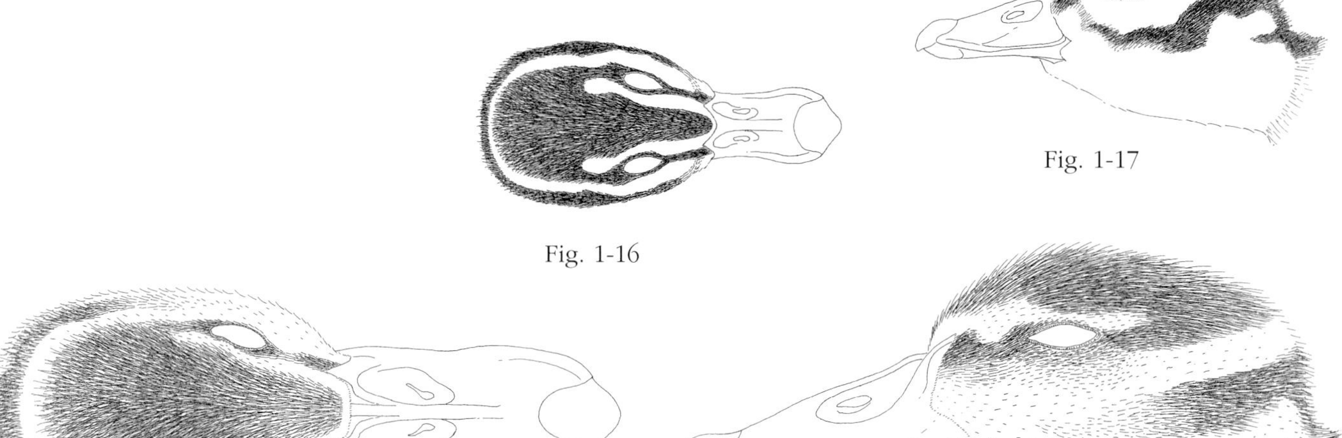

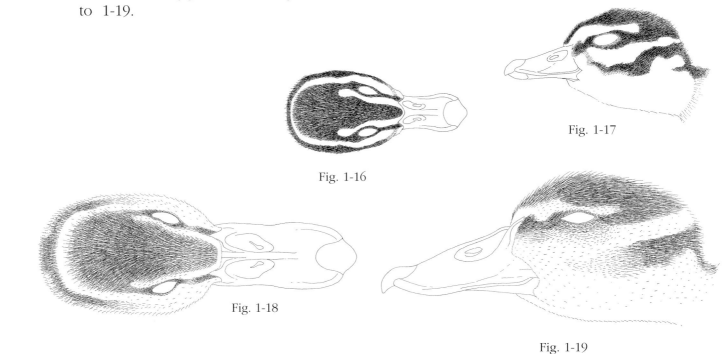

Fig. 1-17

Fig. 1-16

Fig. 1-18

Fig. 1-19

Figs. 1-13 to 1-15 (1 day): captive; figs. 1-16, 1-17 [3-4 days], figs. 1-18, 1-19 [3-4 weeks]: Virgin Islands.

3b. Dark crown seldom separated from dark bill by line of light-colored down (if present, nearly always extremely narrow and inconspicuous); base color of plumage of very young downies often brilliantly yellow (e.g., Munsell 5.5Y 8/12 [=Ridgway's Empire Yellow]). Black-bellied Whistling-duck, *Dendrocygna autumnalis,* figs. 1-20 to 1-26.

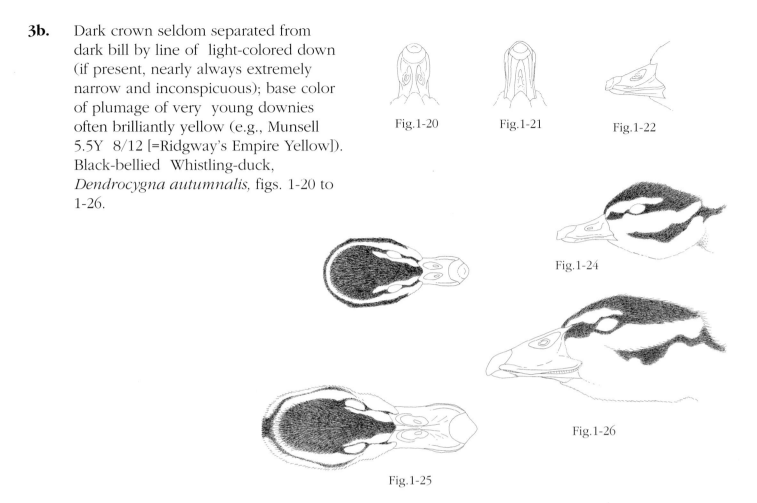

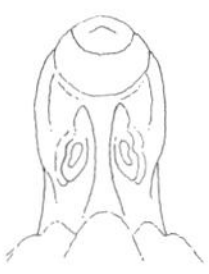

Fig.1-20

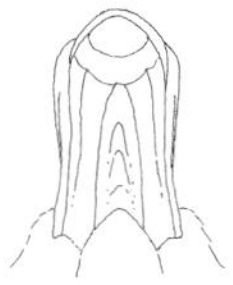

Fig.1-21

Fig.1-22

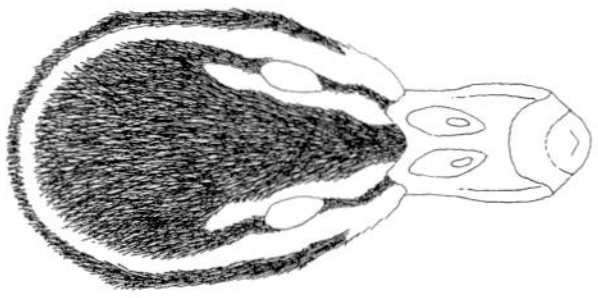

Fig.1-24

Fig.1-26

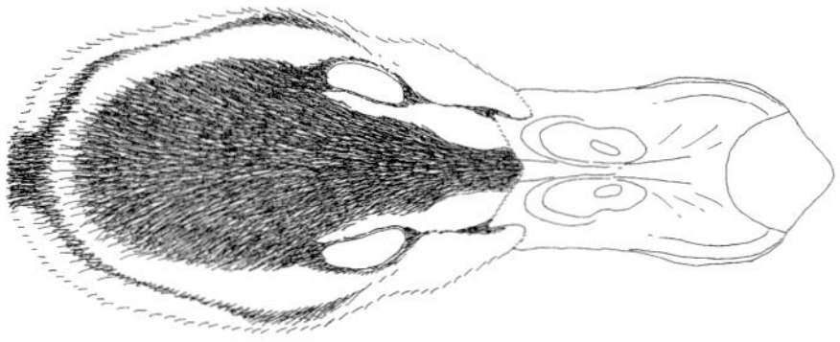

Fig.1-25

Figs. 1-20 to 1-24 (1 day): Texas; figs. 1-25, 1-26 [2 weeks]: Costa Rica. *D. autumnalis fulgens.*

Tribe Cygnini
Genus *Cygnus*

Mute Swan, *Cygnus olor,* figs. 2-1 to 2-7.

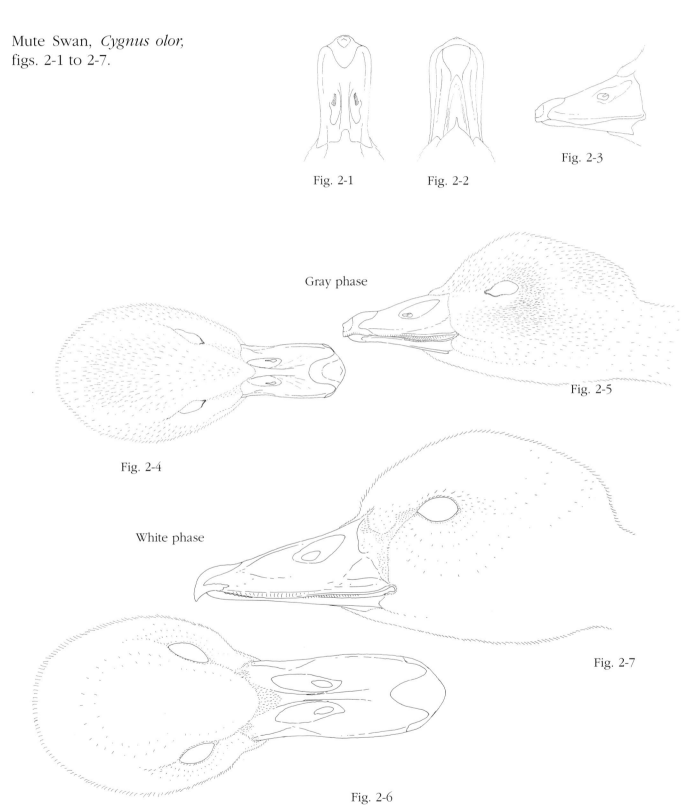

Fig. 2-1

Fig. 2-2

Fig. 2-3

Gray phase

Fig. 2-5

Fig. 2-4

White phase

Fig. 2-7

Fig. 2-6

Figs. 2-1 to 2-3 (1 day), figs. 2-4, 2-5 (2 days): Rhode Island; figs. 2-6, 2-7 [5 weeks]: captive.

Key to *Olor* species

1a. 'Horns' of bill almost never covered by feathers; sharply pointed edges of lateral bill feathering seldom obscured by down (figs. 2-10, 2-11), these feathers short, velvety, but more or less smoothly appressed to head; head down also more or less smooth, not extremely long; upper and lower nails of bill more or less triangular posteriorly (figs. 2-8, 2-9). In very young downies: nostril long, usually asymmetrical oval (fig. 2-10), often somewhat pointed anteriorly. In older downies: using commissure as measure of bill length, rear edge of nostril usually falls within posterior half of bill; bill proportions longer, narrower than in 1b (figs. 2-13, 2-14). Trumpeter Swan, *Olor buccinator,* figs. 2-8 to 2-14.

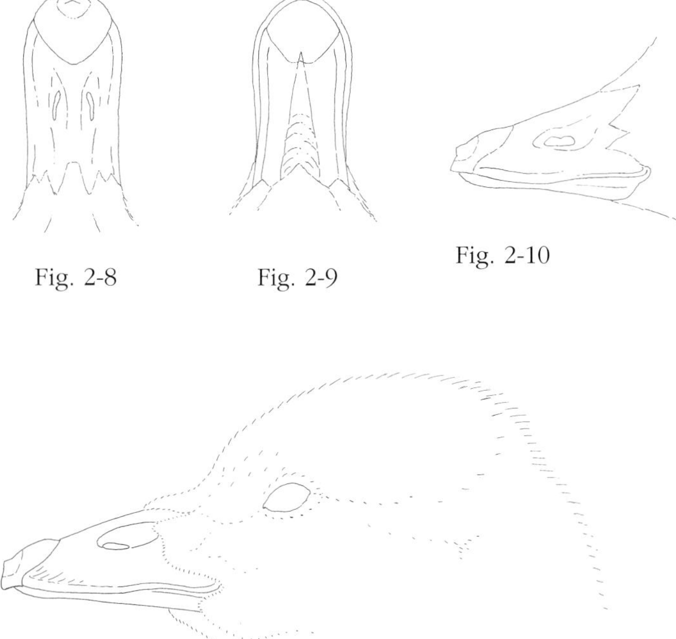

Fig. 2-8

Fig. 2-9

Fig. 2-10

Fig. 2-12

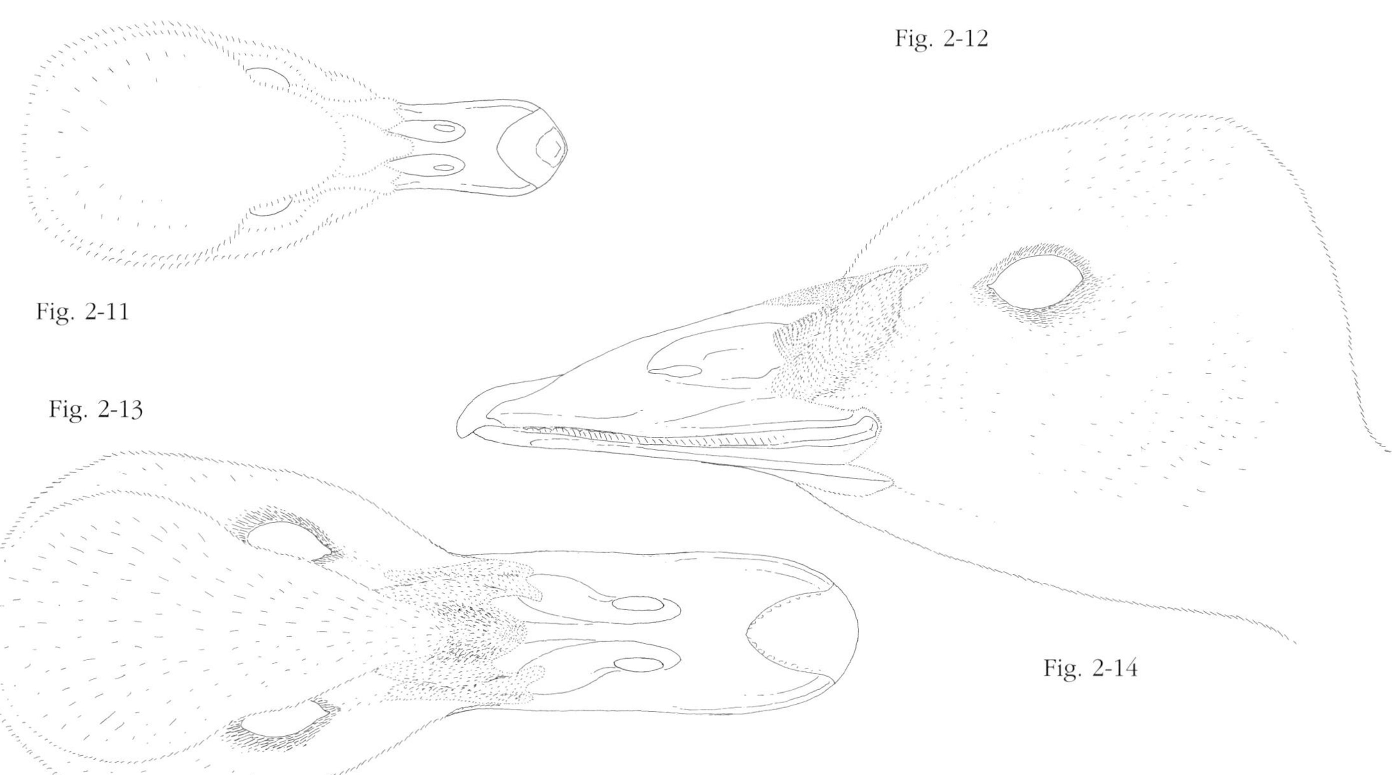

Fig. 2-11

Fig. 2-13

Fig. 2-14

Figs. 2-8 to 2-10 [3 days]: captive (Montana); figs. 2-11, 2-12 [2 days]: Alberta; figs. 2-13, 2-14 [6 weeks]: Montana.

1b. 'Horns' of bill often nearly concealed by feathers; edges of lateral bill feathering usually obscured by down (figs. 2-17, 2-18), these feathers short but fluffy, not smoothly appressed to head; head down also fluffy, often extremely long; upper and lower nails of bill usually more or less rounded posteriorly (figs. 2-15, 2-16). In very young downies: nostril small, symmetrical oval, either rounded or slightly flattened (figs. 2-15, 2-19). In older downies: using commissure as measure of bill length, rear edge of nostril usually falls about halfway along bill; bill proportions shorter, wider than in 1a (figs. 2-20, 2-21). Tundra Swan, *Olor columbianus,* figs. 2-15 to 2-21.

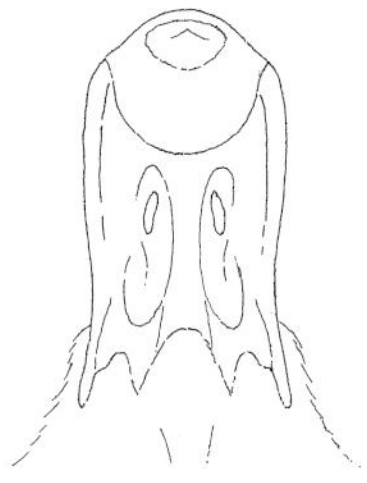

Fig. 2-15

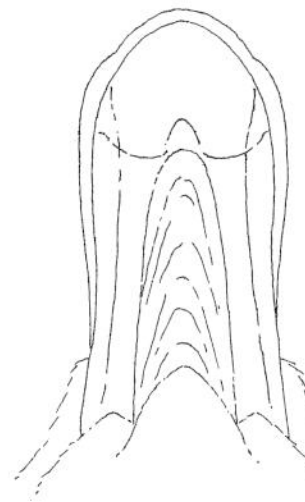

Fig. 2-16

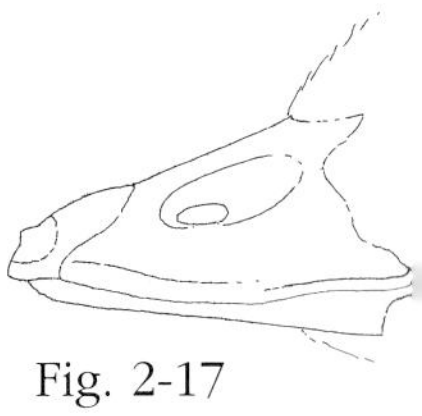

Fig. 2-17

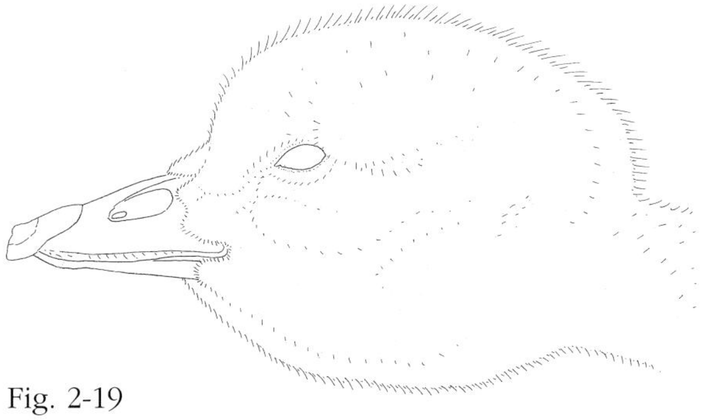

Fig. 2-19

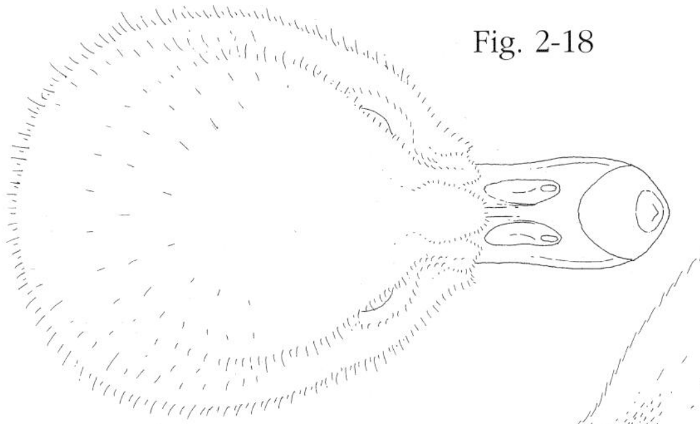

Fig. 2-18

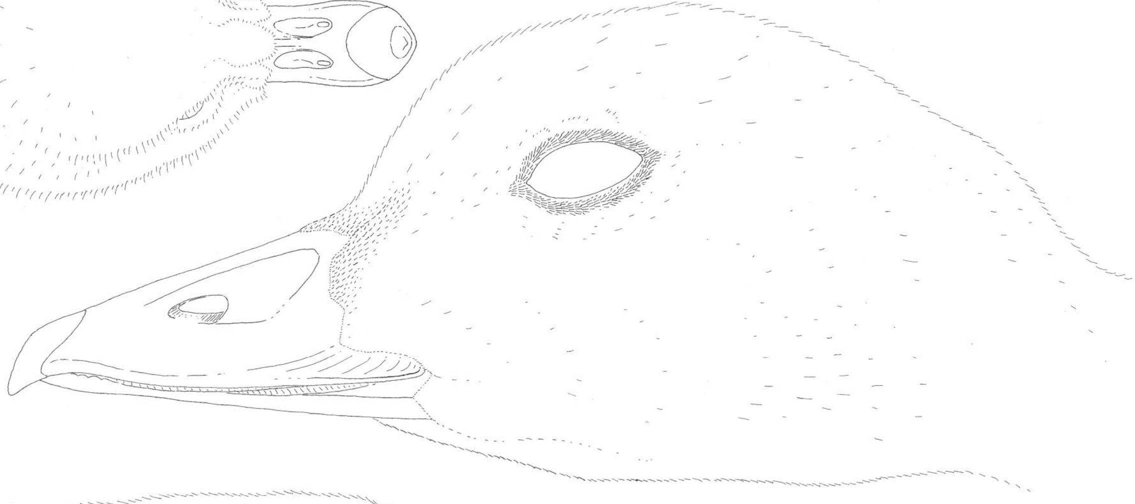

Fig. 2-21

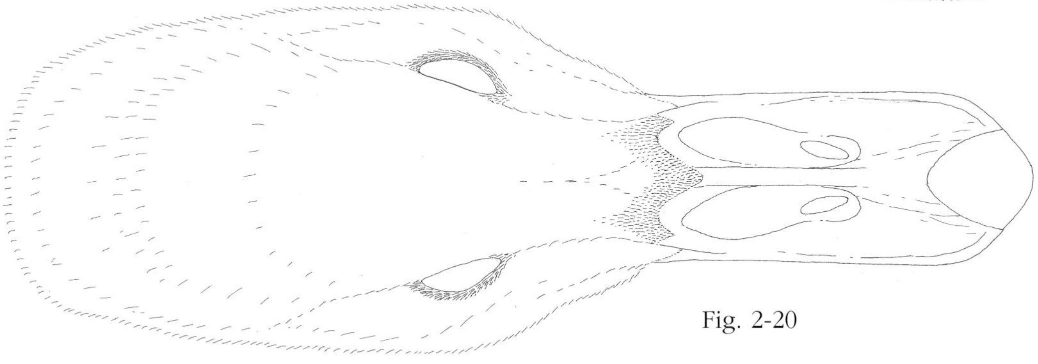

Fig. 2-20

Figs. 2-15 to 2-17 (1 day): Alaska; figs. 2-18, 2-19 [1 day], figs. 2-20, 2-21 [5-6 weeks]: Northwest Territories.
O. c. columbianus.

Tribe Anserini
Key to *Anser* species

Note: The "dark gray", "black-yellow", and rare "white" phases of the Ross' gosling (plumage designations from Ryder 1967: 36) are not included in the key to Anser species, but are shown on plate 3.

1a. Entire plumage blackish or dusky olive, except for bright yellow chin-patch and, in some individuals, yellow patch on nape and/or bright yellow line around bill. Dark phases, "Classes 2 to 4" (plumage designations and characteristics from Cooke and Cooch 1968: 291). Lesser Snow Goose, *Anser c. caerulescens,* figs. 3-1 to 3-5.

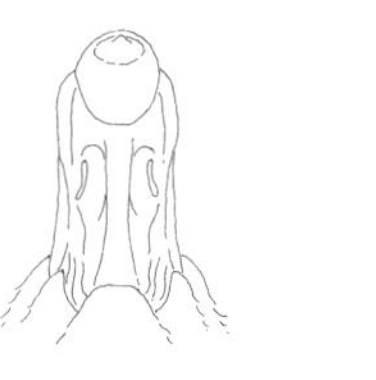
Fig. 3-1

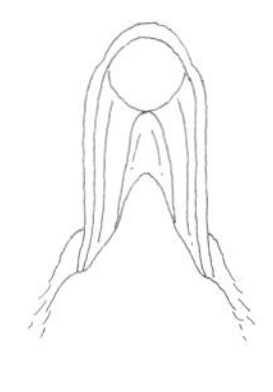
Fig. 3-2

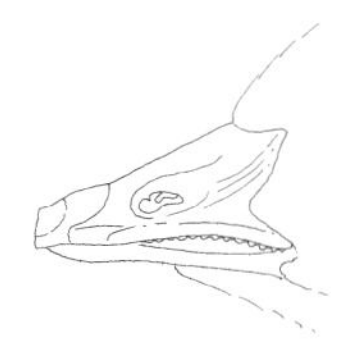
Fig. 3-3

"Class 4"

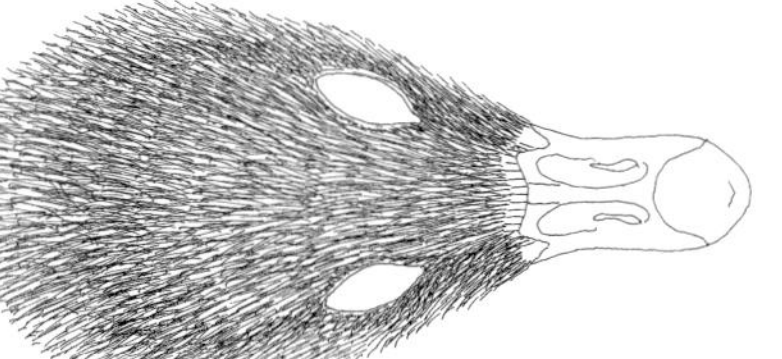
Fig. 3-4

Fig. 3-5

Figs. 3-1 to 3-3 [2 days]: captive; figs. 3-4, 3-5 [2-3 days]: Northwest Territories. *A. c. caerulescens.*

1b. Always a clear *value* difference between colors of upperparts and underparts; yellow base color more generally distributed on head and underparts, not restricted as in la. Go to 2.

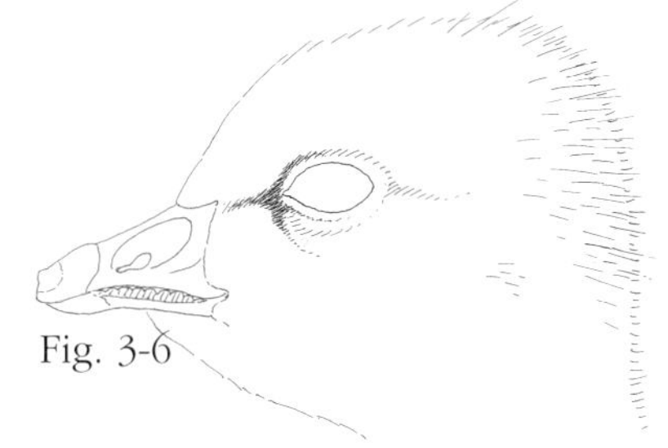
Fig. 3-6

2a. Distinct eye-stripe always present (figs. 3-6, 3-7); in dorsal view, forehead and forepart of crown always light-colored, pattern color forms crescent-shaped patch on posterior crown well behind eye-level, either conspicuous (fig. 3-8), inconspicuous (fig. 3-9), or virtually lacking (fig. 3-10).

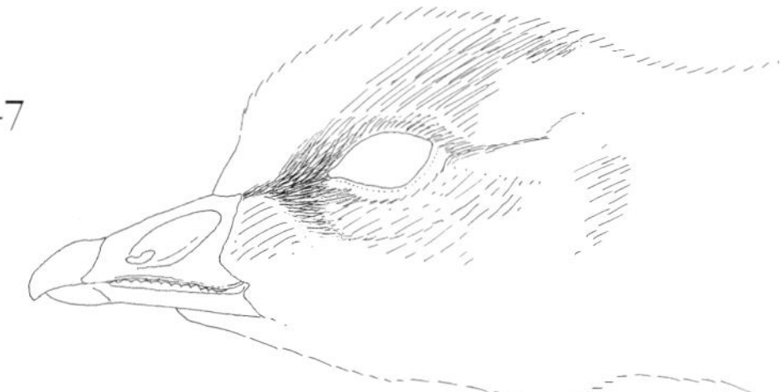

Fig. 3-7

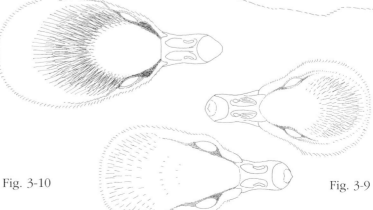

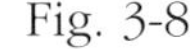
Fig. 3-8

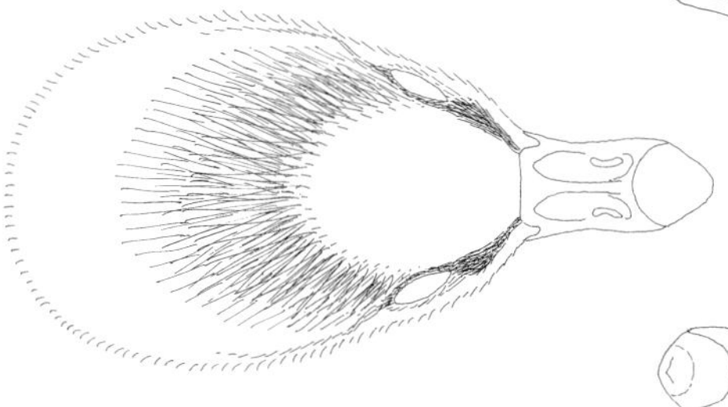

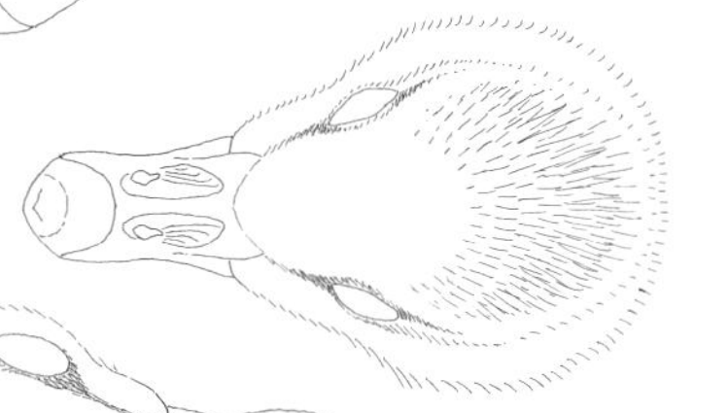

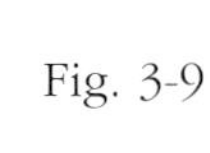
Fig. 3-9

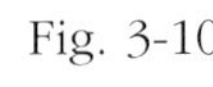
Fig. 3-10

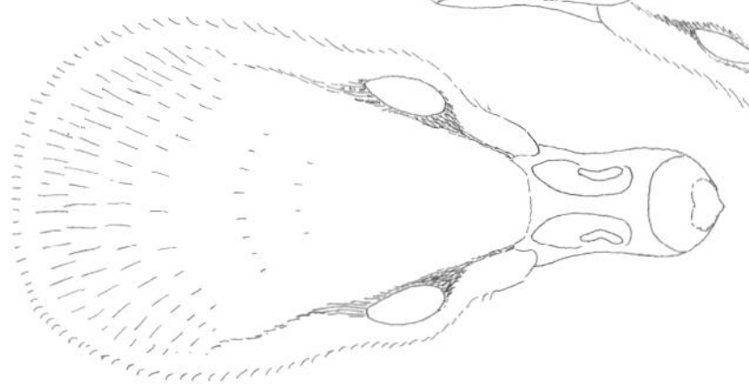

2b. Eye-stripe may be small and fairly distinct (fig. 3-11), somewhat diffuse (fig. 3-12), or heavy and mask-like (fig. 3-14); in dorsal view, forehead usually lighter colored than crown, pattern color forms diffuse patch over entire crown area beginning at eye level (figs. 3-13, 3-15). Go to 5.

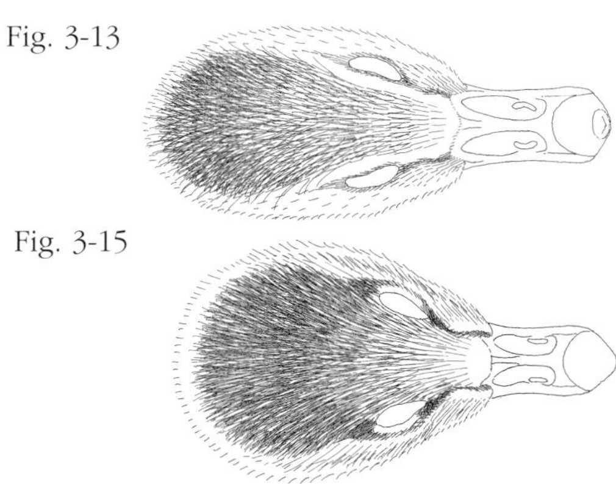
Fig. 3-13
Fig. 3-15

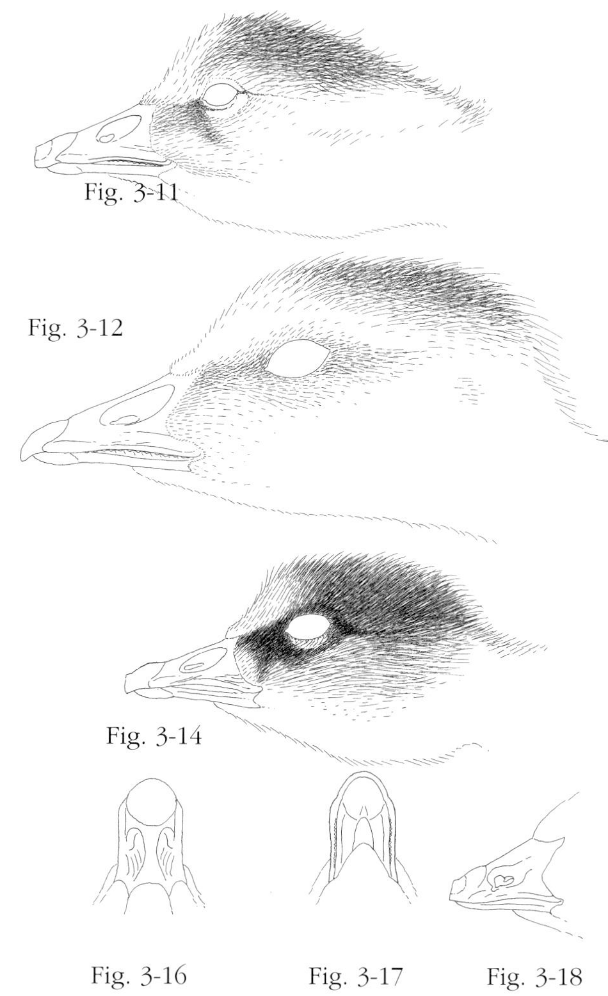
Fig. 3-11
Fig. 3-12
Fig. 3-14
Fig. 3-16 Fig. 3-17 Fig. 3-18

3a. Pattern color of plumage light or medium olive-gray; yellows of base color exceedingly pale (Munsell *value* usually higher than 8.0/) but bright (Munsell *chroma* /8.0 or higher), restricted almost entirely to face and upper breast. Medium gray and "pearly gray" phases (Ryder 1967: 36). Ross' Goose, *Anser rossii*, figs. 3-16 to 3-21.

Figs. 3-16 to 3-18 (1 day): captive (Northwest Territories); fig. 3-19 (1 day), figs. 3-20, 3-21 [1-2 days]: Northwest Territories.

Medium gray

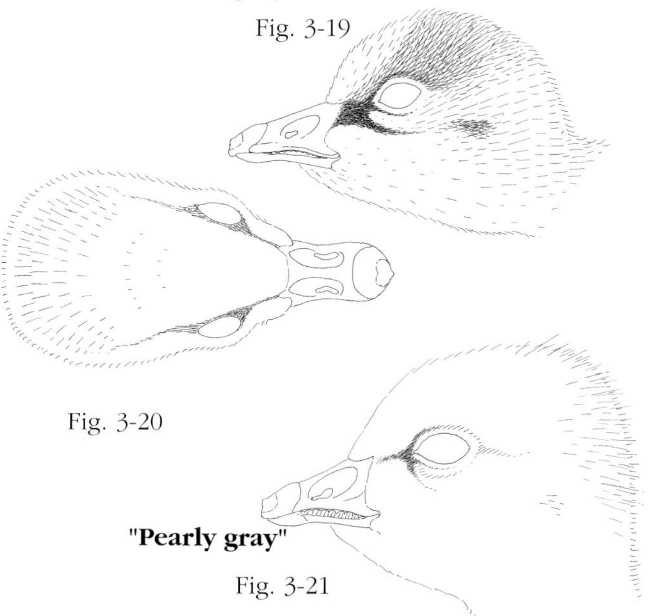
Fig. 3-19
Fig. 3-20
"Pearly gray"
Fig. 3-21

3b. Pattern color of plumage light, medium, or dark grayish yellow-olive; yellows of base color light or pale (but never so pale as in 3a), always bright or brilliant (up to Munsell *chroma* /10.0), always widely distributed throughout plumage. Go to 4.

4a. Over all size small: mean culmen length (EC) of four live wild-caught day-old Ross' goslings=15.3 mm (14.8 mm - 15.6 mm [John Ryder, letter to the author, July 1964]); down extremely long, dense, and fluffy; toes often appear short relative to tarsus length: in live birds, ratio of middle toe with claw (IIIw) to tarsus (TMT)=0.90 (0.81 - 1.04; n=14, SD=0.055, SE=0.014). "Light yellow", "yellow-green", and "dark yellow" phases (Ryder 1967: 36). Ross' Goose, *Anser rossii*, figs. 3-22, 3-23.

Figs. 3-22, 3-23 [1-2 days]: Northwest Territories.

4b. Over all size medium to large: mean culmen length (EC) of four live captive day-old Lesser Snow goslings=17.4 mm (16.5 mm - 18.0 mm); down dense and fluffy but not unusually long; toes do not appear short relative to tarsus length: in live birds, ratio of middle toe with claw (IIIw) to tarsus (TMT)=0.94 (0.84 - 1.00; n=15, SD=0.044, SE=0.011). Yellow phases, "Classes 0 and 1" (Cooke and Cooch 1968: 291). Snow Goose, *Anser caerulescens*, figs. 3-24 to 3-37.

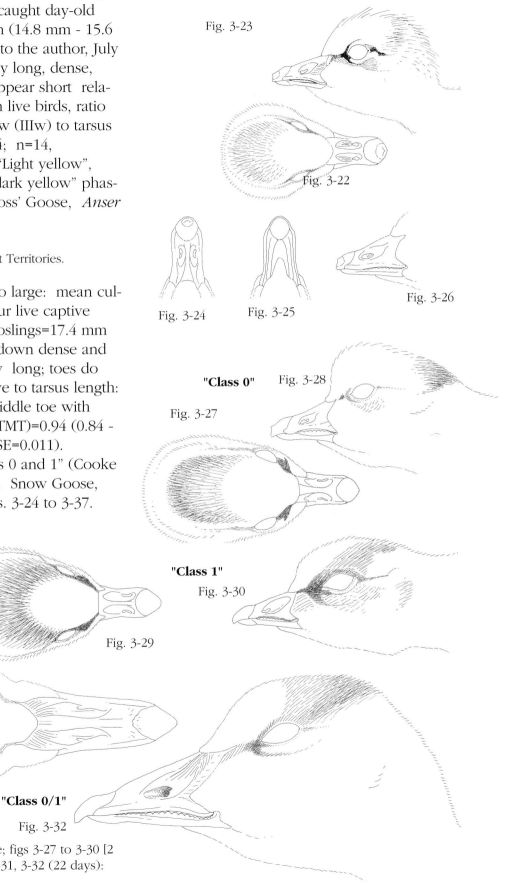

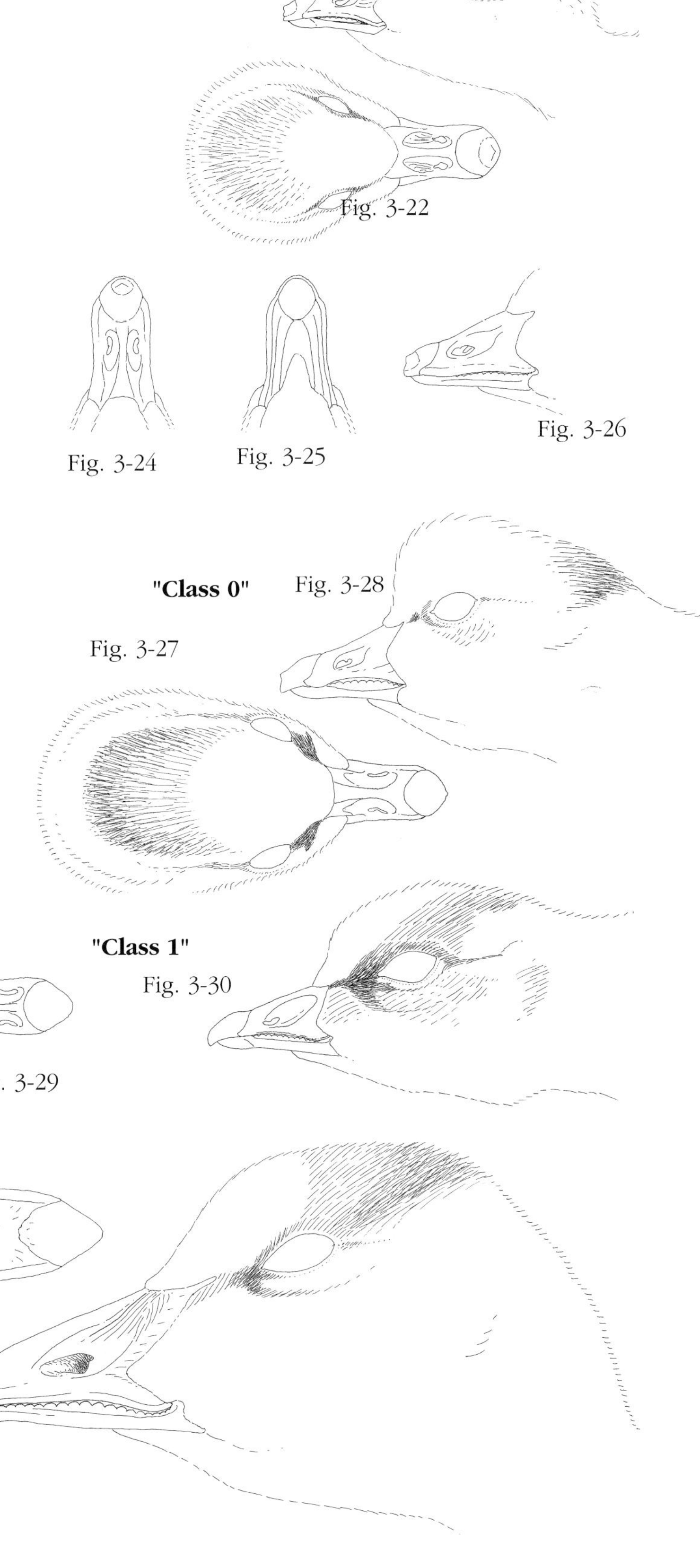

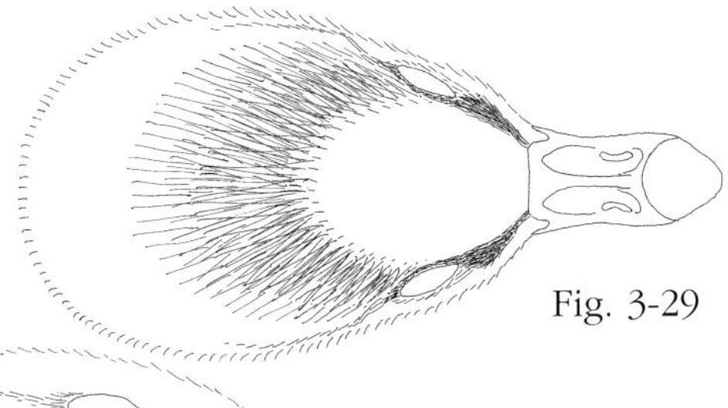

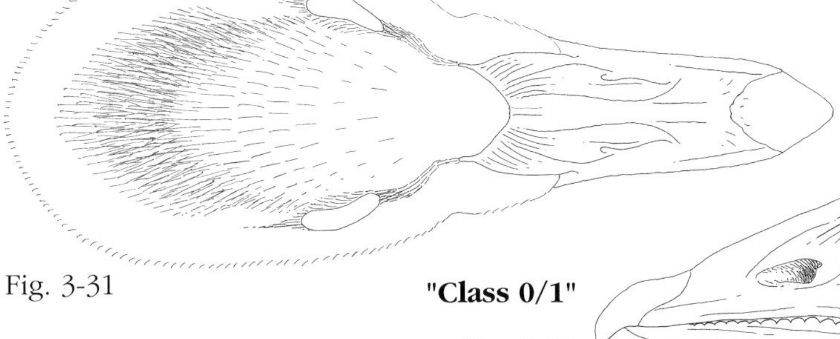

Figs. 3-24 to 3-26 [1-2 days]: captive; figs 3-27 to 3-30 [2 days]: Northwest Territories; figs. 3-31, 3-32 (22 days): captive. *A. c. caerulescens.*

Figs. 3-33 to 3-35 [1-2 days]: captive: figs. 3-36, 3-37 [6 days]: Northwest Territories. *A. c. atlanticus.*

"Class 0/1"

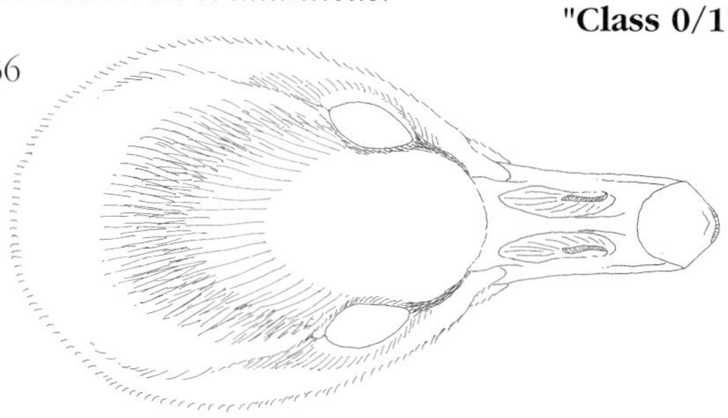

Fig. 3-36

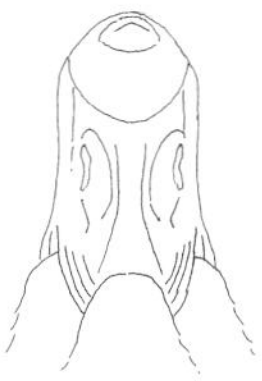

Fig. 3-33

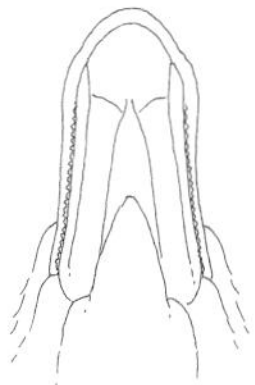

Fig. 3-34

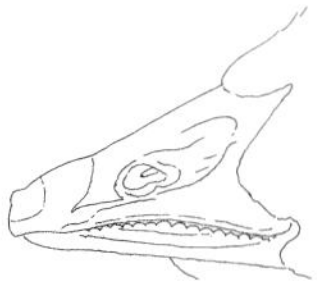

Fig. 3-35

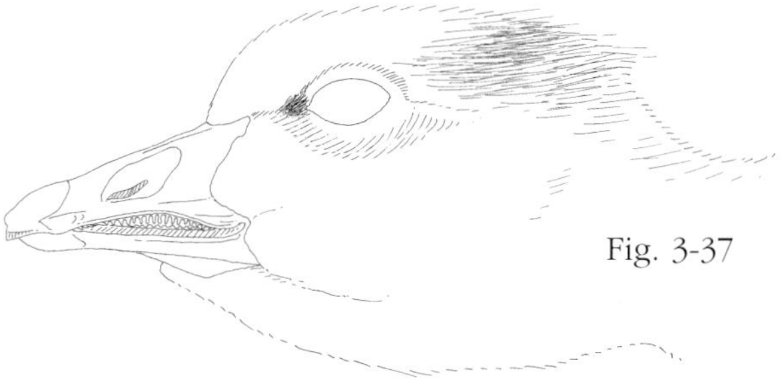

Fig. 3-37

5a. Tarsi essentially dark, monochromatic: seldom more than 1 Munsell step of *value* or *chroma* between base and pattern colors; dark crown color usually extends directly to eye (figs. 3-42, 3-44) except in very pale specimens (figs. 3-39, 3-40); tomium of upper mandible turns markedly downward at rictus, often overlapping lower mandible (figs. 3-40, 3-44, 3-48); eyelid rim in live downies dark-colored, inconspicuous (also noted in adult birds [Bauer and Glutz von Blotzheim 1968]); yellow base color of plumage of young downies sometimes pale but usually clear and bright (often brilliant), almost never extremely dull. In older downies: pronounced dark mask continuous with dark crown nearly always present in dorsal view (figs. 3-43, 3-47). Pink-footed Goose, *Anser brachyrhynchus,* figs. 3-38 to 3-48.

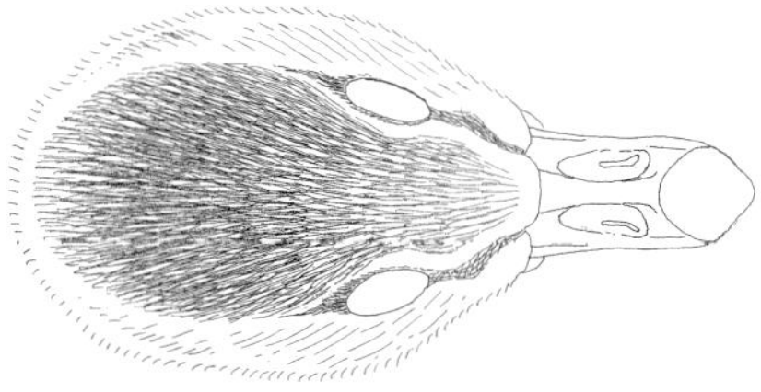

Fig. 3-39

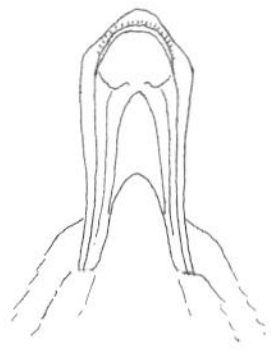

Fig. 3-38

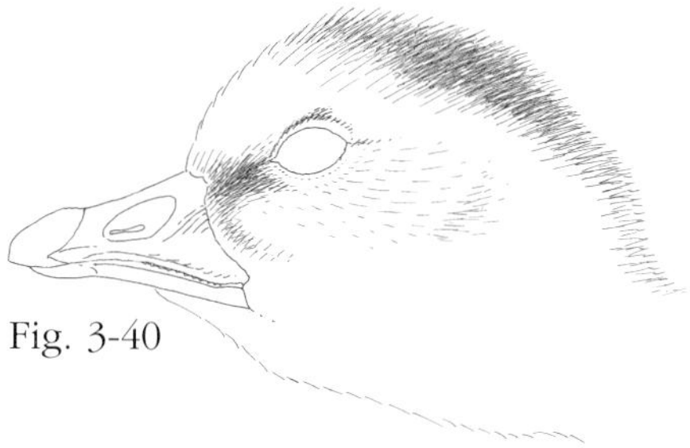

Fig. 3-40

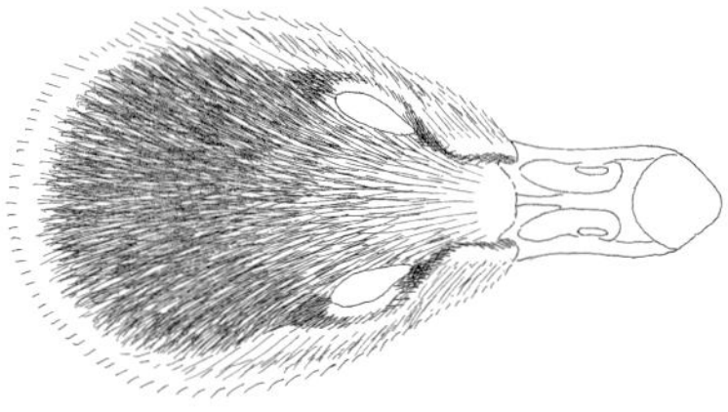

Fig. 3-41

Fig. 3-43

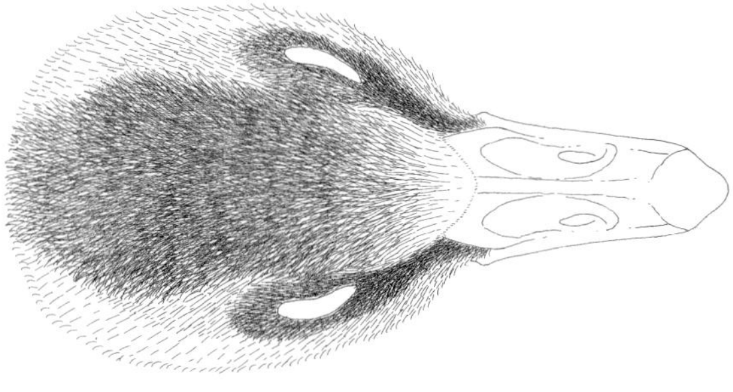

Fig. 3-42

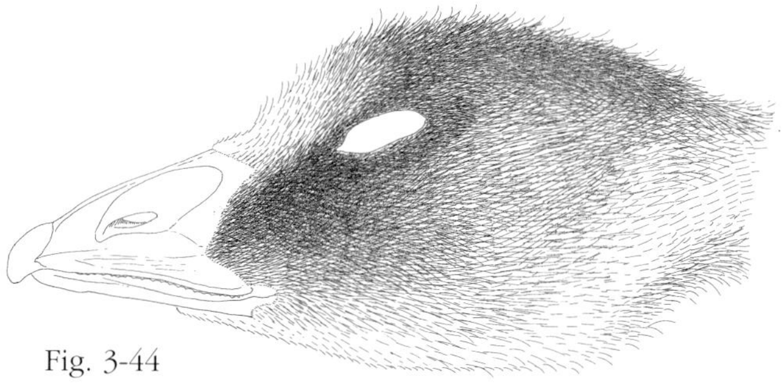

Fig. 3-44

Figs. 3-38, 3-41, 3-42, 3-45, 3-46 [2 days]: Spitsbergen; figs. 3-39, 3-40 (2 days): captive; figs 3-43, 3-44 {3-/2 weeks], figs. 3-47, 3-48 [2-1/2 weeks]: Iceland *A. brachyrhynchus.*

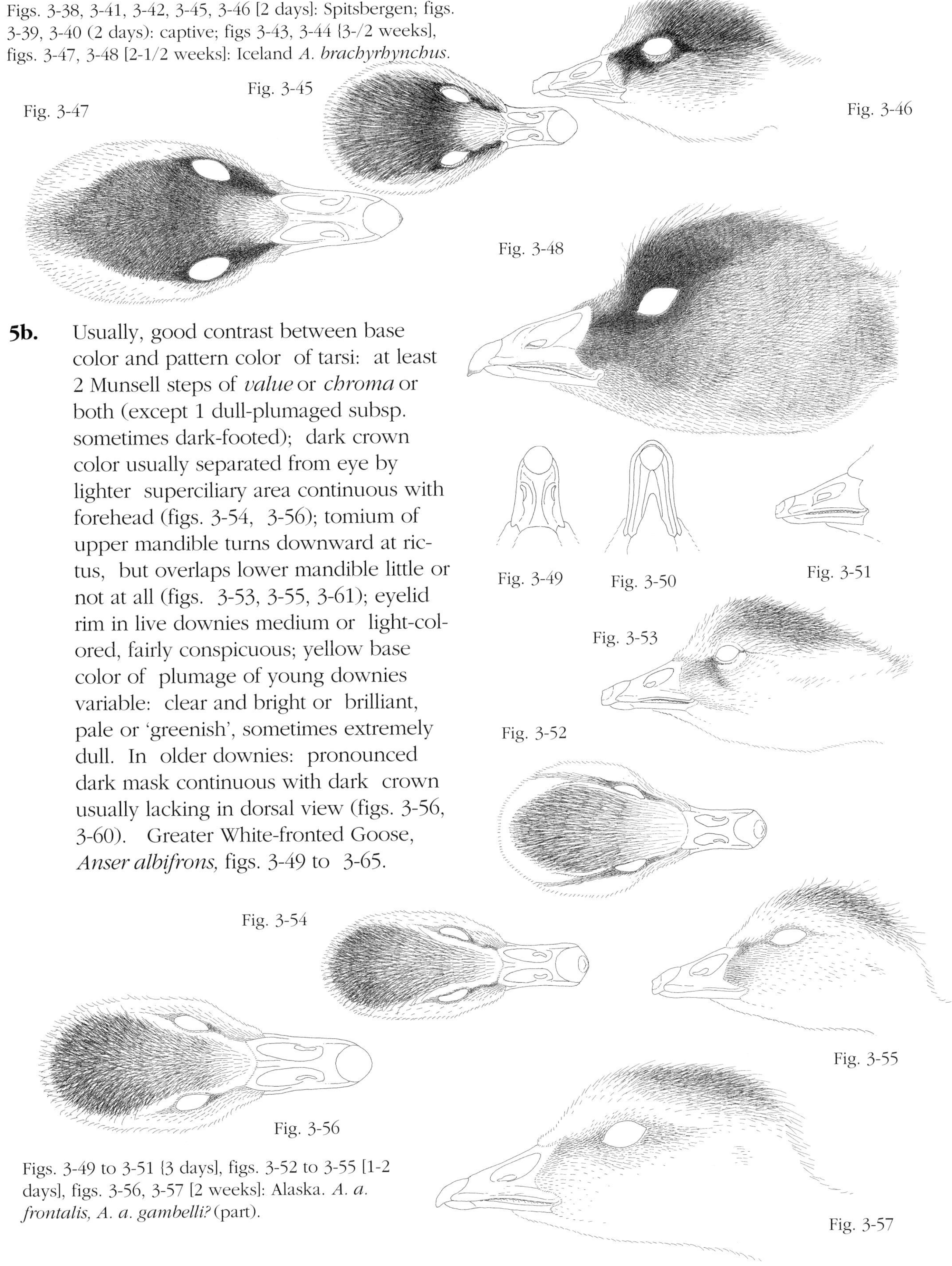

5b. Usually, good contrast between base color and pattern color of tarsi: at least 2 Munsell steps of *value* or *chroma* or both (except 1 dull-plumaged subsp. sometimes dark-footed); dark crown color usually separated from eye by lighter superciliary area continuous with forehead (figs. 3-54, 3-56); tomium of upper mandible turns downward at rictus, but overlaps lower mandible little or not at all (figs. 3-53, 3-55, 3-61); eyelid rim in live downies medium or light-colored, fairly conspicuous; yellow base color of plumage of young downies variable: clear and bright or brilliant, pale or 'greenish', sometimes extremely dull. In older downies: pronounced dark mask continuous with dark crown usually lacking in dorsal view (figs. 3-56, 3-60). Greater White-fronted Goose, *Anser albifrons,* figs. 3-49 to 3-65.

Figs. 3-49 to 3-51 {3 days], figs. 3-52 to 3-55 [1-2 days], figs. 3-56, 3-57 [2 weeks]: Alaska. *A. a. frontalis, A. a. gambelli?* (part).

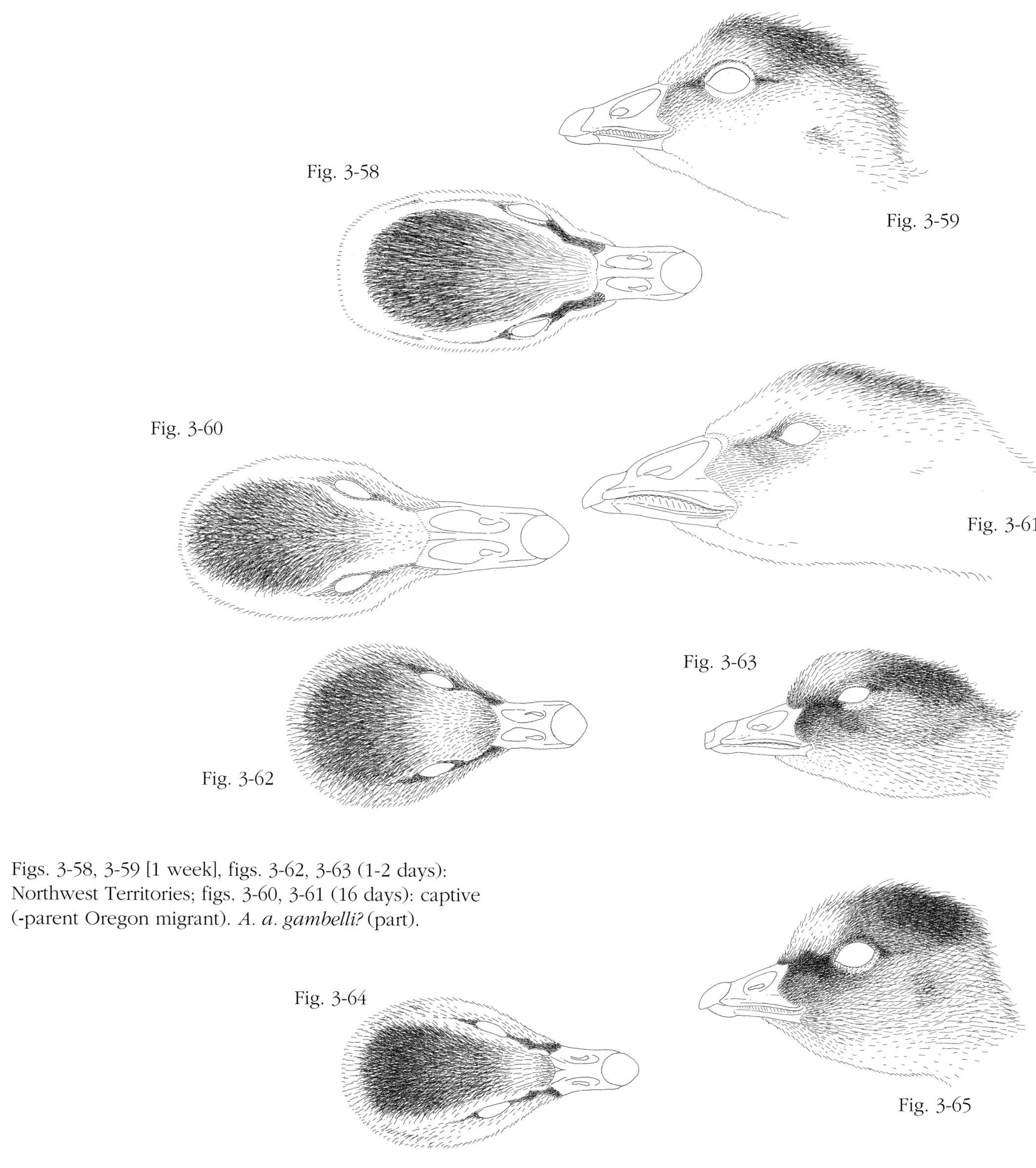

Figs. 3-58, 3-59 [1 week], figs. 3-62, 3-63 (1-2 days): Northwest Territories; figs. 3-60, 3-61 (16 days): captive (-parent Oregon migrant). *A. a. gambelli?* (part).

Figs. 3-64, 3-65 (5 days): captive (Greenland). *A. a. flavirostris.*

Tribe Anserini
Genus *Philacte*

Emperor Goose, *Philacte canagica*, figs. 3-66 to 3-72.

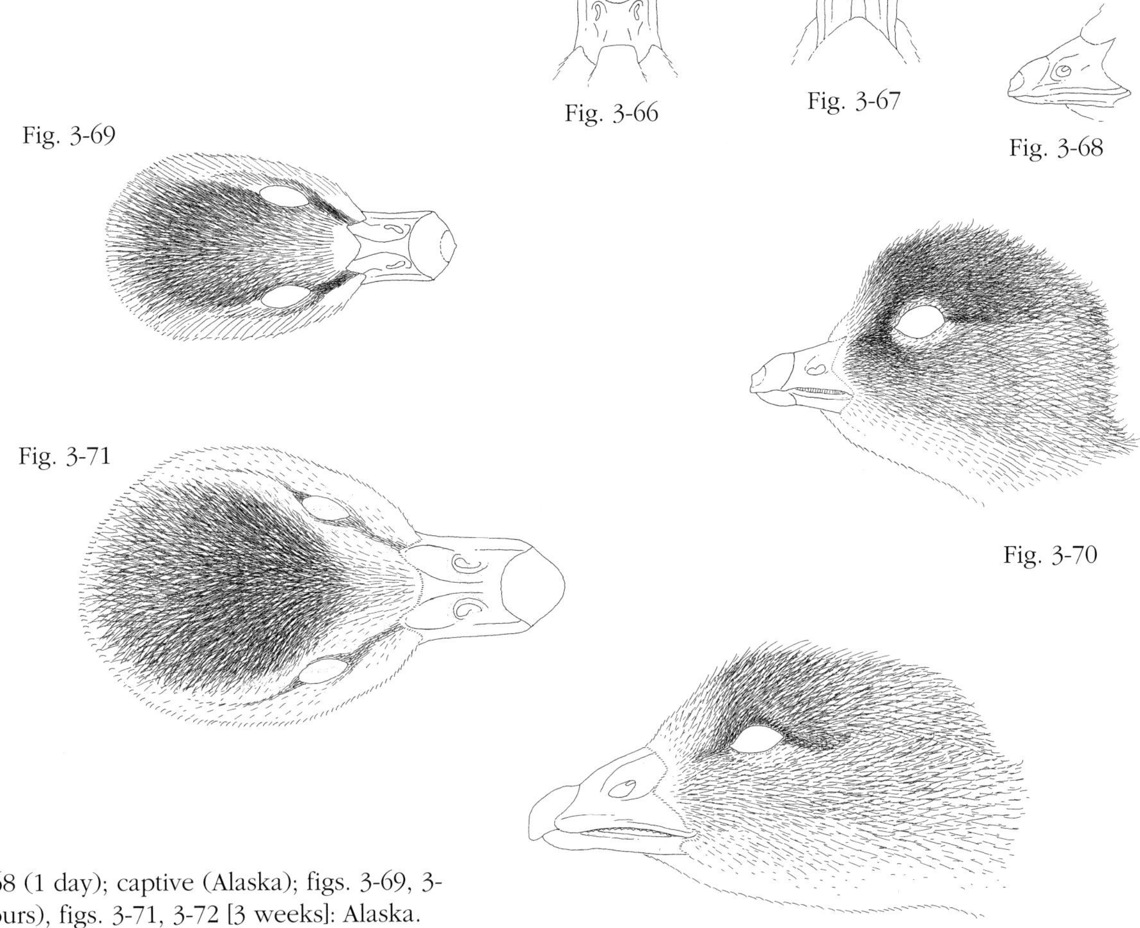

Figs. 3-66 to 3-68 (1 day); captive (Alaska); figs. 3-69, 3-70 (about 36 hours), figs. 3-71, 3-72 [3 weeks]: Alaska.

Key to *Branta* species

1a. Base color of plumage white or creamy (if yellow, extremely pale and confined entirely to head); pattern color gray or olive-gray. Go to 2.

1b. Entire base color of plumage always recognizeably yellow; pattern color always some shade of olive-yellow, brownish olive, or grayish olive. Canada Goose, *Branta canadensis.* Go to 3.

2a. Wide, shallow white 'V' on gray lower breast; base color of plumage white, never pale yellow on face. Brant, *B. bernicla,* figs. 3-73 to 3-86.

Figs. 3-73 to 3-75 (1 day): captive (Northwest Territories): figs. 3-76, 3-77 (3 days), fig. 3-78 [3-4 weeks]: Northwest Territories. *B. b. hrota.*

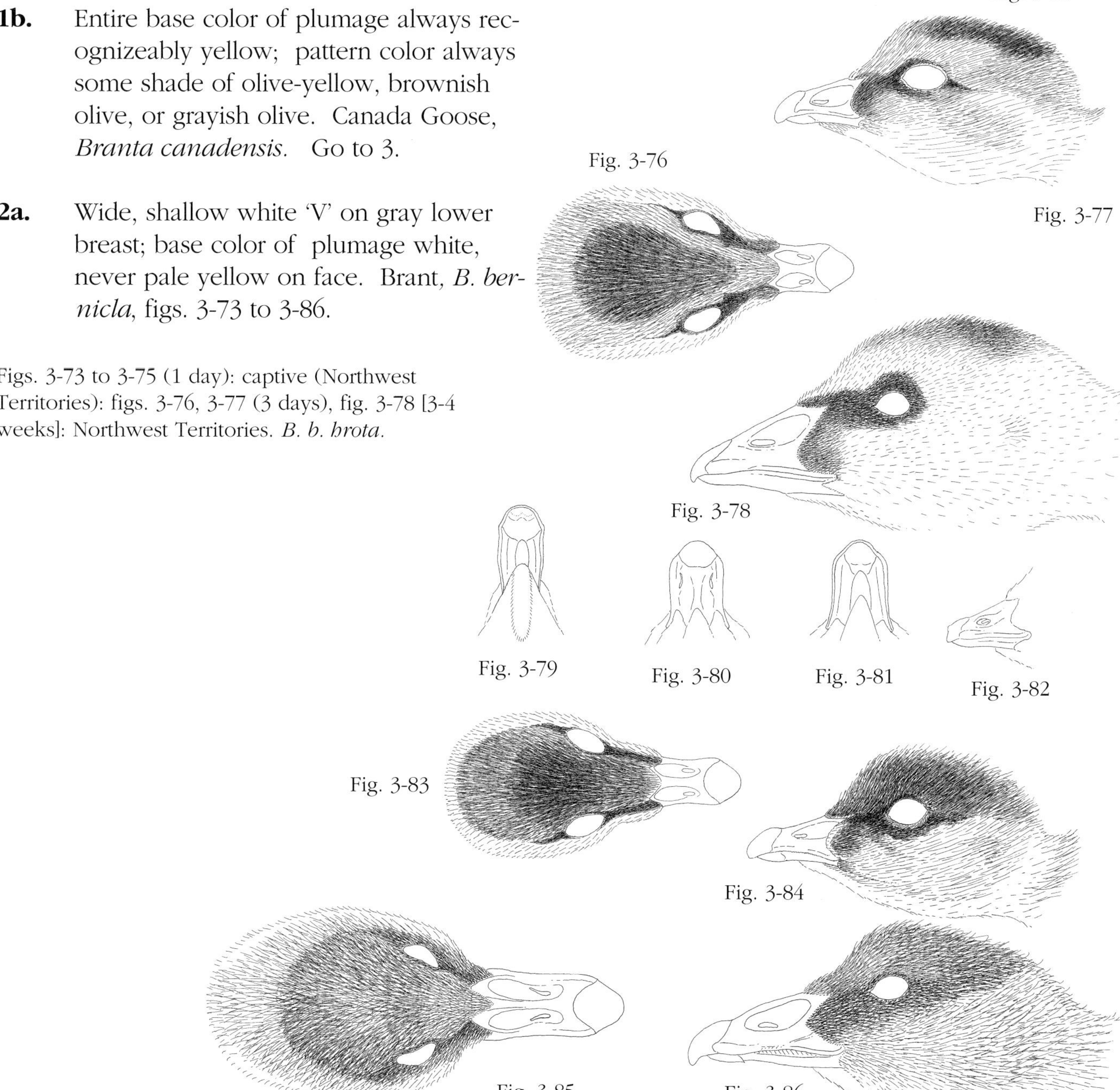
Fig. 3-73 Fig. 3-74 Fig. 3-75 Fig. 3-76 Fig. 3-77 Fig. 3-78 Fig. 3-79 Fig. 3-80 Fig. 3-81 Fig. 3-82 Fig. 3-83 Fig. 3-84 Fig. 3-85 Fig. 3-86

Fig. 3-79 (1 day), figs. 3-85, 3-86 [3-4 weeks]: Northwest Territories; figs. 3-80 to 3-82 [3 days], figs. 3-83 [3-4 days]: Alaska. *B. b. nigricans.*

2b. Prominent gray band on white upper breast; base color of plumage creamy white, extremely pale yellow on face. Barnacle Goose, *B. leucopsis,* figs. 3-87 to 3-93.

Figs. 3-87 to 3-91 (1 day), figs. 3-92, 3-93 [2 weeks]: captive.

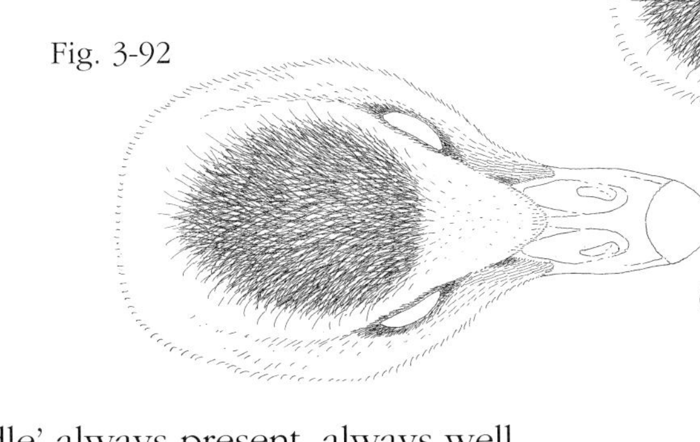

Fig. 3-92

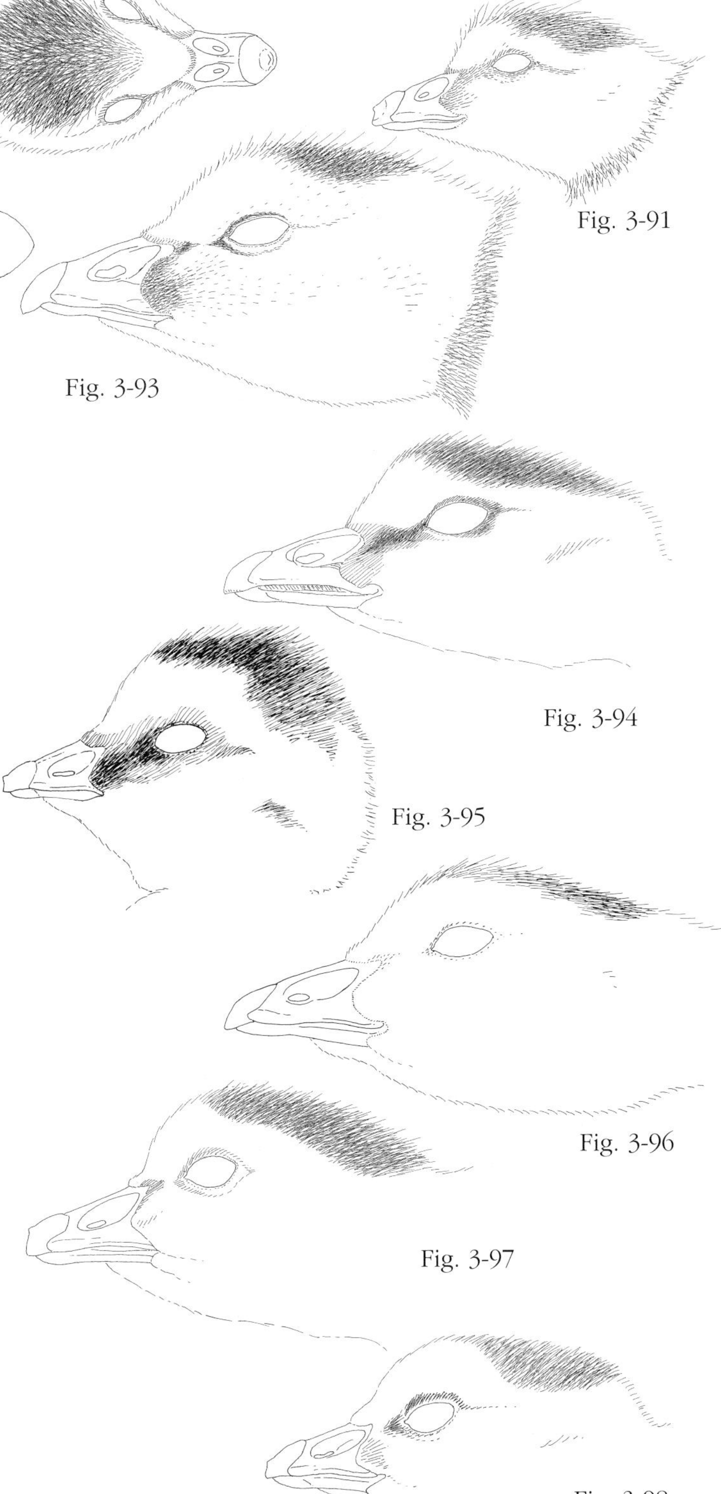

Fig. 3-87 Fig. 3-88 Fig. 3-89 Fig. 3-90 Fig. 3-91 Fig. 3-93 Fig. 3-94 Fig. 3-95 Fig. 3-96 Fig. 3-97 Fig. 3-98

3a. 'Bridle' always present, always well marked (figs. 3-94, 3-95); colors of tarsi and feet always deep, dark, or blackish; base color of plumage in live goslings often bright or brilliant yellow, but usually appears dull and 'greenish' because overlaid by grayish olive down tips; breast-band often present, usually conspicuous; iridescent golden dorsal plumes usually few or lacking. Downies of the dark-bellied Pacific adults described by Delacour (1954; 4 subspp.) and Palmer (1976, vol. 2; 3 subspp.). Go to 4.

3b. 'Bridle' lacking (fig. 3-96), inconspicuous (fig. 3-97), or, if present, less well-marked (fig. 3-98) than in figs. 3-94 and 3-95, above; colors of tarsi and feet light or medium to deep, dark, or blackish; base color of plumage nearly always bright or brilliant yellow, with grayish olive down tips few or lacking; breast-band nearly always lacking, always inconspicuous if present; usually, many iridescent golden dorsal plumes. Downies of the light-bellied Atlantic, interior, and tundra adults described by Delacour (1954; 7 subspp.) and Palmer (1976, vol. 2; 5 subspp.). Go to 6.

4a. Distinct olive-gray breast-band always present; tarsal base color never strong olive-green; over all body size small. Go to 5.

4b. Olive-gray breast-band nearly always absent (if present, usually pale and inconspicuous); tarsal base color often strong olive-green but contrasting poorly with blackish pattern color (as in some Vancouver Island goslings); over all body size medium (as in goslings from N part of range [=Delacour's *occidentalis*]) to large (goslings from S part of range [=Delacour's *fulva*]). Dusky Canada Goose, *B. canadensis occidentalis,* figs. 3-99 to 3-105, and Vancouver Canada Goose, *B. canadensis fulva,* figs. 3-106 to 3-112.

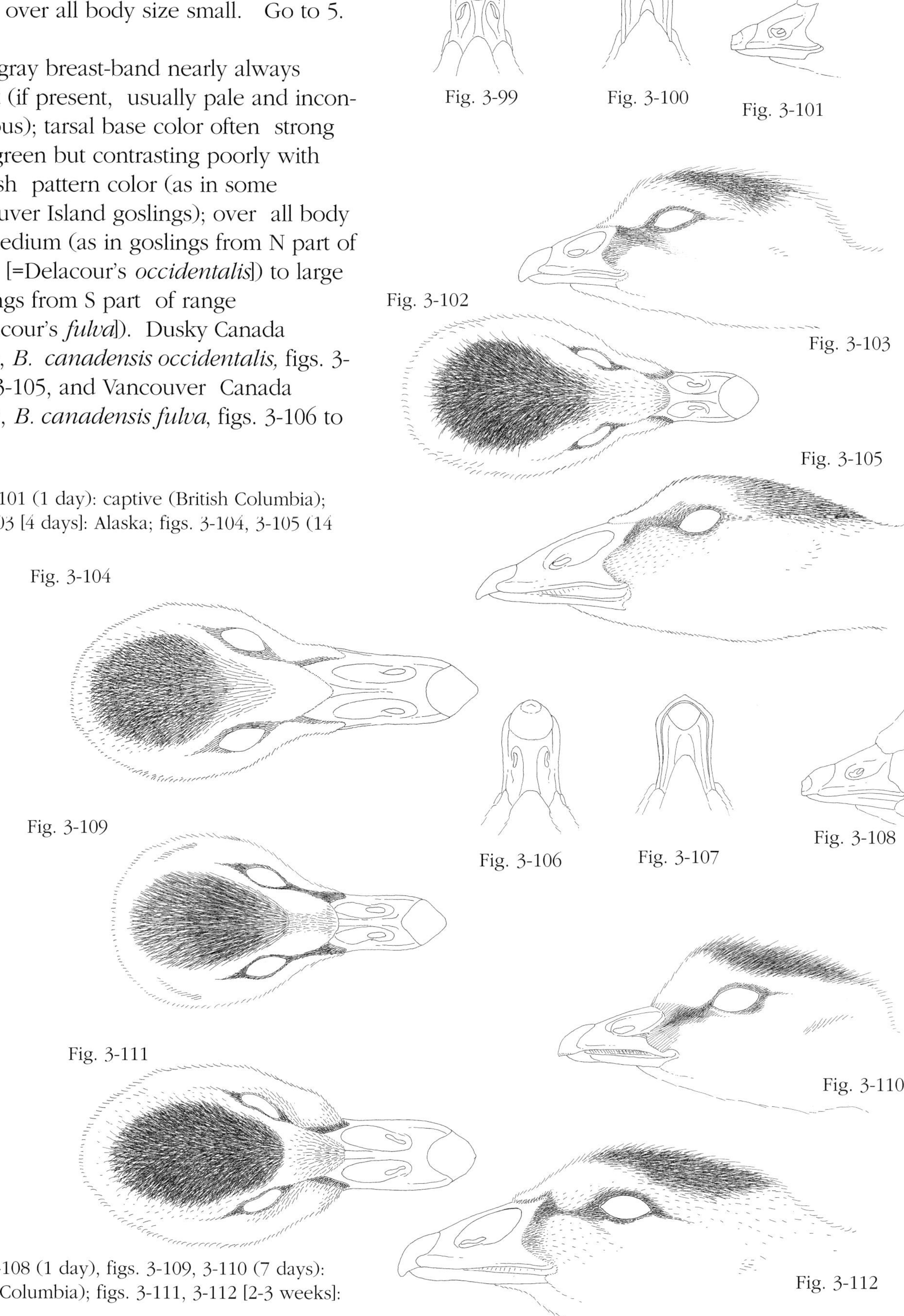

Figs. 3-99 to 3-101 (1 day): captive (British Columbia); figs. 3-102, 3-103 [4 days]: Alaska; figs. 3-104, 3-105 (14 days): captive.

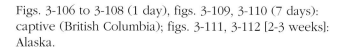

Figs. 3-106 to 3-108 (1 day), figs. 3-109, 3-110 (7 days): captive (British Columbia); figs. 3-111, 3-112 [2-3 weeks]: Alaska.

5a. Bill extremely short (figs. 3-113, 3-116); underbill (UB) about 50% of culmen (EC): in live birds, mean ratio of UB/EC =0.53 (0.42-0.62; n=27, SD=0.049, SE=0.009); colors of tarsi and feet nearly always uniformly dull blackish brown or matte black; mesial line of dark crown color almost never extends all the way to bill (fig. 3-118); down nearly always very long and fluffy. The smallest of the Canada Geese. Cackling Canada Goose, *B. canadensis minima,* figs. 3-113 to 3-119.

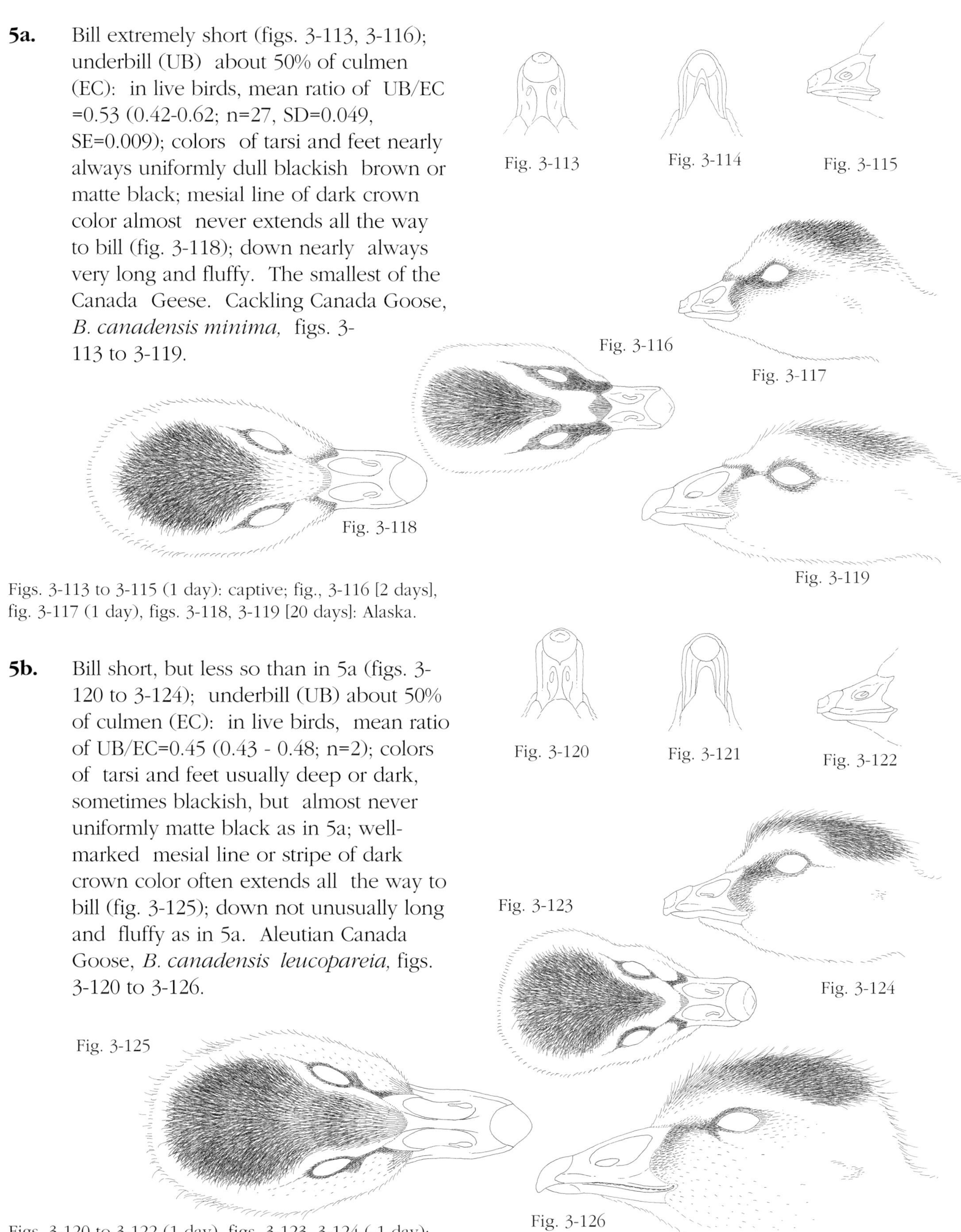

Fig. 3-113

Fig. 3-114

Fig. 3-115

Fig. 3-116

Fig. 3-117

Fig. 3-118

Fig. 3-119

Figs. 3-113 to 3-115 (1 day): captive; fig., 3-116 [2 days], fig. 3-117 (1 day), figs. 3-118, 3-119 [20 days]: Alaska.

5b. Bill short, but less so than in 5a (figs. 3-120 to 3-124); underbill (UB) about 50% of culmen (EC): in live birds, mean ratio of UB/EC=0.45 (0.43 - 0.48; n=2); colors of tarsi and feet usually deep or dark, sometimes blackish, but almost never uniformly matte black as in 5a; well-marked mesial line or stripe of dark crown color often extends all the way to bill (fig. 3-125); down not unusually long and fluffy as in 5a. Aleutian Canada Goose, *B. canadensis leucopareia,* figs. 3-120 to 3-126.

Fig. 3-120

Fig. 3-121

Fig. 3-122

Fig. 3-123

Fig. 3-124

Fig. 3-125

Fig. 3-126

Figs. 3-120 to 3-122 (1 day), figs. 3-123, 3-124 (-1 day): captive (Alaska); figs. 3-125, 3-126 [3-4 weeks]: Alaska.

6a. Base color of plumage brilliant lemon yellow on head and breast, markedly paler and duller on belly and undertail; down rather short but extremely dense and mat-like; bill short, somewhat rounded at tip (figs. 3-129, 3-132); underbill (UB) usually less than 60% of culmen (EC); in live birds, mean ratio of UB/EC=0.57 (0.51-0.61; n=3, SD=0.053, SE=0.031). The smallest of the light yellow Canada goslings. Richardson's Canada Goose, *B. canadensis hutchinsii*, figs. 3-127 to 3-134.

Fig. 3-127

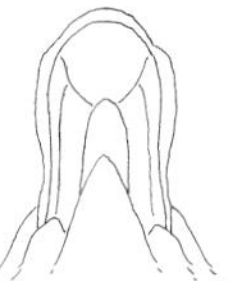
Fig. 3-128

Fig. 3-129

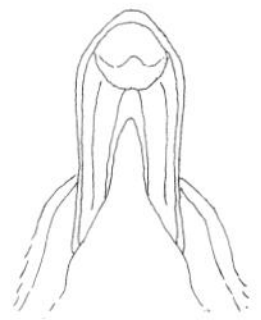

Fig. 3-130

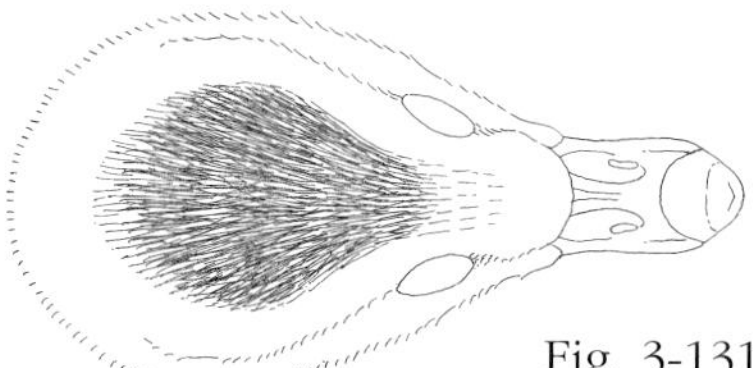
Fig. 3-131

Fig. 3-132

Figs. 3-127 to 3-129, 3-133, 3-134 (-1 day), figs. 3-130 to 3-132 [1 day]: Northwest Territories.

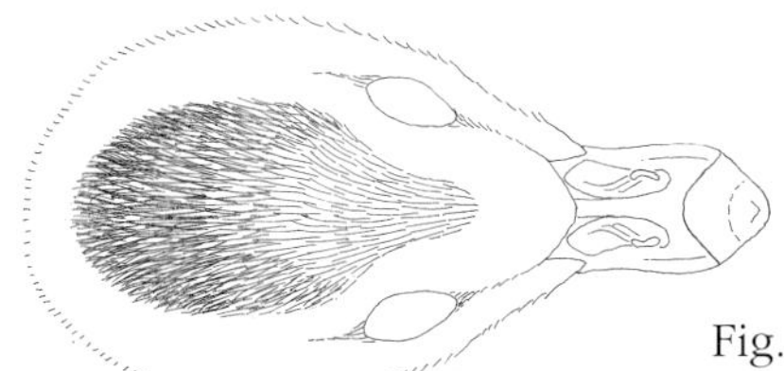
Fig. 3-133

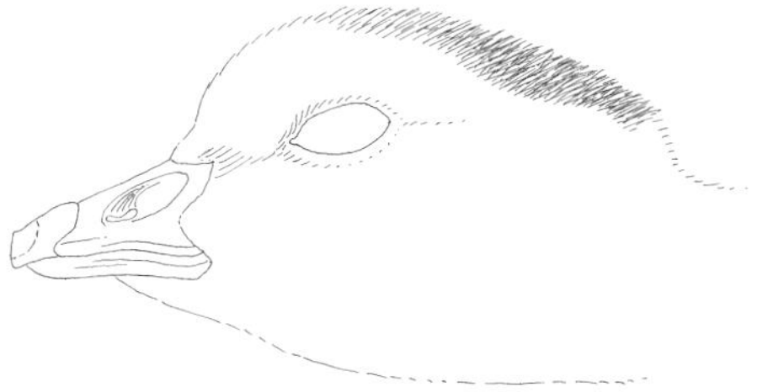

Fig. 3-134

6b. Base color of plumage yellow, green-yellow, or orange-yellow, usually bright or brilliant but sometimes rather dull, not markedly paler on belly and undertail; down long and soft but not dense and mat-like as in 6a; bill medium (fig. 3-135) or long (fig. 3-136), almost never short and rounded as in 6a; underbill (UB) also usually less than 60% of culmen (EC) in two medium-sized subspecies: in live birds, mean ratio of UB/EC=0.57 (0.53-0.62; n=9, SD=0.032, SE=0.011), but nearly always more than 60% in large-sized subspecies: in live birds, mean ratio of UB/EC=0.70 (0.59 - 0.92; n=67, SD=0.062, SE=0.008). Go to 7.

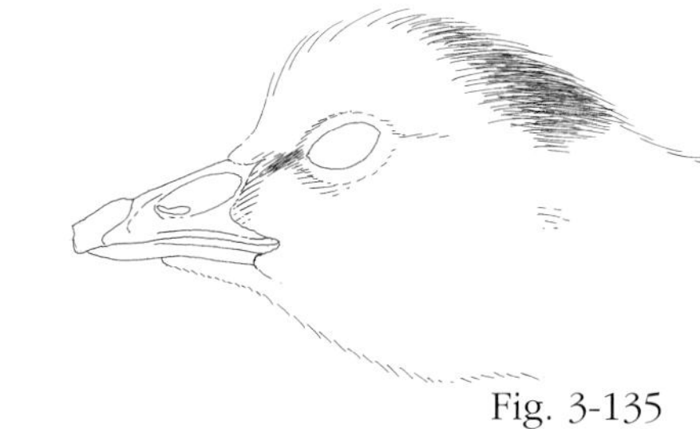
Fig. 3-135

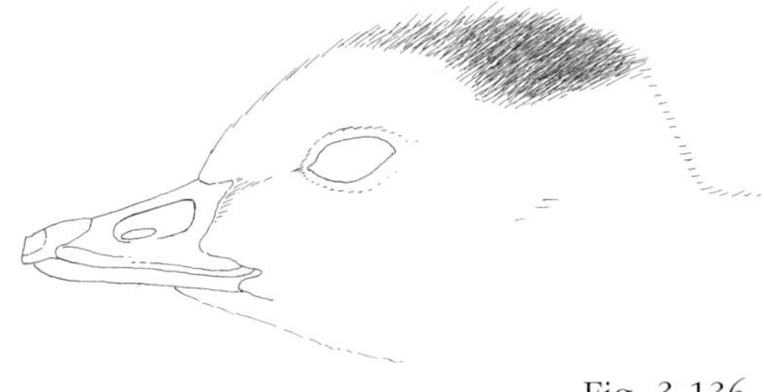
Fig. 3-136

7a. Base color of plumage always bright or brilliant yellow, often with tint of orange or green on face or throughout plumage; breast-band never present; 'bridle' usually lacking, seldom prominent if present; base color of tarsi and feet usually light or medium (most interior birds) but sometimes deep, dark, or blackish (many coastal birds). The largest of the Canada Geese. Atlantic Canada Goose, *B. canadensis canadensis,* figs. 3-137 to 3-141; Todd's Canada Goose, *B. canadensis interior,* figs. 3-142 to 3-145; Giant Canada Goose, *B. canadensis maxima,* figs. 3-146 to 3-152; and Great Basin Canada Goose, *B. canadensis moffitti,* figs. 3-153 to 3-157.

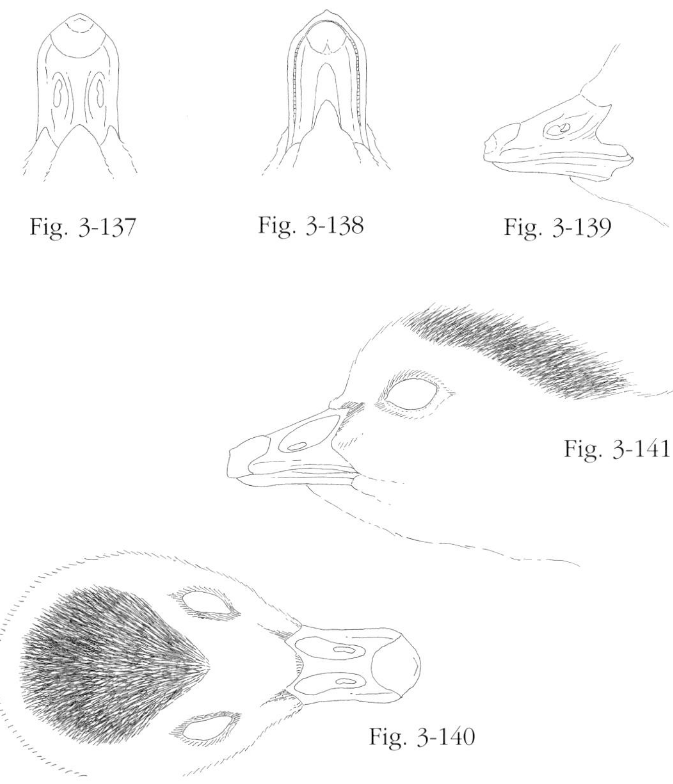

Fig. 3-137 Fig. 3-138 Fig. 3-139 Fig. 3-141 Fig. 3-140

Figs. 3-137 to 3-139 (1 day), figs. 3-140, 3-141 [2-3 days]: Newfoundland.

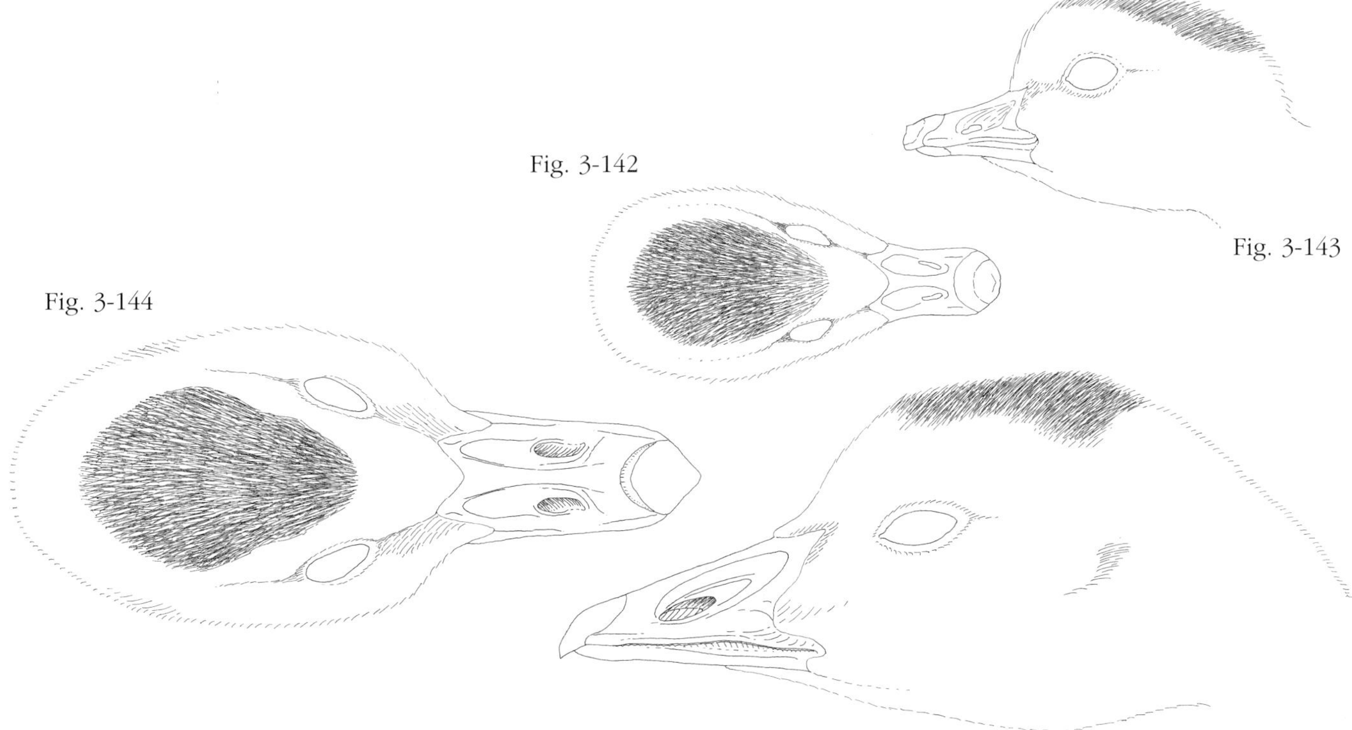

Fig. 3-142 Fig. 3-143 Fig. 3-144 Fig. 3-145

Fig. 3-142, 3-143 [1-2 days]: Manitoba; figs. 3-144, 3-145 [3-4 weeks]: Northwest Territories.

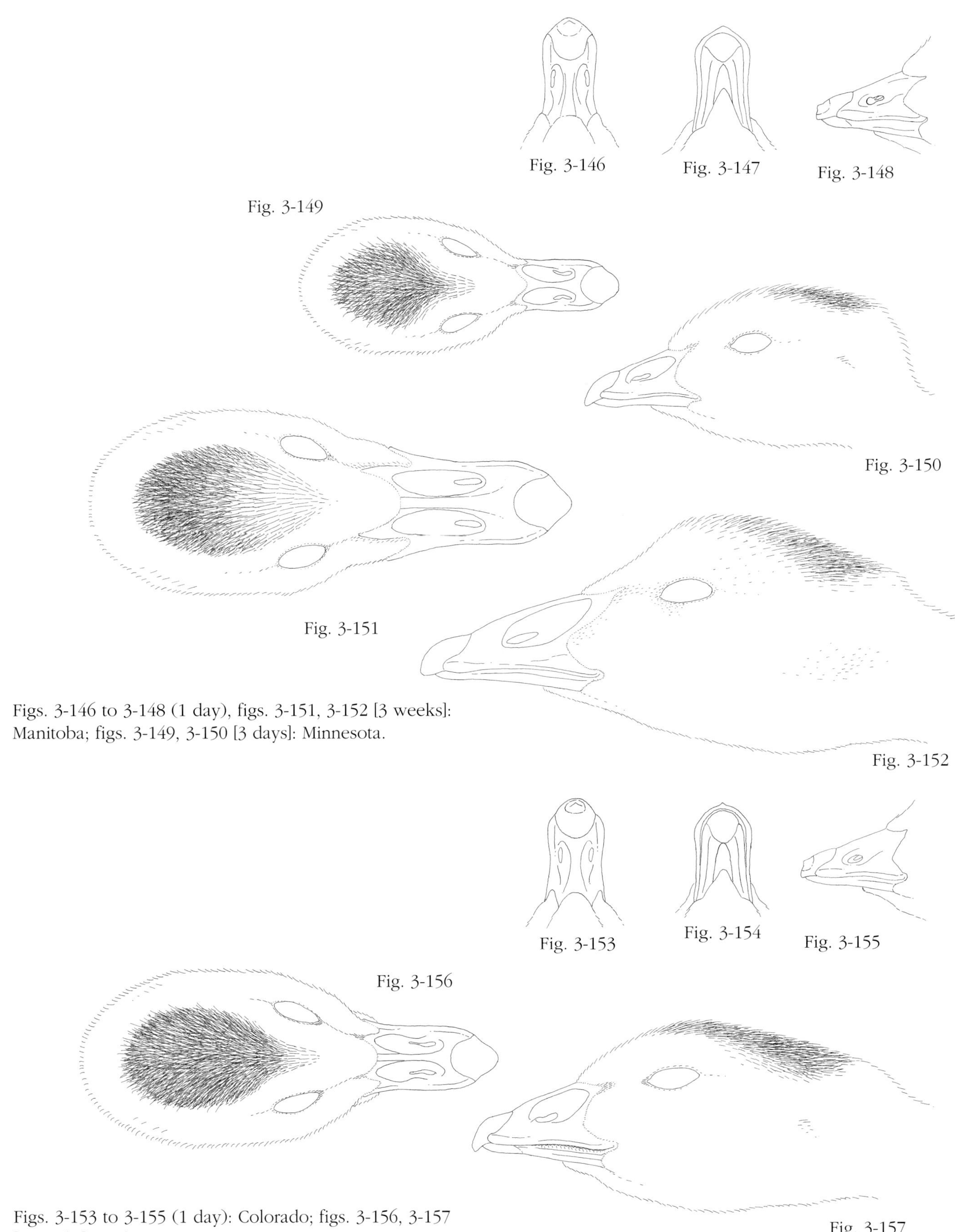

Figs. 3-146 to 3-148 (1 day), figs. 3-151, 3-152 [3 weeks]: Manitoba; figs. 3-149, 3-150 [3 days]: Minnesota.

Figs. 3-153 to 3-155 (1 day): Colorado; figs. 3-156, 3-157 [2 weeks]: Utah.

7b. Base color of plumage often bright but seldom brilliant, usually overlaid by pale grayish down tips or may seem 'greenish'; inconspicuous breast-band occasionally present; 'bridle', if present, usually fairly prominent (fig. 3-171); base color of tarsi and feet variable, usually dark if plumage dull, sometimes blackish; over all size medium. Various middle-sized goslings from W shore Hudson Bay, interior Southampton Island, interior Northwest Territories, Mackenzie Delta, and N and W coasts Alaska as far as Hooper Bay, including Lesser Canada Goose, *B. canadensis parvipes*, figs. 3-158 to 3-166, and Taverner's Canada Goose, *B. canadensis taverneri*, figs. 3-167 to 3-173.

See species account, pp. 53-59, for discussion of variation, and Table 1, Appendix A, for comparative measurements.

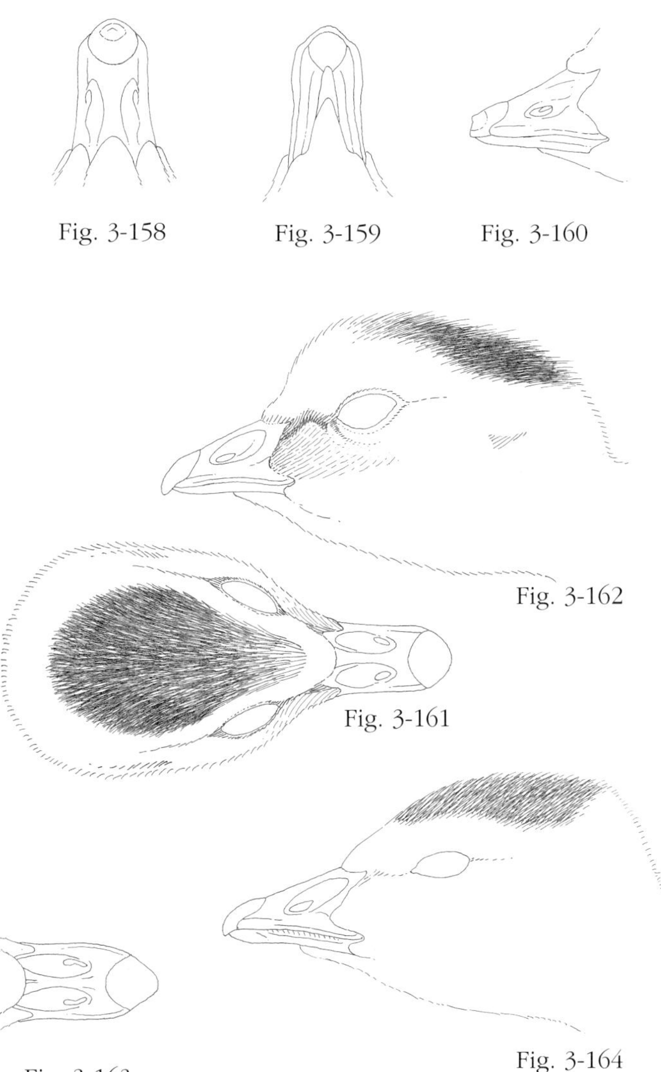

Fig. 3-158 Fig. 3-159 Fig. 3-160

Fig. 3-162

Fig. 3-161

Fig. 3-163

Fig. 3-164

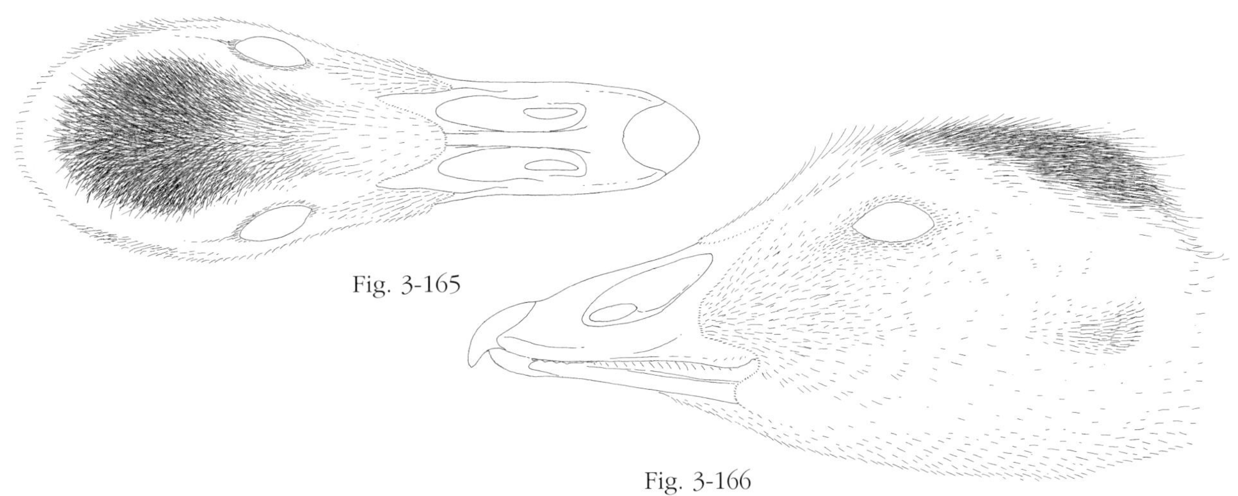

Fig. 3-165

Fig. 3-166

Figs. 3-158 to 3-160 (1 day), figs. 3-163, 3-164 [5-6 days], figs. 3-165, 3-166 [3-4 weeks]: Northwest Territories; figs. 3-161, 3-162 [3-5 days]: Yukon Territories.

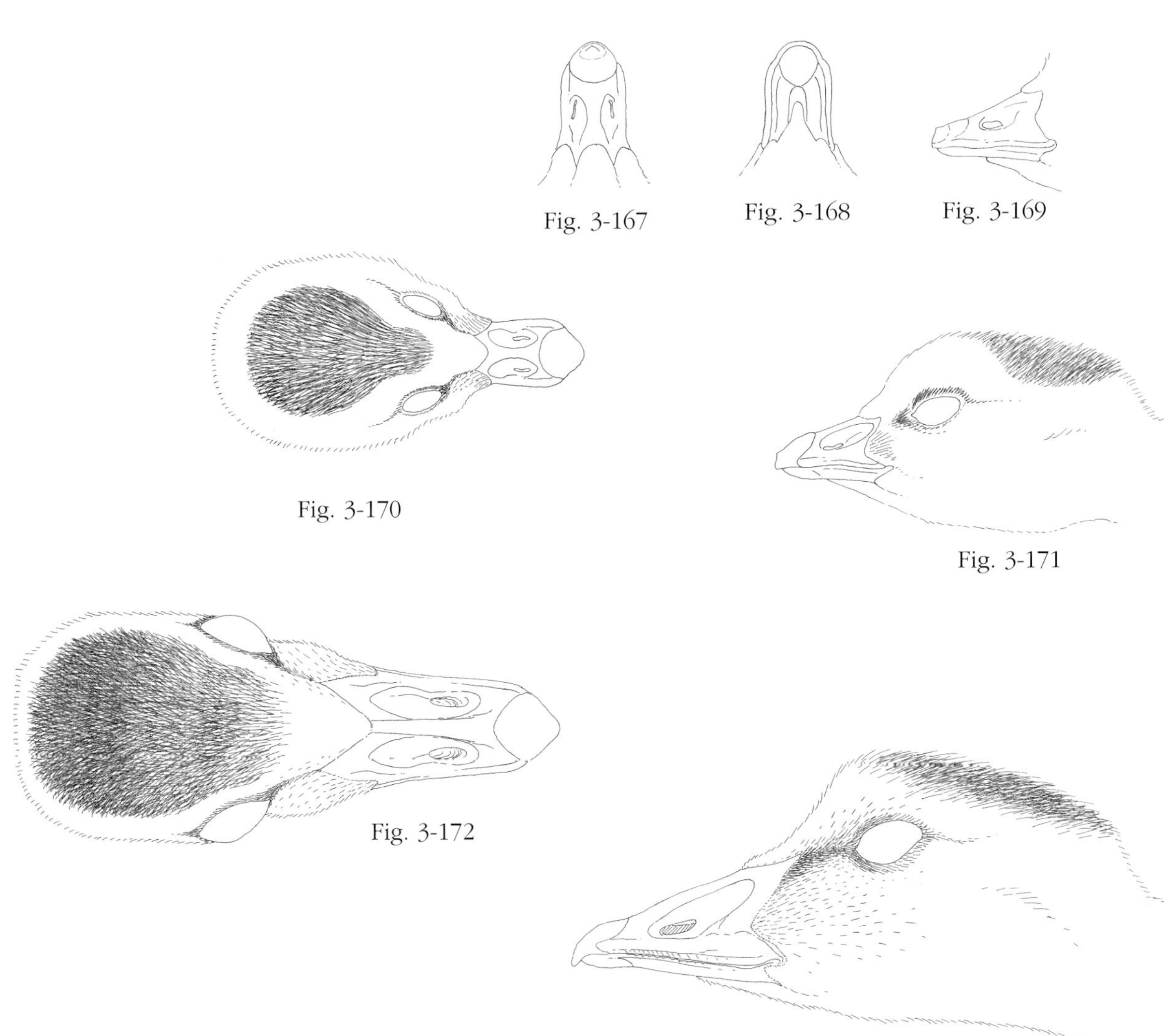

Fig. 3-167

Fig. 3-168

Fig. 3-169

Fig. 3-170

Fig. 3-171

Fig. 3-172

Fig. 3-173

Figs. 3-167 to 3-169 (1 day): captive; figs. 3-170, 3-171 [2-3 days], figs. 3-172, 3-173 [3 weeks]: Alaska.

Genus *Nesochen*

Hawaiian Goose, *Nesochen sandvicensis,* figs. 3-174 to 3-178.

Figs. 3-174 to 3-176 (1 day): captive (Hawaiian Islands); figs. 3-177, 3-178 (2 days): Hawaiian Islands.

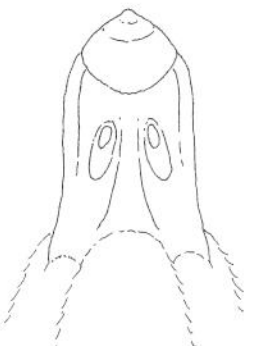
Fig. 3-174

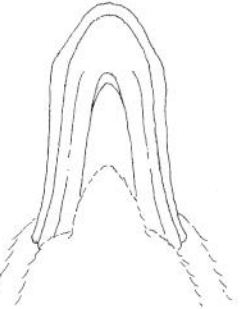
Fig. 3-175

Fig. 3-176

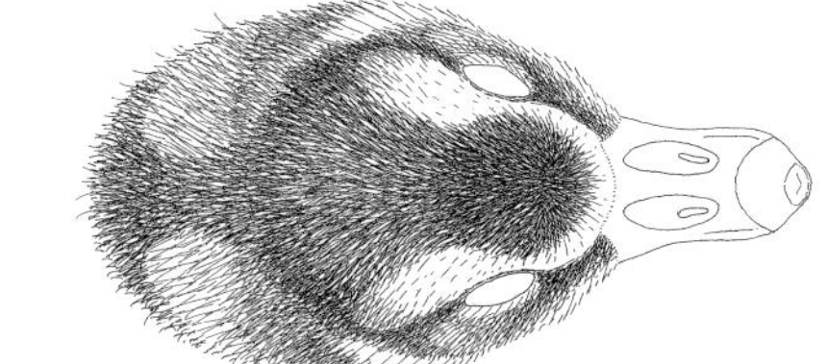
Fig. 3-177

Fig. 3-178

Tribe Cairinini
Genus *Cairina*

Muscovy Duck, *Cairina moschata,* figs. 4-1 to 4-7.

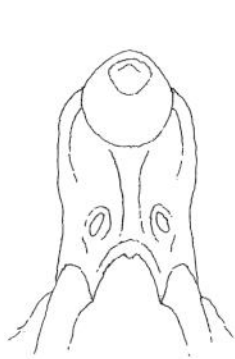
Fig. 4-1

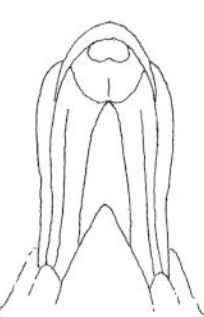
Fig. 4-2

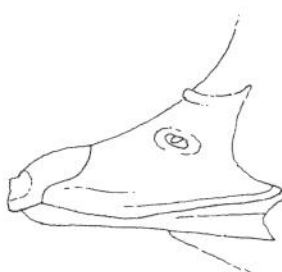
Fig. 4-3

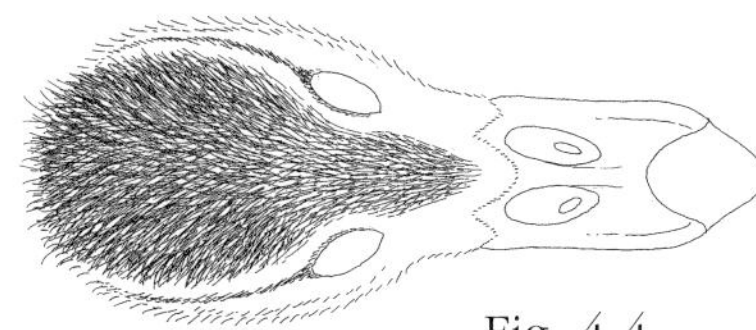
Fig. 4-4

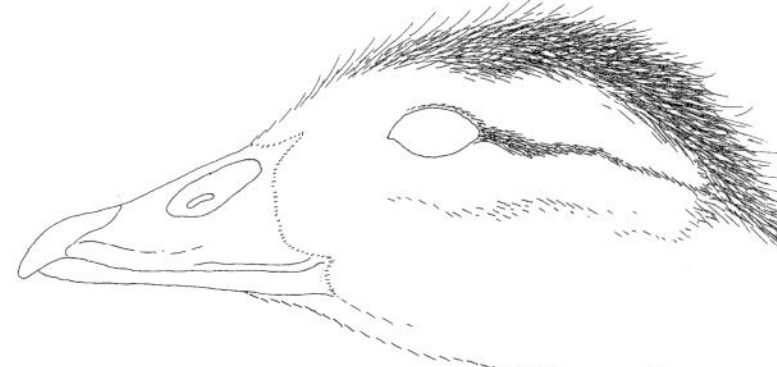
Fig. 4-5

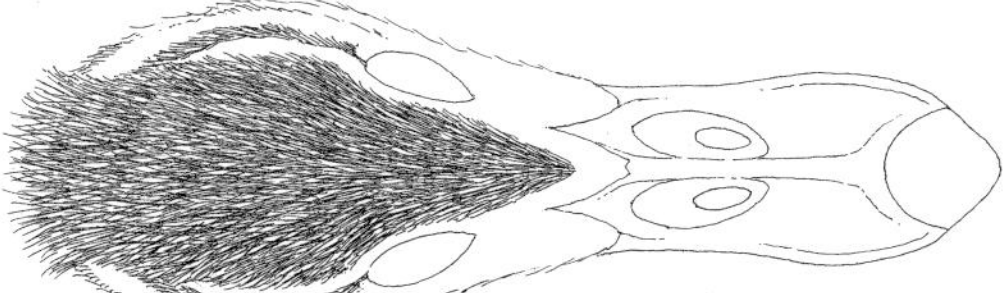
Fig. 4-6

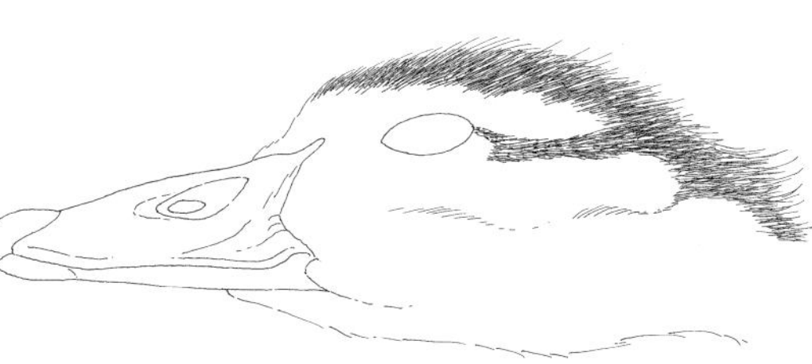
Fig. 4-7

Figs. 4-1 to 4-3 (1 day): captive (Brazil); figs. 4-4, 4-5 [4-6 days]: Brazil; figs. 4-6, 4-7 [12-14 days]: Venezuela.

Genus *Aix*

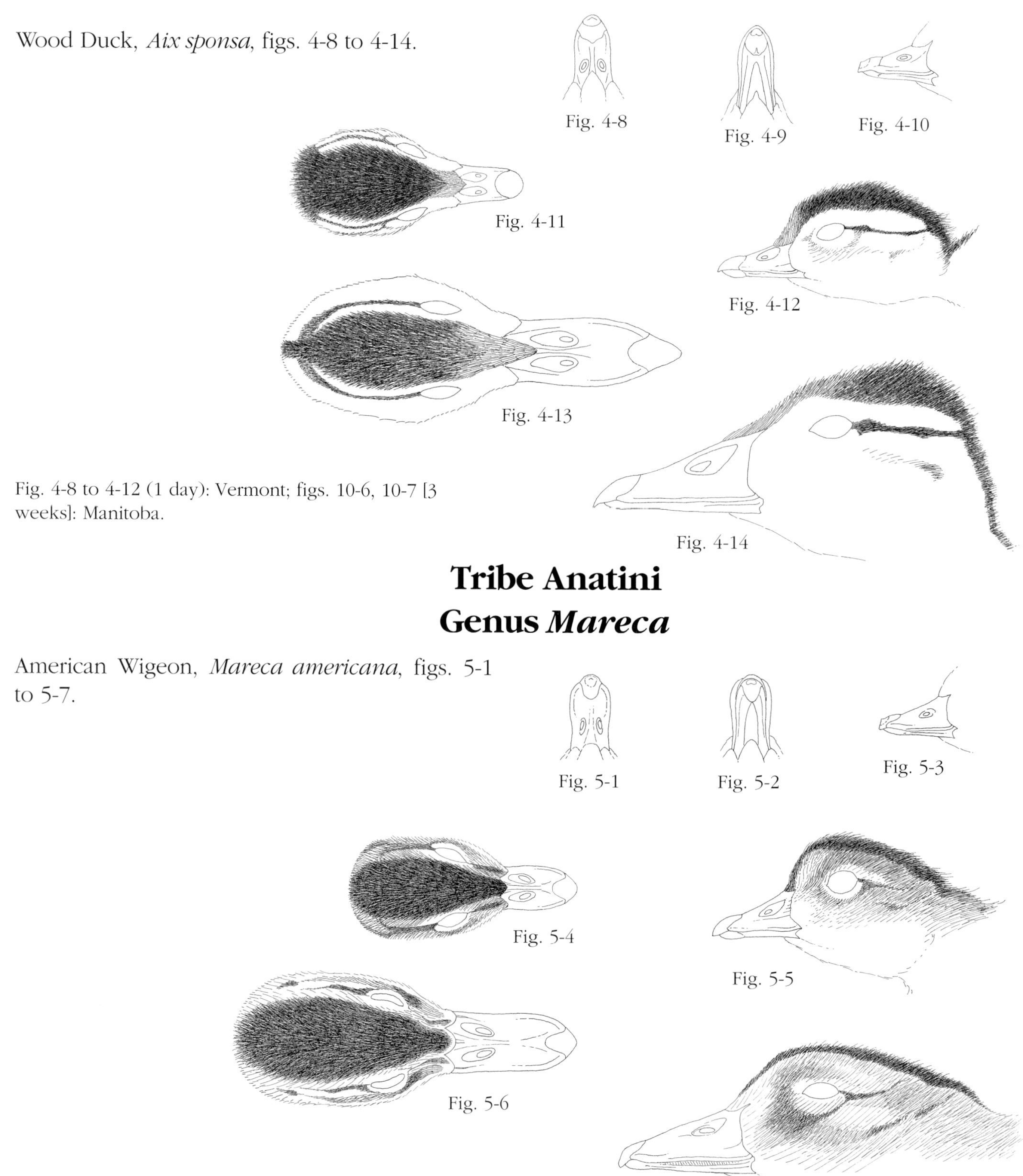

Wood Duck, *Aix sponsa*, figs. 4-8 to 4-14.

Fig. 4-8 to 4-12 (1 day): Vermont; figs. 10-6, 10-7 [3 weeks]: Manitoba.

Tribe Anatini

Genus *Mareca*

American Wigeon, *Mareca americana*, figs. 5-1 to 5-7.

Fig. 5-1 to 5-3 (1 day): Manitoba, figs. 5-4, 5-5 [3 days]: Ontario; figs. 5-6, 5-7 [2 weeks]: Saskatchewan.

Key to *Anas* species

1a. Base color of plumage white or grayish white, with no trace of yellow (rarely a trace of extremely pale yellow on belly); appearance of stripes in dorsal view of head also characteristic (figs. 5-11, 5-13). Northern Pintail, *Anas acuta*, figs. 5-8 to 5-14.

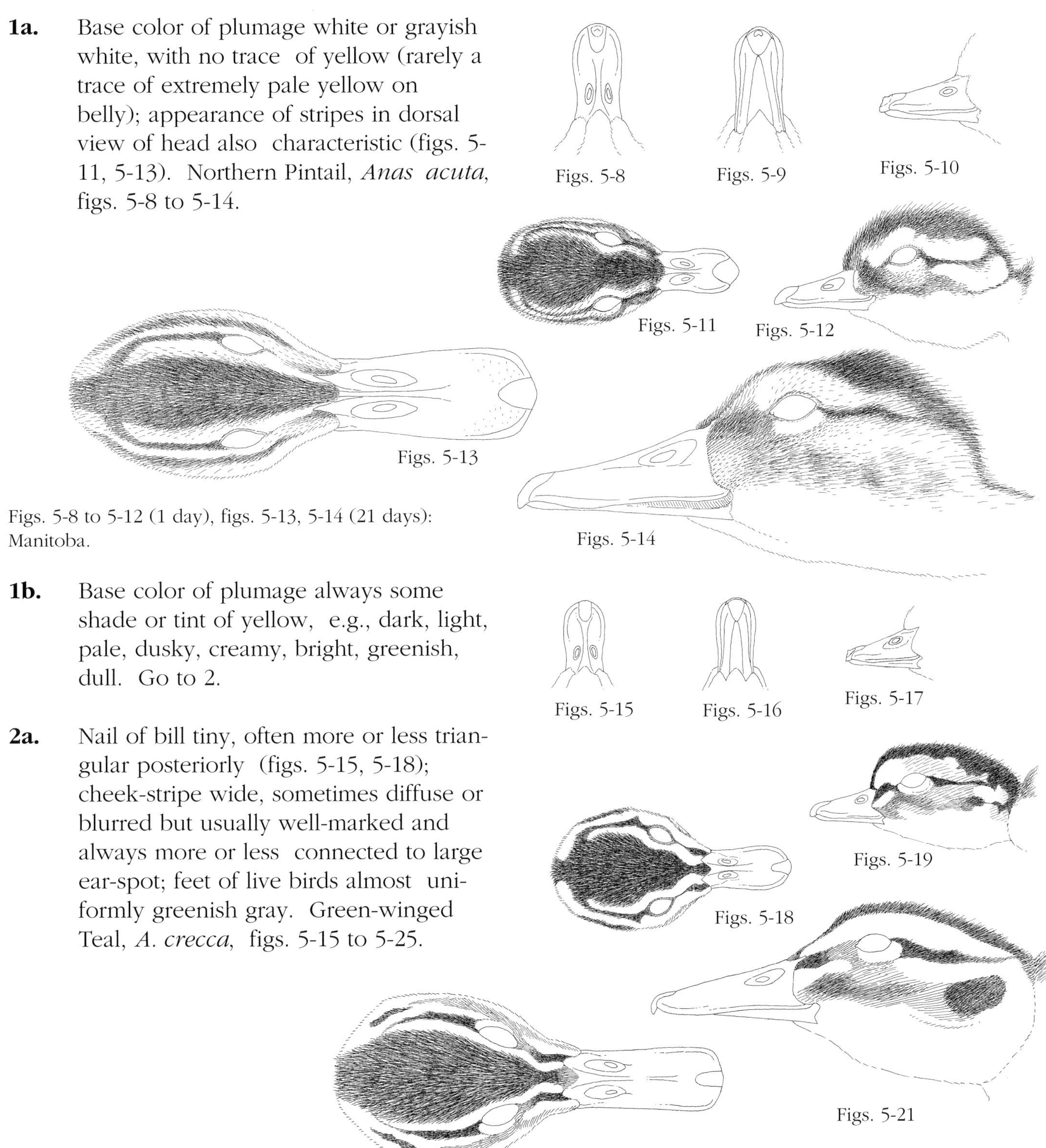

Figs. 5-8 to 5-12 (1 day), figs. 5-13, 5-14 (21 days): Manitoba.

1b. Base color of plumage always some shade or tint of yellow, e.g., dark, light, pale, dusky, creamy, bright, greenish, dull. Go to 2.

2a. Nail of bill tiny, often more or less triangular posteriorly (figs. 5-15, 5-18); cheek-stripe wide, sometimes diffuse or blurred but usually well-marked and always more or less connected to large ear-spot; feet of live birds almost uniformly greenish gray. Green-winged Teal, *A. crecca*, figs. 5-15 to 5-25.

Figs. 5-15 to 5-17, 5-19 (1 day): Manitoba; fig. 5-18 [4 days]: Alberta; figs. 5-20, 5-21 [3 weeks]: Northwest Territories. *A. c. carolinensis.*

Figs. 5-22, 5-23 [5-6 days], figs. 5-24, 5-25 [10-12 days]: Alaska. *A. c. nimia.*

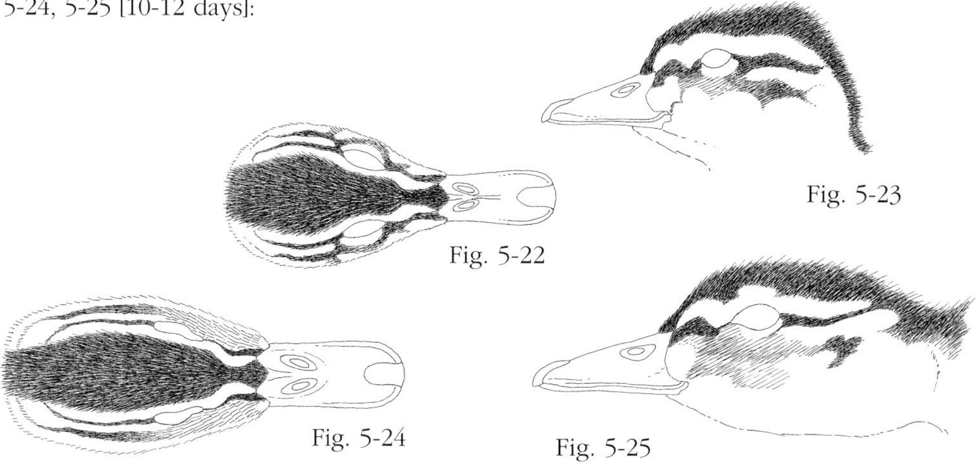

Fig. 5-23

Fig. 5-22

Fig. 5-24

Fig. 5-25

2b. Nail of bill always larger than in 2a; cheek-stripe usually absent or merely suggested as a dull wash, contrasting poorly with base color; feet of live birds never greenish gray. Go to 3.

3a. Bill elongated (figs. 5-29, 5-31) relative to total head length (OBT): in live, day-old birds, mean ratio of culmen (EC) to OBT=0.35 (0.31-0.41; n=45, SD=0.025, SE=0.004; compare EC/OBT ratios of other day-old Anatini in Table 1, Appendix A); bill longer and flaring widely at sides in older downies (figs. 5-33, 5-35); wing-patches usually inconspicuous or lacking; dark wash on cheeks usually present, giving dusky appearance to face (figs. 5-32, 5-34). Northern Shoveler, *A. clypeata*, figs. 5-26 to 5-36.

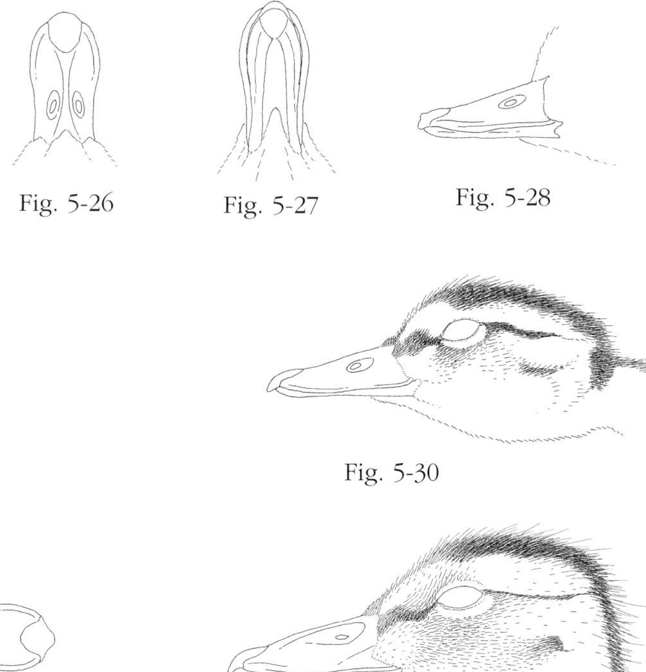

Fig. 5-26

Fig. 5-27

Fig. 5-28

Fig. 5-30

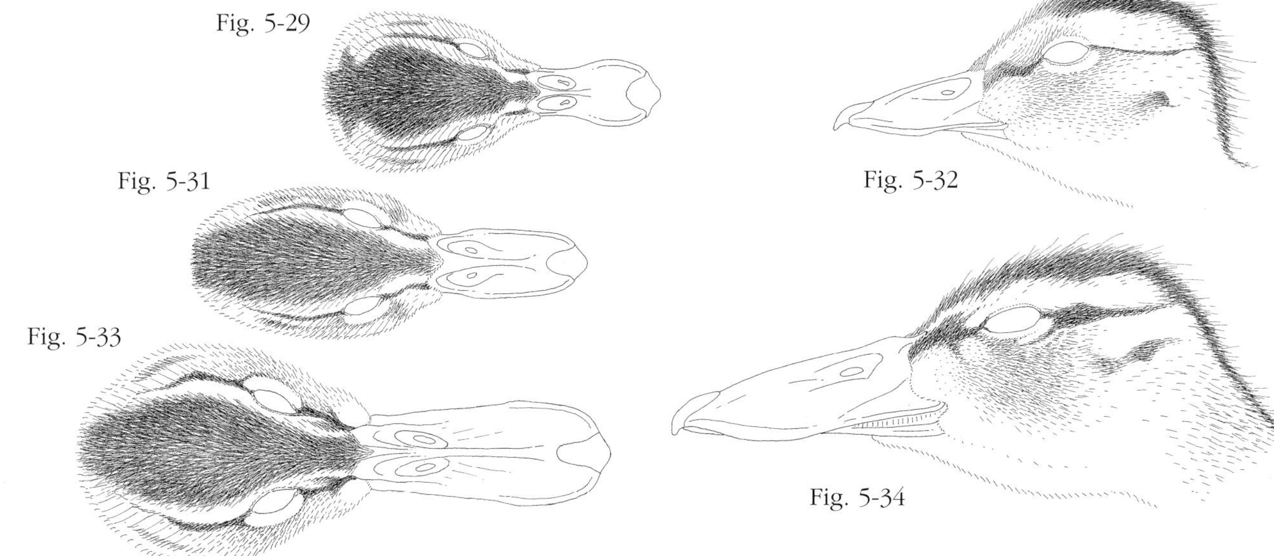

Fig. 5-29

Fig. 5-31

Fig. 5-32

Fig. 5-33

Fig. 5-34

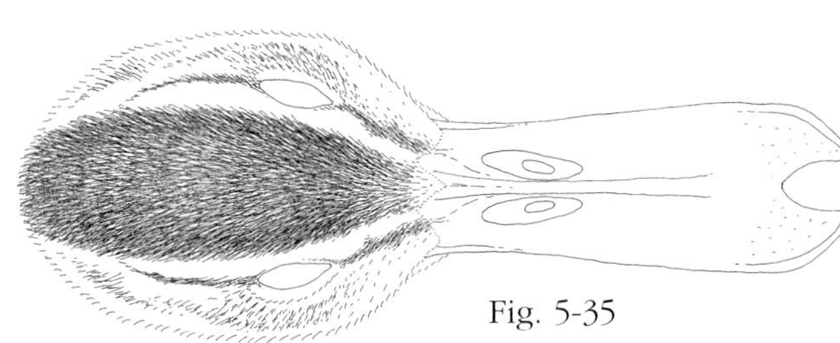

Fig. 5-35

Fig. 5-36

Figs. 5-26 to 5-28, 5-30 (1 day), figs. 5-33, 5-34 [3 weeks], figs. 5-35, 5-36 (29 days): Manitoba; figs. 5-29 [2 days], figs. 5-31, 5-32 [5-6 days]: Saskatchewan.

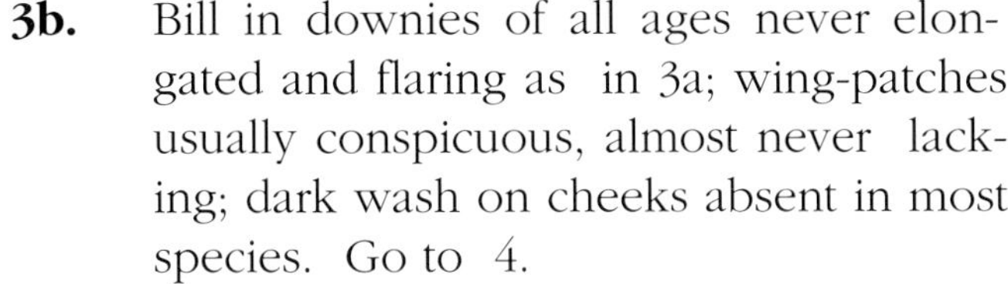

3b. Bill in downies of all ages never elongated and flaring as in 3a; wing-patches usually conspicuous, almost never lacking; dark wash on cheeks absent in most species. Go to 4.

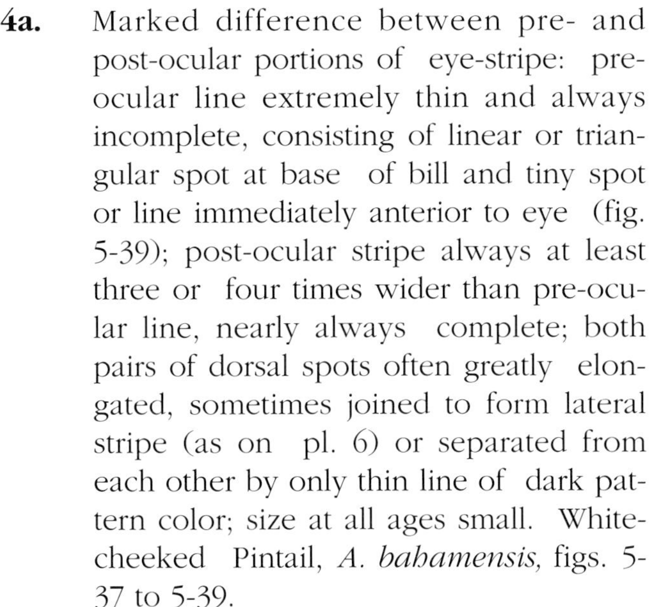

4a. Marked difference between pre- and post-ocular portions of eye-stripe: preocular line extremely thin and always incomplete, consisting of linear or triangular spot at base of bill and tiny spot or line immediately anterior to eye (fig. 5-39); post-ocular stripe always at least three or four times wider than pre-ocular line, nearly always complete; both pairs of dorsal spots often greatly elongated, sometimes joined to form lateral stripe (as on pl. 6) or separated from each other by only thin line of dark pattern color; size at all ages small. White-cheeked Pintail, *A. bahamensis,* figs. 5-37 to 5-39.

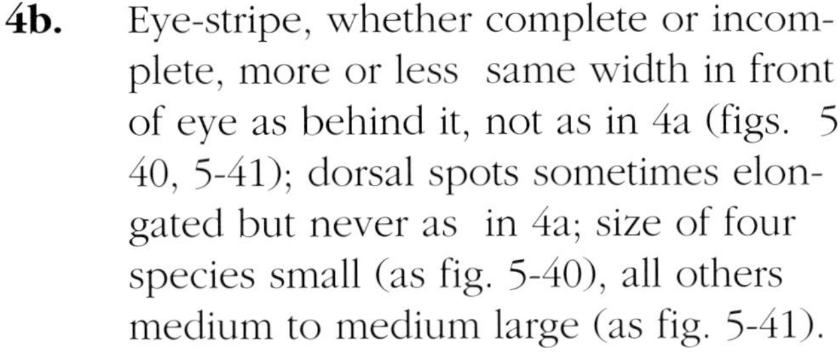

4b. Eye-stripe, whether complete or incomplete, more or less same width in front of eye as behind it, not as in 4a (figs. 5-40, 5-41); dorsal spots sometimes elongated but never as in 4a; size of four species small (as fig. 5-40), all others medium to medium large (as fig. 5-41).

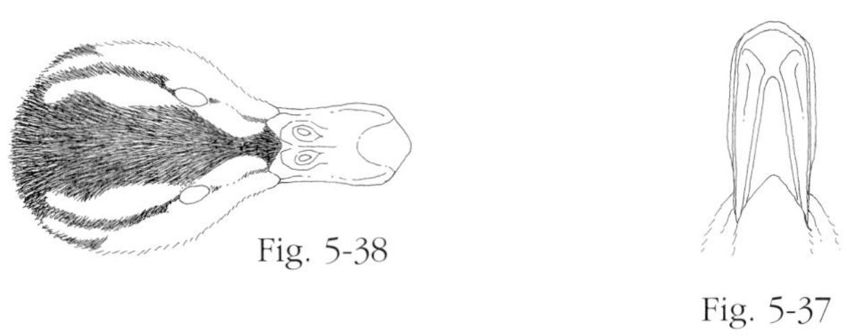

Fig. 5-38

Fig. 5-37

Fig. 5-39

Fig. 5-37 (4 days): captive; figs. 5-38, 5-39 [2 days]: Puerto Rico.

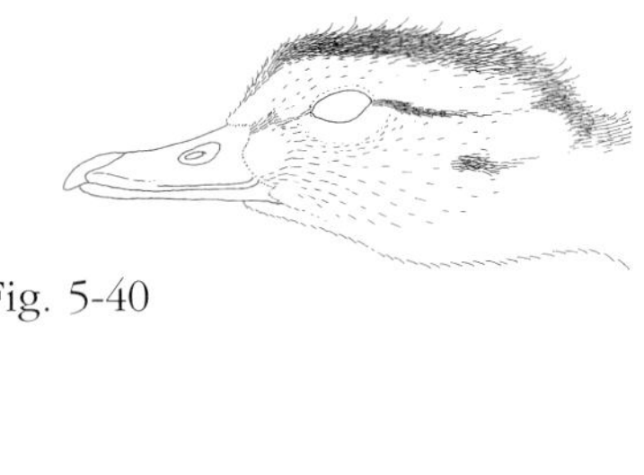

Fig. 5-40

Fig. 5-41

5a. Dark crown color nearly always goes all the way to bill, narrowing on forehead, flaring out again toward 'horns' of bill (fig. 5-42); occasional line of light-colored down above bill extremely narrow and inconspicuous (fig. 5-43); one species small, others medium to medium large; compare relative sizes of small species (figs. 5-110 to 5-129) and medium-large species (figs. 5-53 to 5-77, 5-81 to 5-98). Go to 6.

5b. Dark crown color tapers more or less evenly to forehead, leaving conspicuous line of lighter base color above bill (figs. 5-44, 5-45), almost never goes all the way to bill, seldom flares out toward 'horns' of bill; size at all ages small. Go to 12.

6a. Yellow base color always pale and creamy (bleaches nearly white in older downies); numerous pale or whitish tips of down plumes give mottled appearance to dark back; creamy white dorsal spots prominent; shoulder-spots often more or less connected to longer, wider rump-spots by broken line of pale down plumes; dark crown narrow in dorsal view (figs. 5-49, 5-51): compare with Northern Mallard's crown (figs. 5-89, 5-93); bill narrow and high-bridged at base. Gadwall, *A. strepera,* figs. 5-46 to 5-52.

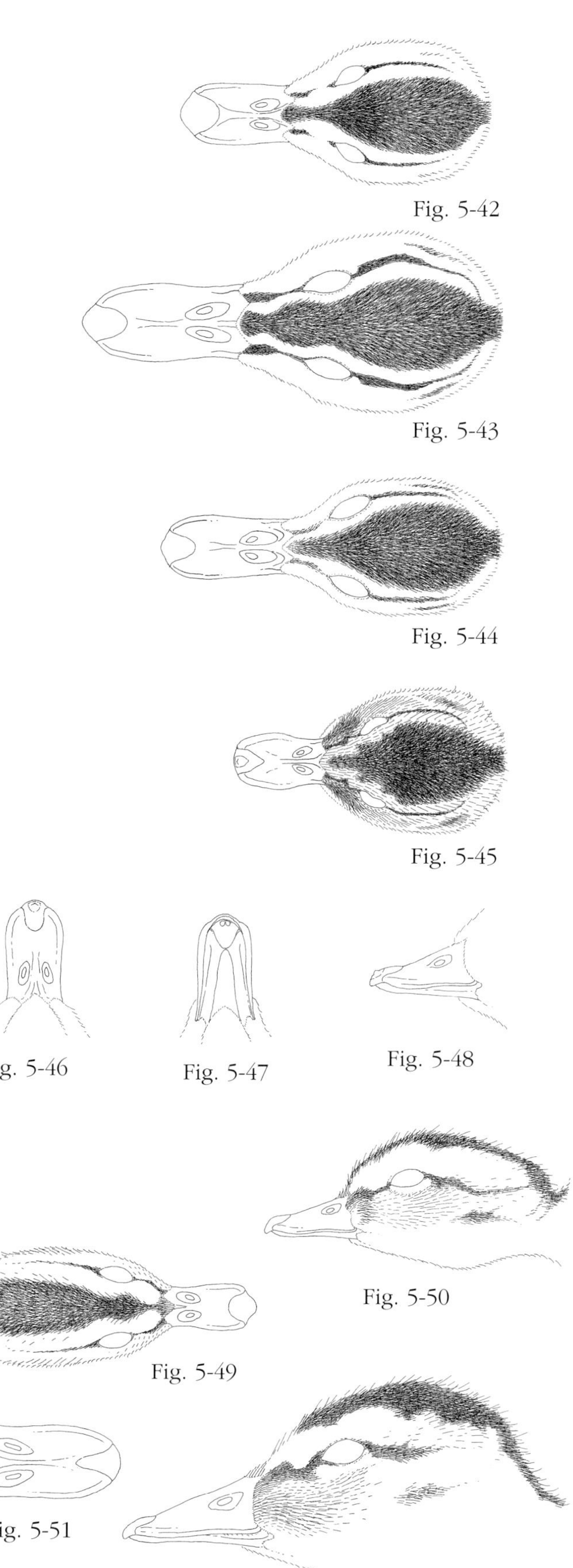

Fig. 5-42

Fig. 5-43

Fig. 5-44

Fig. 5-45

Fig. 5-46

Fig. 5-47

Fig. 5-48

Fig. 5-50

Fig. 5-49

Fig. 5-51

Fig. 5-52

Figs. 5-46 to 5-50 (1 day): Manitoba; figs. 5-51, 5-52 [12 days]: Saskatchewan.

6b. Yellow base color sometimes pale, but never creamy as in 6a; dorsal plumage never with mottled appearance as in 6a; dorsal spots sometimes large but almost never connected as in 6a; bill never narrow and high-bridged at base as in 6a. Go to 7.

7a. Tarsi and feet always dark, often blackish; low contrast between pattern and base colors: one Munsell *value* step or less. Go to 8.

7b. Tarsi and feet more brightly colored than in 8a, sometimes dark but never blackish; nearly always good to fair contrast between pattern and base colors: two or more Munsell *value* steps. Go to 9.

8a. Eye-stripe always heavy, blackish, and well-marked, nearly always complete (figs. 5-57 to 5-65); pattern color blackish olive-brown, with few, if any, lighter yellow-brown plumes on yoke and forehead (fig. 5-60). American Black Duck, *A. rubripes*, figs. 5-53 to 5-65.

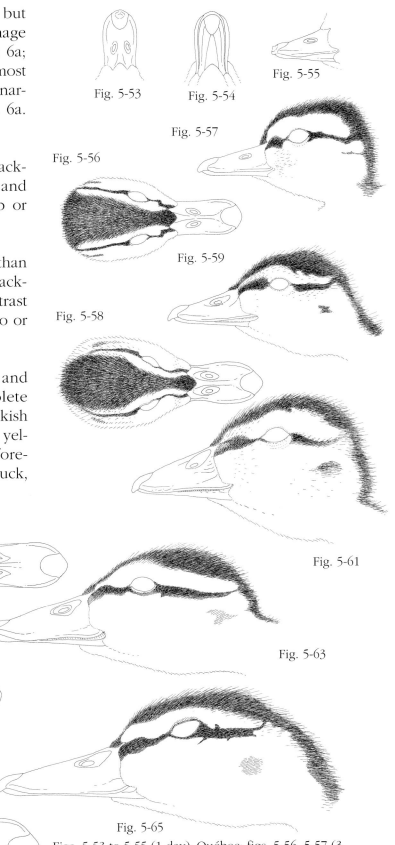

Fig. 5-53 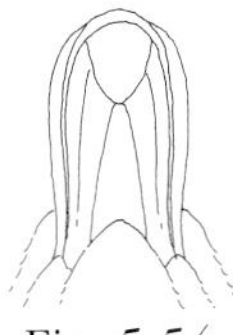 Fig. 5-54 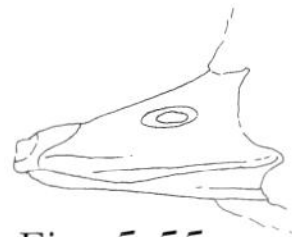 Fig. 5-55

Fig. 5-57

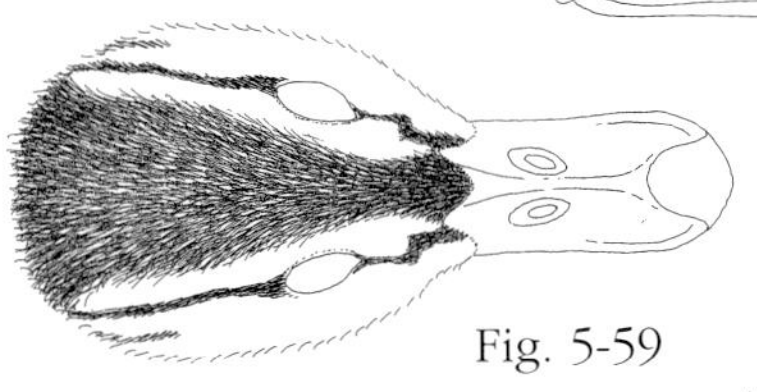

Fig. 5-56

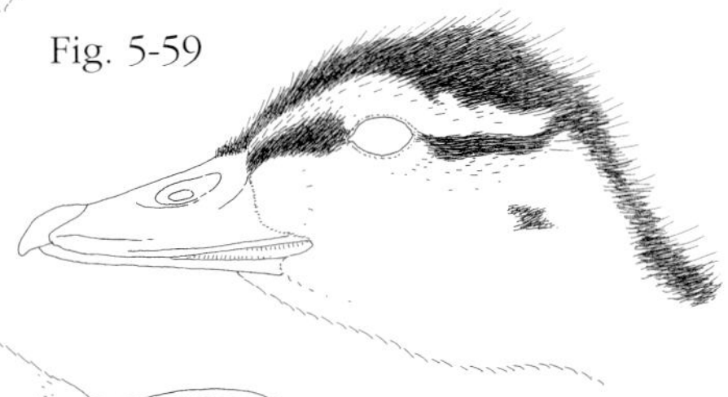

Fig. 5-59

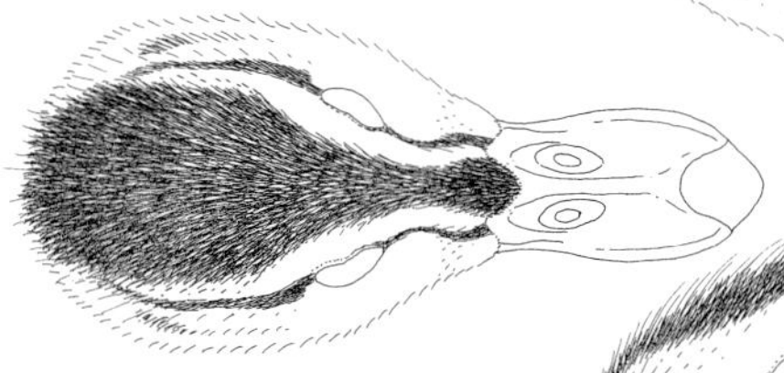

Fig. 5-58

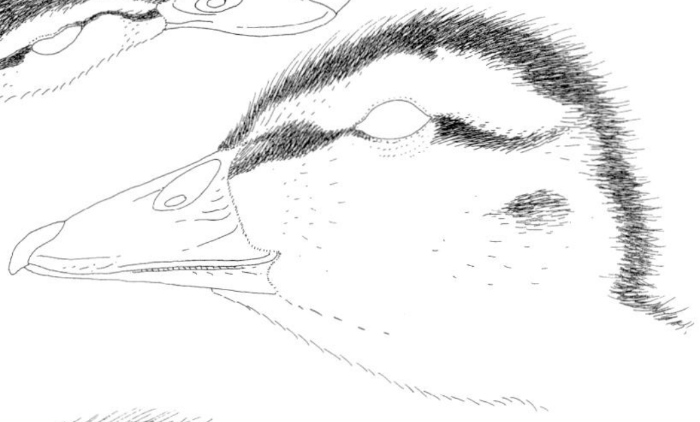

Fig. 5-61

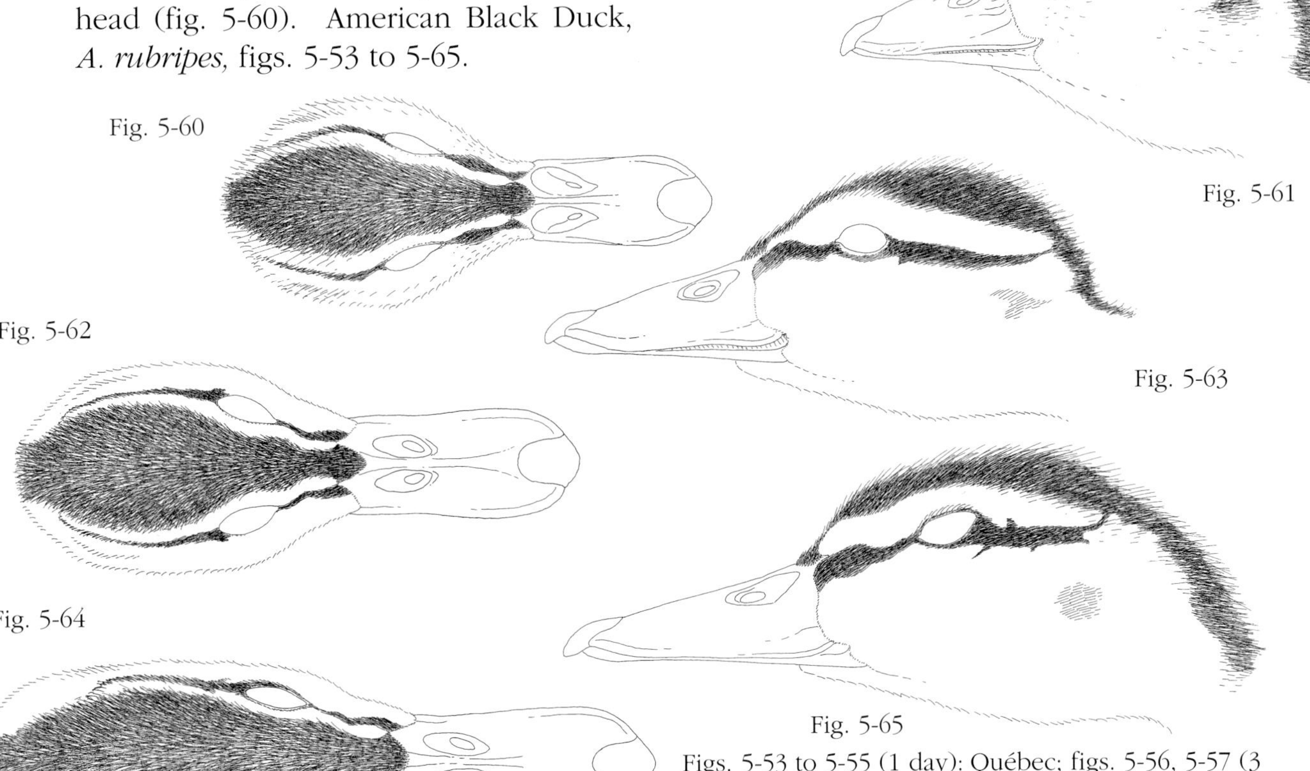

Fig. 5-60

Fig. 5-62

Fig. 5-63

Fig. 5-64

Fig. 5-65

Figs. 5-53 to 5-55 (1 day): Québec; figs. 5-56, 5-57 (3 days), figs. 5-62, 5-63 [2-1/2 weeks], figs. 5-64, 5-56 [3-1/2 weeks]: Ontario; figs. 5-58, 5-59 [6 days]: Michigan; figs. 5-60, 5-61 [10-12 days]: Nova Scotia.

8b. Eye-stripe nearly always thin, brownish, and incomplete, either in front of eye or at occiput or both (figs. 5-70, 5-72, 5-77); pattern color deep, dull olive-brown with many lighter yellow-brown plumes [Munsell 2.5Y 5/6] on yoke and forehead (fig. 5-71). Mottled Duck, *A. fulvigula*, figs. 5-66 to 5-77.

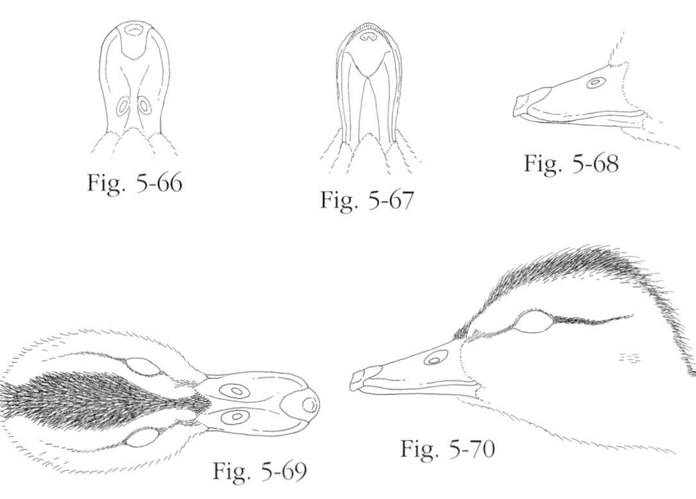

Figs. 5-66 to 5-68 (1 day): captive (Florida); figs. 5-69, 5-70 [1-2 days], figs. 5-71, 5-72 [2 weeks]: Florida *A. f. fulvigula*.

Fig. 5-71

Fig. 5-72

Fig. 5-73

Fig. 5-74

Fig. 5-75

Figs. 5-73 to 5-75 (1 day): Louisiana; 7-76, 5-77 (3 days): Texas. *A. f. maculosa*.

9a. Size small (i.e., teal-sized; compare relative size of teal and Northern Mallard heads in figs. 5-117 to 5-129, and figs. 5-86 to 5-102, respectively); in 2- or 3-day wild duckling (USNM uncat.) length of head from outer edge of dense down on occiput to tip of bill (OBT)=42.8 mm, exposed culmen (EC)=14.3 mm. Hawaiian Duck, *A. wyvilliana*, figs. 5-78 to 5-80.

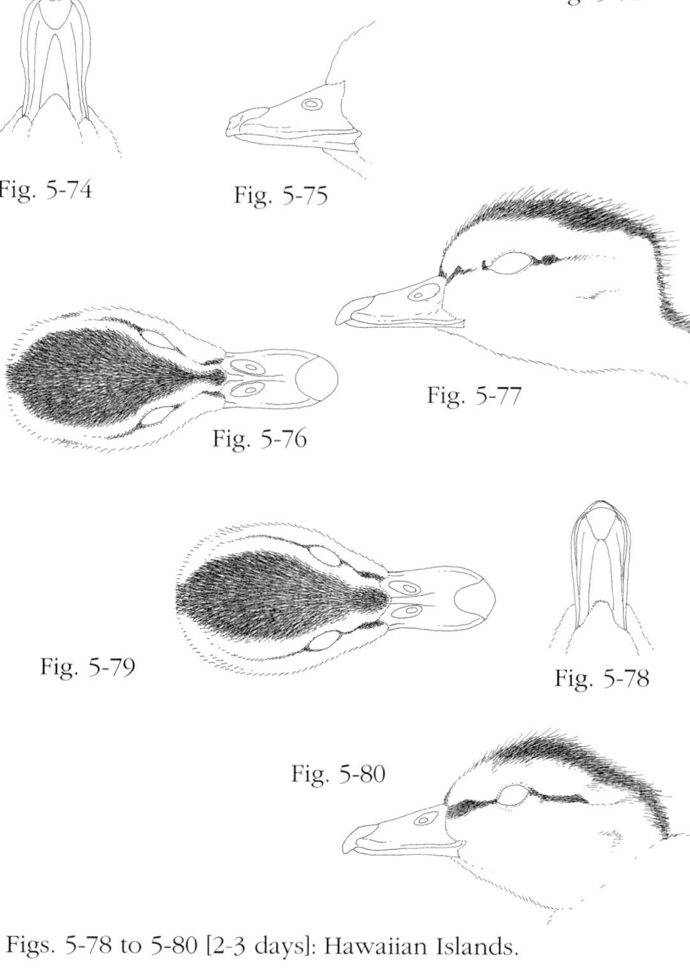

Figs. 5-78 to 5-80 [2-3 days]: Hawaiian Islands.

9b. Size medium-large (observe comparison in 9a): in three 2- or 3-day live captive *A. diazi* ducklings, mean of head lengths (OBT)=51.0 mm, mean of exposed culmens (EC)=18.6 mm. Northern Mallard, *A. p. platyrhynchos*, similar. Go to 10.

10a. Ear-spot always very small and inconspicuous (figs. 5-83, 5-85); eye-stripe always thin, brown, and incomplete, either in front of eye or behind it or both (fig. 5-83); base color nearly always some tint of orange-yellow on face and breast (Munsell *hues* 10YR, 2.5Y), fading to near-neutral parchment color on belly and undertail. In older downies (Class II [2½ to 5 weeks]): underdown of belly nearly always dark to medium gray: Munsell *value* 3.0/ to 4.5/. Mexican Duck, *A. diazi*, figs. 5-81 to 5-85.

Figs. 5-81 to 5-83 [3-5 days], figs. 5-84, 5-85 [2-1/2 weeks]: Mexico.

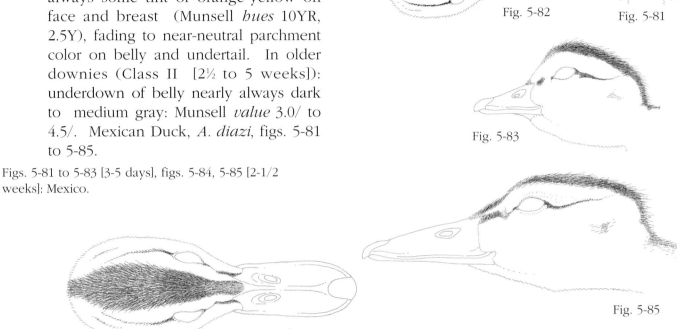

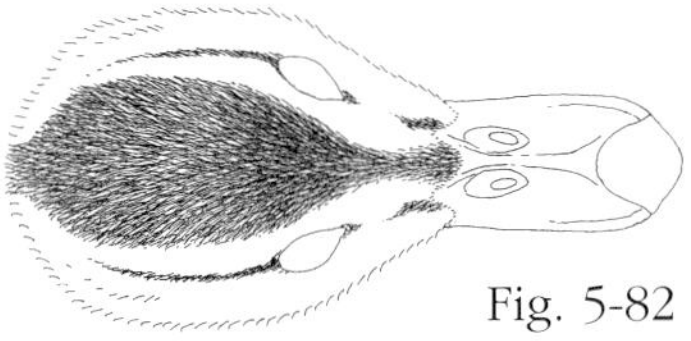

Fig. 5-82

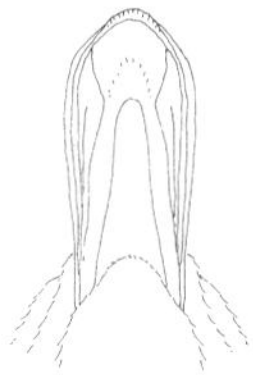

Fig. 5-81

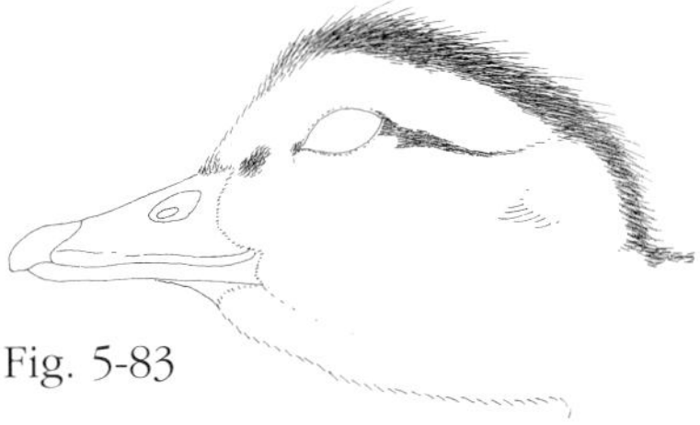

Fig. 5-83

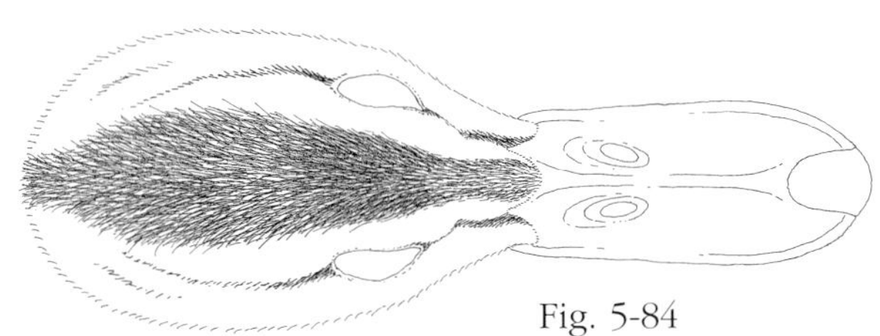

Fig. 5-84

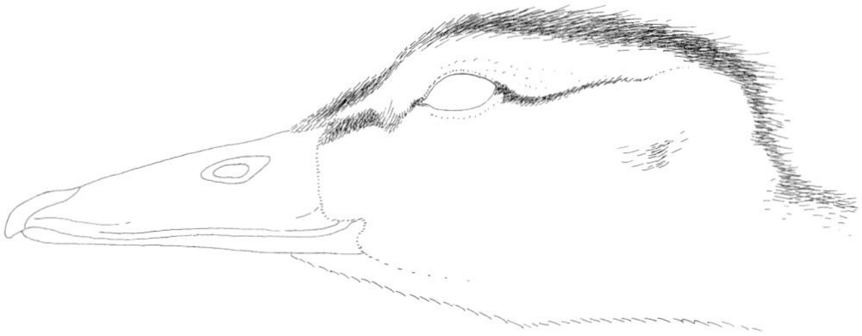

Fig. 5-85

10b. Ear-spot sometimes very small (figs. 5-90, 5-92), but usually well-marked and conspicuous (figs. 5-94, 5-102); eye-stripe sometimes thin and incomplete (fig. 5-92), but usually moderately heavy, blackish brown, and complete (figs. 5-90, 5-96); base color sometimes orange-yellow but usually yellow on face and breast (Munsell *hue* range 2.5Y to 6Y, sometimes 7.5Y), somewhat duller but still clearly yellow on belly and undertail. In older downies (Class II [2½ to 5 weeks]): underdown of belly nearly always light gray (rarely medium): Munsell *value* 5.0/ to 7.0/. Mallard, *A. platyrhynchos*, figs. 5-86 to 5-102.

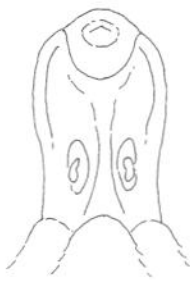

Fig. 5-86

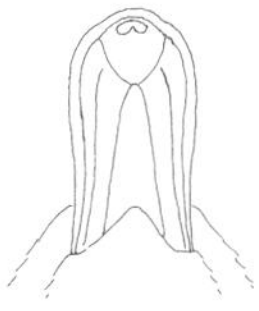

Fig. 5-87

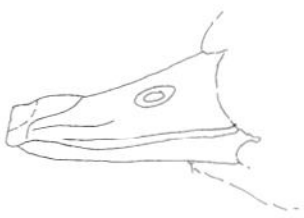

Fig. 5-88

Fig. 5-89

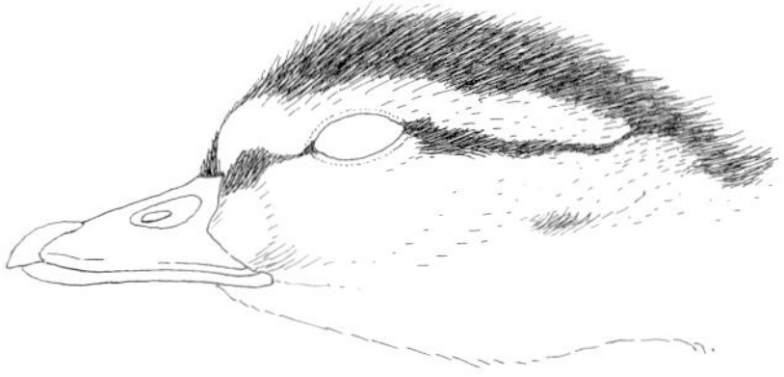

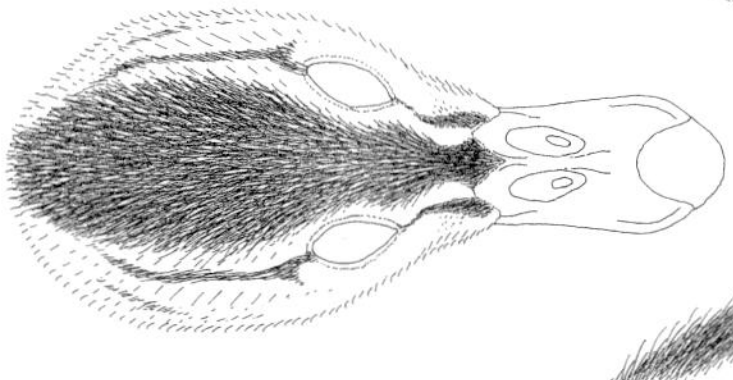

Fig. 5-90

Fig. 5-91

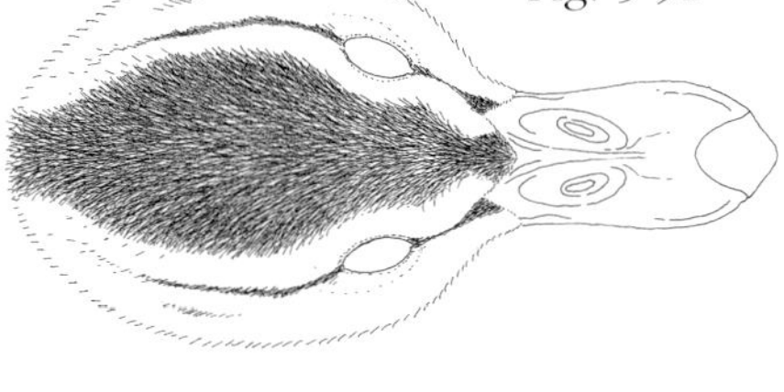

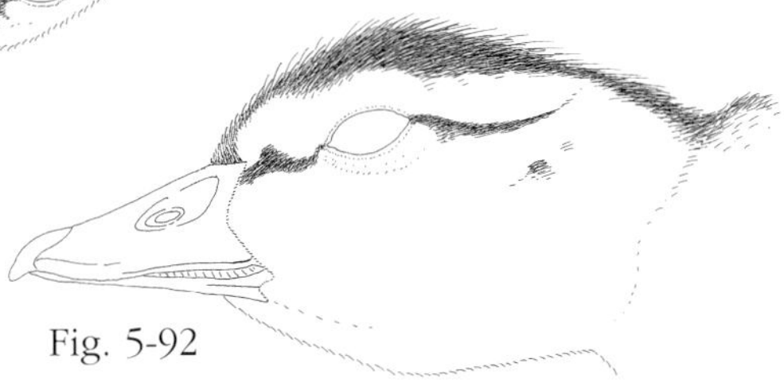

Fig. 5-92

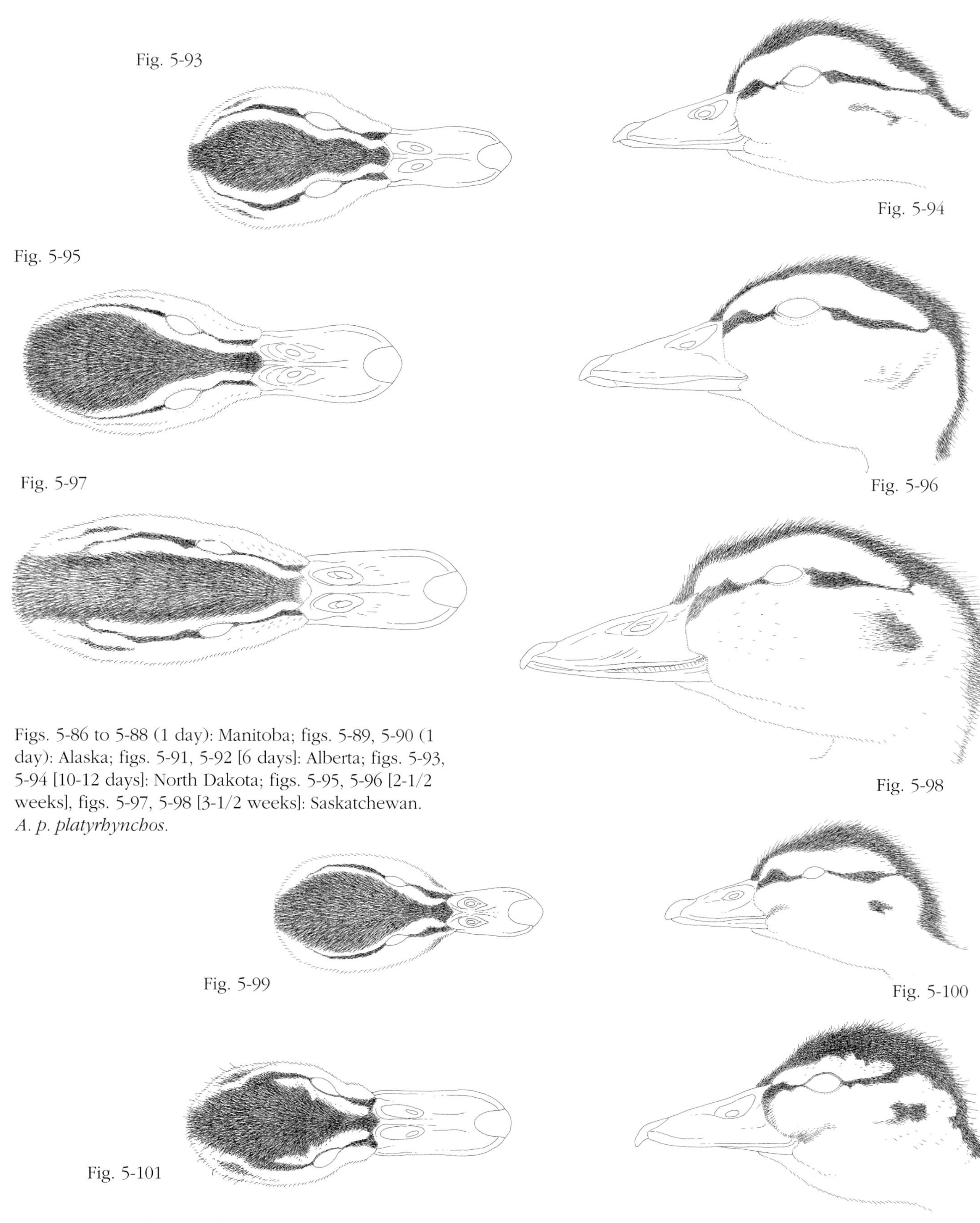

Figs. 5-86 to 5-88 (1 day): Manitoba; figs. 5-89, 5-90 (1 day): Alaska; figs. 5-91, 5-92 [6 days]: Alberta; figs. 5-93, 5-94 [10-12 days]: North Dakota; figs. 5-95, 5-96 [2-1/2 weeks], figs. 5-97, 5-98 [3-1/2 weeks]: Saskatchewan. *A. p. platyrhynchos.*

Figs. 5-99, 5-100 [3-5 days]: Greenland; figs. 5-101, 5-102 (2-1/2 weeks): captive (Greenland). *A. p. conboschas.*

11a. Entire base color of plumage brownish yellow ('gingery'); bill roundly spatulate, posterior of nail triangular, tip of nail flat (fig. 103) or (sometimes) smoothly pointed; small, diffuse, dark 'mustache' at rictus. Laysan Duck, *A. laysanensis,* figs. 5-103 to 5-109.

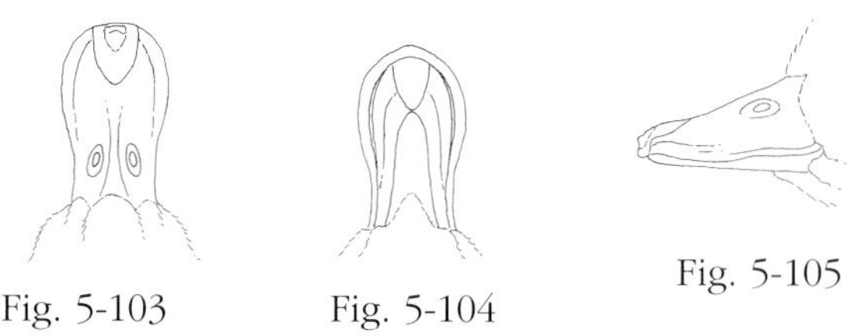

Fig. 5-103 Fig. 5-104 Fig. 5-105

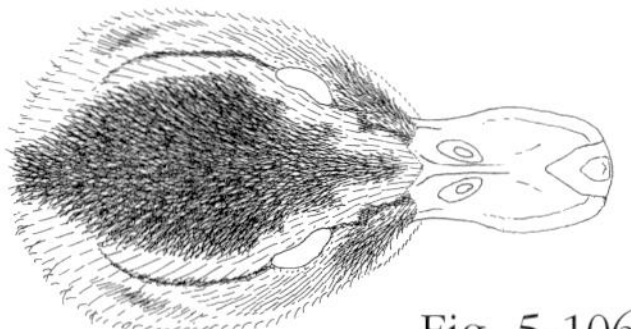

Fig. 5-106

Fig. 5-107

Figs. 5-103 to 5-105 (-1 day), figs. 5-106, 5-107 (1 day), figs. 5-108, 5-109 [2 weeks]: captive (Laysan I).

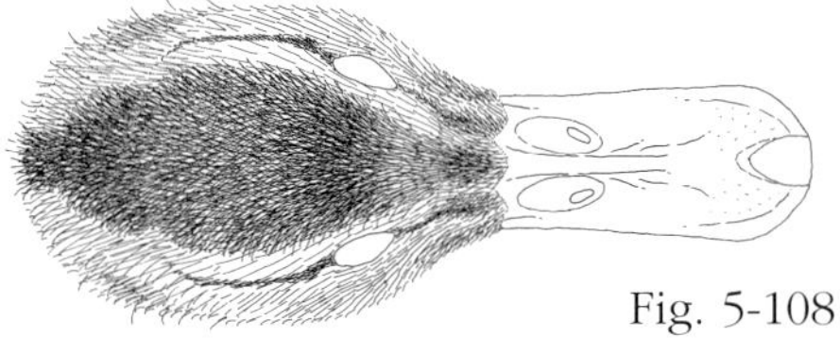

Fig. 5-108

Fig. 5-109

11b. Entire base color of plumage some tint of yellow: light, bright, pale, or dull; bill not roundly spatulate as in 11a, tip of nail has broad, shallow point; small 'mustache' at rictus absent. Go to 12.

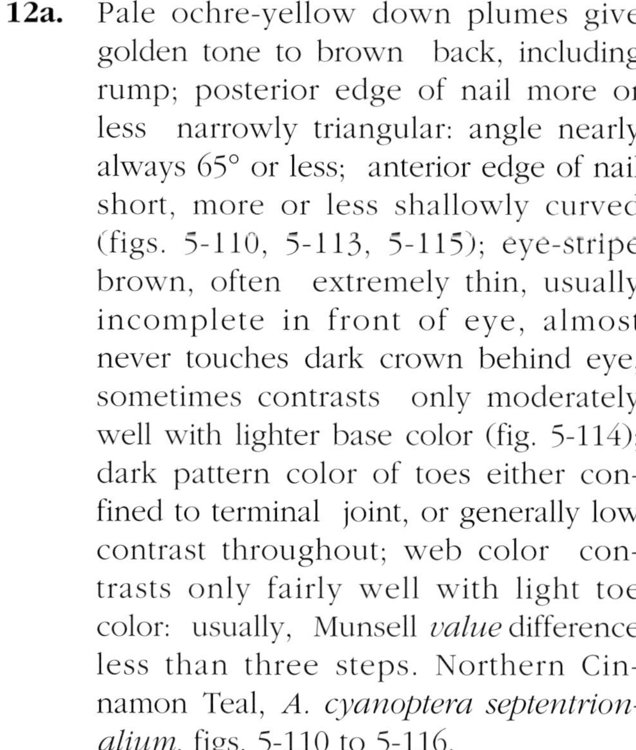

12a. Pale ochre-yellow down plumes give golden tone to brown back, including rump; posterior edge of nail more or less narrowly triangular: angle nearly always 65° or less; anterior edge of nail short, more or less shallowly curved (figs. 5-110, 5-113, 5-115); eye-stripe brown, often extremely thin, usually incomplete in front of eye, almost never touches dark crown behind eye, sometimes contrasts only moderately well with lighter base color (fig. 5-114); dark pattern color of toes either confined to terminal joint, or generally low contrast throughout; web color contrasts only fairly well with light toe color: usually, Munsell *value* difference less than three steps. Northern Cinnamon Teal, *A. cyanoptera septentrionalium,* figs. 5-110 to 5-116.

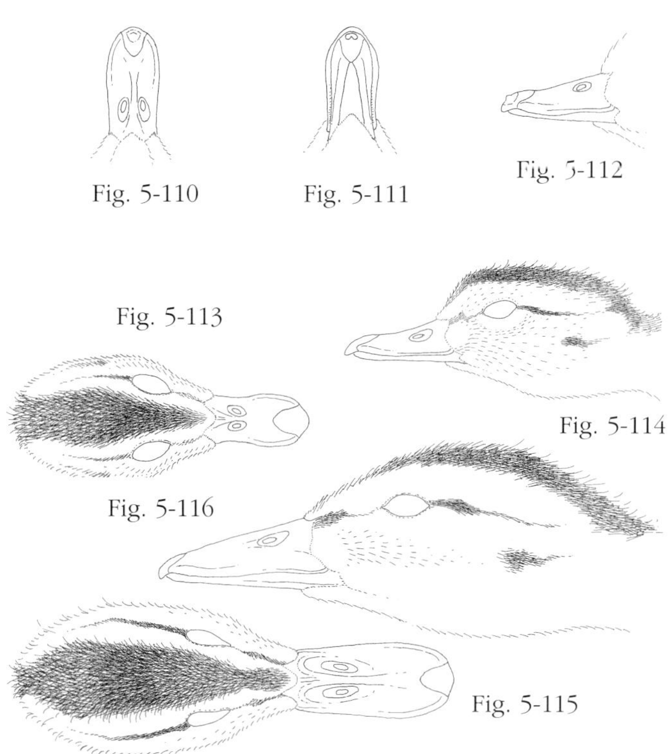

Fig. 5-110 Fig. 5-111 Fig. 5-112

Fig. 5-113 Fig. 5-114

Fig. 5-116

Fig. 5-115

Figs. 5-110 to 5-114 (1 day): captive (Utah); figs. 5-115, 5-116 [2-1/2 weeks]: California . *A. cyanoptera septentrionalium.*

12b. Pale, often dull, yellow down plumes do not give golden tone to blackish brown back, show hardly at all on lower back and rump, which appear dark; posterior edge of nail more or less broadly triangular: angle nearly always more than 65°; anterior edge of nail long, often more or less deeply curved (figs. 5-117, 5-120, 5-126); eye-stripe blackish brown, often thin but usually less so than in 12a, nearly always complete in front of eye, usually touches dark crown behind eye, nearly always contrasts well with lighter base color (fig. 5-121); dark pattern color of toes usually distributed more or less equally on all joints; web color contrasts well with light toe color: nearly always, Munsell *value* difference three or more steps. Blue-winged Teal, *A. discors*, figs. 5-117 to 5-129.

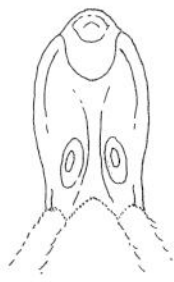

Fig. 5-117

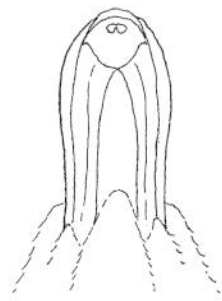

Fig. 5-118

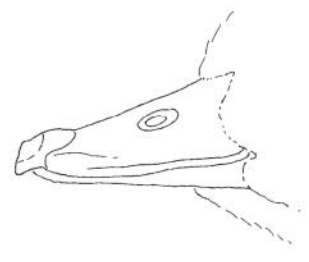

Fig. 5-119

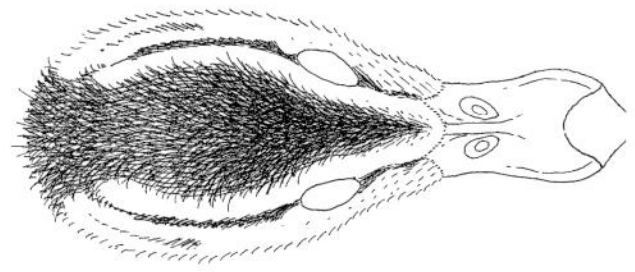

Fig. 5-120

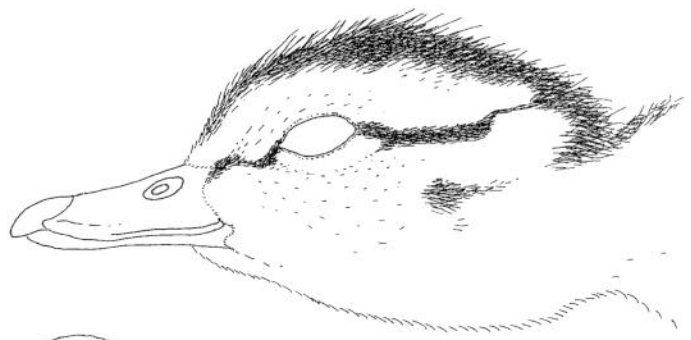

Fig. 5-121

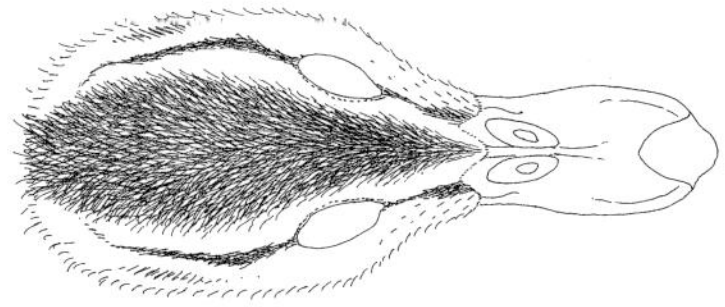

Fig. 5-122

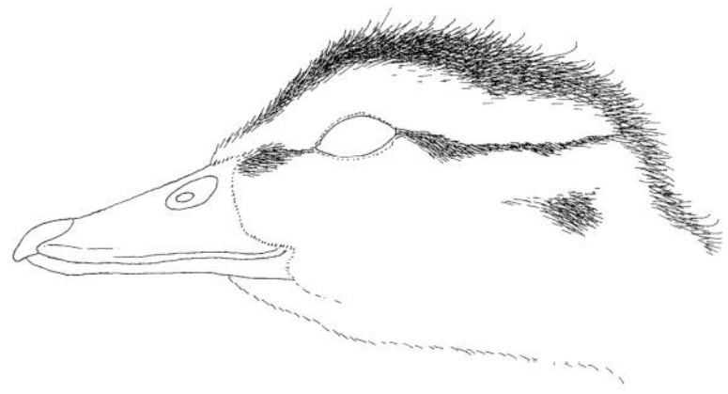

Fig. 5-123

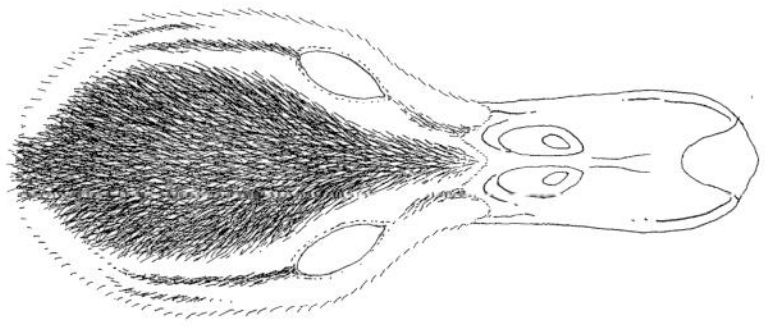

Fig. 5-124

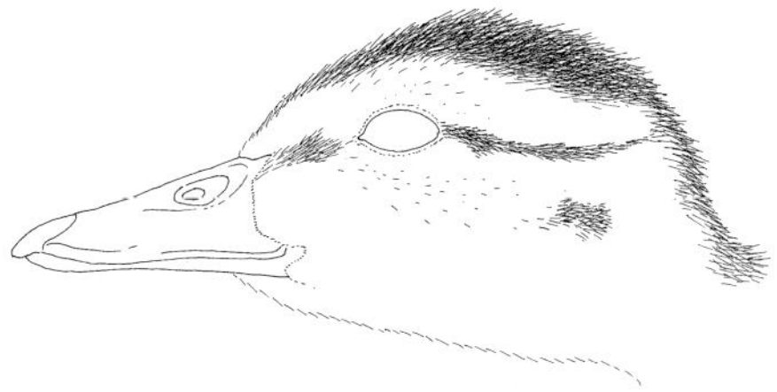

Fig. 5-125

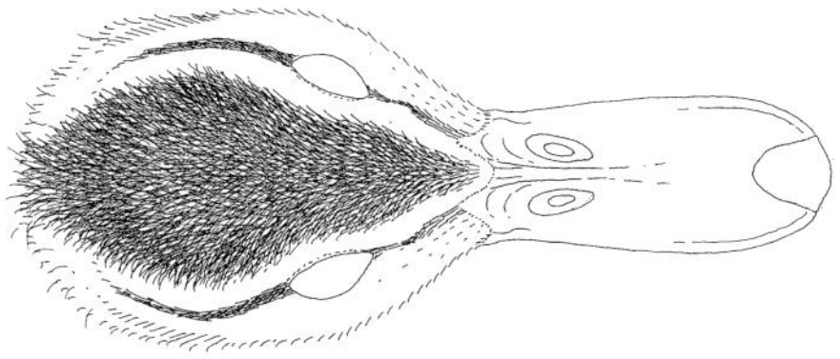

Fig. 5-126

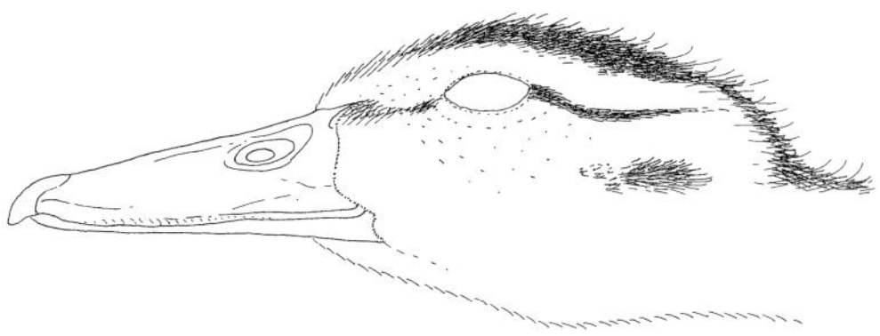

Fig. 5-127

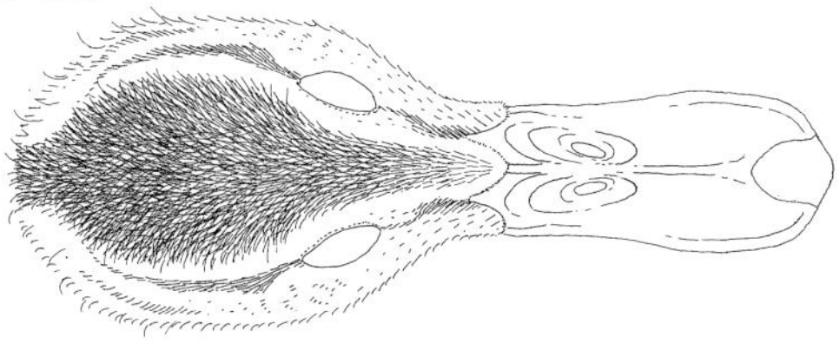

Fig. 5-128

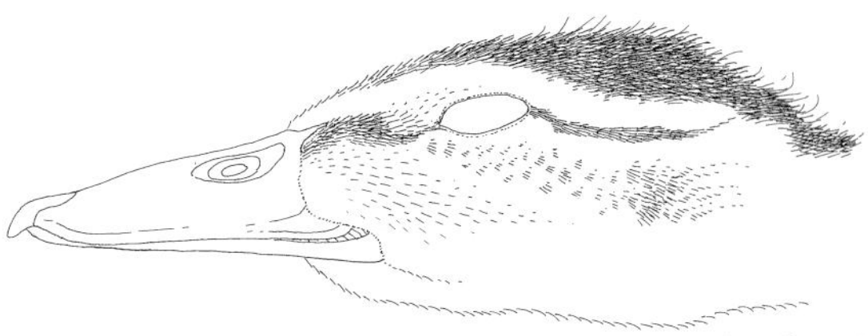

Fig. 5-129

Figs. 5-117 to 5-121 (1 day): Manitoba; figs. 5-122, 5-123 [6 days]: British Columbia; figs. 5-124, 5-125 [10 days]: Saskatchewan; figs. 5-126, 5-127 [2-1/2 weeks]: Ontario; figs. 5-128, 5-129 [3-1/2 weeks]: Montana. *A. d. discors.*

Tribe Aythyini

Key to *Aythya* species

1a. Dorsal spots and wing-patches nearly always large (1 cm or more), light-colored, contrasting well with darker pattern color (fig. 6-1), except one species characteristically low-contrast. 'Bright yellow' pochards. Go to 2.

1b. Dorsal spots nearly always small (5 mm or less), often contrasting poorly with dark pattern color (fig. 6-2); rump-spots and/or wing-patches sometimes entirely lacking. 'Dark yellow' pochards (scaup). Go to 4.

2a. Nail of bill narrow, sides often nearly parallel (figs. 6-3, 6-6); anterior edge of nail almost never curved—nearly always more or less straight; dark crown color always goes clearly and unmistakeably all the way down to bill, sometimes even a short way down sides of bill (fig. 6-7). Canvasback, *Aythya valisineria,* figs. 6-3 to 6-9.

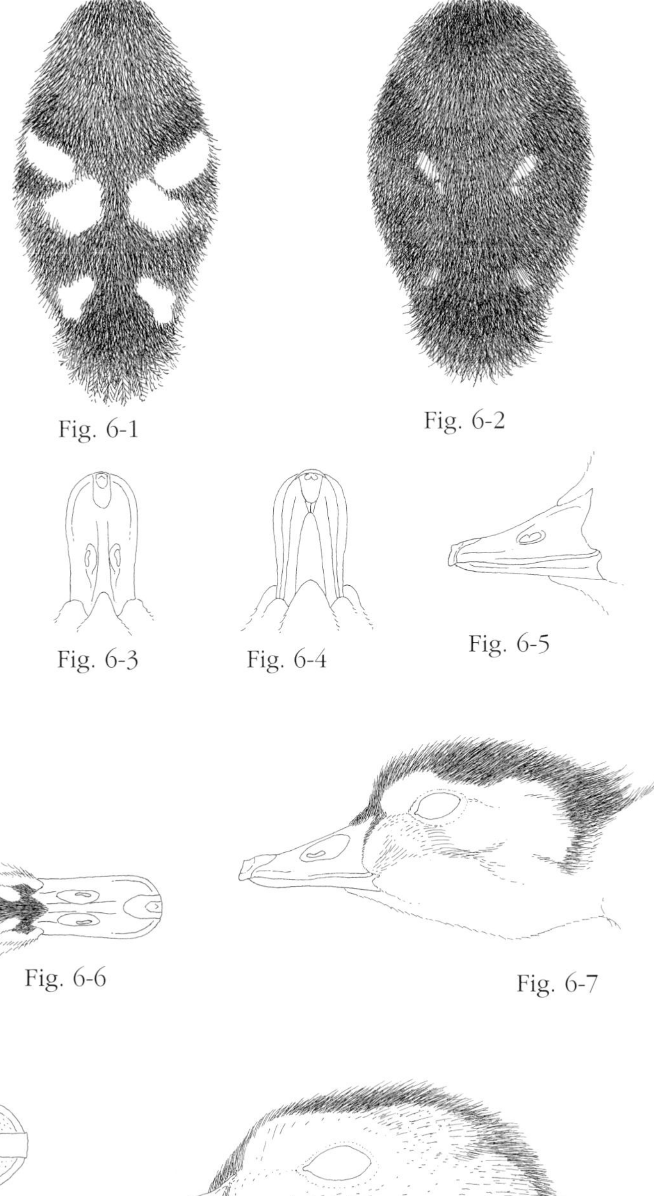

Fig. 6-1

Fig. 6-2

Fig. 6-3

Fig. 6-4

Fig. 6-5

Fig. 6-6

Fig. 6-7

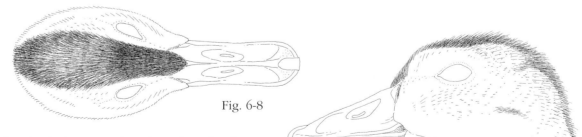

Fig. 6-8

Fig. 6-9

Figs. 6-3 to 6-7 (1 day): Manitoba; figs. 6-8, 6-9 [3 weeks]: Alberta.

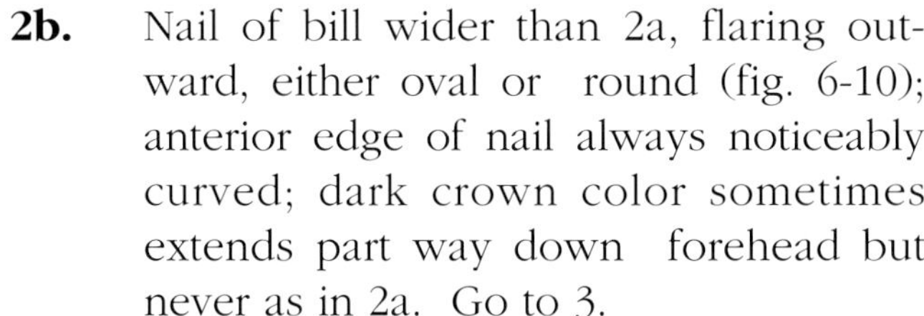

2b. Nail of bill wider than 2a, flaring outward, either oval or round (fig. 6-10); anterior edge of nail always noticeably curved; dark crown color sometimes extends part way down forehead but never as in 2a. Go to 3.

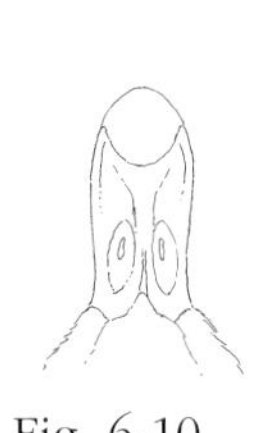

Fig. 6-10

3a. Forehead always light-colored; nail of bill oval; strongly contrasting dorsal spots have most extensive area of any North American *Aythya* species, rump-spots often continuous with base color under tail; olive-brown pattern color of plumage darkest of any North American pochard, yellow base color deep and vivid; nearly always a central dorsal spot a bit forward of the wings (often just a few pale plumes). Ring-necked Duck, *A. collaris,* figs. 6-11 to 6-17.

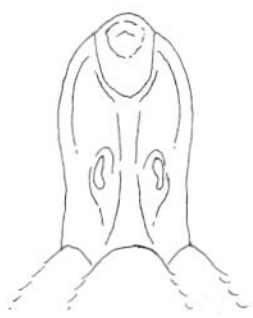

Fig. 6-11

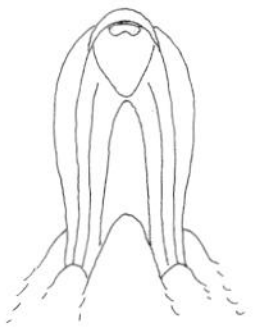

Fig. 6-12

Fig. 6-13

Fig. 6-14

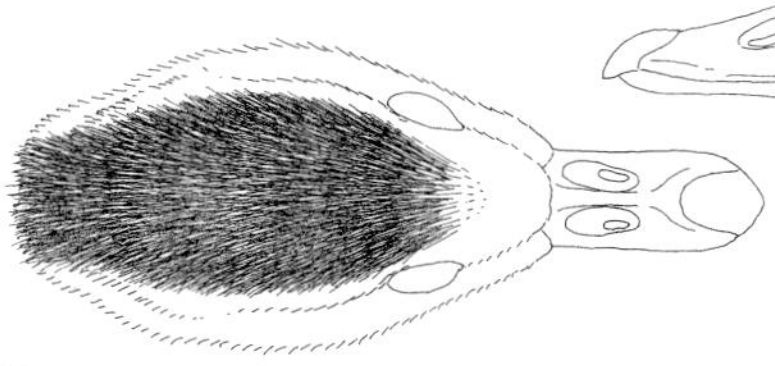

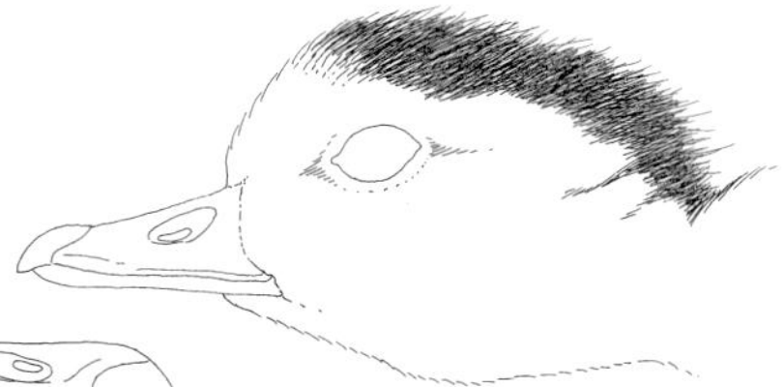

Fig. 6-15

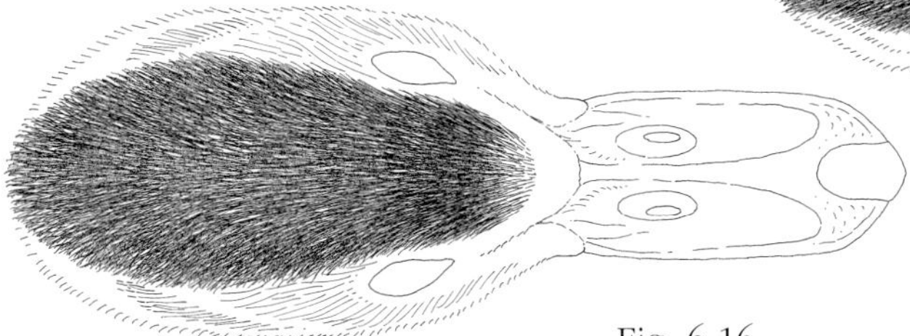

Fig. 6-16

Fig. 6-17

Figs. 6-11 to 6-15 (1 day): Ontario; figs. 6-16, 6-17 [3 weeks]: Minnesota.

3b. Forehead usually light-colored, but sometimes dark crown color extends part way to bill, usually overlaid by pale yellow down tips (fig. 6-23); nail of bill wide, often nearly round; dorsal spots and wing-patches large but low contrast; olive-brown pattern color of plumage lightest of any North American pochard, yellow base color light and brilliant; almost never a central dorsal spot. Redhead, *A. americana,* figs. 6-18 to 6-24.

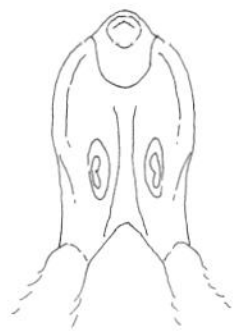

Fig. 6-18

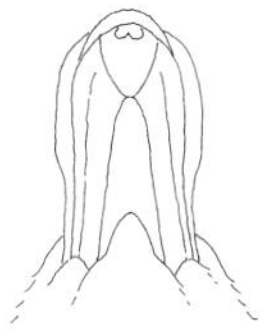

Fig. 6-19

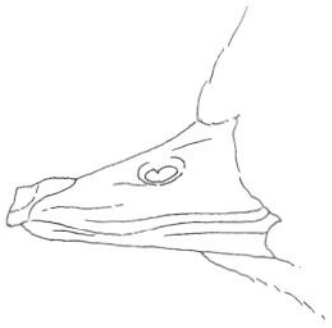

Fig. 6-20

Fig. 6-21

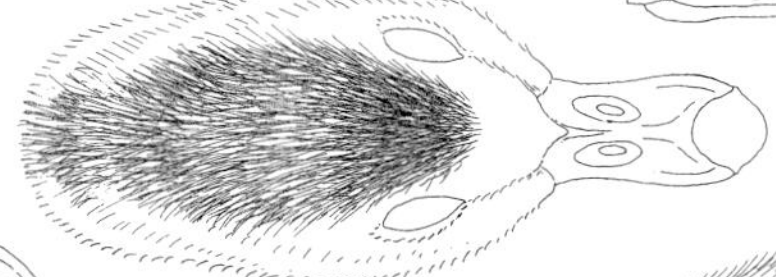

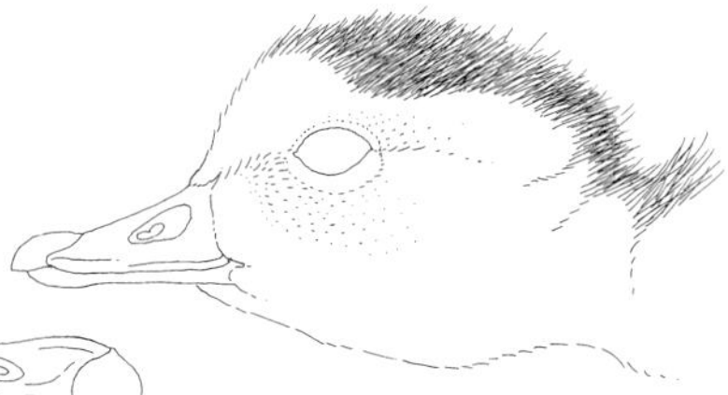

Fig. 6-22

Fig. 6-23

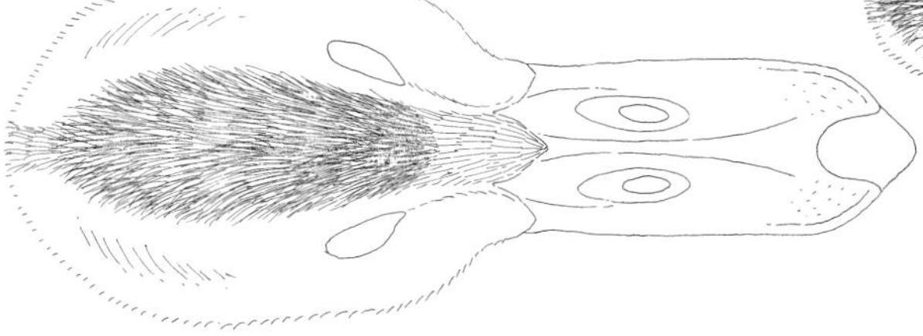

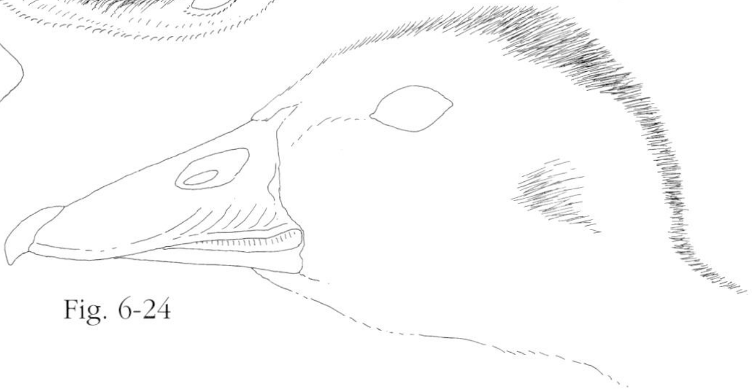

Fig. 6-24

Figs. 6-18 to 6-22 (1 day), figs. 6-23, 6-24 (25 days): Manitoba.

4a. Nail of bill at all ages narrow, usually appears longer than wide (figs. 6-25, 6-28, 6-30, 6-32): ratio of nail 'area', i.e., length of nail (LN) x width of nail (WN), to height of bill at base (HBB) usually less than 3.0 (except for certain very young downies), regardless of age, sex, or status (in day-old ducklings, mean ratio of (LN x WN)/HBB=2.7 [1.8-3.6; n=40, SD=0.54, SE=0.08]; see also (LN x WN)/HBB ratios for ducklings aged 7-28 d. in Table 1, Appendix A); supraorbital stripe usually unbroken, usually contrasts well with dark crown color (difference=3 or more Munsell *value* steps); eye-line usually present and complete, contrasts well with face color; usually four dorsal spots: shoulder-spots fairly conspicuous, rump-spots often inconspicuous but rarely lacking; sides of bill usually taper gracefully from widest point to base: 'slipper-shaped' (older downies, fig. 6-32). In live birds, eye-colors of both sexes during first 10 days brownish gray, grayish brown, or grayish olive (Munsell *hues* 10YR to 5Y), becoming lighter (both sexes), brighter (Munsell *chroma* /4.0 to /8.0, males only), greener (all males, some females), or grayer (other females), with some males having bright greenish yellow (7.5Y) or yellowish green (2.5GY, 5GY) eyes as early as four weeks. Lesser Scaup, *A. affinis,* figs. 6-25 to 6-33. ***Caution*:** Check hallux; if flattened lobe is less than 3 x wider than hallux bone, and if tarsus (TMT) is about 80% length of middle toe with claw (IIIw), specimen may be an American Wigeon, *Mareca americana* (compare TMT/IIIw ratios of scaup spp. [TMT/IIIw=ca. 70%] and *M. americana* in Table 1, Appendix A). If suspected misidentification, return to 8a and 8b in Key to Genera and re-examine specimen.

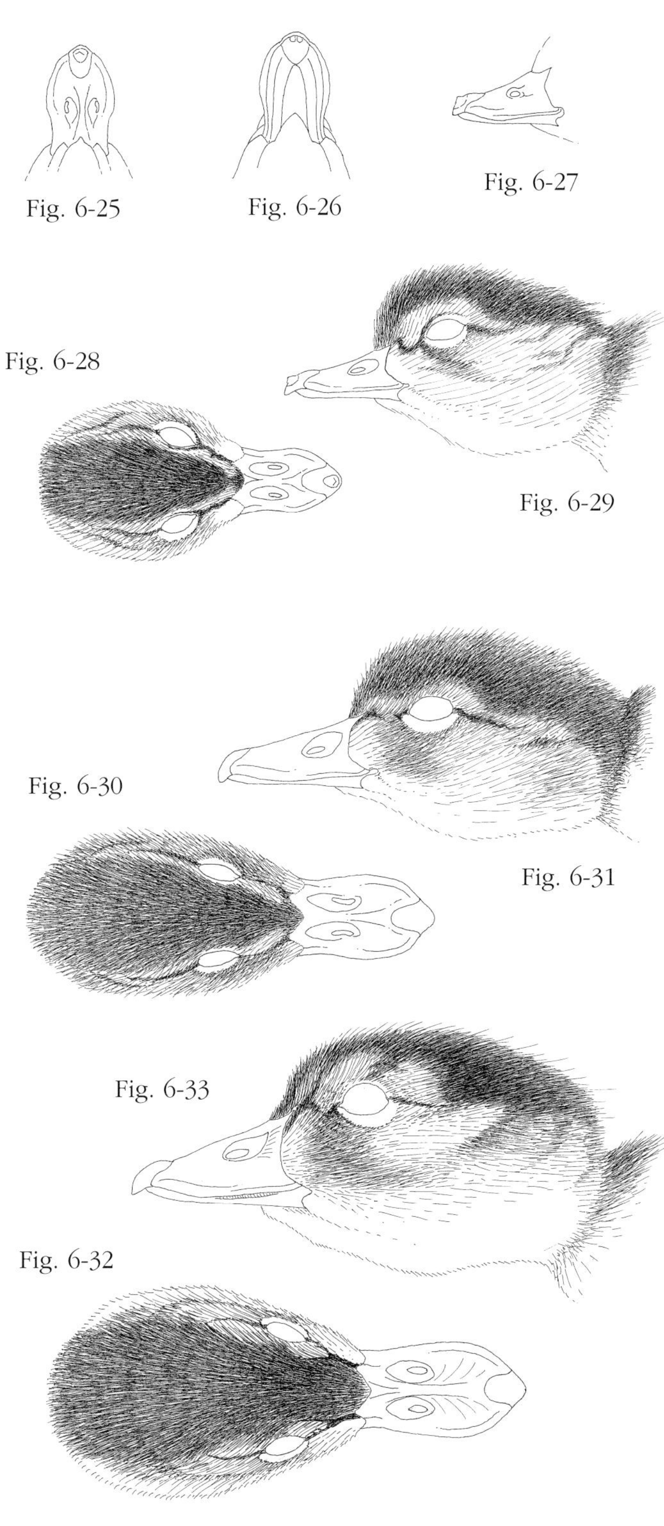

Figs. 6-25 to 6-27 (1 day): Manitoba; figs. 6-28, 6-29 [1-2 days], figs. 6-30, 6-31 [10 days]: Alberta; figs. 6-32, 6-33 [2-1/2 weeks]: Saskatchewan.

4b. Nail of bill at all ages large, often appears nearly as wide as long (figs. 6-37, 6-41): ratio of nail 'area', i.e., length of nail (LN) x width of nail (WN), to height of bill at base (HBB) usually 3.0 or higher, regardless of age, sex, or status (in day-old ducklings, mean ratio of (LN x WN)/HBB =3.7 [2.8-4.6; n=27, SD=0.52, SE=0.10]; see also (LN x WN)/HBB ratios for ducklings aged 7-28 d. in Table 1, Appendix A); supraorbital stripe often broken above eye, usually contrasts less well than 4a with dark crown color (difference=3 or fewer Munsell *value* steps); eye-line, if present, usually contrasts poorly with face color, may be incomplete behind eye and/or absent, incomplete, or smudged in front of eye; two or four dorsal spots; shoulder-spots often inconspicuous, rump-spots often nearly indiscernible or lacking; sides of bill usually taper slightly and evenly from widest point to base: 'spade-shaped' (older downies, fig. 6-41). In live birds, eye-colors of both sexes during first 10 days olive-gray, grayish yellow-green, or grayish yellowish brown (Munsell *hues* 10YR to 5GY), becoming lighter (both sexes), 'bluer' (at 2-3 weeks, eyes of males light olive-gray, eyes of females pale blue, grayish blue, or bluish gray), then 'greener' (at 5-6 weeks, eyes of males 2.5GY to 5GY, eyes of females 2.5BG to 5BG), but remaining very dull, i.e., 'bluish', in both sexes (Munsell *chroma* nearly always less than /2.0). Greater Scaup, *A. marila*, figs. 6-34 to 6-42. Observe ***Caution*** as in 4a.

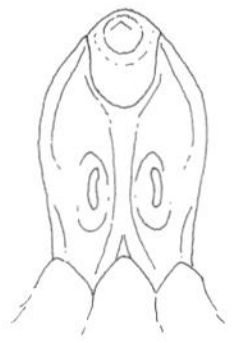

Fig. 6-34

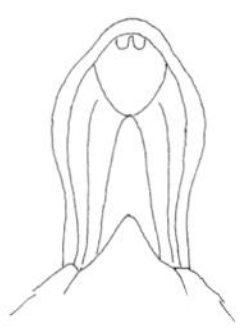

Fig. 6-35

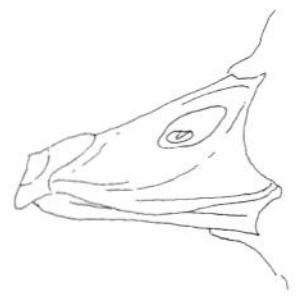

Fig. 6-36

Fig. 6-38

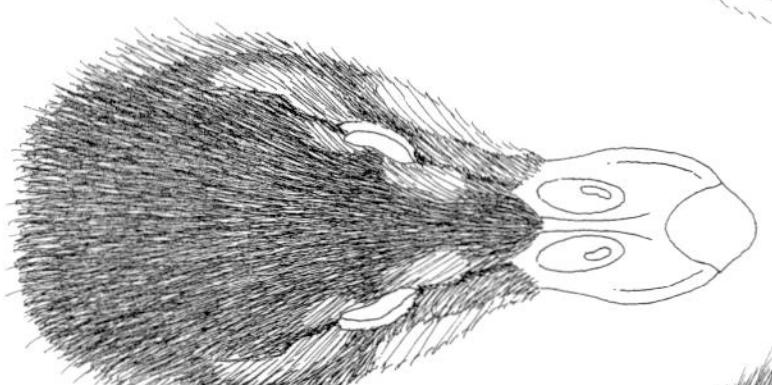

Fig. 6-37

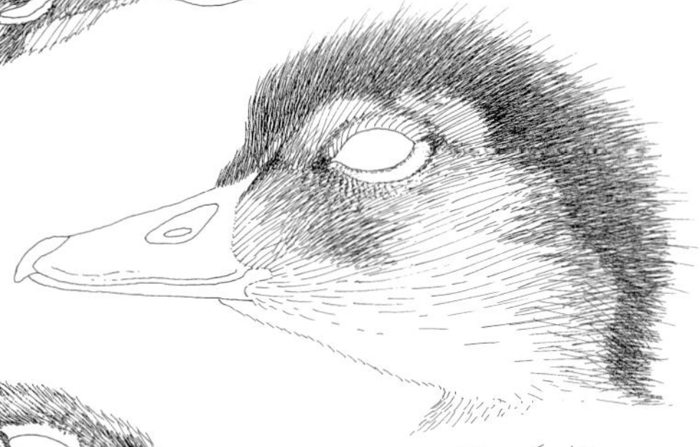

Fig. 6-40

Fig. 6-39

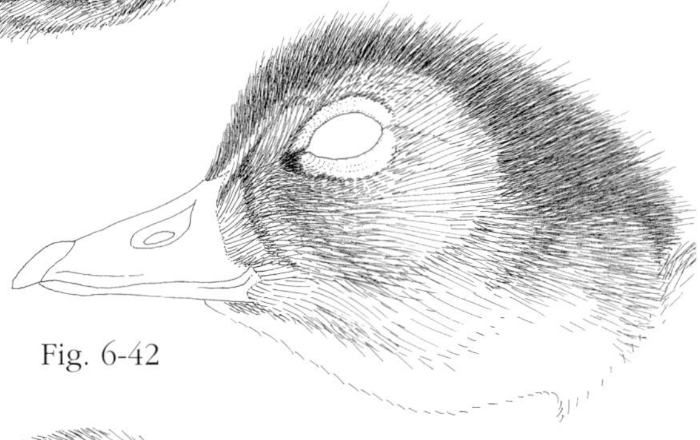

Fig. 6-42

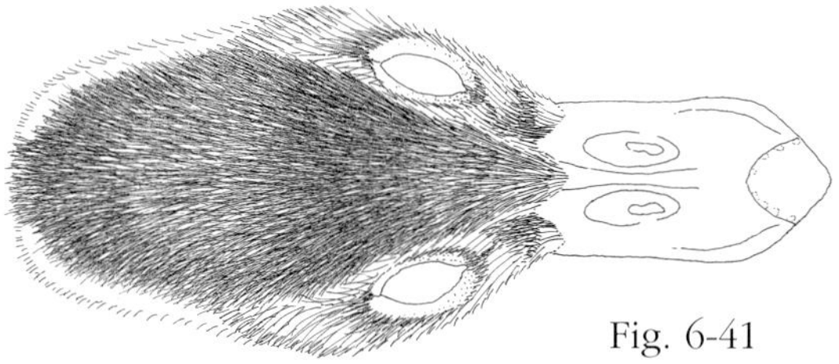

Fig. 6-41

Figs. 6-34, 6-36 (1 day), figs. 6-41, 6-42 [2 weeks]: Manitoba; figs. 6-37, 6-38 [2 days]: Alaska; figs. 6-39, 6-40 [7-9 days]: Ontario. *A. m. nearctica*. Fig. 6-35 (1 day): Iceland. *A. m. marila*.

Tribe Somateriini
Key to *Somateria* species

1a. Entire eye surrounded by well-defined dark-feathered 'spectacle' (young downies; fig. 7-5) or bi-colored 'spectacle' (older downies; fig. 7-7). Spectacled Eider, *Somateria fischeri*, figs. 7-1 to 7-7.

Figs. 7-1 to 7-3 [2-3 days], figs. 7-4, 7-5 [5 days], figs. 7-6, 7-7 (19-20 days): Alaska.

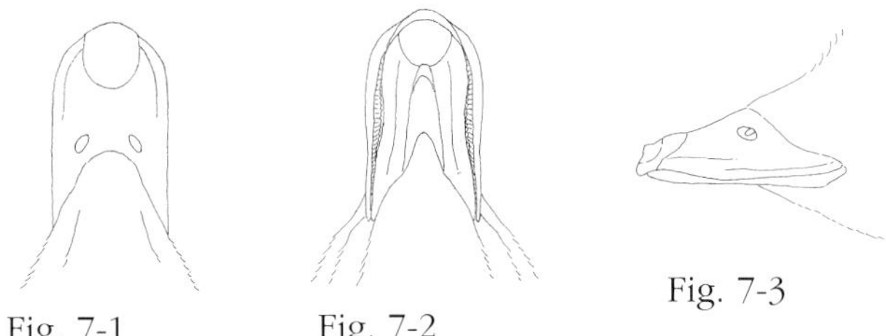

Fig. 7-1 Fig. 7-2 Fig. 7-3

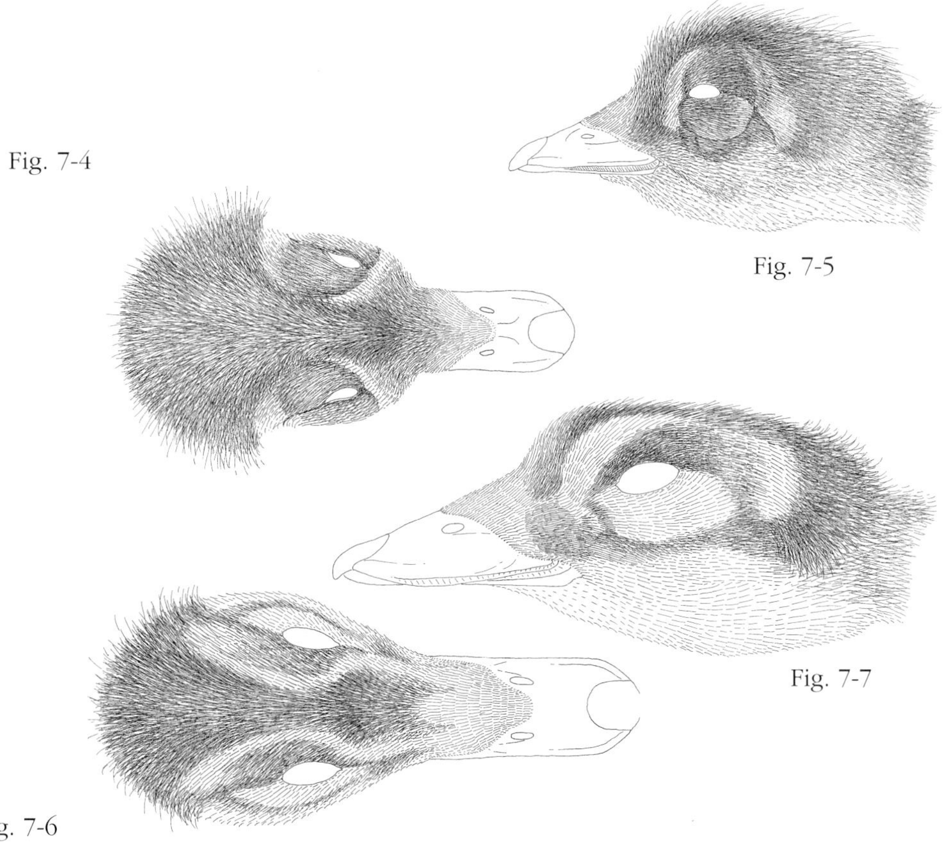

Fig. 7-4

Fig. 7-5

Fig. 7-7

Fig. 7-6

1b. 'Spectacle' lacking; light-colored supraorbital stripe extends from bill to level above ear or to occiput (fig. 7-8). Go to 2.

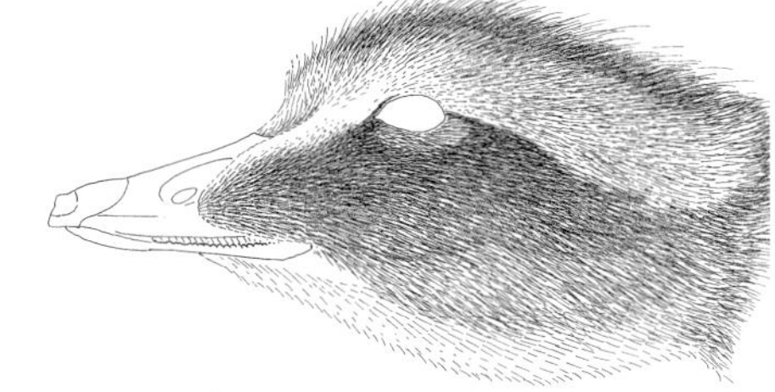

Fig. 7-8

2a. Mesial feathering on bill extends beyond lateral feathering (figs. 7-9, 7-14). King Eider, *S. spectabilis,* figs. 7-9 to 7-15.

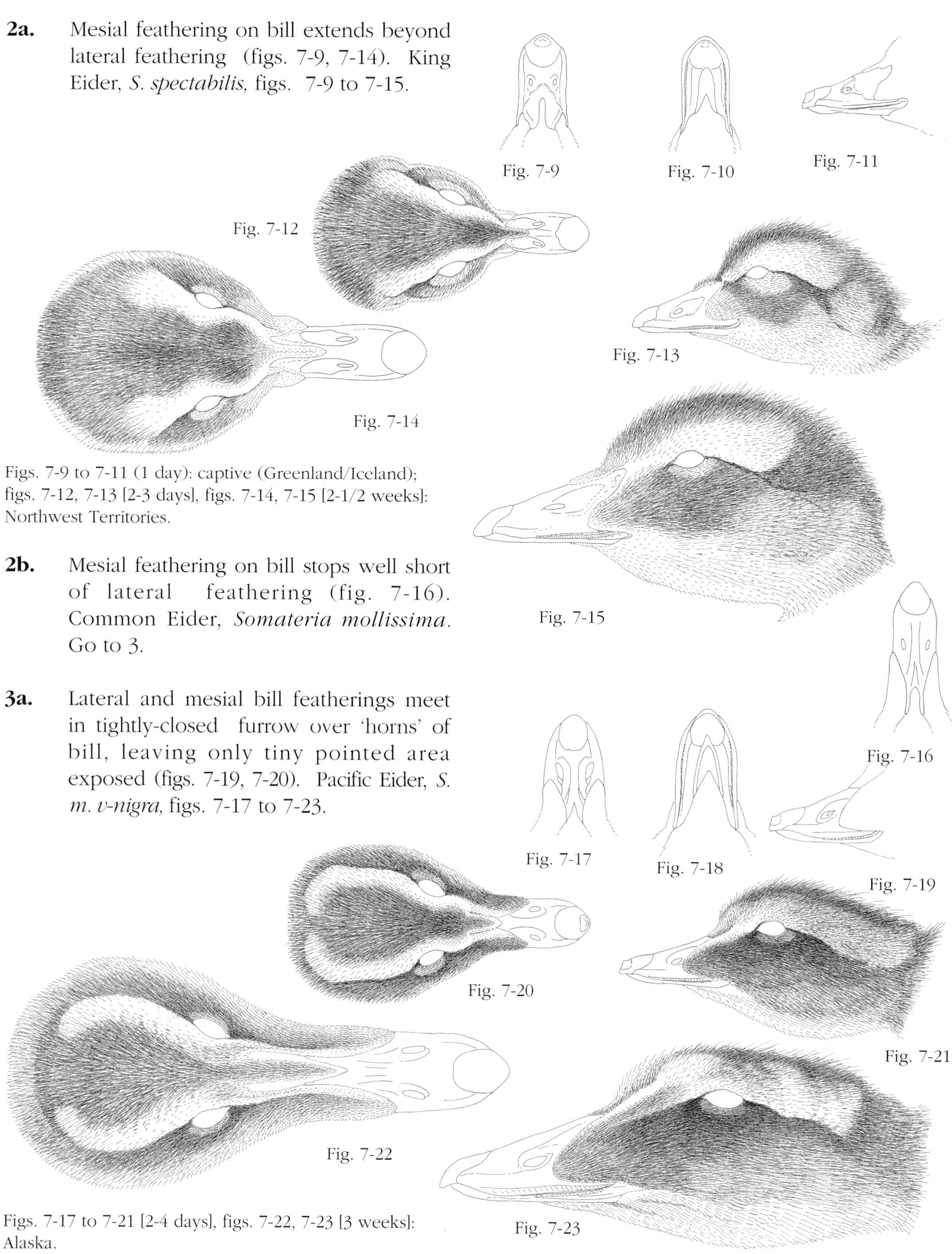

Figs. 7-9 to 7-11 (1 day): captive (Greenland/Iceland); figs. 7-12, 7-13 [2-3 days], figs. 7-14, 7-15 [2-1/2 weeks]: Northwest Territories.

2b. Mesial feathering on bill stops well short of lateral feathering (fig. 7-16). Common Eider, *Somateria mollissima.* Go to 3.

3a. Lateral and mesial bill featherings meet in tightly-closed furrow over 'horns' of bill, leaving only tiny pointed area exposed (figs. 7-19, 7-20). Pacific Eider, *S. m. v-nigra,* figs. 7-17 to 7-23.

Figs. 7-17 to 7-21 [2-4 days], figs. 7-22, 7-23 [3 weeks]: Alaska.

3b. Lateral and mesial featherings conceal 'horns' only partly or not at all (except one dark subspecies sometimes with feathered 'horns'). Go to 4.

4a. 'Horns' of bill usually long and rounded, nearly always fully exposed, more prominent in older downies (figs. 7-24, 7-25). Go to 5.

4b. 'Horns' of bill shorter than in 4a and more or less pointed, usually partly exposed (fig. 7-26), but sometimes concealed (fig. 7-27) or fully, if narrowly, exposed (fig. 7-28), longer and more prominent in older downies (fig. 7-29). Go to 6.

5a. Base color in young downies always light or pale and extremely dull (forehead and supraorbital stripe often appear nearly white in front view): in well-prepared study skins under artificial N daylight, mean Munsell *value* of supraorbital stripe=6.8 (6.0-7.5; n=17, SD=0.43, SE=0.10), mean Munsell *chroma*=2.4 (1.0-4.0; n=17, SD=1.05, SE=0.25); pattern color appears brownish gray or grayish brown, almost never blackish: mean Munsell *value* of rump =3.1 (2.5-3.8; n=26, SD=0.32, SE=0.06). The palest, grayest, and—with *v-nigra*—the largest downy of the North American eider subspecies. Hudson Bay Eider, *S. m. sedentaria*, figs. 7-30 to 7-36.

Figs. 7-30 to 7-32 (1 day): Manitoba; figs. 7-33, 7-34 [2-3 days], figs. 7-35, 7-36 [2 weeks]: Northwest Territories.

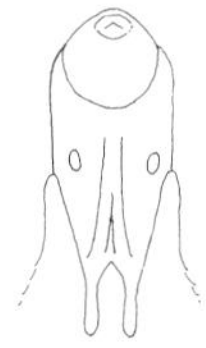

Fig. 7-24

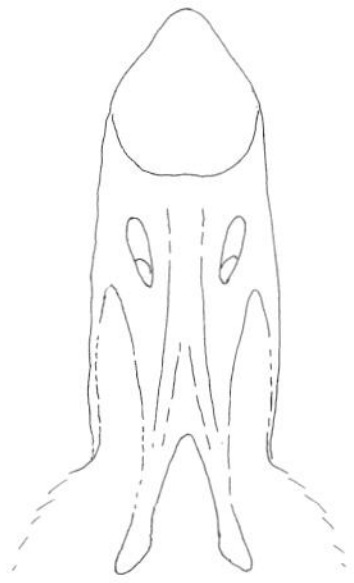

Fig. 7-25

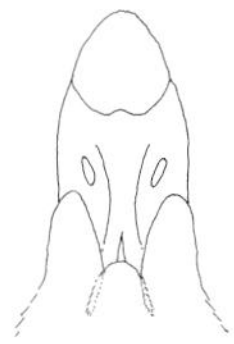

Fig. 7-26

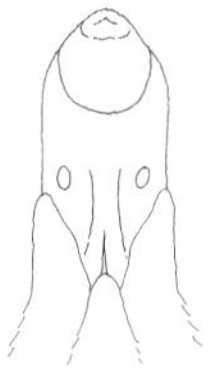

Fig. 7-27

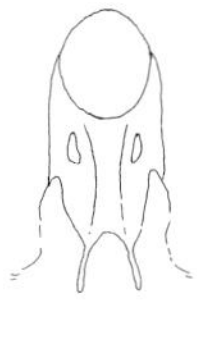

Fig. 7-28

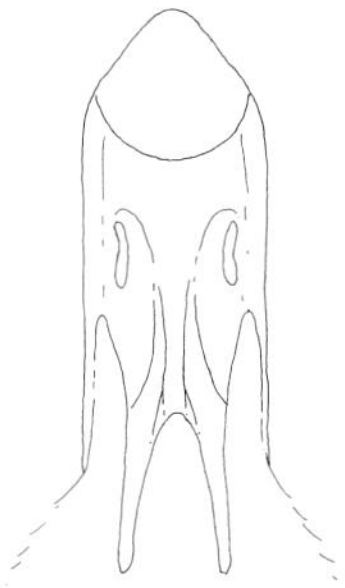

Fig. 7-29

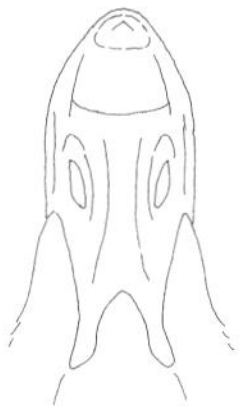

Fig. 7-30

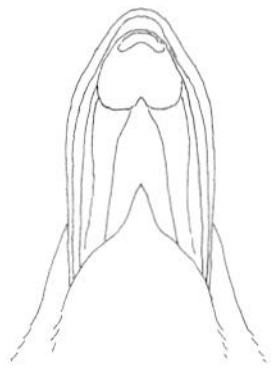

Fig. 7-31

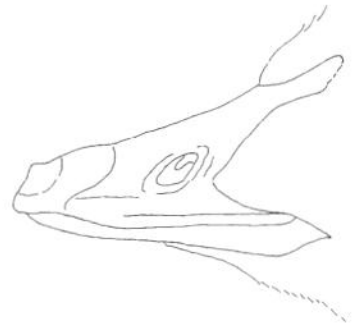

Fig. 7-32

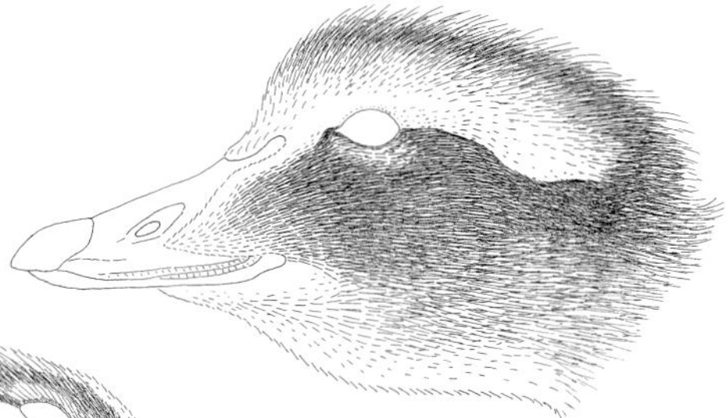

Fig. 7-33

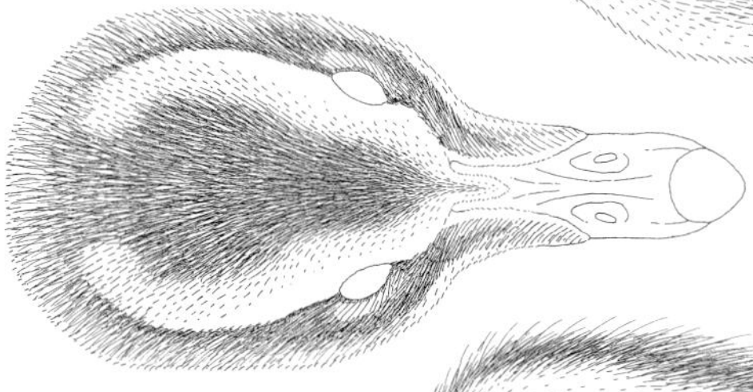

Fig. 7-34

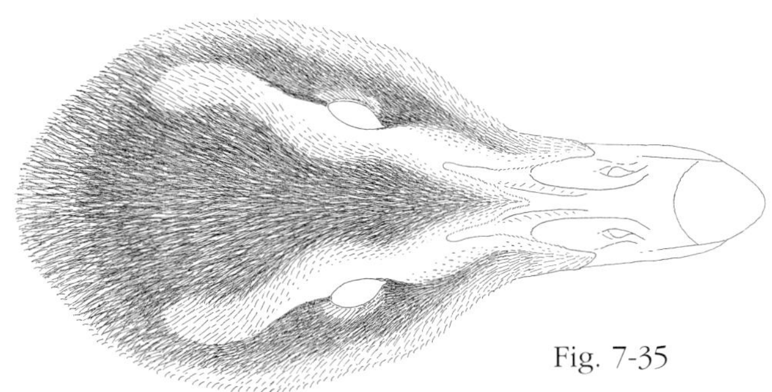

Fig. 7-35

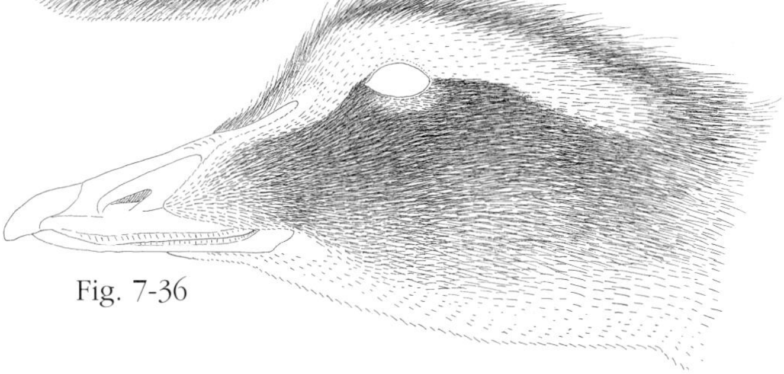

Fig. 7-36

5b. Base color in young downies moderate to light, seldom extremely dull (forehead and supraorbital stripe almost never appear nearly white in front view): in well-prepared study skins under artificial N daylight, mean Munsell *value* of supraorbital stripe= 6.1 (5.4-7.0; n=22, SD=0.46, SE=0.10), mean Munsell *chroma*=3.2 (2.0-4.0; n=22, SD=0.47, SE=0.10); pattern color dark brownish gray or dark grayish brown, often blackish: mean Munsell *value* of rump=2.4 (2.0-3.0; n=23, SD=0.28, SE=0.06). The darkest downy—with *islandica*—of the North American eider subspecies. Dresser's Eider, *S. m. dresseri,* figs. 7-37 to 7-43.

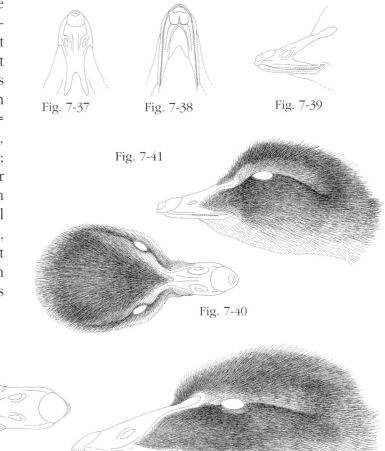

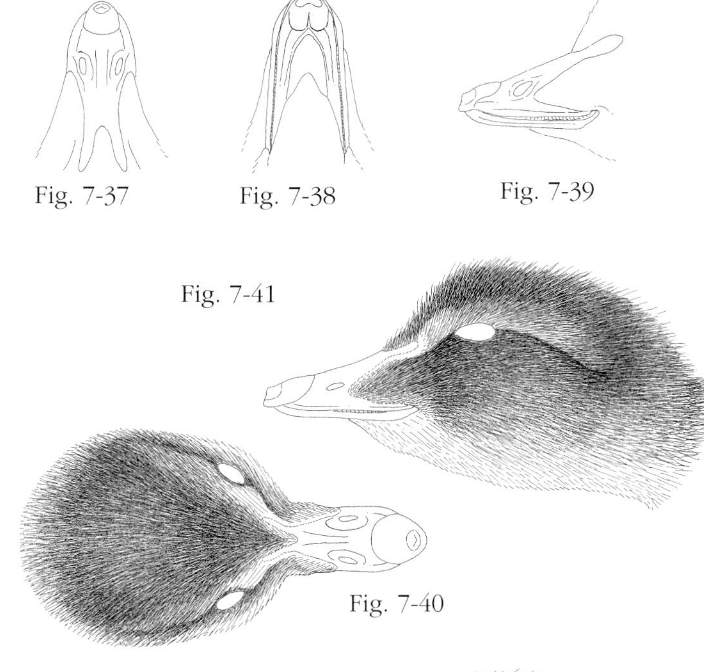

Fig. 7-37 Fig. 7-38 Fig. 7-39

Fig. 7-41

Fig. 7-40

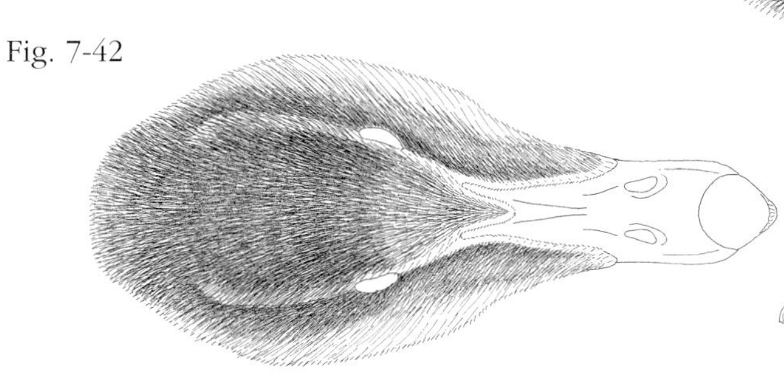

Fig. 7-42

Fig. 7-43

Figs. 7-37 to 7-39 (1 day0, figs. 7-40, 7-41 [1-2 days], figs. 7-42, 7-43 [2-1/2 weeks]: Quebec.

6a. Pattern color very dark or blackish: in well-prepared study skins under artificial N daylight, mean Munsell *value* of rump=2.2 (2.0-2.4; n=5, SD=0.22, SE=0.10); base color moderate: mean Munsell *value* of belly plumes=5.3 (5.0-5.6; n=4, SD=0.35, SE=0.17). The darkest downy—with dresseri—of the North American eider subspecies. Icelandic Eider, *S. m. islandica,* figs. 7-44 to 7-46.

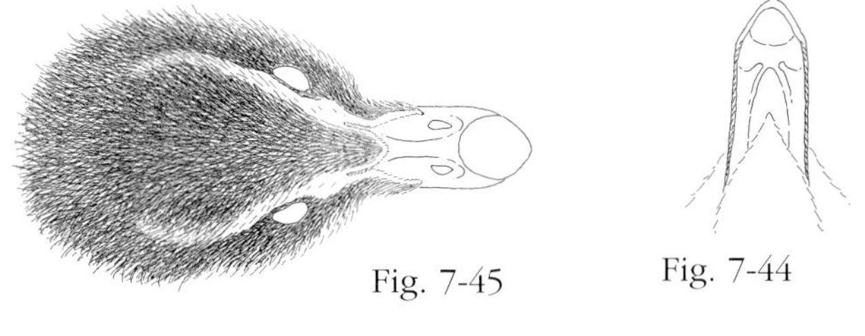

Fig. 7-45 Fig. 7-44

Figs. 7-44 to 7-46 [1-2 days]: Iceland.

Fig. 7-46

6b. Pattern color moderately dark, seldom blackish: in well-prepared study skins under artificial N daylight, mean Munsell *value* of rump=2.8 (2.4-3.5; n=11, SD=0.35, SE=0.10); base color light to pale: mean Munsell *value* of belly plumes=6.9 (6.5-7.5; n=11, SD=0.42, SE=0.13). Northern Eider, *S. m. borealis,* figs. 7-47 to 7-51.
See species account, pp. 000-000, for discussion of variation.

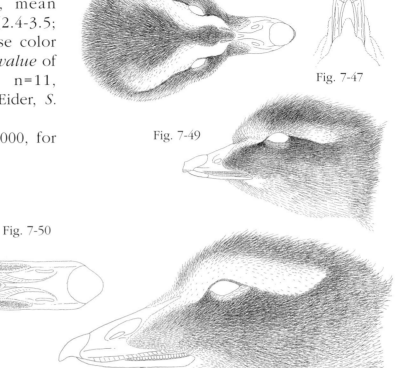

Fig. 7-48

Fig. 7-47

Fig. 7-49

Fig. 7-50

Fig. 7-51

Genus *Polysticta*

Steller's Eider, *Polysticta stelleri,* figs. 7-52 to 7-56.

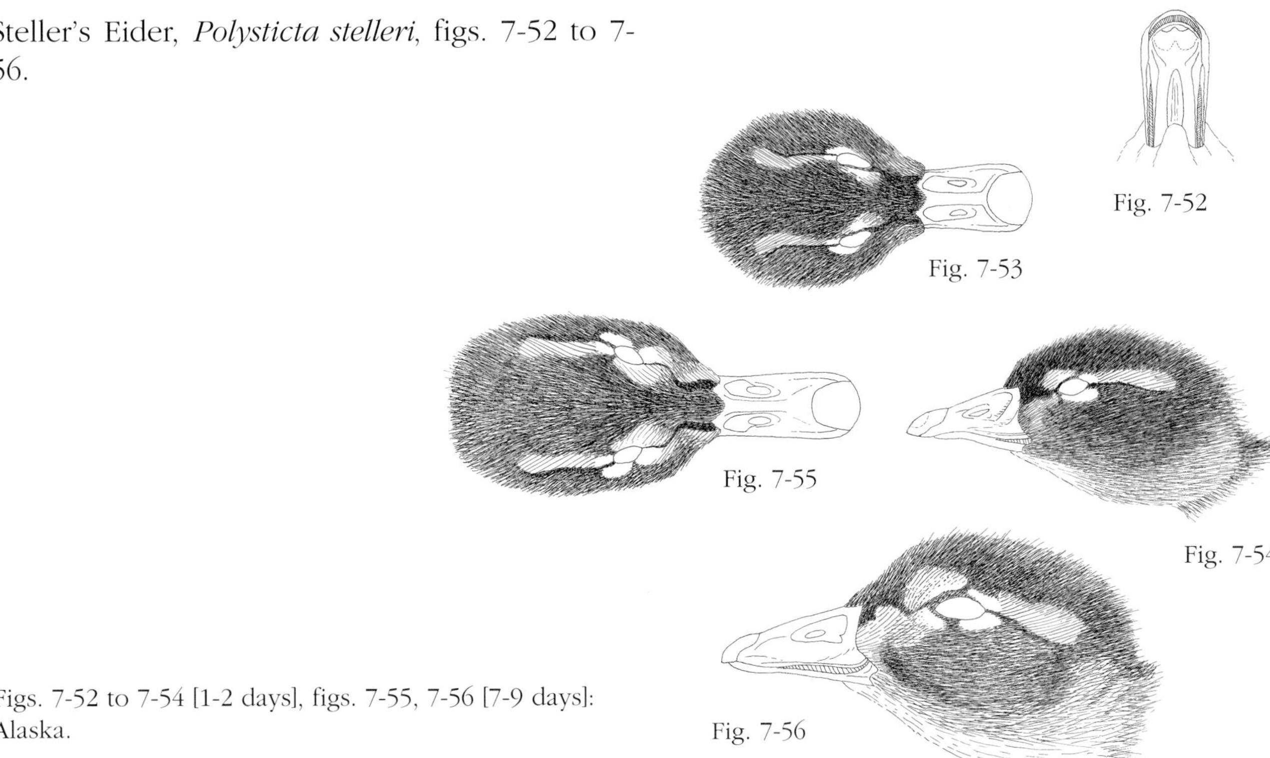

Fig. 7-52

Fig. 7-53

Fig. 7-55

Fig. 7-54

Fig. 7-56

Figs. 7-52 to 7-54 [1-2 days], figs. 7-55, 7-56 [7-9 days]: Alaska.

Tribe Mergini
Genus *Histrionicus*

Harlequin Duck, *Histrionicus histrionicus*, figs. 8-1 to 8-7.

Fig. 8-1

Fig. 8-2

Fig. 8-3

Fig. 8-4

Fig. 8-5

Fig. 8-6

Fig. 8-7

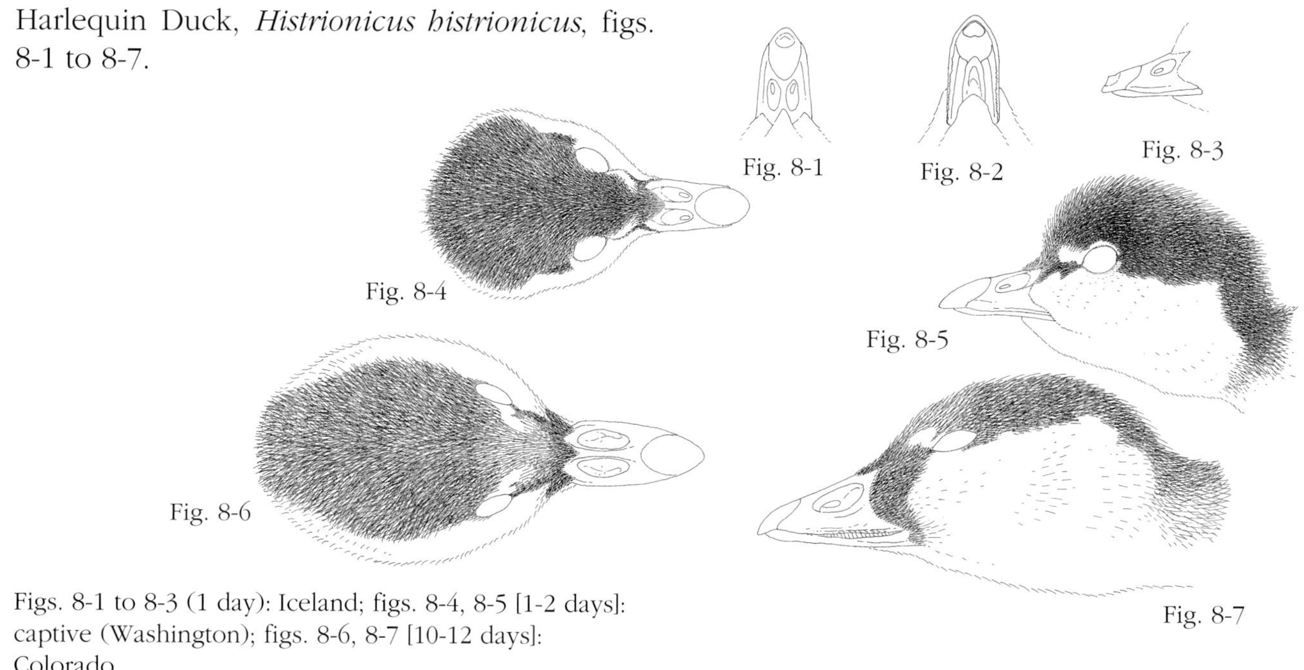

Figs. 8-1 to 8-3 (1 day): Iceland; figs. 8-4, 8-5 [1-2 days]: captive (Washington); figs. 8-6, 8-7 [10-12 days]: Colorado.

Genus *Clangula*

Oldsquaw, *Clangula hyemalis,* figs. 8-8 to 8-14.

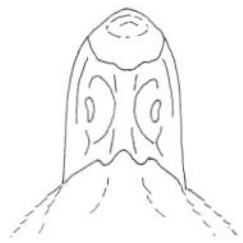

Fig. 8-8

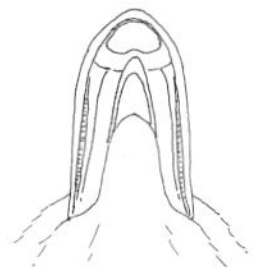

Fig. 8-9

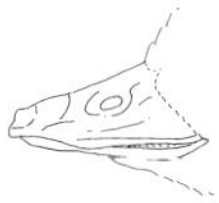

Fig. 8-10

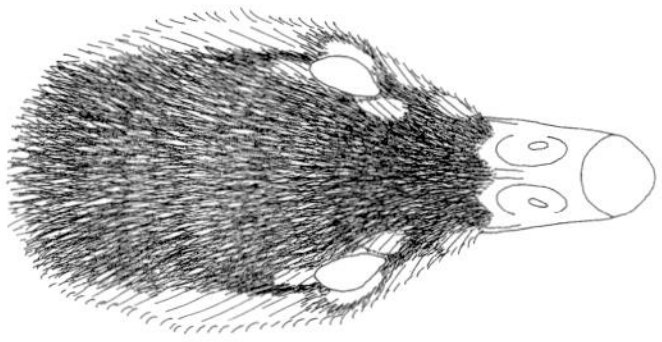

Fig. 8-11

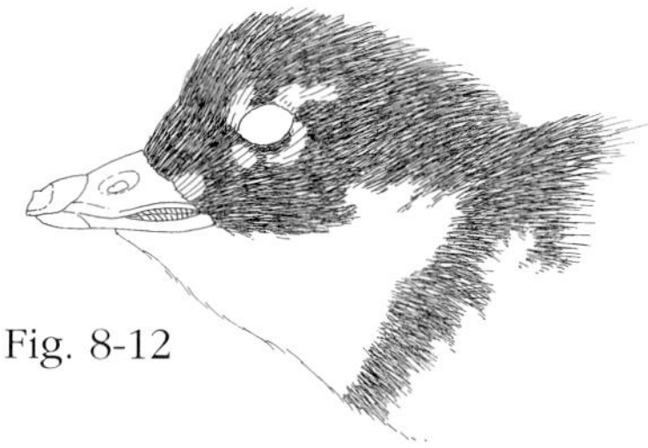

Fig. 8-12

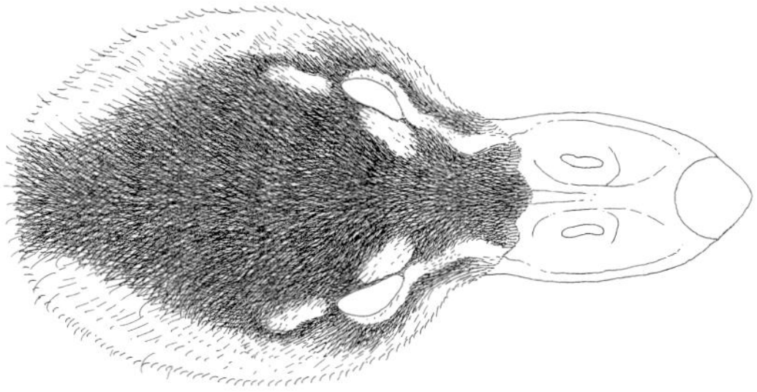

Fig. 8-13

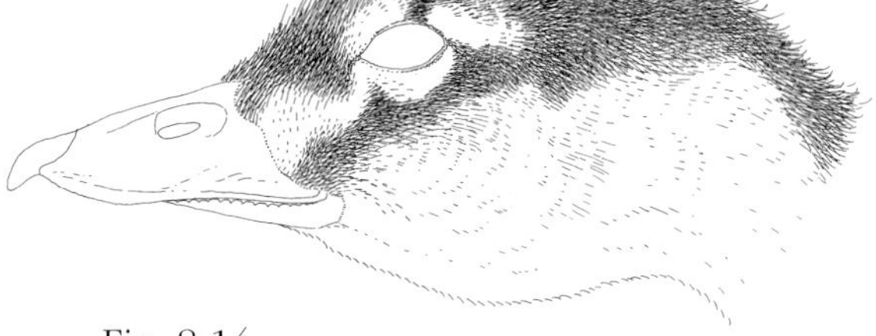

Fig. 8-14

Figs. 8-8 to 8-10, 8-12 (1 day): Manitoba; fig. 8-11 (1-2 days): Alaska; figs. 8-13, 8-14 (19 days): Ontario.

Key to *Melanitta* species

1a. Lateral feathering extends markedly onto sides of bill, almost to nostrils (figs. 8-17). White-winged Scoter, *Melanitta fusca;* figs. 8-15 to 8-21.

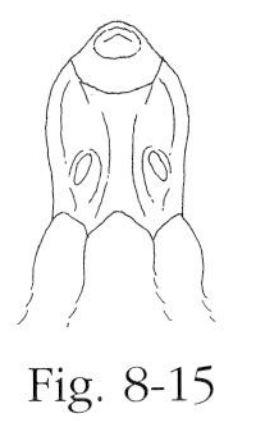

Fig. 8-15

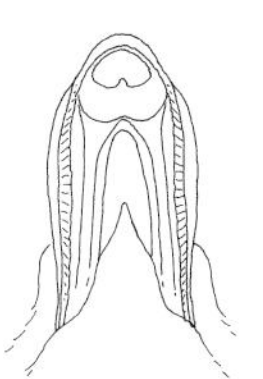

Fig. 8-16

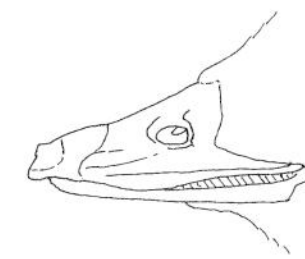

Fig. 8-17

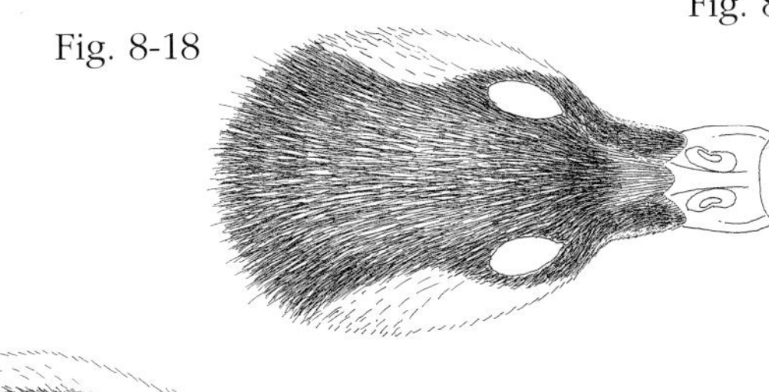

Fig. 8-18

Fig. 8-19

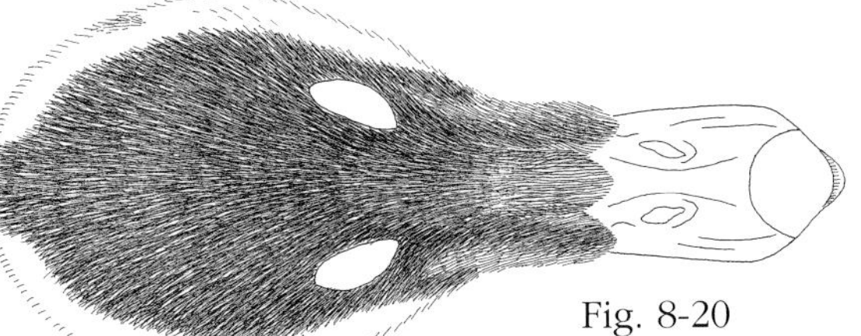

Fig. 8-20

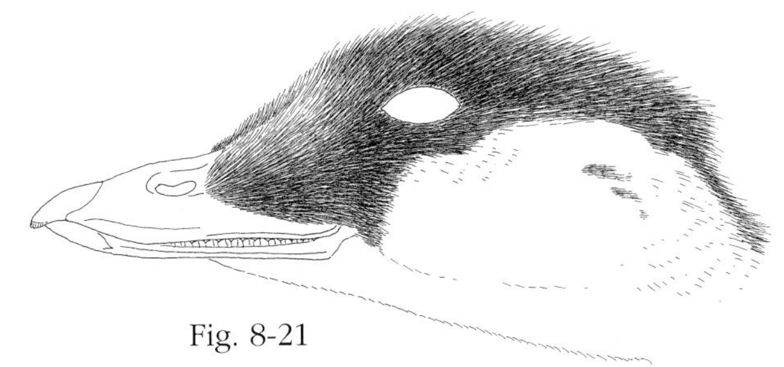

Fig. 8-21

Figs. 8-15 to 8-17 (1 day), fig. 8-19 (4-1/2 days): Alberta; fig. 8-18 [2-3 days]: Northwest Territories; figs. 8-20, 8-21 [3 weeks]: Alaska. *M. f. deglandi.*

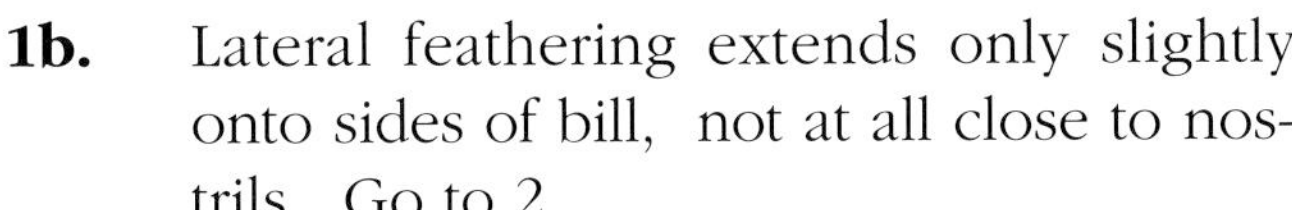

1b. Lateral feathering extends only slightly onto sides of bill, not at all close to nostrils. Go to 2.

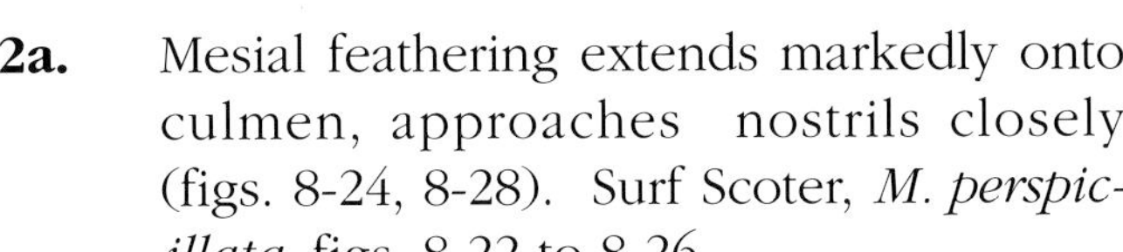

2a. Mesial feathering extends markedly onto culmen, approaches nostrils closely (figs. 8-24, 8-28). Surf Scoter, *M. perspicillata,* figs. 8-22 to 8-26.

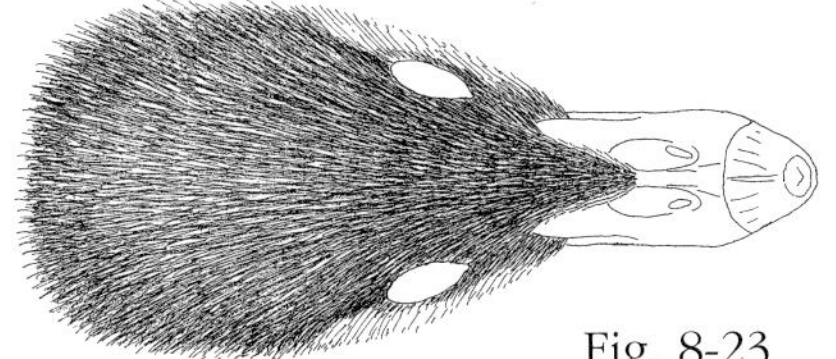

Fig. 8-23

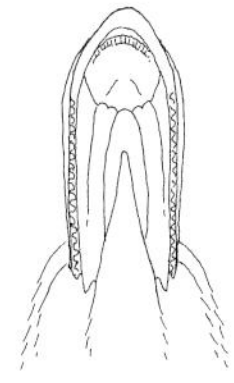

Fig. 8-22

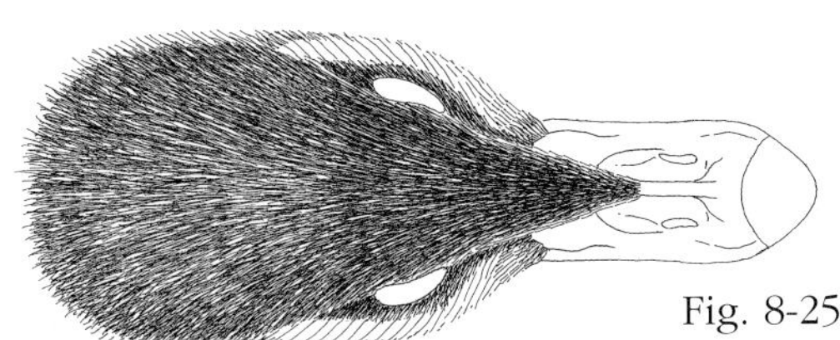

Fig. 8-25

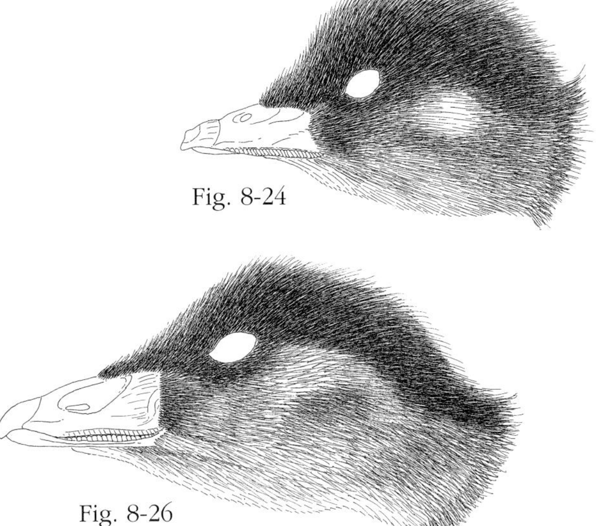

Fig. 8-24

Fig. 8-26

Fig. 8-22 to 8-24 [1-2 days]: Saskatchewan; figs. 8-25, 8-26 [1-=12 days]: Northwest Territories.

2b. Mesial feathering extends only slightly if at all onto culmen, does not approach nostrils closely (fig. 8-31). Black Scoter, *M. nigra,* figs. 8-27 to 8-33.

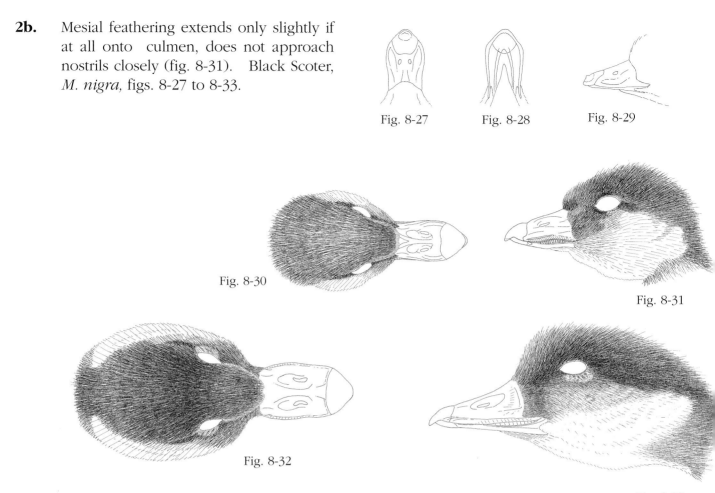

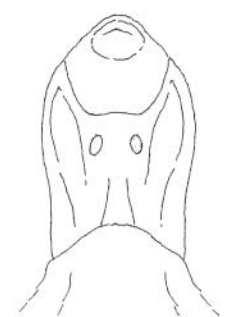

Fig. 8-27

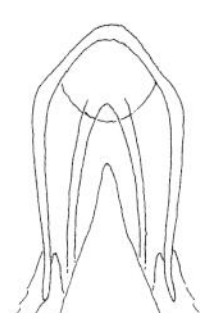

Fig. 8-28

Fig. 8-29

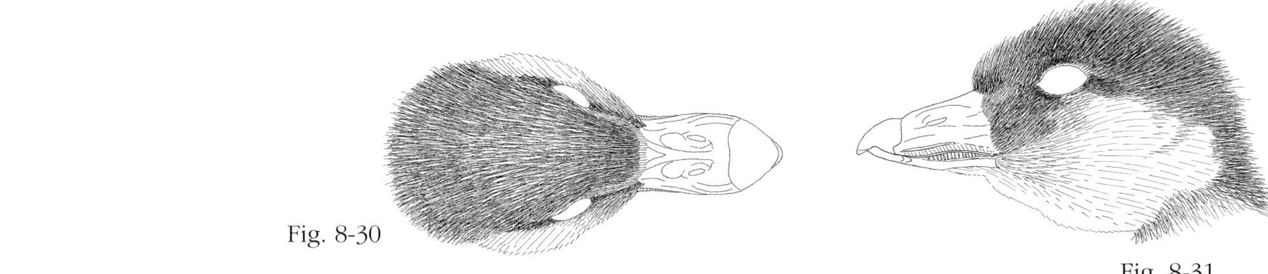

Fig. 8-30

Fig. 8-31

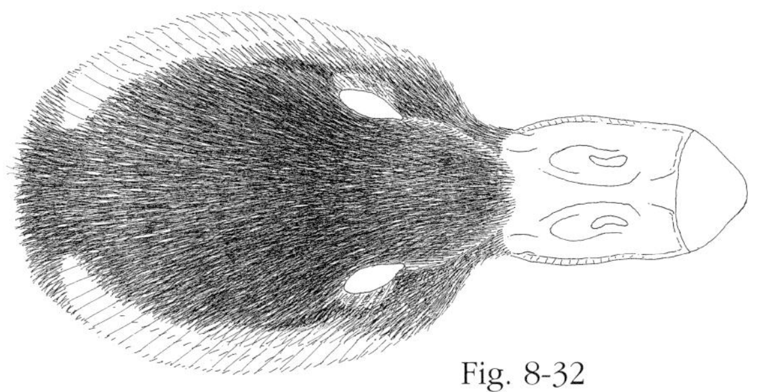

Fig. 8-32

Fig. 8-33

Figs. 8-27 to 8-29 (1 day): Iceland. *M. n. nigra.*

Figs. 8-30, 8-31 [5-7 days]: Alaska; figs. 8-32, 8-33 {3 weeks]: Newfoundland. *M. n. americana.*

Key to *Bucephala* species

1a. In very young downies: using commissure as measure of bill length, rear edge of nostril is nearly always within anterior half of bill; underbill (UB) usually shorter than culmen (EC), sometimes equal to it, almost never longer (fig. 8-34); in live downies, mean ratio of UB/EC=0.87 (0.69-1.10; n=64, SD=0.071, SE=0.009). In live downies of all ages, white cheek-patch remains well below eye-level in ear region. Go to 2.

1b. In very young downies: using commissure as measure of bill length, rear edge of nostril is nearly always within posterior half of bill; underbill (UB) usually equal to or longer than culmen (EC), seldom shorter (fig. 8-39); in live downies, mean ratio of UB/EC=1.00 (0.09-1.07; n=9, SD=0.050, SE=0.018). In live downies of all ages, white cheek-patch rises to eye-level in ear region, but turns abruptly downward along nape. Bufflehead, *Bucephala albeola,* figs. 8-35 to 8-43.

Figs. 8-35 to 8-37 (1 day), fig. 8-38 (8 days): Alberta; fig. 8-39 [4-5 days]: British Columbia; figs. 8-40, 8-41 [12-14 days]: Yukon Territory; figs. 8-42, 8-43 [3 weeks]: Saskatchewan.

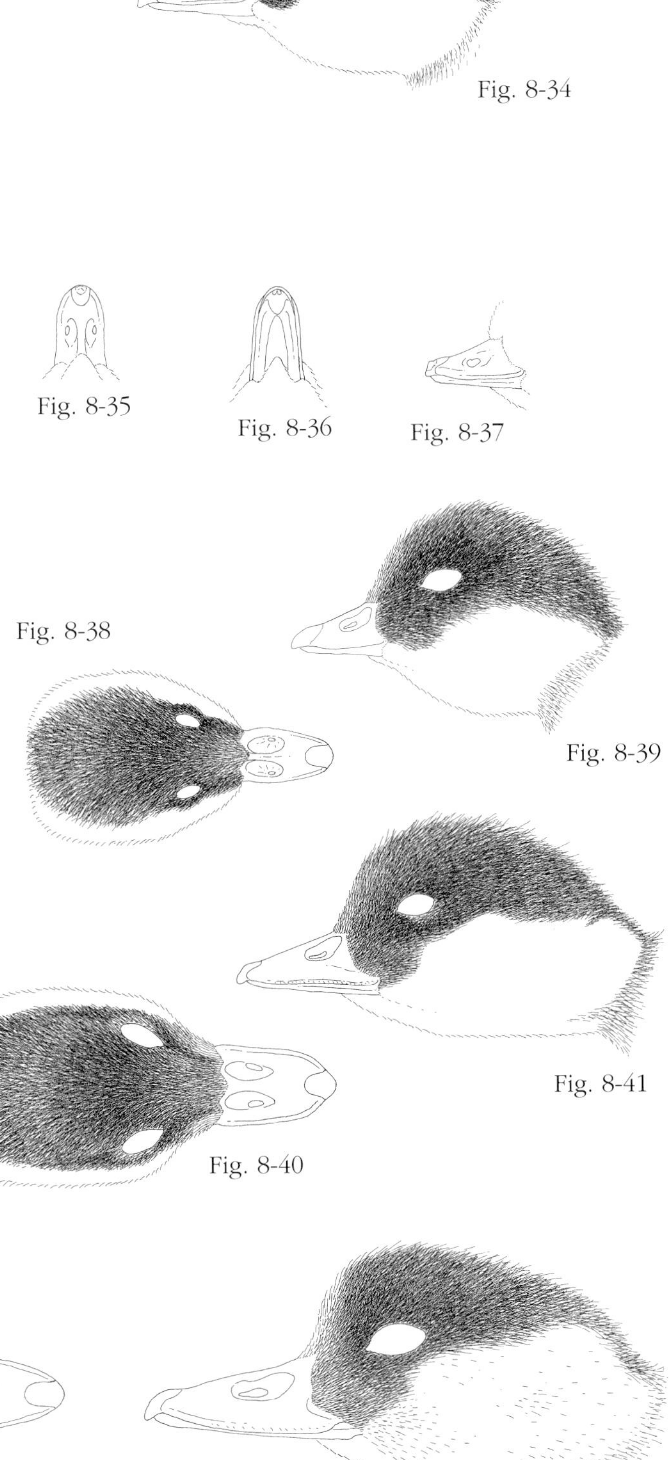

Fig. 8-34

Fig. 8-35

Fig. 8-36

Fig. 8-37

Fig. 8-38

Fig. 8-39

Fig. 8-41

Fig. 8-40

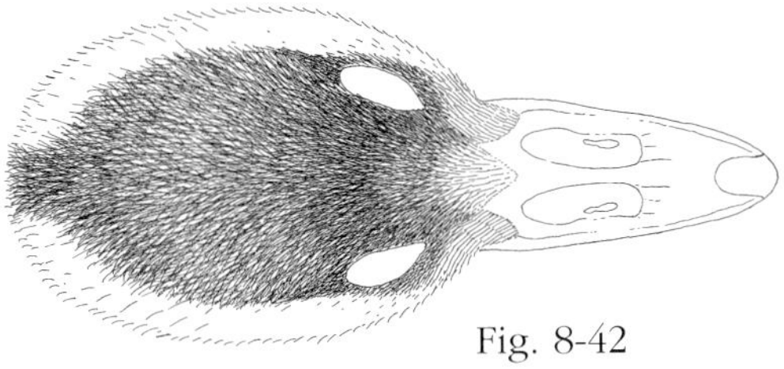

Fig. 8-42

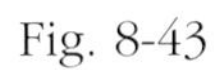

Fig. 8-43

2a. In live downies 1-2 days old (upper or lower or both egg-teeth present): Fjeldså's (1977: 77) ratio (width of nail [WN] to distance between anterior corners of nostrils [DACN])=1.03 (0.88-1.20; n=31, SD=0.077, SE=0.014); in downies older than 2-3 days, ratio of nail 'area', (length of nail [LN] x width of nail [WN], to width of bill at posterior edge of nail [WBPN]) nearly always larger than 4.0 regardless of sex or status (in live ducklings 4 d., mean ratio of (LN x WN)/WBPN=4.5 [4.1-4.8; n=21, SD=0.21, SE=0.05]; see also (LN x WN)/WBPN ratios for ducklings aged 1-28 d. in Table 1, Appendix A); nail often as wide as long (very young downies; figs. 8-44, 8-47) and raised above surrounding bill surface (older downies; figs. 8-50, 8-52), with anterior edge long and deeply curved (figs. 8-47, 8-49, 8-51), and posterior border broadly rounded or broadly triangular; nostril large, irregularly round or triangular, raised above surrounding bill surface in live downies of all ages. Barrow's Goldeneye, *B. islandica,* figs. 8-44 to 8-52.

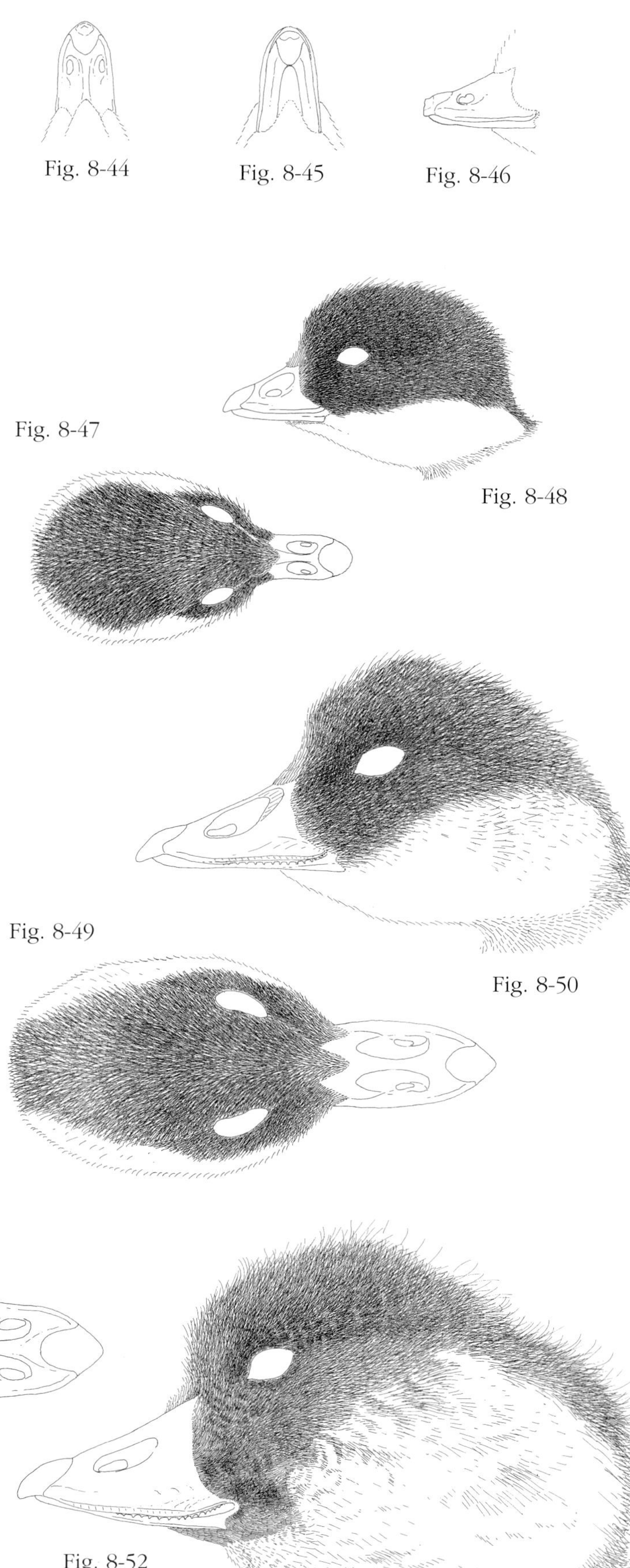

Figs. 8-44 to 8-46 (1 day), figs. 8-51, 8-52 [5-6 weeks]: British Columbia; fig. 8-47 [1-2 days]: Montana; fig. 8-48 [2 days]: Alberta; figs. 8-49, 8-50 [3 weeks]: Alaska.

2b. In live downies 1-2 days old (upper or lower or both egg-teeth present); Fjeldså's (1977: 77) ratio (width of nail [WN] to distance between anterior corners of nostrils [DACN])=0.64 (0.57- 0.71; n=4, SD=0.061, SE=0.030); in downies older than 2-3 days, ratio of nail 'area', (length of nail [LN] x width of nail [WN], to width of bill at posterior edge of nail [WBPN]) nearly always smaller than 4.0 regardless of sex or status (in live ducklings 4 d., mean ratio of (LN x WN)/WBPN=3.3 [2.8-3.9; n=10, SD=0.30, SE=0.09]; see also (LN x WN)/WBPN ratios for ducklings aged 1-26 d. in Table 1, Appendix A); nail medium or narrow, almost never as wide as long, raised little or not at all above surrounding bill surface (all ages), nearly always with anterior edge short and shallowly curved, and posterior border narrowly rounded or (sometimes) sharply triangular; nostril a rather small, flattened oval, raised above surrounding bill surface in young, live downies but little or not at all in older live downies. Common Goldeneye, *B. clangula,* figs. 8-53 to 8-61.

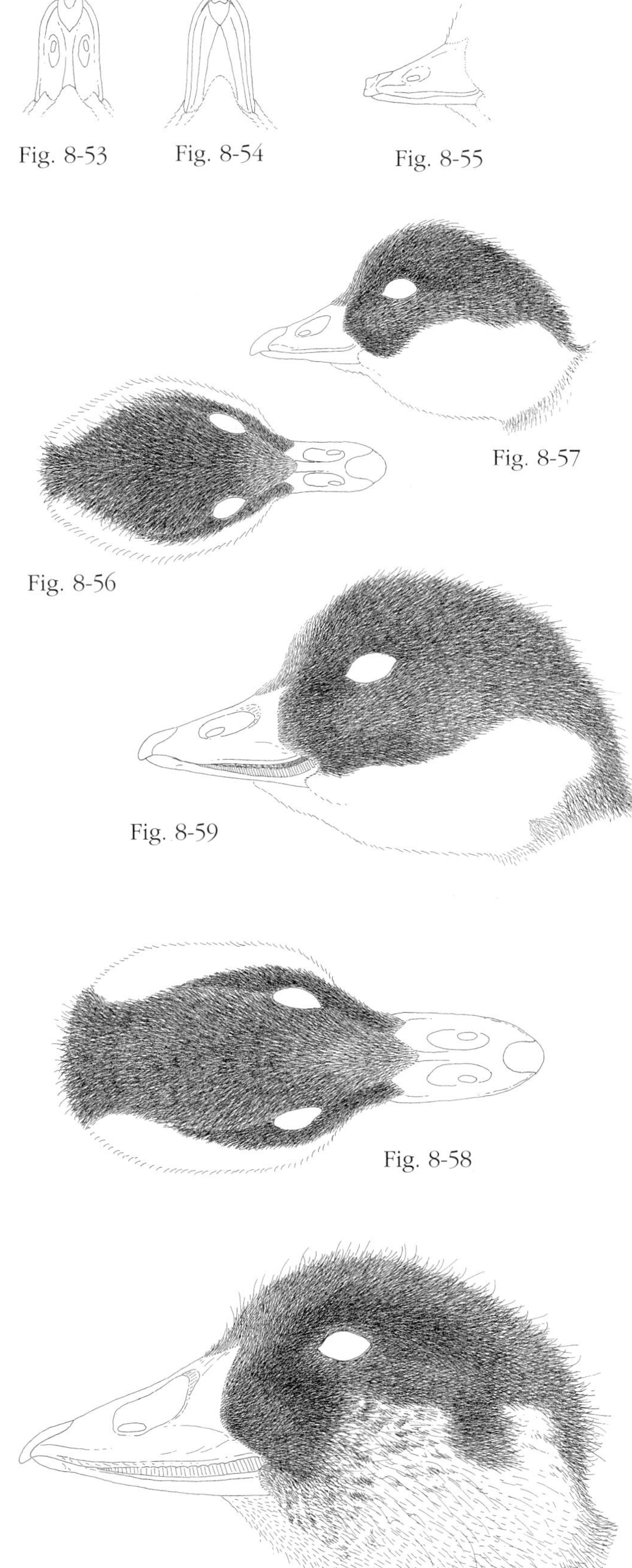

Fig. 8-53 Fig. 8-54 Fig. 8-55

Fig. 8-57

Fig. 8-56

Fig. 8-59

Fig. 8-58

Fig. 8-60

Fig. 8-61

Fig. 8-53 to 8-55 (1 day): Manitoba; figs. 8-56, 8-57 [2 days]: Alberta; figs. 8-58, 8-59 [12-14 days], figs. 8-60, 8-61 [4 weeks]: Ontario. *B. c. americana.*

Genus *Lophodytes*

Hooded Merganser, *Lophodytes cucullatus,* figs. 8-62 to 8-68.

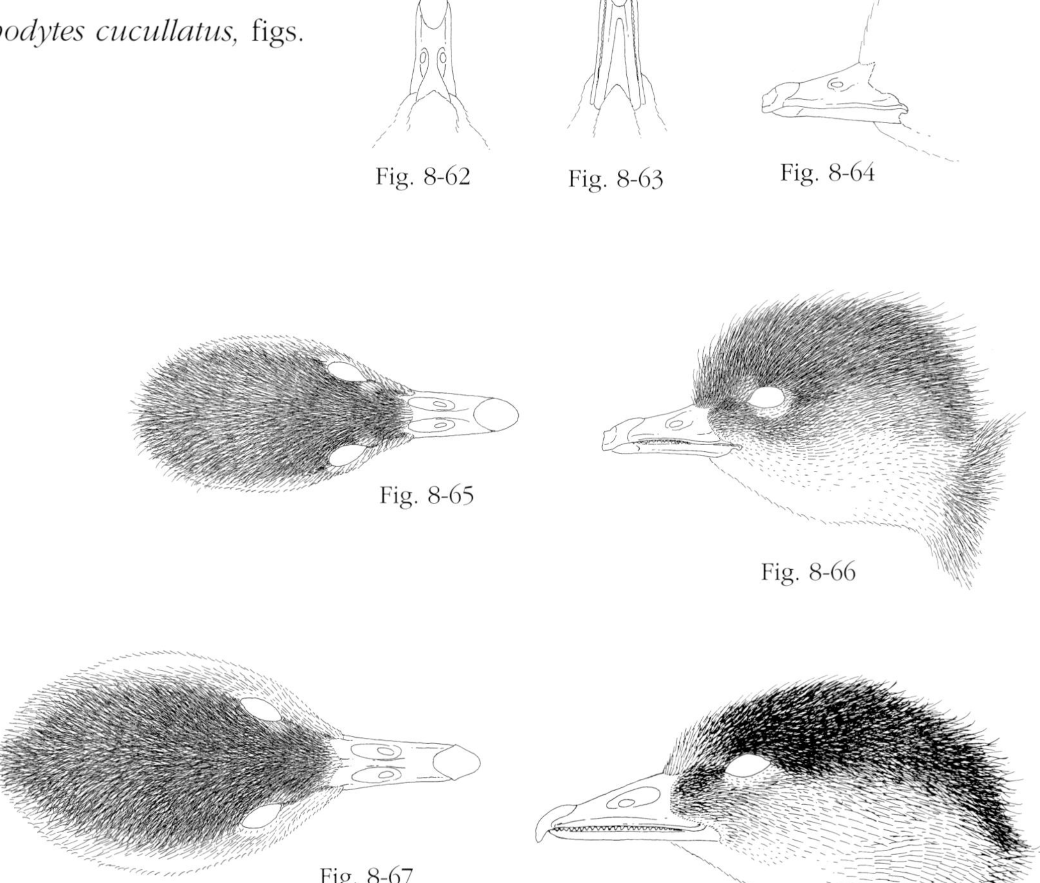

Fig. 8-62 Fig. 8-63 Fig. 8-64

Fig. 8-65

Fig. 8-66

Fig. 8-67

Fig. 8-68

Figs. 8-62 to 8-64, 8-66 (1 day): Vermont; fig. 8-65 (1 day): captive; figs. 8-67, 8-68 [10-12 days]: Ontario.

Key to *Mergus* species

1a. In young downies, upper mandible blackish red-brown, lower mandible and tomia pale to light reddish brown; lateral bill feathering nearly always extends beyond apex of mesial feathering (figs. 8-72, 8-78); dark elements of face pattern tend to 'bleed' light reddish onto whiter areas, except around eyes, where white area usually forms conspicuous subocular crescent (fig. 8-75); using commissure as measure of bill length, entire nostril usually lies clearly in posterior half of bill in very young downies, and in posterior third of bill in large older downies (and adults; Taverner 1945). Red-breasted Merganser, *Mergus serrator,* figs. 8-69 to 8-79.

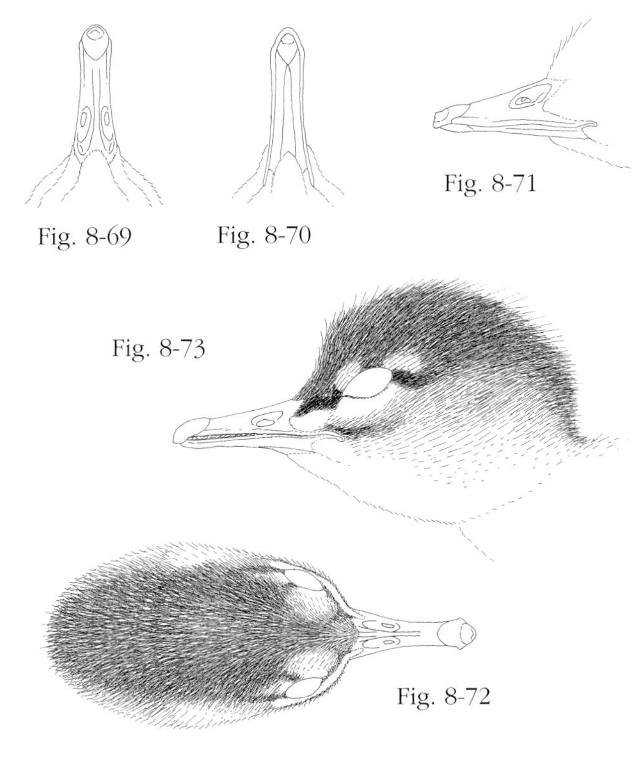

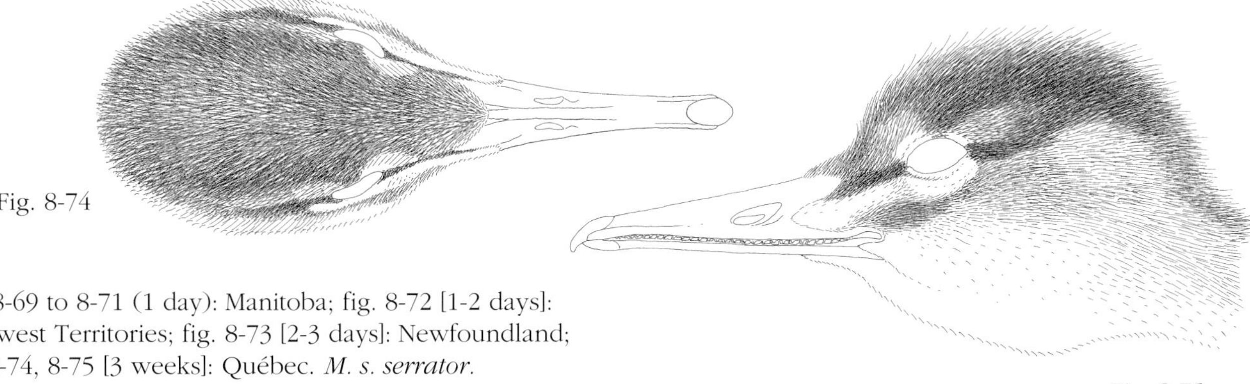

Figs. 8-69 to 8-71 (1 day): Manitoba; fig. 8-72 [1-2 days]: Northwest Territories; fig. 8-73 [2-3 days]: Newfoundland; figs. 8-74, 8-75 [3 weeks]: Québec. *M. s. serrator.*

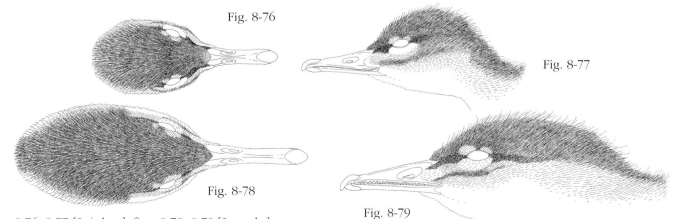

Fig. 8-76

Fig. 8-77

Fig. 8-78

Fig. 8-79

Figs. 8-76, 8-77 [3-4 days], figs. 8-78, 8-79 [2 weeks]: Greenland. *M. s. schioleri.*

1b. In young downies, upper and lower mandibles blackish (except lower mandibles becoming more like 1a in older downies); apex of mesial feathering on culmen nearly always extends slightly beyond lateral feathering (fig. 8-80); dark elements of face pattern remain more or less separate from white areas in young downies, but may lighten and 'bleed' in older downies; white subocular crescent nearly always lacking (figs. 8-84, 8-86); using commissure as measure of bill length, entire nostril usually more or less centered on bill in very young downies; anterior edge of nostril approaches center of bill in large older downies (and adults; Taverner 1945). Common Merganser, *M. merganser,* figs. 8-80 to 8-86.

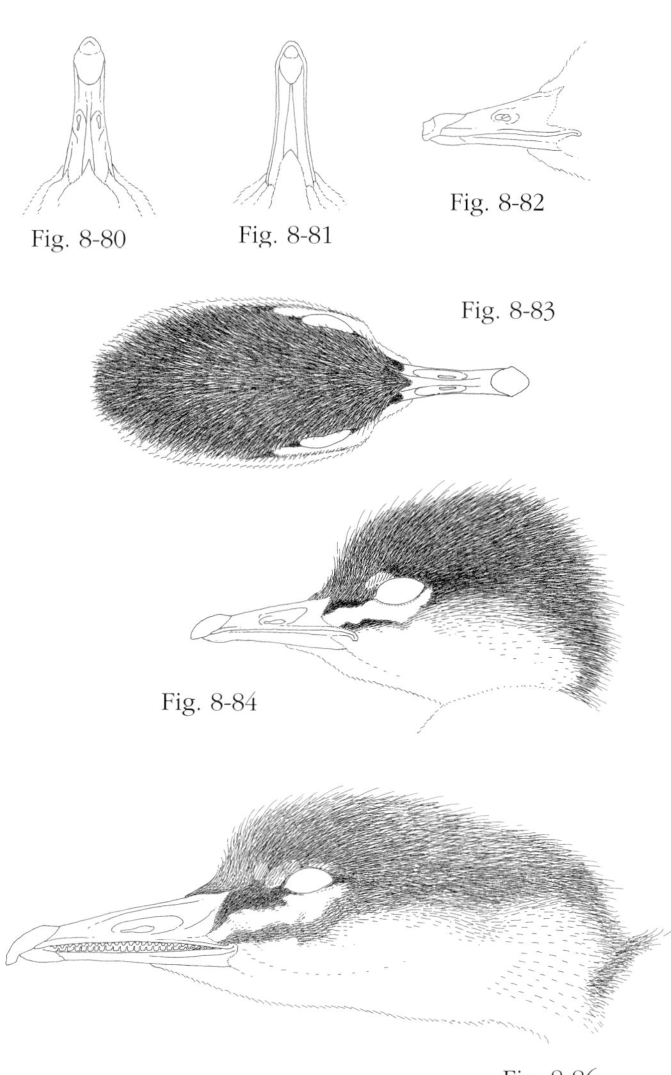

Fig. 8-85

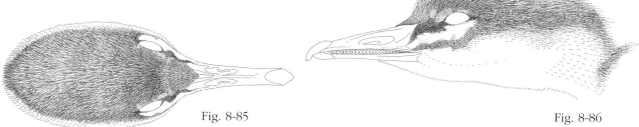

Figs. 8-80 to 8-82 (1 day): Manitoba; fig. 8-83 [2-3 days]: California; fig. 8-84 [3-4 days]: Minnesota; figs. 8-85, 8-86 [2 weeks]: Ontario. *M. m. americanus.*

Tribe Oxyurini

Genus *Nomonyx*

Masked Duck, *Nomonyx dominicus,* figs. 9-1 to 9-3.

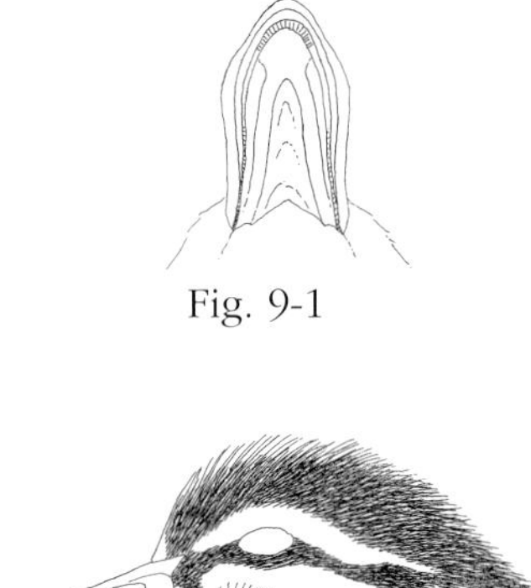

Fig. 9-1

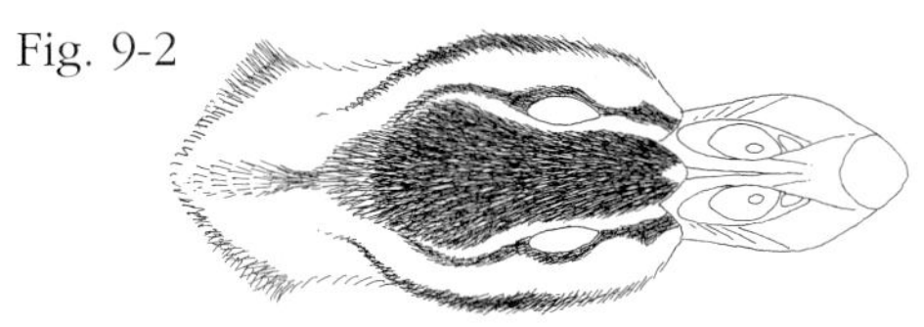

Fig. 9-2

Fig. 9-3

Figs. 9-1 to 9-3 (4 days): Cuba.

Genus *Oxyura*

Ruddy Duck, *Oxyura jamaicensis,* figs. 9-4 to 9-10.

Fig. 9-4

Fig. 9-5

Fig. 9-6

Fig. 9-7

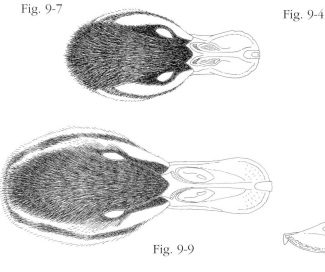

Fig. 9-8

Fig. 9-9

Fig. 9-10

Figs. 9-4 to 9-6 (1 day), fig. 9-8 (7-8 days), figs. 9-9, 9-10 [4 weeks]: Manitoba; fig. 9-7 [1-2 days]: Alberta. *O. j. rubida.*

Definitive plate numbers (**bold**) and definitive figure numbers (*italics*) follow entries for both scientific names and English common names. French and Spanish common names have cross-references to English common names.

A

B

E

H

I

J

K

L

M

N

O

P

R

S

T

V

W

Y